D1548558

EDITOR: Richard Raimondo
ILLUSTRATOR: Shiz Horii
ART DIRECTOR: John P. Fornieri

ISBN 0-87350-501-8

Completely Revised 1983

©Copyright 1938 - 1954 - 1959 - 1977 - 1983

MILADY PUBLISHING COMPANY
Tarrytown, NY

Printed in United States of America
All Foreign Rights Reserved

10 9 8 7 6

Standard Textbook of
PROFESSIONAL
BARBER-STYLING

A practical and complete basic course of training
in the science and practice of barber-styling
for students in training and professional barber-stylists

Milady PUBLISHING COMPANY
220 White Plains Road, Tarrytown, NY 10591

FOREWORD

The material contained in this new edition of the Standard Textbook of Professional Barber-Styling has been completely revised and modernized with respect to both the science and practice of barber-styling.

The **science** of barber-styling denotes the great fund of knowledge available in this field. The science of barber-styling has been developed into a systematic and coherent body of related barber-styling information.

The **practice** deals with the manual skills and dexterity demonstrated by the professional practitioner in the performance of the various barber-styling services.

The **theory** and information contained in this text have been prepared to allow great flexibility and adaptability to whatever system or routine is followed in either school or shop. The materials presented are not designed nor intended to standardize all barber-styling practice. They are not designed nor intended to in any way stifle initiative in barber-styling education or method. Rather, they are presented in such a manner as to encourage teachers to be flexible, modern, and alert to change and improvements.

The text clearly presents the step-by-step instructions in the art and practice of basic services. Many illustrations, charts, review examination questions and a glossary have been included to facilitate teaching and learning. Phonetic pronunciations also have been provided for difficult and technical terms.

Barber-styling school graduates who used this text in their studies have found themselves better prepared to cope with the great demands of the modern practice of barber-styling.

We wish to express our sincerest appreciation to the many state board members, barber-styling educators, and stylists who contributed their time, knowledge, and talents to the revision of this textbook.

BARBER-STYLING TEXTBOOK COMMITTEE

CONTENTS

v

Dedicated to the Advancement of Barber-Styling Education

WELCOME TO THE BARBER-STYLING PROFESSION WITH ITS MANY OPPORTUNITIES

Congratulations for making the wise decision to study barber-styling. By enrolling for a course of study in this school, you have taken the first important step toward a career in a most satisfying and interesting profession.

Barber-styling offers the unique opportunity for a lifetime career in one of our most respected industries. After completing a comparatively very short training period, you will be prepared to embark upon a career offering a fairly good income for your entire working life.

FOR THE YOUNG BARBER-STYLIST

The opportunities available for men and women are far greater in the field of barber-styling than in any other field comparable in preparation time and expense. Barber-styling offers a lucrative, exciting and growth-filled future for the alert and ambitious individual. Furthermore, the practice of barber-styling offers the rare opportunity for a career filled with personal pleasure and satisfaction. It appeals to the artistic and esthetic needs of the practitioner. It encourages the free exercise of the individual's personal talent and ability. And, most important, it combines job satisfaction with financial stability.

Barber-styling presents a vocation which can be tailored to fit into the pattern of a person's private life. For example, if a female barber-stylist wishes to leave the profession to raise a family, or pursue other interests (such as attending college), she can do so fully confident that she can return at a later date, and continue her profession. The same is true for the male barber-stylist. If he chooses to leave the profession for any length of time and for any reason, he can return to the profession with the same confidence as the female stylist.

WELCOME

We, therefore, extend a most sincere welcome to you. We are certain that you will be pleased with your decision in selecting this fascinating career.

How well you succeed will depend to a large degree upon your own talents and your own ambitions. The field and the opportunities are unlimited. You have opened the door to a new, exciting world; now, enter.

Unlimited career opportunities are available in the field of barber-styling for the well-trained individual.

The doors are thrown open to many fascinating and exciting careers for the qualified barber-stylist. Passing through anyone of these doors presents an opportunity for a lucrative career in some branch of this dynamic and fascinating field.

An examination of the following chart will present some idea of the many career areas available to the qualified barber-stylist.

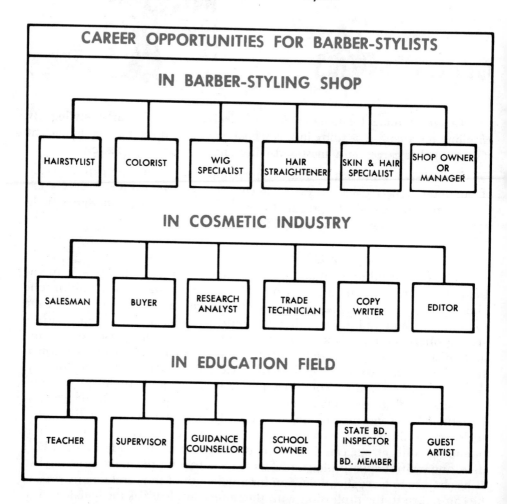

CAREER OPPORTUNITIES FOR BARBER-STYLISTS

IN BARBER-STYLING SHOP

HAIRSTYLIST | COLORIST | WIG SPECIALIST | HAIR STRAIGHTENER | SKIN & HAIR SPECIALIST | SHOP OWNER OR MANAGER

IN COSMETIC INDUSTRY

SALESMAN | BUYER | RESEARCH ANALYST | TRADE TECHNICIAN | COPY WRITER | EDITOR

IN EDUCATION FIELD

TEACHER | SUPERVISOR | GUIDANCE COUNSELLOR | SCHOOL OWNER | STATE BD. INSPECTOR — BD. MEMBER | GUEST ARTIST

SUMMARY

Barber-styling is as exciting as it is profitable. It represents to many men and women a profession that will bring much happiness and financial independence.

BARBER-STYLING IS A CREATIVE PROFESSION

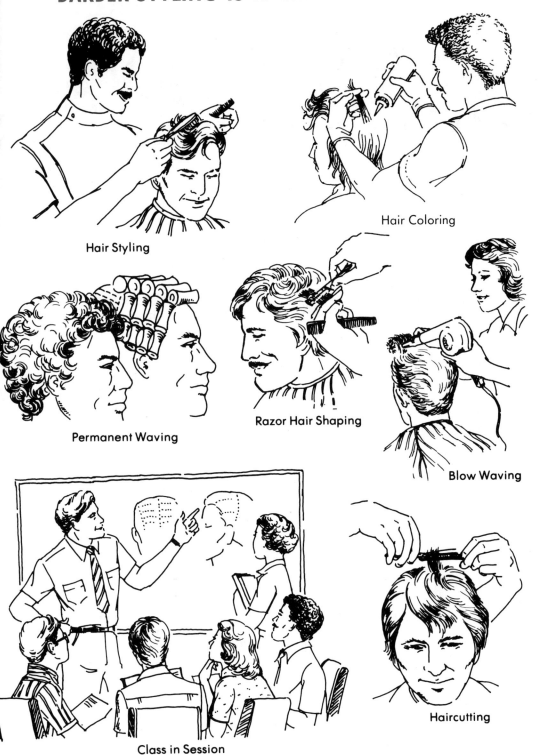

Hair Styling

Hair Coloring

Permanent Waving

Razor Hair Shaping

Blow Waving

Class in Session

Haircutting

You, Too, Can Be A Professional Barber-Stylist

To be successful — you must learn to do the little things and extend those courtesies that will make clients like you. In addition, you must be well groomed and proficient in your skills as a professional barber-stylist.

Barbering refers to the performance of those techniques and arts, such as haircutting, shaving, massaging, facial treatments, and trimming and styling the beard and mustache, which make up the major services performed in the barber-styling shop.

Location — The premises where the art of barbering and hairstyling is practiced is also known by various titles. The most popular of these titles are barber shop, barber-styling shop, hairstyling shop, barber-styling center, barber stylists, gentlemen's stylist, etc. The various titles are used interchangeably, as well as the words "shop" and "salon," to indicate the premises where the professional technician offers services.

TO HELP YOU IN YOUR STUDY

Phonetic pronunciations are given to difficult and technical terms throughout the text.

KEY TO PRONUNCIATION

Vowels and consonants have their ordinary English sounds. Vowels (a, e, i, o, u) are pronounced short, unless a macron (a short line) is placed over the vowel, in which case it is pronounced long. Example: bloodstream (blud'strēm); back-comb (bak'kōm).

The accent mark (') following a syllable denotes that this syllable is to receive more emphasis than the other syllables.

Chapter 1

HYGIENE AND GOOD GROOMING

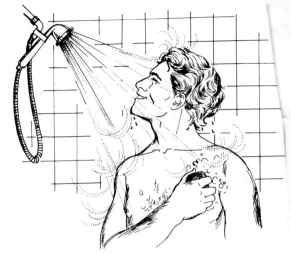

INTRODUCTION

Good health is required for the successful practice of barber-styling. Without it, one cannot work efficiently or be able to satisfy the needs of clients. With it, the practitioner will find it possible to work effectively and constructively.

In accordance with the general concepts of the profession, the barber-stylist should be a living example of good health. The stylist should be capable and qualified to advise clients on how hygienic living contributes to good health. Thus, the stylist will increase in professional worth to the employer, to clients, and to the community.

Hygiene has been defined as the branch of applied science which concerns itself with healthful living. Its major purpose is to preserve health. It includes **personal hygiene,** which pertains to the **individual,** and **public hygiene,** which relates to the group or the **community** at large.

It is essential that the barber-stylist be keenly aware of the importance of hygiene. Failure to abide by the proper rules of hygiene could result in the failure of the body organs and appendages, including hair and skin, to function properly. Neglect of hygienic practices can result in disorders of the skin or hair, as well as causing organic diseases.

Personal hygiene is concerned with the intelligent care given by the individual to the preservation of good health by following the rules of healthful living, such as:

1. Cleanliness
2. Oral hygiene
3. Posture
4. Exercise
5. Relaxation
6. Adequate sleep
7. Balanced diet
8. Wholesome thoughts

Public hygiene (sanitation) refers to the hygienic conditions created for the community at large. These are not only the efforts made by the barber-stylist to maintain sanitary conditions and prevent the spread of disease, but also the actions taken by the government to promote public health. In order for the government to protect the health, safety and welfare of its citizens, steps are taken to assure:

1. Pure air
2. Pure food
3. Pure water
4. Adequate disposal of sewage
5. Control of disease
6. Adequate medical facilities

The barber-stylist should be concerned with all problems involving the rvation of good health. The barber-stylist is constantly in direct contact clients. In the regular course of shop duties, the stylist uses instruments osmetic preparations on client after client, constantly placing the stylist anger of contracting some communicable disease from a client or vertently transmitting an infection from client to client. It is, therefore, ious that one of the most important responsibilities of the barber-stylist constantly and carefully practice all the rules of sanitation and hygiene.

The health of the body is very closely related to the condition of the skin d hair. The complexion of the skin is said to be the outward expression inner health. Good health reflects itself in a clear complexion and clear es. However, a dull, sallow complexion is indicative of:

1. Sluggish circulation   3. Irregular elimination   5. Poor health
2. Lack of fresh air   4. Improper diet

HYGIENIC RULES

In order to maintain good health and vitality, it is essential to follow hygienic rules of living.

Eating well-balanced meals at regular intervals and drinking a sufficient amount of water will help keep the digestive system functioning properly. One of the basic causes of poor health is a faulty diet. Avoid such poor eating habits as:

1. **Not eating enough** of the **right kinds of food.** This may lead to loss of weight, lowered resistance or nutritional diseases.
2. **Overeating,** because it taxes the digestive system.

Exercise and recreation in the form of walking, dancing, sports and gym activities tend to develop the muscles and help to keep the body fit. A few of the benefits resulting from regular and non-strenuous exercises are:

1. An improvement in nutrition
2. An improvement in blood circulation
3. The body is supplied with more life-giving oxygen due to the increased action of the lungs.

Sunshine. Any form of recreation in the sunshine adds vigor as well as helping to supply the body with the essential vitamin "D." However, recent studies show that too much sun may cause certain types of skin cancer. Make certain to allow for only a moderate intake of sun.

Fatigue or tiredness, resulting from work, exercise, mental effort or the strain caused by hurry and worry, should always be followed by a period of rest or relaxation. Over-exertion and lack of rest tend to drain the body of its vitality. Therefore, an adequate amount of sleep, not less than seven hours, is necessary. This allows the body to recover from the fatigue of the day's activities and to replenish itself with renewed energy.

HEALTHY THOUGHTS

The mind and the body operate as a unit. A well-balanced condition of body and mind contributes to good health. This enables them to perform all

2

of their functions normally. A pleasant attitude is an asset to health, whereas a morose, despondent spirit is a liability and a handicap to health. Healthy thoughts can be cultivated by conscious effort and by self-control. In place of worry and fear, the health-giving qualities of cheerfulness, courage and hope should be developed. Outside interests, rest and recreation relieve the strain of monotony and hard work.

Thoughts and **emotions** influence body activities. A thought may cause the face to turn red and increase the heart action. A thought may either stimulate or depress the functions of the body. Strong emotions, such as worry and fear, have a harmful effect on the heart, arteries and glands. Mental depression weakens the functions of the organs, thereby lowering the resistance of the body to disease.

A WELL-GROOMED BARBER-STYLIST

A well-groomed barber-stylist is one of the best advertisements of an effectively run barber-stylist shop.

To keep your appearance at its best, you must give daily attention to all the important details that make for a clean, neat, and pleasing personality.

Daily Bath and Deodorant: Keep the body cleansed and odor free by taking a daily shower or bath and by using an underarm deodorant.

Oral Hygiene: Clean and brush the teeth regularly. Use mouth wash to sweeten the breath.

Hair: Keep your hair clean, styled and neatly combed.

Clothes: Wear a uniform that is clean, neat, and properly fitted. Wear fresh underclothes. Men should wear clean socks. Women should wear clean, unwrinkled pantyhose.

Hands and Naisl: Keep your hands clean, and always have your nails well-manicured.

Face: Men should shave daily. If you wear a mustache and/or a beard, keep them trimmed and neatly styled. Women should wear makeup, but not overdone.

Shoes: Wear shoes that are well-fitted and sensibly styled. Keep the shoes shined and in good condiltion. Women should wear low heels.

Many barber-styling shop owners consider appearance, visual poise, and personality to be as important as technical knowledge and manual skills.

A WELL-GROOMED FEMALE STYLIST

Proper grooming is also important to female barber-stylists. Give careful attention to cleanliness of uniform, skin, hair, hands, and teeth. Keep breath sweet with mouth wash. Keep your body free of odor by taking a shower or bath daily, and by using an underarm deodorant. Wear low-heeled shoes that are well-fitted and sensibly styled. Keep the shoes shined and in good condition. Watch out for hosiery wrinkles.

PERSONAL CLEANLINESS

Personal cleanliness is an important hygienic requirement. The barber-stylist must observe cleanliness in the following ways:

1. Keep the body clean by taking a daily bath or shower.
2. Avoid body odors by using a deodorant.
3. Keep teeth and gums in good condition. Brush teeth twice daily with a good dentifrice.
4. Have dental examination every six months.
5. Avoid bad breath by rinsing mouth with a good mouth wash.
6. Keep your shoes clean and in good condition.
7. Wear clean undergarments and a clean uniform each day.
8. Keep hair well-groomed.
9. Keep hands and fingernails in good condition.
10. Wash hands before and after serving each client and after visiting the toilet.
11. Avoid the use in common of towels, drinking cups, hair brushes and combs.

MAINTAIN GOOD HEALTH

In order to maintain good health, observe the following rules:

1. Breathe air of good quality.
2. Drink sufficient amount of water each day.
3. Follow a balanced diet. Do not overeat.
4. Have a regular and daily elimination.
5. Stand, sit and walk with good posture.
6. Obtain adequate sleep.
7. Have recreation and outdoor exercise.
8. Have regular physical examinations.

TO PROTECT PUBLIC HEALTH

To protect public health, any person suffering from an infectious or contagious disease must not be allowed to attend school or work in a barber-styling shop. The public **must never** be served by one with an infectious or contagious disease.

POSTURE

"It's not what you do, it's the way that you do it," goes the old line, and it's nowhere truer than in reference to good posture. If you find yourself worn out and beat at the end of a working day, it may not be due to the amount of work you have done. Very possibly the reason for your weariness may lie in the way you stand, walk and sit. Good posture adds to good appearance, but it also adds to physical stamina and lets you put in a full day's work without collapsing at the end of the day.

THE SPINE

The spine is divided into three sections.

1. The first seven vertebrae, cervicals (sur'vi-kals), are involved in the posture problem known as kyphosis (ki-fo'sis) (hunchback). The head is held forward, the shoulders droop and the chest is caved in.

2. The middle twelve vertebrae, the thoracic (tho-ra'sik), are involved in swayback, lordosis (lor-do'sis).

3. The lowest five vertebrae, the lumbar, hold your pelvis in balance.

Scoliosis (sko-le-o'sis) is a combination of swayback and hunchback. It is the worst condition of poor posture. Scoliosis confuses body functions, creates a bad impression on others and contributes to the fact that your clothes don't seem to fit you correctly.

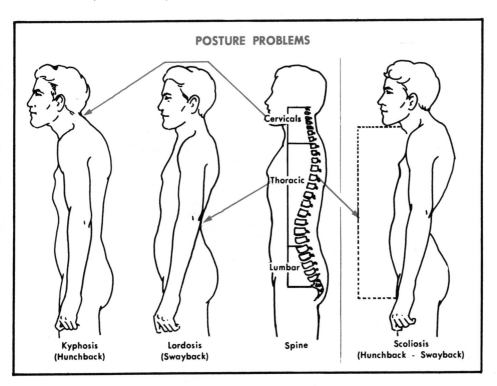

POSTURE PROBLEMS

| Kyphosis (Hunchback) | Lordosis (Swayback) | Spine | Scoliosis (Hunchback - Swayback) |

POSTURE CORRECTION

Get a mirror, and after you have noted the defects that need to be corrected, try to shape up to the following good posture rules. Sheer practice is the best exercise, and most of the general physical fitness exercises will help tremendously in developing the muscles that hold the body erect.

RULES FOR CORRECT POSTURE

1. The weight should be carried on the balls of the feet, not the heels. Imagine a plumb-line falling from your shoulder and stand so that it falls just forward of the ankle.
2. Keep your shoulders back. You don't have to stand at attention, but you should be close to it.
3. Hold stomach in. Even if you're not overweight, poor posture can give you a potbelly.
4. Head should be held high. This gives you the appearance of confidence and reduces aching shoulders as well.

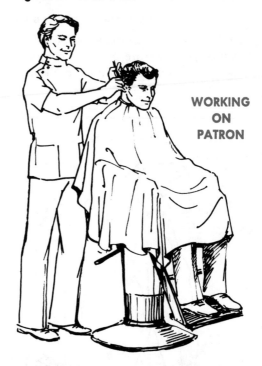

WORKING
ON
PATRON

BENEFITS OF GOOD POSTURE

Some of the advantages of good posture are:
1. It gives a feeling of confidence. To BE confident, you must ACT confidently.
2. Good posture builds good health by allowing the inner organs room to function properly.
3. "Standing tall" helps to improve your speech by freeing the power source of your voice, the diaphragm (di′a-fram).
4. Proper body alignment makes for a dynamic personality, both mentally and physically.

CORRECT SITTING POSTURE

Just as there is a mechanically correct posture for standing, so is there one for sitting. It is highly important that you sit correctly. Learn to sit "in balance."

1. Place your feet on the floor directly under your knees
2. Have the seat of the chair even with your knees. This will allow the upper and lower legs to form a 90-degree angle at the knees.

3. Allow your feet to carry the weight of your thighs.
4. Rest the weight of your torso on the thigh bones, not on the end of your spine.
5. Keep your torso erect.
6. Make sure your desk is at the correct height so that the upper and lower parts of your arm form a right angle when you are writing.

CORRECT LIFTING TECHNIQUE

When you lift something heavy, be sure to use the weight-lifter's method, or you may cause a rupture or a slipped disk. Lift with your back straight, pushing with the heavy thigh muscles, never the back muscles.

CAUTION:

Have some idea of the weight of the object you are lifting. You can hurt your back just as severely by lifting a light object your muscles expect to be heavy as you can by lifting a heavy object incorrectly.

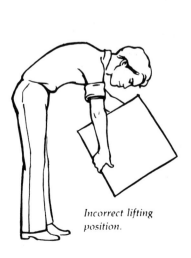

Incorrect lifting position.

Correct lifting position.

7

The major cause of poor posture is laziness, but there are other causes as well. Our soft easy chairs, our mattresses, our daily posture habits—all these contribute to muscles that are trained and used in the wrong way.

Our day-to-day habits of standing, sitting and walking vitally influence our posture not only while we are doing them, but for days, weeks and years thereafter. Therefore, it is important that you observe correct posture while working, standing, walking or sitting.

NORMAL AND WEAK ARCHES

Normal arch.

A normal foot is narrow in the middle and wide at the heel and toes. Good arches are characteristic of the normal footprint.

A weak foot is caused by a weak arch. Its footprint is wider in the middle than a normal footprint.

Weak arch.

Fallen arches, or **flat feet,** is a common foot ailment. The flat foot leaves a footprint that is almost the same throughout its entire length.

Weak and flat feet may be strengthened by means of massage and exercise, or may be helped by the wearing of arch supports and proper shoes. These remedial measures should be taken only after consultation with a foot specialist.

Flat foot.

YOUR PERSONALITY CHART

An **attractive personality** is one of your greatest assets in life and is revealed in your speech, appearance, behavior, and manners. It is the total effect you have on other people. How you behave in school, business, or social life can either add or take away from your personality.

Try to make your answers to the following questions project a true picture of your inner and outer self. First evaluate yourself. If your rating is low, consult your teacher, friends, or doctor to find out what can be done to enrich and improve it. Analyze your personality every three months to find out what progress you are making.

Check the proper boxes in this Personality Quiz to find out if you have the personality qualities listed below:

1. **Female.** Do you give careful attention to personal grooming, such as your clothes, hair, makeup, hosiery, and shoes?
   ☐ Always ☐ Sometimes ☐ Never

   Male. Do you give careful attention to personal grooming, such as your clothes, socks, shoes, hair, shave, mustache, hair in nose?
   ☐ Always ☐ Sometimes ☐ Never

2. Do you check your posture when sitting, standing, and walking?
   ☐ Always ☐ Sometimes ☐ Never

3. Do you change undergarments daily and avoid halitosis and body odor at all times?
   ☐ Always ☐ Sometimes ☐ Never

4. Are you loyal to others?
   ☐ Always ☐ Sometimes ☐ Never

5. Are you friendly and courteous to others?
   ☐ Always ☐ Sometimes ☐ Never

6. Are you truthful in dealing with others?
   ☐ Always ☐ Sometimes ☐ Never

7. Can you get along and work well with others?
   ☐ Always ☐ Sometimes ☐ Never

8. Can you accept responsibility?
   ☐ Always ☐ Sometimes ☐ Never

9. Do you have confidence in your knowledge and ability?
   ☐ Always ☐ Sometimes ☐ Never

10. Do you have a good tone of voice and choice of words?
    ☐ Always ☐ Sometimes ☐ Never

RATING YOUR PERSONALITY

Give yourself 10 points for **Always**; 5 points for **Sometimes**; and zero (0) for **Never**. Compare your final rating with the following standards:

Excellent Personality 85-100%

Good Personality 75- 85%

Fair Personality 60- 75%

Poor Personality ....59% or less

Note: About two-thirds of all job dismissals are due to bad manners, poor personality and inability to get along with people. It would be to your advantage, therefore, to do all you can to improve your personality.

RECORD OF PERSONALITY IMPROVEMENT

	Now	After 3 Months	After 6 Months	After 9 Months	After 1 Year
RATING					

QUESTIONS ON HYGIENE AND GOOD GROOMING

1. Define hygiene.
2. Define personal hygiene.
3. Define public hygiene.
4. List eight basic requirements for good personal hygiene.
5. List six basic requirements for good public health under the supervision of the government.
6. Which three mental qualities promote good health?
7. Which two emotions can injure health?
8. A daily bath or shower keeps the body ....
9. Avoid body odors by using a ....
10. Sweeten the breath by rinsing mouth with a good ....
11. The public must never be served by a barber-stylist having an infectious or .... disease.

Chapter 2
PROFESSIONAL ETHICS

INTRODUCTION

The practice of modern barber-styling is a combination of scientific knowledge and artistic ability. **Science** consists in the knowing, **art** in the doing.

The **art of barber-styling** calls for the application of manual skills and dexterity in order to produce pleasing and satisfactory results.

The **science** consists of the essential knowledge required to give the skin and hair a clean, healthy and well-groomed appearance.

The successful barber-stylist is one who is well versed in both the science and art of this important profession.

Barber-styling as a **professional career** offers many opportunities and rewards to those students who receive and absorb thorough training in both the science and art of the profession, and who develop pleasing appearances and agreeable personalities, observe proper professional ethics and exercise proper practical skills.

ETHICAL CONDUCT

Ethical conduct deals with the proper behavior and business dealings of practitioners in relation to their employers, patrons and co-workers.

Proper ethical practices help to build confidence and increase business and income. The barber-stylist should abide by the following rules of ethical conduct:

1. Give courteous and friendly service to all clients.
2. Treat all clients honestly and fairly; do not show favoritism.
3. Be fair and courteous, and show respect for the feelings and rights of others.
4. Keep your word and fulfill your obligations.
5. Cherish a good reputation. Set an example of proper conduct and behavior.
6. Be loyal to your employer, manager, school and associates.
7. Cooperate with the school personnel and fellow students.

11

8. Comply with school or shop rules and regulations.
9. Practice good sanitary habits of work at all times.
10. Obey all provisions of the state law.
11. Maintain a professional attitude and practice it faithfully and sincerely.

A PROFESSIONAL ATTITUDE TOWARDS PATRONS

Greet the patron by name, with a pleasing tone of welcome in your voice. See that his personal belongings are properly cared for. Study his mood. Often, the client will prefer quiet and relaxation. If he wishes to talk, be a good listener. Never repeat gossip as he may lose confidence in you. Never gossip about anyone.

Off-color stories are distasteful and have no place in a barber-styling shop.

Good habits and practices acquired during your school training will lay the foundation for a successful career in barber-styling. To become successful as a professional barber-stylist you should:

1. Follow the rules of good ethics.
2. Make a good impression on others.
3. Cultivate confidence and a pleasing personality.
4. Pay attention to the minor details which will make clients like you.
5. Adopt a cordial manner in greeting clients in person and over the telephone.
6. Address clients by their names, i.e., "Mr. Smith." Never use very familiar terms or nicknames.
7. Handle your clients with tact. Develop an even temperament.
8. Be punctual and proficient in your work.
9. Set a good example of what you are selling. Your personal appearance is your best advertisement.
10. Develop business and sales abilities along with common sense.
11. Be prompt and judicious in adjusting clients' complaints and grievances.
12. Listen attentively when others speak.
13. Learn to talk intelligently about your work.
14. Cultivate a pleasing voice.
15. Wear immaculately clean, freshly laundered clothes and uniforms.
16. Keep shoes well shined.
17. Keep fingernails short, well trimmed and clean.
18. Wash your hands before and after serving a client.

TO BE SUCCESSFUL you must learn to do the little things that will make people like you.

TO BE SUCCESSFUL you must learn to . . .

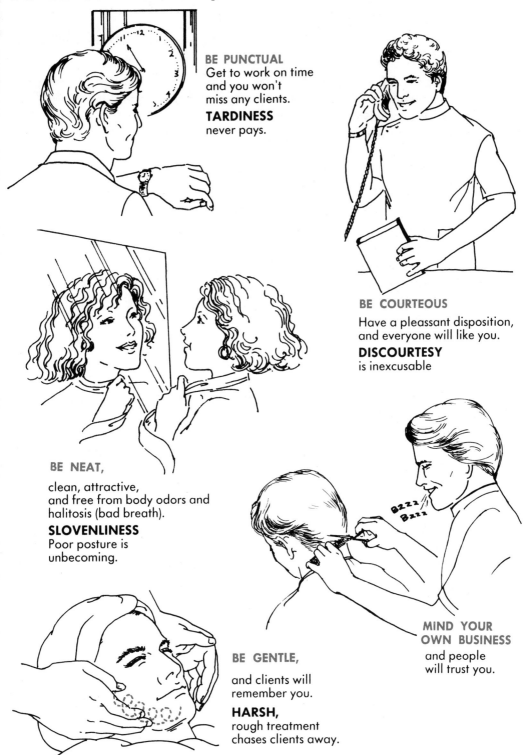

BE PUNCTUAL
Get to work on time
and you won't
miss any clients.
TARDINESS
never pays.

BE COURTEOUS

Have a pleassant disposition,
and everyone will like you.
DISCOURTESY
is inexcusable

BE NEAT,

clean, attractive,
and free from body odors and
halitosis (bad breath).
SLOVENLINESS
Poor posture is
unbecoming.

BE GENTLE,

and clients will
remember you.

HARSH,
rough treatment
chases clients away.

**MIND YOUR
OWN BUSINESS**

and people
will trust you.

13

POOR ETHICS

POOR ETHICS. *Questionable practices, extravagant claims and broken promises violate the rules of good ethical conduct. They cast an unfavorable light on the profession in general and the individual student, practitioner and barber-styling shop in particular.*

To prevent unethical practices:

1. Do not criticize your fellow workers to clients.
2. Do not misrepresent products.
3. Do not use profane language.
4. Do not become sarcastic with unpleasant clients.
5. Do not serve clients merely for the sake of tips.
6. Do not break the laws governing the practice of the profession.
7. Do not break the rules and regulations of the school.
8. Do not criticize the barber-styling profession.
9. Do not be dishonest.
10. Do not gossip.
11. Do not acquire a poor reputation.
12. Do not be careless in your habits of sanitation.

Be Careful to Avoid

1. Bad breath and body odors.
2. Smoking in the presence of clients.
3. Speaking in a loud or harsh voice.
4. Condemning the work of fellow workers.
5. Discussing personal problems with clients.
6. Lounging on the arms of chairs or on other furniture.
7. Poor posture when working, and shuffling the feet while walking.
8. Playing the radio or television too loudly in the presence of clients.
9. Carrying on a conversation with someone else while serving a client.

GUIDES FOR STUDENT SUCCESS

1. Speak in the classroom only when recognized by the teacher.
2. School regulations are important — obey them all.
3. Personal calls interfere with teaching and learning.
4. Be careful with all school equipment.
5. Be clean and well-groomed at all times.
6. Cooperation with teachers is essential for good learning.
7. Notebooks and workbooks are important review aids.
8. Loafing or loitering makes a poor impression on others.
9. Be courteous and considerate at all times.
10. Be tactful and polite to clients.
11. Observe safety rules and prevent accidents.
12. Develop a pleasing personality.
13. Think and act positively.
14. Attend trade shows and conventions to add to learning.
15. Carefully complete all homework assignments.
16. Clothes and uniform should be spotless.
17. Follow teacher's instructions and techniques.
18. Show patrons that you are interested and sincere.
19. Maintain good attendance.
20. Ask for clarification if you do not understand.
21. Bathe daily and use a body deodorant.
22. Develop and exhibit good manners at all times.
23. Be respectful to your teachers and supervisors.
24. Be careful when using school equipment and supplies.
25. The development of good work habits is essential to success.

The successful barber-stylist extends **courtesy** to state board members and inspectors. These people are acting in the line of duty and they contribute to the higher standards of barber-styling.

STATE BOARD LAWS

The successful barber-stylist must know the laws, rules and regulations governing the profession and must comply with them. Compliance is necessary, because they are designed to contribute to the health, welfare and safety of the community.

QUESTIONS ON PROFESSIONAL ETHICS

1. Define ethics.
2. Check which ones you consider as ethical practices.
   ☐ Courtesy   ☐ Honesty   ☐ Extravagant claims   ☐ Broken promises
   ☐ Obeying the law   ☐ Keeping your word
3. Why is it important that the barber-stylist avoid bad breath and body odor?
4. Why must the barber-stylist never repeat gossip to clients or co-workers?
5. Why should the barber-stylist avoid the use of profane language?
6. Why should the barber-stylist extend courtesy to state board members?
7. Why should the barber-stylist comply with the law?

Chapter 3
BACTERIOLOGY STERILIZATION AND SANITATION

LOUIS PASTEUR (1822-1895), French chemist who devised a method to destroy bacteria.

Sterilization (ster-i-li-zā′shun) and **sanitation** (san-i-tā′shun) are subjects of practical importance to barber-stylists because they have a direct bearing on their own as well as the clients' welfare. To **protect** individual and public health, barber-stylists should know when, why and how to utilize sterilization and sanitation.

If barber-stylists are to understand the importance of sanitation and sterilization they must first have a knowledge of bacteriology.

BACTERIOLOGY

Bacteriology (bak-tē-rē-ol′ō-jē) is that science which deals with the study of the micro-organisms called bacteria.

Barber-stylists must understand how the spread of disease can be prevented and become familiar with the precautions which must be taken to protect their own as well as their clients' health. They must understand the **relation** of bacteria to the **principles** of barber-styling shop cleanliness and sanitation. The State Barber Boards and the Health Department require the application of sanitary measures while serving the public. Contagious diseases, skin infections and blood poisoning are caused either by the conveyance of infectious material from one individual to another or by unsanitized implements (such as combs, brushes, clippers, shears, razors, etc.) which have been used first on an infected person and then on another person. Other sources of contagion are dirty hands and fingernails.

Bacteria (bak-tē′rē-ah) are minute, one-celled vegetable microorganisms (mī′krō-or′gan-izms) found nearly everywhere, and being especially numerous in dust, dirt, refuse and diseased tissues. Bacteria are also known as **germs** (jurmz) or **microbes** (mī′krōbs).

17

Bacteria exist everywhere, particularly on the skin of the body, in water, in air, in decayed matter, in the secretion of body openings, on the clothing and beneath the nails.

Ordinarily, bacteria are not visible except with the aid of a microscope (mĭ'krō-skōp). They are so minute in size that fifteen hundred rod-shaped bacteria will barely reach across a pinhead.

THE TWO TYPES OF BACTERIA

There are hundreds of different kinds of bacteria. However, bacteria are classified into two types, depending on their **beneficial** (harmless) or **harmful** (disease-producing) qualities.

1. **Non-pathogenic** (non-path-ō-jen'ik) **organisms** (**microbes or germs**) (beneficial or harmless type) constitute the majority of all bacteria. They perform many useful functions, such as decomposing refuse and improving the fertility of the soil. To this group belong the **saprophytes** (sap'rō-fīts) which live on dead matter and do not produce disease.

2. **Pathogenic** (path-ō-jen'ik) **organisms** (**microbes or germs**) (harmful type), although in the minority, cause considerable damage by invading plant or human tissues. Pathogenic bacteria are harmful because they produce disease. To this group belong the **parasites** (par'a-sīts) which require living matter for their growth.

It is because of the pathogenic bacteria that the practice of cleanliness and sanitation is necessary in a barber-styling shop or school.

CLASSIFICATION OF PATHOGENIC BACTERIA

Bacteria show distinct forms or shapes which aid in their identification. However, we are concerned with pathogenic bacteria, classified as follows:

1. **Cocci** (singular, **coccus**) are round-shaped organisms which appear singly or in groups as follows:
   a) **Diplococci** (singular, **diplococcus**) grow in pairs. They cause pneumonia and gonorrhea (gon-o-re'ah).
   b) **Streptococci** (singular, **streptococcus**) are pus-forming organisms which grow in chains. They are found in blood poisoning.
   c) **Staphylococci** (singular, **staphylococcus**) are pus-forming organisms which grow in bunches or clusters. They are present in abscesses, pustules and boils.

2. **Bacilli** (singular, **bacillus**) are rod-shaped organisms which present either a short, thin or thick structure. They are the most common and produce such diseases as tetanus (lockjaw), influenza, typhoid fever, tuberculosis and diphtheria. Many bacilli are **spore** producers.

3. **Spirilla** (singular, **spirillum**) are curved or corkscrew-shaped organisms. They are further subdivided into several groups, of chief importance being the **Treponema pallida,** the causative agent in syphilis. (sif'ilis).

THREE GENERAL FORMS OF BACTERIA

COCCI

BACILLI

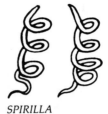

SPIRILLA

GROUPINGS OF BACTERIA

DIPLOCOCCI

STREPTOCOCCI

STAPHYLOCOCCI

SIX DISEASE-PRODUCING BACTERIA

TYPHOID BACILLUS
SHOWING FLAGELLA

TUBERCLE BACILLUS
(Tuberculosis)

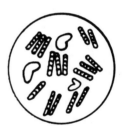

DIPHTHERIA
BACILLUS

INFLUENZA
BACILLUS

CHOLERA
(Microspira)

TETANUS BACILLUS
WITH SPORES

TO AVOID THE SPREAD OF DISEASE

KEEP YOURSELF CLEAN. KEEP YOUR SURROUNDINGS CLEAN. KEEP EVERYTHING YOU COME IN CONTACT WITH CLEAN. SEE THAT EVERYTHING YOU USE IS CLEAN.

Singular	*Plural*
coccus (kok'us)	cocci (kok'sī)
bacillus (basil'us)	bacilli (ba-sil ī)
spirillum (spī-ril'um)	spirilla (spī-ril'ah)
staphylococcus (staf-i-lō-kok'us)	staphylococci (staf-i-lō-kok'sī)
streptococcus (strep-tō-kok'us)	streptococci (strep-tō-kok'sī)
diplococcus (dip-lō-kok'us)	diplococci (dip-lō-kok'sī)
gonococcus (gon-o-kok'us)	gonococci (gon-o-kok'si)
	treponema pallida (trep-o-ne'mah pal'i-dah)

BACTERIAL GROWTH AND REPRODUCTION

Bacteria consist of an outer cell wall and internal protoplasm. They manufacture their own food from the surrounding environment, give off waste products and grow and reproduce.

Bacteria may exhibit two distinct phases in their life cycle: the **active** or **vegetative** stage and the **inactive** or **spore-forming** stage.

Active or Vegetative Bacteria

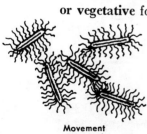

During the active stage, bacteria grow and reproduce. These microorganisms multiply best in warm, dark, damp and dirty places where sufficient food is present.

When conditions are favorable, bacteria reproduce very fast. As food is absorbed, the bacterial cells grow in size. When the limit of growth is reached, the bacterial cells divide crosswise in half, thereby forming two daughter cells. From one bacterium, as many as sixteen million germs may develop in half a day.

Reproduction of bacteria

When favorable conditions cease to exist, bacteria either die or become inactive.

Inactive or Spore-Forming Bacteria

Certain bacteria (such as the anthrax and tetanus bacilli), during their inactive stage and in order to withstand periods of famine, dryness and unsuitable temperature, form **spherical spores** having tough outer coverings. In this stage, spores can be blown about in the dust and are not harmed by disinfectants, heat or cold.

When favorable conditions are restored, the spores **change into the active or vegetative** form and then start to grow and reproduce.

Movement of Bacteria

The ability to move about is limited to the bacilli and spirilla, for the cocci rarely show active mobility. Wherever any mobility of bacteria is shown, we find hairlike projections, known as **flagella** or **cilia,** extending from the sides, or sides and ends. A whiplike motion of these hairs propels the bacteria about in liquid.

Movement of bacteria

BACTERIAL INFECTIONS

Pathogenic bacteria become a menace to health when they invade the body. An **infection** occurs if the body is unable to cope with the bacteria and their harmful toxins. **A local infection** is indicated by a boil or a pimple that contains pus. **A general infection** results when the bloodstream carries the bacteria and their toxins to all parts of the body, as in blood poisoning or syphilis.

The presence of **pus** is a sign of infection. **Staphylococci** are the most common pus-forming bacteria. Found in pus are bacteria, waste matter, decayed tissue, body cells and blood cells, both living and dead.

A disease becomes **contagious** or **communicable** when it spreads from one person to another by contact. Some of the more common contagious disorders which would prevent a barber-stylist from working are tuberculosis, common cold, ringworm, scabies, head lice, and virus infections.

The chief source of contagion are unclean hands, unclean implements, open sores, pus, mouth and nose discharges, and the common use of drinking cups and towels. Uncovered coughing or sneezing and spitting in public also spread germs.

Through personal hygiene and public sanitation, infections can be prevented and controlled.

There can be no infection without the presence of **pathogenic** bacteria.

Pathogenic bacteria may enter the body by way of:

1. A break in the skin, such as a cut, pimple or scratch
2. Breathing or by swallowing (air, water or food)
3. The nose (air)   4. The eyes or ears (dirt)

The **body fights infection** by means of its defensive forces:

1. The unbroken skin, which is the body's first line of defense
2. Body secretions, such as perspiration and digestive juices
3. White blood cells within the blood, to destroy bacteria
4. Antitoxins, to counteract the toxins produced by bacteria

Other Infectious Agents

Filterable viruses (fil'ter-a-b'l vi'ru-sez) are living organisms so small that they will pass through the pores of a porcelain filter. They cause the common cold and other respiratory (re-spir'a-to-re) and gastro-intestinal infections.

Parasites are plants or animals which live upon another living organism without giving anything in return.

Plant (vegetable) **parasites** or **fungi** (fun'jī), such as molds, mildews and yeasts, can produce such contagious diseases as ringworm and favus.

Animal parasites, such as certain insects, are responsible for such contagious diseases as scabies, due to the itch mite and pediculosis (pe-dik-ū-lō'sis), caused by lice.

Contagious diseases caused by parasites should never be treated in a barber-styling shop. Clients should be referred to their physicians.

Immunity (i-mū'ni-tē) is the ability of the body to resist invasion and destroy bacteria once they have gained entrance. Immunity against disease is a sign of good health. It may be natural or acquired. **Natural immunity** means natural resistance to disease, being partly inherited and partly developed by hygienic living. **Acquired immunity,** being artificial, is secured after the body has overcome certain diseases by itself or when it has received certain kinds of animal injections.

Human disease carrier is a person immune to a disease and yet harboring germs which can infect other people. **Typhoid** (tī'foid) **fever** and **diphtheria** (dif-thē're-ah) may be transmitted in this manner.

The destruction of bacteria may be accomplished by disinfectants and intense heat, such as boiling, steaming, baking or burning, and ultra-violet rays. This subject is covered in the next chapter.

TO AVOID THE SPREAD OF DISEASE

KEEP YOURSELF CLEAN; KEEP YOUR SURROUNDINGS CLEAN; KEEP EVERYTHING YOU COME IN CONTACT WITH CLEAN, AND SEE THAT EVERYTHING YOU USE IS CLEAN.

QUESTIONS ON BACTERIOLOGY

1. Define bacteriology.
2. What are bacteria?
3. Name and briefly describe two types of bacteria.
4. Why are bacteria not visible to the naked eye?
5. Name three general forms of bacteria and the shape of each.
6. Name five principal routes through which bacteria may enter the body.
7. How do bacteria multiply?
8. Name two common pus-forming bacteria.
9. Why does the barber-stylist study bacteria in connection with the practice of sterilization?
10. Define the following terms: a) pathogenic; b) non-pathogenic.
11. What is a contagious or communicable disease?
12. What will destroy bacteria?
13. Differentiate between natural and acquired immunity.
14. What causes an infection?
15. What is the difference between local infection and general infection?
16. By what other terms are bacteria known?
17. a) Briefly describe spore-forming bacteria. b) Name two.
18. a) What are parasites? b) Name a disease produced by an animal parasite; plant parasite.
19. How can infection be prevented in the barber-styling shop?
20. What is immunity?
21. What is a human disease carrier? Give two examples.
22. Name four common contagious diseases that prevent a barber-stylist from working.
23. List four of the body's defensive forces for fighting infection.
24. Why should the student and barber-stylist practice strict sanitary rules?

STERILIZATION

Sterilization (ster-i-liza'shun) is the process of making an object germ-free by the destruction of all kinds of bacteria, whether beneficial or harmful.

Health Departments and State Barber Boards recognize that it is impossible to completely sterilize implements and equipment in the barber-stylist school and shop. Therefore, it is generally recognized that implements and equipment are SANITIZED and not sterilized.

Throughout the entire text the term SANITIZE will be used to indicate all forms of sanitation.

Sterilization is of practical importance to the barber-stylist because it deals with methods used to prevent the growth of germs or to destroy them entirely, particularly those which are responsible for infections and communicable (ko-mu'ni-ka-b'l) diseases.

METHODS OF STERILIZATION AND SANITATION

There are five well-known methods of sterilization and sanitation. These may be grouped under two main headings:

1. **Physical agents:**
   a) **Moist heat.**
      1. **Boiling water** at 212° Fahrenheit (far'en-hīt) for twenty minutes. (This method is no longer used in barber-styling shops.)
      2. **Steaming**—requires a steam pressure sterilizer. It is used in the medical field to kill bacteria and spores.
   b) **Dry heat** (baking) is used in hospitals to sterilize sheets, towels, gauze, cotton and similar materials.
   c) **Ultra-violet rays** in an electrical sanitizer may be used in a barber-styling shop to keep sanitized implements sanitary.

2. **Chemical agents:**
   a) **Antiseptics** and **disinfectants** are used in barber-styling shops.
   b) **Vapors** (fumigants) in a cabinet sanitizer are used to keep sanitized implements sanitary.

Chemicals are the most **effective** sanitizing agents that may be used in barber-styling shops for destroying or checking bacteria. The chemical agents used for sanitizing purposes are antiseptics and disinfectants.

1. An **antiseptic** (an-ti-sep'tik) is a substance which **may kill,** or **retard the growth** of bacteria without killing them. Antiseptics can, as a general rule, be used with safety on the skin.
2. A **disinfectant** (dis-in-fek'tant) destroys bacteria and is used to sanitize implements.

Several chemicals can be classed under both heads: a **strong solution** may be used as a disinfectant and a **weak solution** as an antiseptic. (Example: Formalin, alcohol or "quats.")

Requirements of a good disinfectant:

1. Convenient to prepare
2. Quick acting
3. Preferably odorless
4. Non-corrosive
5. Economical
6. Non-irritating to skin

There are many chemical disinfectant agents on the market, prepared and ready for use. Consult with your state board of barber-styling or health department for a list of approved disinfectants to be used in a shop or school. Chemicals commonly used in the barber-styling shop include:

1. Sodium Hypochlorite (household bleach) - Liquid; immerse implements in 10% solution for 10 or more minutes.
2. Quarternary Ammonium Compounds - Liquid or tablet; immerse implements in 1:1000 solution for 20 or more minutes.
3. Formalin - Liquid; immerse implements or sanitize electrodes and sharp cutting edges in 70% solution for 10 or more minutes. After removing implements, allow excess moisture to evaporate. Never use cloth, tissue, or cotton to dry.

The following rules must be followed to keep the barber - styling shop implements sanitized:

1. Chemical solutions in sanitizers should be changed regularly.
2. Combs and brushes must be sanitized after each client has been serviced.
3. Shampoo bowls must be sanitized after each use.
4. Sanitize electrical appliances by rubbing surface with a cotton pad dampened with 70% alcohol.

A **wet sanitizer** is any receptacle large enough to hold a disinfectant solution in which the objects to be sanitized are completely immersed. Wet sanitizers come in various sizes and shapes.

Before immersing objects in a wet sanitizer containing a disinfectant solution, be sure to:

1. Remove loose hair from combs.
2. Wash thoroughly with hot water and soap.
3. Rinse thoroughly.

This procedure prevents contamination of the solution. Besides, soap and hot water remove most of the bacteria.

Wet Sanitizer

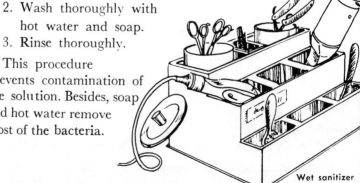

Wet sanitizer

After the implements are removed from the disinfectant solution, they should be rinsed in clean water, wiped dry with a clean towel and stored in a dry or cabinet sanitizer.

Dry or cabinet sanitizer is an airtight cabinet containing an active fumigant. The sanitized implements are kept clean by placing them in the cabinet until ready for use.

How fumigant is prepared. Place one tablespoonful of borax and one tablespoonful of Formalin on a small tray or blotter on the bottom of the cabinet. This will form formaldehyde vapors. Replace chemicals regularly as they lose their strength, depending on how often the cabinet door is opened and closed.

Formalin is also available in tablet form. Follow manufacturer's directions.

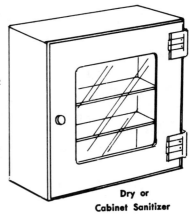

Dry or Cabinet Sanitizer

Ultra-Violet Ray Sanitizer

ULTRA-VIOLET RAY ELECTRICAL SANITIZER

Ultra-violet ray electrical sanitizers are effective for keeping combs, brushes and implements clean until ready for use. Combs, brushes and implements must be sanitized before they are placed in the ultra-violet sanitizer. Follow manufacturer's directions for proper use.

CHEMICAL SANITIZING AGENTS

QUATERNARY AMMONIUM COMPOUNDS (QUATS)

(kwa-ter'na-rē a-mo̅'ne̅-um kom'pounds—kwats)

This group of compounds is effective as disinfectants. They are available under different trade and chemical names.

The **advantages** claimed are: short disinfection time, odorless and colorless, non-toxic and stable. A 1:1000 solution is commonly used to sanitize implements. **Immersion time** ranges from one to five minutes, depending upon the strength of the solution used.

CAUTION. Before using any "quat," read and follow manufacturer's directions on label and accompanying literature. Find out if product can be used in naturally soft or hard water or water that has been softened. Inquire whether it contains a rust inhibitor. Should the product lack a rust inhibitor (in-hib'i-tor), the addition of ½% of sodium nitrite (so̅'de̅-um ni̅'trit) to the solution prevents the rusting of metallic implements.

How to Prepare a 1:1000 Strength Solution of a Quaternary Ammonium Compound

10% active ingredient, add 1¼ oz. "quat" solution to 1 gallon of water.

12½% active ingredient, add 1 oz. "quat" solution to 1 gallon of water.

15% active ingredient, add ¾oz. "quat" solution to 1 gallon of water.

FORMALIN

Formalin (for'ma-lin) will function as a sanitizing agent and can be used either as an antiseptic or disinfectant, depending on its percentage strength. As purchased, Formalin is approximately 37% to 40% formaldehyde (for-mal'dē-hĭd) gas in water.

Formalin may be used in various strengths, as follows:

25% solution (equivalent to 10% formaldehyde gas)—used to sanitize implements. Immerse them in the solution for at least ten minutes. (Preparation: 2 parts Formalin, 5 parts water, 1 part glycerine.)

10% solution (equivalent to 4% formaldehyde gas)—used to sanitize combs and brushes. Immerse them for at least twenty minutes. (Preparation: 1 part Formalin, 9 parts water.)

5 % solution (equivalent to 2% formaldehyde gas)—used to cleanse the hands after they have been in contact with wounds, skin eruptions, etc. Also used to sanitize shampoo bowls and chairs. (Preparation: 1 part Formalin, 19 parts water.)

SANITIZING WITH CHEMICAL DISINFECTANTS

1. Wash implements thoroughly with soap and hot water.
2. Rinse with plain water to remove all traces of soap.
3. Immerse implements in a wet sanitizer (containing approved disinfectant) for the required time.
4. Remove implements from wet sanitizer, rinse in water and wipe dry with clean towel.
5. Store sanitized implements in individually wrapped cellophane envelopes, or keep in a cabinet sanitizer or in ultra-violet ray cabinet until ready **for use.**

SANITIZING WITH ALCOHOL

Implements having a fine cutting edge are best sanitized by rubbing the surface with a cotton pad dampened with 70% alcohol. This application prevents the cutting edges from becoming dull.

Electrodes (ē-lek'trōdz) may be safely sanitized by gently rubbing the exposed surface with a cotton pad dampened with 70% alcohol.

After sanitizing, place implements into a dry sanitizer until ready for use.

SANITIZING FLOORS, SINKS AND TOILET BOWLS

The disinfection of floors, sinks and toilet bowls in the barber-styling shop calls for the use of such commercial products as Lysol, CN, pine needle oil or similar disinfectants. **Deodorants** are also useful to offset offensive smells and for imparting a refreshing odor.

Whatever disinfectant is being used, make **sure** that it is properly diluted as suggested by the manufacturer.

IT IS ALWAYS A PLEASURE FOR CLIENTS TO RECEIVE SERVICES IN A BARBER-STYLING SHOP THAT IS SPOTLESS. GET INTO THE HABIT NOW. KEEP EVERYTHING CLEAN AND IN ORDER.

TABLE OF EQUIVALENTS

Ordinary Measured Glass	8 ozs.
One Pint	16 ozs.
One Quart	32 ozs.
Half Gallon	64 ozs.

✚ SAFETY PRECAUTIONS ✚

The use of chemical agents for sanitation involves certain dangers, unless safety measures are taken to prevent mistakes and accidents. Follow these safety rules:

1. Purchase chemicals in small quantities and store them in a cool, dry place; otherwise they deteriorate due to contact with air, light and heat.
2. Weigh and measure chemicals carefully.
3. Keep all containers labeled, covered and under lock and key.
4. Avoid spilling when diluting chemicals.
5. Keep a complete first aid kit on hand.

DEFINITIONS PERTAINING TO SANITATION

1. **Sterilize** (ster'i-līz)—to render sterile; to make free from all bacteria (harmful or beneficial) by the act of sterilizing.
2. **Sterile** (ster'il)—free from all germs.
3. **Antiseptic** (an-ti-sep'tik)—a chemical agent which may kill or retard the growth of bacteria.
4. **Disinfect** (dis-in-fekt')—to destroy bacteria on any object.
5. **Disinfectant** (dis-in-fek'tant)—a chemical agent having the power to destroy bacteria (germs or microbes).
6. **Bactericide** (bak-tē'ri-sīd)—a chemical agent having the power to destroy bacteria (germs or microbes).
7. **Germicide** (jur'mi-sīd)—a chemical agent having the power to destroy germs (bacteria or microbes).
8. **Asepsis** (a-sep'sis)—freedom from disease germs.
9. **Sepsis** (sep'sis)—poisoning due to pathogenic bacteria.
10. **Fumigant** (fū'mi-gant)—vapor used to keep clean objects sanitary.
11. **Sanitize** (san'i-tīz)—to render objects clean and sanitary.

SANITIZING RULES

1. **Chemical solutions** in sanitizers should be changed when necessary.
2. **All articles** must be clean and free from hair before being sanitized.
3. **Combs, brushes, razors, shears, clipper blades and tweezers** must be sanitized after each client has been served.
4. **Shampoo bowls** must be sanitized before and after each use.
5. **Sanitize electrical appliances** by rubbing surface with a cotton pad dampened with 70% alcohol.

Note—The immersing of implements in a chemical solution should conform to State Board regulations issued by your state.

DISINFECTANTS COMMONLY USED IN BARBER-STYLING SHOPS

NAME	FORM	STRENGTH	USES
Quaternary Ammonium Compounds ("Quats")	Liquid or tablet	1:1000 solution	Immerse implements into solution for 20 or more minutes.
Formalin	Liquid	25% solution	Immerse implements into solution for 10 or more minutes.
Formalin	Liquid	10% solution	Immerse implements into solution for 20 or more minutes.
Ethyl or Grain Alcohol	Liquid	70% solution	Sanitize sharp cutting implements and electrodes for 10 or more minutes.
Cresol (Lysol)	Liquid	10% soap solution	Cleanse floors, sinks and toilets.
Sodium Hypochlorite	Liquid	10% solution	Immerse implements into solution for 10 or more minutes.

ANTISEPTICS COMMONLY USED IN BARBER-STYLING SHOPS

NAME	FORM	STRENGTH	USES
Boric Acid	White crystals	2-5% solution	Cleanse the eyes.
Tincture of Iodine	Liquid	2% solution	Cleanse cuts and wounds.
Hydrogen Peroxide	Liquid	3-5% solution	Cleanse skin and minor cuts.
Ethyl or Grain Alcohol	Liquid	60% solution	Cleanse hands, skin and minute cuts. Not to be used if irritation is present.
Formalin	Liquid	5% solution	Cleanse hands, shampoo bowl, cabinet, etc.
Chloramine-T (Chlorazene; Chlorozol)	White crystals	½% solution	Cleanse skin and hands and for general use.
Sodium Hypochlorite (Javelle water; Zonite)	White crystals	½% solution	Rinse the hands.

It is advisable to check the above and other approved disinfectants and antiseptics that are being used in barber-styling shops with your State Board or Health Department.

SANITATION

Public Sanitation is the application of measures to promote public health and prevent the spread of infectious diseases.

The importance of sanitation cannot be over-emphasized. Rendering barber-styling services requires direct contact with the client's skin, scalp and hair. Understanding sanitary measures **insures** the **protection** of the client's health.

Various governmental agencies protect community health by providing for a wholesome food and water supply and the quick disposal of refuse. These steps are only a few of the ways in which the public health is safeguarded.

The Barber Board and **Board of Health** in each state or locality have formulated sanitary regulations governing **barber-styling shops.** Every barber-stylist must be familiar with these regulations in order to obey them.

A person with an infectious disease is a source of contagion to others. Hence, a barber-stylist having a cold or any contagious disease must not be permitted to serve clients. Likewise, clients obviously suffering from an infectious disease must not be accommodated in a barber-styling shop. In this way, the best interests of other clients may be served.

Water for drinking purposes should be odorless, colorless, and free from any foreign matter. Crystal clear water still may be unsanitary because of the presence of pathogenic bacteria, which cannot be seen with the naked eye.

VENTILATION IN THE BARBER-STYLING SHOP

The **air within a barber-styling shop** should be neither dry nor stagnant, nor have a stale, musty odor. Room temperature should be about 70 degrees Fahrenheit.

The shop should be ventilated with the aid of an exhaust fan or an air conditioning unit. Air conditioning is an advantage that permits changes in the quality and quantity of air brought into the shop. The temperature and moisture content of the air may also be regulated by means of air conditioning.

RULES OF SANITATION

Adherence to the following rules of sanitation will result in cleaner and better service to the public.

1. Every barber-styling shop **must** be well-lighted, heated and ventilated, in order to keep it in a clean and sanitary condition.
2. The walls, floors and windows in the shop **must** be kept clean.
3. All barber-styling establishments must be supplied with running hot and cold water.
4. All plumbing fixtures should be properly installed.
5. The premises should be kept free from rodents, flies or other similar insects.
6. Dogs, cats, birds or other pets **must not be permitted** in a shop.

7. The barber-styling shop is **not to be used** for eating, sleeping or living quarters.

8. All hair, cotton or other waste material **must be removed** from the floor without delay, and deposited in a closed container. Remove them from the premises at frequent intervals.

The public has learned the importance of sanitation and is now demanding that every possible sanitary measure be used in the barber-styling shop for the promotion of public health. Adopting the above rules of sanitation will result in cleaner and better service to the public.

The responsibility of sanitation rests with **each student** in the school and **each barber-stylist** in the shop. The manager must provide the necessities for school and shop sanitation.

SANITARY MEASURES

1. Clean and sanitize all implements used and return to their proper place.
2. Clean work bench, chairs and mirrors.
3. Remove all hair and waste materials from floor.
4. The rest rooms **must be kept** in a sanitary condition.
5. Each barber-stylist **must wear** a clean uniform while working on clients.
6. The barber-stylist **must cleanse** his hands thoroughly **before** and **after** serving a client.
7. The barber-stylist **must wash** his hands **after** leaving the toilet.
8. A freshly laundered towel or fresh paper towel **must be used** for each client. Towels ready for use must be stored in a clean, closed cabinet. All soiled linen towels and used paper towels must be placed in their respective containers used for this purpose. Keep dirty towels away from clean towels.
9. Headrest coverings and neck strips or towels **must be changed** for each patron.
10. Use neckstrip to prevent chaircloth from coming in contact with the client's skin.
11. The **use in common** of hair brushes on more than one person is **prohibited,** unless sanitized after each client.
12. The **common use** of drinking cups, styptic pencils or shaving mugs is prohibited.
13. Lotions, ointments, creams and powders **must be kept** in clean, closed containers. Use a sanitized spatula to remove creams or ointments from jars. Use sterile cotton pledgets to apply lotions and powders. Re-cover containers after each use.
14. Combs or implements **must not** be carried in pockets of uniform.
15. Combs, shears and razors **must be sanitized** after each use.
16. All instruments and articles used, **must first be sanitized** and then placed in a dust-proof or air-tight container or a cabinet sanitizer.
17. Objects dropped on the floor **are not to be used** until sanitized.

QUESTIONS ON SANITATION AND STERILIZATION

1. What is sterilization?

2. Sanitization involves the use of agents which are both physical and ....

3. Name two methods of keeping objects clean after sanitization has taken place.

4. What type of bacteria makes necessary the practice of sanitation in the barber-styling shop?

5. What are the dangers of using unsanitary implements and linens on patrons?

6. Distinguish between asepsis, sterile and sepsis.

7. Wash implements thoroughly with soap and .... water.

8. Formaldehyde is the active gas found in ....

9. What is an antiseptic?

10. What is a disinfectant?

11. What is a fumigant?

12. About how long does it take to sanitize implements when using: a) quats; b) 25% Formalin; c) 10% Formalin?

13. What is a wet sanitizer; how is it best used?

14. When using a disinfectant how are objects sanitized?

15. List six requirements of a good disinfectant.

16. What should be done with implements after sanitization in a disinfectant solution?

17. How should combs and brushes be kept after sanitization?

18. What is a dry or cabinet sanitizer?

19. What is the proper way to produce formaldehyde vapors in a cabinet sanitizer?

20. What is the composition of Formalin?

21. What is the best way to sanitize sharp implements and prevent their dulling?

22. What is a safe way to sanitize electrodes?

23. Effective sanitization in the barber-styling shop prevents the spread of ....

24. What strengths Formalin solution are recommended to: a) sanitize implements; b) cleanse hands?

25. a) What are four advantages of using "quats" as a sanitizer? b) In what strength are "quats" commonly used?

26. In measuring liquids: a) How many ounces equal one ordinary measuring glass; b) How many ounces equal 1 pint?

27. List five safety precautions when using chemical agents.

28. Is there a difference in the action of a disinfectant, germicide, or bactericide? Give reason for your answer.

SANITATION

1. Define sanitation.

2. Which unsanitary practices may spread disease in the barber-styling shop?

3. How should the hands be treated after touching a client suspected of having a skin or scalp infection?

4. What are five sanitary requirements of a barber-styling shop?

5. Which rule of sanitation should be observed regarding the use of headrests?

6. Why are neck strips or towels required?

7. What is the sanitary way to keep lotions, ointments, creams and powders?

8. What is the sanitary way to remove creams and ointments from their containers?

9. Where should towels be kept after laundering?

10. Where should dirty towels be kept?

11. Which supplies must be changed for each client?

12. Why should styptic pencils never be used in common?

13. If a towel or an implement is accidentally dropped on the floor, how should it be treated?

14. Why is it important to have a pure water supply?

15. How should loose hair and other waste material be disposed of?

16. What is the objection to the use of the common towel?

Chapter 4

IMPLEMENTS

A barber-stylist can be no better than the tools selected and used. Limitations and defects in equipment are not only hazardous, but usually result in work of poor quality. The purchase of standard materials helps to improve the quality and efficiency of the stylist's work. The barber-stylist should buy and use only superior implements from a reliable manufacturer. However, careless or improper use will quickly destroy the efficiency of any implement regardless of how perfectly it was made at the factory.

In order to give satisfactory professional services, the barber-stylist has occasion to use three principal implements, namely: razors, shears and clippers. In addition to these major implements, a number of accessory implements such as combs and brushes are employed.

The important facts to know about each implement are as follows:

1. Its main parts
2. The material of which it is made
3. Its various types and sizes
4. Its proper use and care

RAZORS

Razors are the sharpest and most delicate cutting implements used by barber-stylists. There are two types of straight razors, the regular straight razor and the straight razor with a safety guard.

The safety razor and the electric razor are not used professionally.

STRAIGHT RAZORS

The straight razor is one of the most important implements used by the barber-stylist. Over the years, the razor has undergone improvements in quality and design. For superior service, the barber-stylist should use only the highest quality razor.

The barber-stylist's tool kit should include several high grade razors. In the event that one razor becomes unfit for use, an immediate replacement should be available. Besides, razors receive less wear and better care when they are changed regularly.

Selecting the right kind of razor is a matter of personal choice. The best guides for buying high quality razors are:

1. Consult with a reliable company or salesman who can recommend the type of razor best suited for your work.
2. Consult with more experienced practitioners as to which razors they have found best for shaving.

To judge the value of a razor in any other way may be misleading. Merely observing the color or design of a razor does not reveal the true quality of the implement, nor does the ring of a razor have any significance as far as its hardness or softness is concerned. Ornamental handles on razors sometimes hide inferior quality.

The important points to know about a straight razor are: the main parts, the balance, the temper, the size (length and width of blade), the grind, the style and the finish.

The straight razor is constructed of a hardened steel blade attached to a handle by means of a pivot. The handle is made of either hard rubber, plastic

STRUCTURAL PARTS OF RAZOR

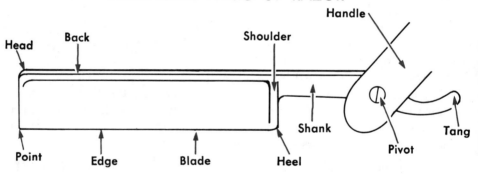

or bone. When the blade is closely examined, the following eleven parts can be seen, namely: the head, back, shoulder, tang, shank, heel, edge, point, blade, pivot and handle.

Razor Balance

The balance of a razor refers to the relative weight and length of the blade as compared with that of the handle.

A straight razor is properly balanced when the weight of the blade is equal to that of the handle. Proper balance means greater ease in handling the razor during shaving.

The balance may be determined by opening the razor and resting it on the first finger at the pivot. If the razor is not well balanced, the head of the razor will move upward or downward.

Razor Grinds

The grind of a razor represents the shape of the blade after it has been ground by the manufacturer. There are two general types of grind, namely: the concave and the wedge grind. The concave grinds come in full concave, ½ concave and ¼ concave.

The concave grind is generally preferred by most barber-stylists. It presents a hollow appearance when observed between the back and edge of the razor, being slightly thicker between the hollow part and the extreme edge. It is often referred to as the **hollow ground razor.** The resistance of the beard can more easily be felt with the hollow ground razor, thus warning the practitioner to check the sharpness of the cutting edge.

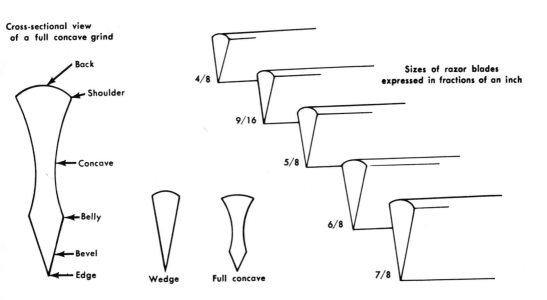

The ½ and ¼ concave grinds have less hollowness than the full concave. However, there will not be any more thickness between the concave and the extreme edge of the razor.

The wedge grind has no hollowness or concavity, both sides of the blade forming a sharp angle at the extreme edge of the razor. Most old type razors were made with a wedge grind. For most barber-stylists, learning how to sharpen a wedge grind is quite difficult. However, once they get accustomed to using it, they usually find that it produces an excellent shave. It is especially preferred for men with coarse, heavy beards.

Razor Tempers

Tempering the razor involves a special heat treatment given by the manufacturer. When a razor is properly tempered, it acquires the proper degree of hardness required for a good cutting edge. Razors can be purchased with either a hard, soft or medium temper. From this assortment, the barber-stylist can select the kind of temper which produces the most satisfactory shaving results.

The **hard tempered razor** will hold an edge longer, but is very difficult to sharpen once the edge is down.

The **soft tempered razor** is very easy to sharpen, but the sharp edge does not last long.

Razor Sizes

The **size of the razor** deals with the length and width of the blade. The width of the razor is measured in eighths or sixteenths of an inch, but most generally in eighths, such as 4/8, 5/8, 6/8 and 7/8. The 5/8 and 9/16 inch are the two most common sizes, with the 5/8 inch size leading in demand.

Razor Styles

The **style of a razor** indicates its shape and design. The modern razor has such features as a straight, parallel back and edge, a round heel, a square point, a flat or slightly round handle. To prevent scratching the skin, the barber-stylist usually rounds off the square point of the razor slightly by drawing the point of the razor along the edge of the hone.

Razor Finish

The **finish of a razor** is the condition of its surface, which may be either plain steel, crocus (polished steel) or metal plated (nickel or silver). Of these types, the crocus finish is usually the choice of the discriminating barber-stylist. Although the crocus finish is more costly, it usually lasts longer and does not show any signs of rust. The metal plated razors are undesirable because the finish wears off quickly and often hides a poor quality steel.

Razor Care

Care of razors. Razors will maintain their cutting quality if care is taken to prevent corrosion of the extremely fine edge. After use, they should be stropped and a little castor oil applied over the cutting edge, thus preventing the corrosive action of moisture. Be careful not to drop the razor, as the blade may be damaged. When closing the razor, be careful that the cutting edge does not strike the handle.

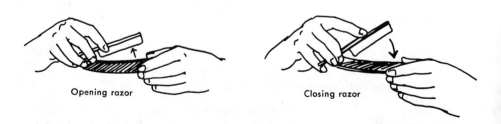

Opening razor   Closing razor

CHANGEABLE STRAIGHT RAZOR BLADE

A very popular type of razor being used by barber-stylists is the straight razor with a changeable blade. This type of razor appears the same, and is employed in the same manner as the conventional razor. However, once the blade has reached the stropping stage, it is discarded and replaced with a new blade.

The blades can be obtained with a square point, a rounded point, or one end rounded and the other end square. The razor may be used with or without a guard.

Many barber-stylists prefer this new type of razor because it eliminates honing and saves them time.

Follow manufacturer's directions for inserting a new blade or removing an old blade from this type of razor.

CHANGING BLADE WITH A GUARD

Removing the guard. With left hand, hold razor firmly above joint. Catching the blade in the teeth on upper part of guard, push blade out.

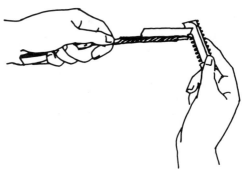

Slide blade into groove, pushing the end with your fingers. Place the tooth end of guard into the blade notch and slide the blade in until it clicks into position.

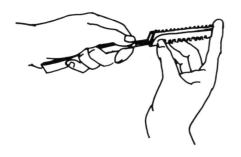

Slide the guard over blade, making sure the open end of the guard is over cutting edge of blade.

HAIRCUTTING SHEARS

The two most general kinds of shears used by barber-stylists are the German type, without a finger brace, and the French type, with a brace for the small finger. The French type is used to a greater extent than the German type.

The main parts. These shears are composed of two blades, one movable and the other still, fastened with a screw which acts as a pivot. Other parts of the shears are the cutting edges of the blades, two shanks, finger grip, finger brace, and thumb grip.

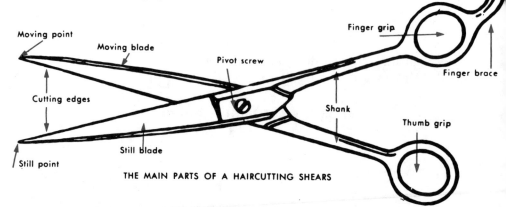

THE MAIN PARTS OF A HAIRCUTTING SHEARS

Size. Shears differ both in their length and size. The most popular lengths of shears are 7 and 7½ inches. The barber-stylist selects the one which he finds most convenient for easy handling.

A shorter 5 inch shears has been developed which some barber-stylists find very efficient for styling work.

Grinds. There are two types of shear grinds, the plain and the corrugated. The plain grind is most frequently used. It may be finished either smooth (knife edge), medium or coarse.

Set. The correct set of the shears is just as important as the grind of the blades. Shears with even the finest cutting edges are very poor cutting implements if the blades are not properly set.

Haircutting shears with detachable blade are becoming very popular with barber-stylists. With these shears, old blades are removed and replaced with new ones. This does away with the necessity of sending shears out to be sharpened. Practitioners find that it is more economical to replace the blades than to re-sharpen them.

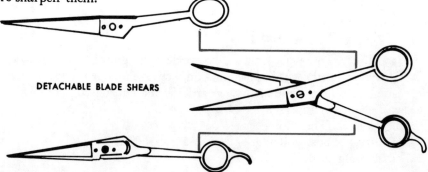

DETACHABLE BLADE SHEARS

THINNING SHEARS

Thinning or serrated shears are used occasionally by barber-stylists to reduce the bulkiness of the hair. There are two general types of thinning or serrated shears available.

The first type has notched teeth on the cutting edge of one blade, while the other blade has a straight cutting edge.

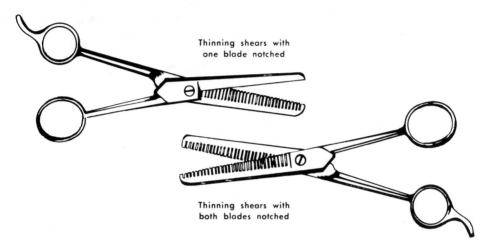

Thinning shears with
one blade notched

Thinning shears with
both blades notched

The second type has overlapping notched teeth on the cutting edges of both blades.

Thinning shears also differ in respect to the number of notched teeth on the cutting blade. The greater the number of notched teeth, the finer the hair strands can be cut.

The most common type used is the single serrated blade having 30 to 32 notched teeth. (Thinning shears are also available with detachable blades.)

CLIPPERS

The two types of hair clippers used by barber-stylists are the hand clipper and the electric clipper. However, the electric clippers are preferred in nearly all barber-styling shops.

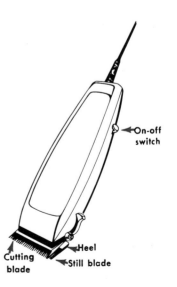

On-off switch

ELECTRIC CLIPPERS

The electric clippers operate either by means of a motor or by magnetic action. They have either a detachable cutting head or a non-detachable cutting head. The magnetic electric clippers are the most popular among barber-stylists. The visible parts of an electric clipper are: cutting blade, still blade, heel, switch, set screw and conducting cord.

Heel

Cutting blade

Still blade

Magnetic Type Clippers

The magnetic type clipper has one single cutting head. The barber-stylist can achieve different cutting thicknesses by placing his comb under the clipper blade or by attaching various size comb attachments, as pictured on the following page.

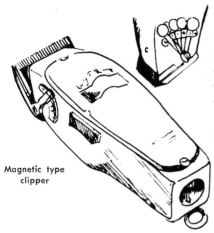

Magnetic type
clipper

Some vibratory type clippers have side adjustments for the purpose of:

1. Slowing down or speeding up their operation, or
2. Changing the cutting thickness of the blade

This clipper is usually preferred for use on children because of its noiseless operation.

Outliner or edger is a magnetic type clipper. It has a very fine cutting head for making the outline around the ear. This method of arching is much faster, as it eliminates the use of a razor. However, it does not cut as close as a razor would.

The outliner or edger is a very valuable implement for use in the styling of a client's hair or in those cases where the client does not want the arch around his ears or the back of his neck shaved.

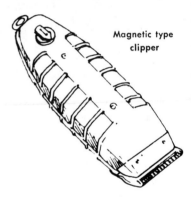

Magnetic type
clipper

Motor Driven Clippers

The motor driven clipper has interchangeable cutting heads available in all the various size heads. This design has a definite advantage, as the blade may be removed and sanitized. The motor driven type clipper is powerful and has the ability to cut very thick hair at a steady rate. Being a heavy duty clipper, it can give the barber-stylist many years of trouble-free service.

Motor driven
clipper

Cordless Clippers

A number of manufacturers have produced **clippers** as well as **outliners** which do not require an electric cord.

These machines are designed to rest in a special unit which replenishes (recharges) their power. The cordless clippers are a very important innovation for barber-stylists when working in rather close quarters.

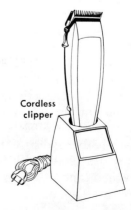

Cordless
clipper

DIFFERENT SIZE BLADES

Illustrated below are the various clipper blades. Each manufacturer has his own method of blade identification. A distinguishing number for a particular blade does not necessarily mean that the same number on another brand represents the same cutting size. Care must be taken when ordering.

Manufacturers are constantly improving their clipper blades to permit faster and better haircutting. Always be on the lookout for the newest developments in haircutting implements.

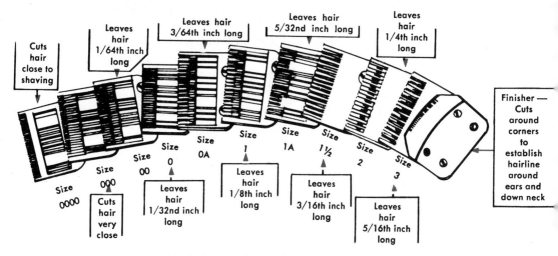

CARE OF ELECTRIC CLIPPERS

Magnetic type clippers do not require greasing. Occasionally, apply only one or two drops of oil between the blades. If a vibratory clipper is cutting exceptionally slow or is pulling the hair, immerse the blades into **clipper oil** and then turn the clipper on and off. This will clean the blades and oil them at the same time. The clipper may also be immersed in a cleaning solvent and then a few drops of oil added to the blades.

Motor driven clippers. To detach the cutting blade from the still blade, slide the still blade out from under the compression spring. The blades may be washed under hot water, reassembled and a drop of oil placed in the two holes found in the compression plate. Remove the name plate and check the grease. The grease chamber should be kept about 2/3 full. If the gears should come out, be careful to reassemble them the same way as they were originally. Remove the carbon brush knobs and check the carbon brushes. If they are worn down, replace them with new brushes. Add a few drops of oil weekly to the oiler at the rear of the clipper. Clean the hair from the oil vents surrounding the switch, to ensure proper ventilation.

WARRANTY

If an electric clipper is running incorrectly, do not attempt to repair it, for this may nullify your guarantee. Return the clipper to the manufacturer for professional, guaranteed service.

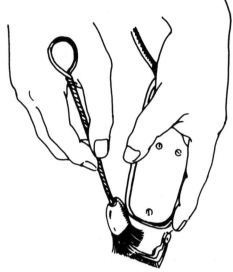

Whenever clipper blades are oiled, remove the excess oil with a dry cloth. Remember, a little oil on the blades will reduce the cutting ability of the blades. Clipper blades are difficult to sharpen. Therefore, it is advisable that this be done by an expert. Keep in mind that repeated sharpenings will lessen the cutting thickness of the blade.

Care of electric clippers. Properly cared for, electric clippers can last several years. Manufacturer's directions should be followed carefully, to assure best use and to keep the manufacturer's warranty valid for a specified period.

The clipper brush has stiff bristles. It is used to remove loose hair clippings from the clipper, keeping it clean and sanitary.

Cleaning clippers with a clipper brush

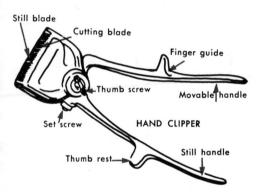

HAND CLIPPER

While hand clippers are rarely used in the modern barber-stylist shop, practitioners should have a hand clipper available in the event the electric clipper goes out of order.

These clippers are equipped with cutting blades ranging from #0000 to #3. The #0000 is the shortest and the #3 is the longest. Because of the time required to change the blades, the barber-stylist using hand clippers usually employs two pairs. The #000 and the #1 cutting blades are the most commonly used.

Care of the hand clipper. The thumb screw must be adjusted to maintain the proper tension between the blades. If this is not done, hair will get between the two sets of blades and cause the clipper to pull the hair. Should this occur, remove the thumb screw, the spring washer, the compression plate and the cutting blade. Wash both blades with hot water, dry them thoroughly and reassemble the clipper. A drop of oil may be applied toward the heel of the blades on the still blade. Bear in mind that over-oiling will also allow the hair to enter between the blades. The set screw must be altered, to adjust the tension between the two blades. If the set screw is too tight your hand muscles will tire quickly. If the set screw is too loose, the moving handle will not return, causing the clipper to "jam" in the hair. Should this occur, the movable handle must be forced back to its original position. The hand clipper would then have to be disassembled, cleaned and reassembled as above.

BARBER-STYLING ACCESSORIES USED IN SHAVING

HONES

Various types of hones (honz) are available for the purpose of sharpening razors. A hone is primarily a rectangular block composed of abrasive material. Since it is harder than steel, the abrasive in the hone is capable of cutting or filing an edge on the razor.

The final choice of hone rests mainly with the practitioner. The question often arises as to which type of hone will best serve to sharpen a razor. As a general rule, any type of hone is satisfactory, provided it is properly used and is capable of producing a sharp cutting edge on the razor.

As a result of their experiences, barber-stylists may prefer one type of hone to another. The student usually practices with a slow-cutting hone, while the experienced practitioner generally prefers a faster cutting hone.

In selecting a hone, the barber-stylist must consider that the finer the abrasive in a hone, the slower its action in developing an effective edge on the razor.

Depending on their source, hones are divided into three main groups: natural hones, synthetic hones and combination hones.

Natural Hones

Natural hones are derived from natural rock deposits. These hones are usually used wet with either water or lather.

Water hone is a natural hone cut out of rock formations, usually imported from Germany. Accompanying the water hone is a small piece of slate of the same texture, called the rubber. As the rubber is applied over the hone, which is moistened with water, a proper cutting surface is developed. Care must be taken when using the rubber hone not to work a bevel into the hone.

Water hone

The water hone is primarily a **slow-cutting hone.** When used as directed by the manufacturer a smooth and lasting edge can be formed on the razor. Its color may be either grey or brown. Of the two colors, the brown **water hone** is considered to be a slightly better grade, and also exerts a slightly faster cutting action.

The Belgian (bel'jan) **hone** is a natural hone cut out of rock formation found in Belgium. It is a slow-cutting hone, but a little faster than the water hone. It is capable of putting a very sharp edge on the razor. Lather is generally applied to the hone when honing, to facilitate movement of the razor.

Belgian hone

One type of Belgian hone consists of a top **light yellowish colored rock** glued on to the back of a **dark red slate.** The principal advantage is to yield a keen cutting edge on the razor. It can be used either **wet or dry.**

Synthetic Hones

Synthetic or manufactured hone

Synthetic (sin-thet'ik) **hones,** such as the **Swaty hone** and the carborundum hone, are manufactured products. These hones can be used dry, or a lather can be spread over them before use.

Because it cuts faster than the water hone, the synthetic hone has the advantage of producing a keen cutting edge on the razor in less time.

Carborundum hone

Carborundum (kar-bor-un'dum) **hone** is a synthetic hone produced in this country. The barber-stylist has a choice of several types, ranging from a slow-cutting hone to a fast-cutting hone. Many practitioners prefer the fast cutting type of hone because of its quick sharpening action. The carborundum hone should not be used by a beginning student because it may produce a very rough edge if not handled properly.

Combination Hones

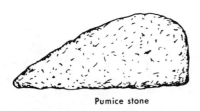

Combination hone

Combination hones consist of a water hone and synthetic hone. The synthetic side is dark brown in color and is used first to develop a good cutting edge. To give the razor a finished edge, it is stroked over the side of the water hone. With this type of hone, the practitioner can use the synthetic hone when the razor is bad, use the water hone when the razor needs a little touching-up, or use both hones together, simply by turning it over.

Most barber-stylists use either the carborundum or the combination hones. It is advisable, however, to be familiar with the other types of hones and understand the benefits of each.

GENERAL INFORMATION ON HONES

Hones are to a large extent a matter of choice, and the type of steel in a razor may make some difference as to whether a good edge can be put on it with a particular type of hone. There are a great many other hones available, besides the several mentioned, which will give very satisfactory results.

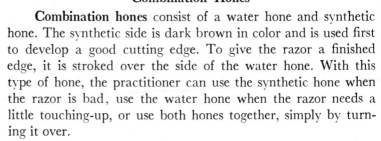

Pumice stone

Care of hone. Always clean the hone before using. Whenever a hone fills with tiny steel particles they must be removed. In order to obtain satisfactory results the best method is by using water and a **pumice stone.** If a new hone is very rough, the same method can be used to work it into shape.

When wet honing is done, the hone should always be **wiped dry** after each usage. This aids in cleaning the hone and also wipes away the tiny particles of steel that adhere to its cutting surface.

STROPS

Unlike the hone, which is designed to grind the edge of the razor, the strop is intended to bring the razor to a smooth, whetted edge.

A good strop is made of durable and flexible material, has the proper thickness and texture, and shows a smooth finished surface. Some barber-stylists like a thin strop, whereas others prefer a thick, heavy strop. Most strops are made in pairs, one side being leather and the other side being canvas. The best assurance for a good strop is the reliability of the manufacturer.

Various types of strops are available to the barber-stylist. Depending upon the material they are made from, they fall into the following groups: French or German, canvas, cowhide, horsehide and imitation leather. The better grade strops are broken in by the manufacturer. Let us consider these one at a time.

French or German Strop

This is a combination strop with leather on one side and a finishing strop on the other. This strop is used by many barber-stylists to facilitate the stropping of their styling razors.

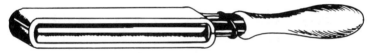

French or German Strop

Canvas Strop

Canvas (kan'vas) **strop.** It is composed of high quality linen or silk woven into a fine or coarse texture. A fine-textured linen strop is most desirable for putting a lasting edge on a razor.

To obtain the best results, a new canvas strop should be thoroughly broken in. A daily hand finish will keep its surface smooth and in readiness for stropping.

For a **hand finish,** the canvas strop is given the following treatment:

1. Attach the swivel end of the strop to a fixed point, such as a nail.
2. Hold the other end tightly over a smooth and level surface.
3. Rub a bar of dry soap over strop, working it well into the grain of the canvas.
4. Rub a smooth glass bottle over the strop several times, each time forcing the soap into the grain and also removing any excess soap.

Leather and canvas strop

Cowhide Strop

The cowhide strop was originally imported from Russia. To this day it still bears the name **Russian strop,** even though it may be manufactured in this country. This name usually implies that the strop is made of cowhide and that the Russian method of tanning was employed.

The cowhide or Russian strop is one of the best strops in use today. When new, it requires a daily hand finish until such time as it is thoroughly broken in. There are several ways of breaking in a Russian strop. A method frequently used is as follows:

1. Rub dry pumice stone over the strop in order to remove the outer nap and develop a smooth surface.
2. Rub stiff lather into the strop.
3. Rub dry pumice stone over the strop until smooth.
4. Clean off the strop.
5. Rub fresh stiff lather into the strop.
6. Rub a smooth glass bottle over the strop several times until a smooth surface is developed.

Another method of breaking in a Russian strop is to omit the pumice stone. Instead, stiff lather is rubbed into the strop with the aid of a smooth glass bottle or with the palm of the hand.

Horsehide Strop

Strops made of horsehide are divided into two main groups: ordinary horsehide strop and the shell.

1. An **ordinary horsehide strop** is of medium grade and has a fine grain. It has a tendency to be very smooth. In this condition it does not readily impart the proper edge to the razor. For this reason, it is not recommended for professional use. However, it is suitable for private use.
2. The other type of horsehide strop is called **shell** or **Russian shell**. This is a high quality strop taken from the rump area of the horse. Although it is quite expensive, it makes one of the best possible strops for the barber-stylist. It always remains smooth and requires very little, if any, breaking in.

Imitation Leather Strop

Imitation leather. This type of strop has not proven too satisfactory. Because of the availability of high-quality strops, it is wise to avoid strops made of **imitation leather.**

STROP DRESSING

Strop dressing serves a useful purpose in the barber-styling shop. It cleans the leather strop, preserves the finish and also improves the draw and sharpening qualities. For proper use, apply a very small amount of dressing to the leather strop. Rub well into the pores and remove the surplus. Always wait at least 24 hours between applications.

LATHER RECEPTACLES

Lather receptacles are containers used to produce the lather necessary for shaving. The most commonly used shaving receptacles are:

1. Electric latherizer.
2. Press button can latherizer.
3. Lather mug with paper lining.

Lather-making devices, such as the **electric latherizer,** are far superior to the lather mug. Not only are these machines cleaner and more sanitary, but they are more convenient and easier to operate. Clients are favorably impressed by the clean, sanitary preheated lather coming from these modern machines. For satisfactory performance follow the manufacturer's instructions on their proper use and care.

Lather mug with Paper lining   Press Button Can   Electric latherizer Cream soap type

The **electric latherizer** is the most widely used lather-making device employed in barber-styling shops. This method is now used to the practical exclusion of all other lather-making methods.

Lather mugs are receptacles made out of glass, earthenware, rubber or metal. When the lather mug is to be used, shaving soap and warm water are thoroughly mixed with the aid of the lather brush. Since the lather mug is continually exposed and collects dirt easily, it requires a thorough cleansing after each client.

To be sanitary, a separate **paper lining** should be used in the lather mug for each client.

Lather mugs or press button cans come in handy in the absence or breakdown of electrical lather-making devices.

Note: Lather mugs have a very limited use in the modern styling shop.

LATHER BRUSHES

The **lather brush** serves to apply the soap lather which softens the beard. Most barber-stylists favor the number three type of lather brush. However, some barber-stylists use the larger sizes. The vulcanized type of lather brush is the most durable, since its bristles will not fall apart in hot water.

To protect the public against contaminated brushes, many states have passed laws requiring that brushes made from animal hair be free from anthrax germs at the time of purchase. These brushes must contain the imprint "Sterilized" to show that the manufacturer has taken necessary steps to destroy the anthrax germs. The lather brush must be sanitized after each use.

Note: Like the lather mug, the lather brush has very limited use in the modern barber-styling shop.

Lather brush

SHAVING SOAP

Shaving soaps are presented in great detail in the chapter on **Chemistry.**

OTHER BARBER-STYLING ACCESSORIES

The barber-stylist uses the following accessories to make his work more efficient.

1. Hydraulic chair.
2. Combs.
3. Hair brushes and neck dusters.

4. Tweezers.
5. Comedone extractor.
6. Electric hair vacuum.

HYDRAULIC CHAIR

A **hydraulic chair** is an essential fixture for rendering comfortable services to clients. To meet the practitioner's needs, it can be easily adjusted both in height and position. Generally, such chairs are spaced about 4½ to 5 feet apart from center to center.

To use the chair properly,
1. Lower and lock the chair before a client gets into or out of it.
2. Always lock the chair during any type of service.
3. Rotate the chair to the proper position and lock it.
4. Operate the chair's hand pump in a skillful and quiet way.
5. Press the release when removing or adjusting the headrest.

For effective operation, follow the manufacturer's instructions at all times.

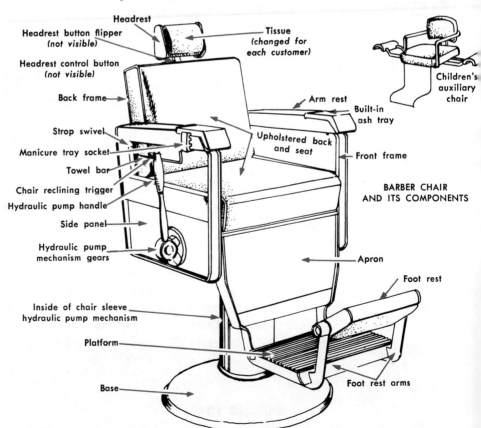

Headrest
Headrest button flipper (not visible)
Tissue (changed for each customer)
Headrest control button (not visible)
Children's auxiliary chair
Back frame
Arm rest
Built-in ash tray
Strop swivel
Manicure tray socket
Upholstered back and seat
Front frame
Towel bar
Chair reclining trigger
Hydraulic pump handle
BARBER CHAIR AND ITS COMPONENTS
Side panel
Hydraulic pump mechanism gears
Apron
Foot rest
Inside of chair sleeve hydraulic pump mechanism
Platform
Base
Foot rest arms

COMBS

Combs are available in a variety of shapes and sizes. The correct size to use depends on the choice of the barber-stylist. Combs are made of hard rubber, bone or plastic. Because of the cost, the combs made from bone are not very popular. Plastic combs are combustible and not as durable as the other kinds of combs. Combs made of **hard rubber** are the most popular and are used by barber-stylists.

Utility should be the most important consideration in the selection of combs. Hair-stylists could make their work somewhat easier by using light-colored combs when servicing clients with dark hair, and dark combs when servicing clients with light hair.

The teeth of the comb may be fine (close together) or coarse (far apart). To keep combs in good condition, avoid contact with heat and moisture, and store them in a cool, dry place. It is important that the teeth of the combs have rounded ends to avoid scratching or irritating a client's scalp.

Haircutting comb used for cutting or trimming. It has desired features: size, shape, weight and balance. It is usually 7½ inches long.

Haircutting comb

Wide tooth comb for flat-tops. Takes widest clippers.

Wide tooth comb

Handle comb with wide teeth. Can be used to spread the relaxer in chemical hair straightening.

Handle comb

All-purpose comb may be used for general hair cutting and styling. Popular size comes 7¾ inches long.

All-purpose comb

STYLING BRUSHES

Hair brush

Barber-stylists use a number of different brushes in their work. The texture of such brushes vary with the type of service they are expected to perform and their quality. Hair brushes used by the barber-stylist are usually firm and stiff.

Hair brushes are made out of plastic, wood or metal and contain either natural or artificial bristles, such as nylon. If made of natural bristles, the brush must bear the marking "sterilized."

The professional barber-stylist most often uses a **metallic brush,** preferably of aluminum. Its split back enables the barber-stylist to cleanse and sanitize the brush. **Plastic brushes** are not recommended for professional use. **Wooden brushes** are an improvement over the plastic brushes.

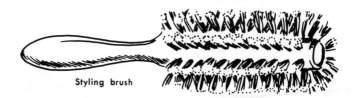

Styling brush

REMINDER

The use of hair brushes, shaving brushes and hair dusters (neck dusters) are forbidden in a number of states. Since they are used in common on a number of clients, some states consider them to be health hazards and forbid their use. If permitted, brushes must be sanitized after each use.

Electric vibrator

ELECTRIC VIBRATORS

The **vibrator** is an electric appliance used in facial and scalp massage to produce mechanical manipulations. (For additional information see "Electrical Equipment" in the chapter on **Electricity.**)

COMEDONE EXTRACTOR

The **comedone extractor** is a metallic implement having a screwed attachment at each end. A fine needle point is at one end and the opposite end is round, has a hole in the center and is used to press out blackheads.

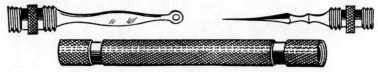

Blackhead (comedone) extractor

REMOVING LOOSE HAIRS

Since a number of states have forbidden the use of hair dusters, other methods have been employed to remove loose hairs from clients.

1. A small towel, properly folded, can be manipulated to dust off loose hairs.
2. Paper neck strips are popularly used to remove loose hairs.
3. Small electric hand vacuums and air hoses are also being employed to clean out loose hairs.

All of these methods are in compliance with state and local health codes.

ELECTRIC HAIR VACUUM

The electric hair vacuum provides quick clean-up service after a haircut. By its powerful action, it can remove all loose hair and some loose dandruff. It is particularly suitable after a crew cut and for going over the forehead and around the neck and ears. Make sure to sanitize the nozzle applicator after each use and empty the container as hair accumulates in it.

Tweezer

TWEEZERS

The tweezer is a metallic implement having two blunt prongs at one end. The blunt prongs of the tweezer are used to pluck unsightly hair. To remove hair, pull it in the same direction in which it grows. For added comfort, the treated area can be steamed and a little cold cream applied. The tweezer may also be used to pull out ingrown hairs.

The automatic tweezer is a more recent development which is quickly gaining in popularity. The automatic tweezer is set and a "spring action" quickly and painlessly extracts the hair.

ELECTRIC HAIR DRYER

The electric hair dryer delivers hot, medium or cold air for the proper and rapid drying of the hair.

Note: For electrical air-waving devices with and without attachments, consult chapter on **Air-waving.**

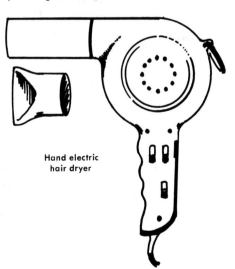

Hand electric hair dryer

QUESTIONS

IMPLEMENTS

1. Name the principal implements used in barber-styling.
2. Name the accessory implements used by the barber-stylist.
3. What should the barber-stylist look for in the purchase of implements?

STRAIGHT RAZORS

1. Name eight important points to be learned about razors.
2. Name the eleven important parts of a razor.
3. Describe the standard style of a razor.
4. Why should the barber-stylist round off the sharp point of a razor?
5. Which razor widths are used by barber-stylists?
   Which widths are the most commonly used?
6. Which part of the razor is ground by the manufacturer?
7. What is meant by the finish of a razor?
8. What is a crocus finish?
9. Why is balance important in a razor?
10. What is meant by the temper of a razor?
11. What is the proper way to care for razors?

SHEARS

1. Name the important parts of haircutting shears.
2. Distinguish between the German and French types of haircutting shears.
3. How are the lengths of shears usually measured? Which sizes are mostly used?
4. What are the two main types of shear grinds, and which type is mostly used?
5. Give the finish of the various plain grinds. Which one is preferred by the barber-stylist?

CLIPPERS

1. Name two types of hair clippers.
2. Name two types of electric clippers.
3. Name the visible parts of an electric clipper.
4. Which type of clipper is recommended for making the outline around the ear?
5. What size clipper blade gives the shortest cut?

ACCESSORY IMPLEMENTS

1. What is a hone?
2. Name three types of hones available to barber-stylists.
3. Name two kinds of natural hones.
4. Describe the water hone.
5. Describe the Belgian hone.
6. Which natural hones are usually used wet, either with water or lather?
7. Which hones may be used either dry or with lather?
8. What is a fast-cutting hone? Give an example.
9. Which strops can be used by barber-stylists?
10. Of what are combs made?
11. Which kind of comb is most commonly used by barber-stylists?
12. Name three shaving soap receptacles.

Chapter 5

HONING
AND STROPPING

A barber-stylist who knows the right way to hone and strop razors has mastered an important professional skill. To acquire the right technique in honing and stropping requires constant practice and long experience under the guidance of a qualified instructor. It should be emphasized that regardless of the technical knowledge possessed by the practitioner, a good shave cannot be given with a dull razor.

HONING

Honing (hōn′ing) is the process of sharpening a razor blade on a hone. The main object in honing is to obtain a perfect cutting edge on the razor. For the beginner a slow-cutting hone is preferable to a fast-cutting hone.

Prepare hone for honing. Honing will be more satisfactory if the razor and hone are kept at room temperature. Depending on which hone is used, it may be moistened with water or lather, or kept dry. When in use, the hone should be kept perfectly flat. Sufficient space should be provided to permit free arm movements in honing.

TECHNIQUE OF HONING

The razor blade is sharpened by honing the razor with smooth, even strokes of equal number and pressure on both sides of the blade. The angle at which the blade is stroked must be the same for both sides of the blade. An old, useless razor may be used for practicing the various movements.

How to hold the razor. Grasp the razor handle comfortably in the right hand as follows:

1. Rest index finger on top of the side part of the shank.
2. Rest ball of thumb at the joint.
3. Place second finger back of the razor near the edge of the shank.
4. Fold remaining fingers around the handle to permit easy turning of the razor.

How to hold the hone. Lay the hone flat in your left hand. Hold the hone firmly with the index finger and the little finger.

CAUTION. Make sure that the fingertips do not project above the hone. If you do, you will cut them.

Turning the razor. Place razor on hone with razor edge facing left. Turn razor from one side to the other. The rolling movement across back of razor is produced with the fingers, rather than the wrist. Practice the turning action until it is mastered.

First stroke in honing. The razor blade must be stroked diagonally across the hone, drawing the blade towards the cutting edge and heel of the razor.

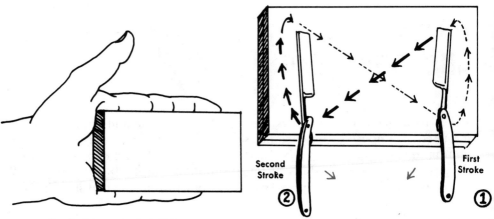

Fig. 1—Proper way to hold hone   Fig. 2—Proper honing of a razor

Second stroke in honing. After the completion of the first stroke, the razor is turned on its back with the fingers in the same manner as you would roll a pencil, without turning the wrist. As the razor is rolled over on its back, slide it upwards from left-bottom of hone to left-top of hone.

Completing the second stroke. Draw razor from left-top corner of hone to right-bottom corner of hone so that the edge faces to the right and the heel leads. Keep equal pressure on the razor at all times. As the razor is rolled over on its back, slide it upwards from right-bottom to right-top.

Repeat strokes. In going from one step to the other, try to maintain four different movements, rather than a sweeping movement. The number of strokes required in honing depends on the condition of the razor's edge.

Testing razor on moistened thumb nail. Depending on the hardness of the hone and the number of strokes taken, the razor edge may be either blunt, keen, coarse or rough. Different sensations are felt when the razor is passed lightly across the thumb nail, moistened with water or lather. (See Fig. 3.)

Magnified razor edge. While honing, the abrasive material makes small cuts in the sides of the razor blade. The small cuts resemble the teeth of a saw and they point in the same direction as the stroke, as shown in Fig. 4.

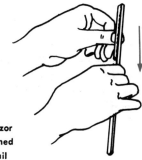

Fig. 3—Testing razor
on moistened
thumbnail

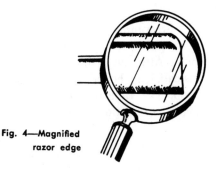

Fig. 4—Magnified
razor edge

To test the razor edge, place it on the nail of the thumb and slowly draw it from the heel to the point of the razor.

1. **A perfect or keen edge** has fine teeth and tends to dig into the nail with a smooth steady grip.
2. **A blunt or dull razor edge** passes over the nail smoothly, without any cutting power.
3. **A coarse razor edge** digs into the nail with a jerky feeling.
4. **A rough or overhoned edge** has large teeth which stick to the nail and produce a harsh, grating sound.
5. **A nick in the razor.** A feeling of a slight gap or unevenness in the draw will indicate a nick in the razor.

Correcting an overhoned razor. To eliminate an overhoned edge, draw the razor backward in a diagonal line across the hone, using the same movement and pressure as in regular honing. One or two strokes each way will usually remove the rough edge. This is called **back honing.** The razor is then honed again, being careful to prevent overhoning.

CARE OF THE HONE

The barber-stylist should know how to use and take care of the particular type of hone he has selected. The manufacturer's instructions offer a reliable guide for keeping the hone in good, serviceable condition.

After using any kind of hone, always wipe the surface clean and cover it. Make sure that all adhering steel particles resulting from the honing are completely removed. Whenever a dry hone has been used, rub its surface with water and pumice (pum'is) stone, wipe clean and keep covered.

A new hone may require a preliminary treatment to put it into good working shape. If a new hone is very rough, rub its surface with water and pumice stone. No preliminary treatment is required for the water hone, as it is ready for immediate use.

Before using, make sure that the surface of the hone is smooth and clean, as this will greatly diminish normal time required to put an edge on the razor. Use the hone either moist or dry, as directed by the manufacturer.

STROPPING

Stropping a razor is a fine art developed by repeated practice. The aim in stropping is to smooth and shape the razor's edge into a keen cutting implement. After being honed, the razor seldom needs any stropping on the canvas. Instead, the honed razor is stropped directly over the surface of the leather strop. The time to use the canvas strop is when the razor develops a smooth edge from continued use. The effect of the canvas strop is similar to mild honing.

THE TECHNIQUE OF STROPPING

Hold the end of the strop firmly in the left hand so it cannot sag. Hold it close to the side, and as high as it is comfortable. Take razor in right hand, well up in the hand. Hold the razor so that the first finger is on the shank, the second finger is on the handle and the thumb rests slightly on both parts. At the same time, the first finger of the right hand rests at the edge of the strop.

Turning the razor. Place the razor on the strop, turning it with fingers and thumb. Practice turning action until it is mastered.

In stropping the razor, use a long diagonal stroke with even pressure from the heel to the point.

Note: The direction of the razor in stropping is the reverse of that used in honing.

First stroke. Start stroke at top edge of strop closest to the chair (Fig. 1). Draw the razor perfectly flat, with back leading, straight over the surface of strop.

Bear just heavy enough on the strop to feel the razor draw. Do not worry about speed. This will come automatically with practice.

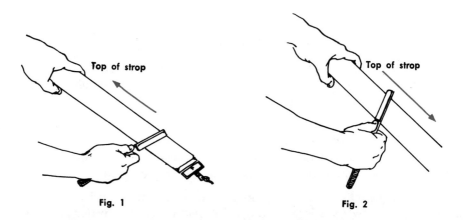

Fig. 1   Fig. 2

Second stroke. When the first stroke is completed, turn the razor on the back of the blade by rolling it in the fingers without turning the hand, as in Fig. 2. Now draw the razor away from you, towards the hydraulic chair, thus completing the second stroke in stropping.

Final testing of razor on moistened tip of thumb, prior to shaving. Touch the razor edge lightly, as in Fig. 3, and note the reaction. A dull edge produces no drawing feeling. A razor that has the proper cutting edge tends to stick to the thumb and will not slide along it.

If the razor edge produces a rough, disagreeable sound upon testing, it indicates that the cutting edge is still coarse. To correct this condition, additional finishing on the leather strop is necessary.

Should the razor edge yield a smooth feeling upon testing, finish it again on the canvas strop, followed by a few more strokes on the leather strop.

Fig. 3

CARE OF STROPS

A leather strop becomes better or worse according to the care it is given. Do not fold a strop, but keep it suspended or attached to a swivel, or laid flat. When a leather strop appears rough, it needs a hand finish to make it smooth. Various types of strop dressings are available for the purpose of cleaning and conditioning the leather side of the strop. A canvas strop needs a daily hand finish to keep it in good condition. (For information on how to break in strops, see chapter on **Implements.**)

A strop is sanitary if it is kept clean. Accumulated grit is removed from a canvas strop by rubbing it with lather. To remove imbedded dirt, the leather strop is softened with lather and then scraped with the back side of the shear blade or similar implement.

QUESTIONS ON HONING AND STROPPING

1. How does the barber-stylist acquire the right technique of honing and stropping?
2. What is accomplished by proper honing?
3. Describe the manner of stroking a razor on a hone.
4. Describe the first stroke used in honing.
5. How is the second stroke performed in honing?
6. What happens to the razor edge as it is honed?
7. Why should the honed razor be tested on a moist thumb nail?
8. What is the sign of a keen edge or a properly honed razor?
9. What is the sign of a blunt razor edge?
10. What is the sign of a coarse razor edge?
11. What is the sign of a rough or overhoned razor edge?
12. What is the proper care of hones?
13. What is the purpose of stropping the razor after honing?
14. How does stropping differ from honing?
15. Which strop is used on a freshly honed razor?
16. What is the proper way to hold the strop?
17. How should the razor be held for stropping?
18. Where should the first stroke be started?
19. Describe the movements used in stropping.
20. Which fingers are used in rolling and turning the razor in the hand?
21. How much pressure should be applied in stropping?
22. How is the razor edge tested after stropping?
23. What is the sign of a smooth, sharp razor edge?
24. What is the sign of a dull razor edge?
25. How can the canvas strop be kept clean and smooth?
26. What is the purpose of stropping the razor before shaving?
27. In what position should the strops be kept?
28. What is used to clean a dirty leather strop?

Chapter 6
SHAVING

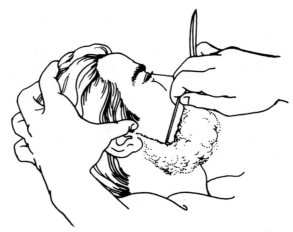

Shaving is one of the basic services performed in the barber-syling shop. It is an important service and deserves a great deal of attention and skill. With the wide use of safety razors and electric razors, shaving has greatly declined in the barber-styling shop volume of service.

Face shaving is necessary for hygienic, business and social reasons. To feel clean and look their best, nearly all men require daily shaving. Since there is a universal need for this service, every effort should be made to again attract men to the shop for this professional service.

FUNDAMENTALS OF SHAVING

The object of shaving is to remove the visible part of the hair extending over the surface of the skin of the face and neck in such a manner as not to cause irritation to the skin. The professional barber-stylist employs a straight razor and warm lather when shaving a client.

Although there are certain general principles of shaving which apply to all men, there are nevertheless particular exceptions. Account should be taken of the texture of the hair (coarse, medium or fine), the grain of the beard and the sensitivity of the skin to the razor edge, shaving cream, hot towels and astringent lotion. Hot towels should not be used when the skin is chapped or blistered from heat or cold. **A person having any infection of the beard must not be shaved, as this may be the means of spreading the infection.**

FOUR STANDARD SHAVING POSITIONS AND STROKES

To obtain the best cutting stroke, the razor must glide over the surface at an angle with the grain of the hair. It should be drawn in a forward movement with the point of the razor in the lead.

To shave the face and neck with the greatest of ease and efficiency, the practitioner employs the following standard positions and strokes:

1. Free hand position and stroke.
2. Back hand position and stroke.
3. Reverse free hand position and stroke.
4. Reverse back hand position and stroke.

Under each of the standard shaving positions and strokes, consideration should be given to:

1. When to use a particular shaving stroke.
2. How to hold the razor for each stroke.
   a) Position of right hand with razor.
   b) Position of left hand.
3. How to stroke the razor.

Review the proper method of honing and stropping the razor before learning each shaving stroke.

OPENING AND CLOSING THE RAZOR

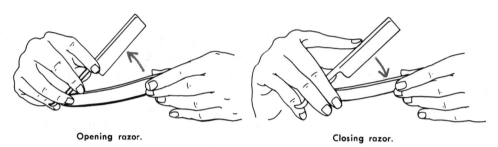

Opening razor.   Closing razor.

CAUTION. When closing the razor, be careful that the cutting edge does not strike the handle.

Exercise No. 1

FREE HAND POSITION AND STROKE

In the first lesson, the student learns the correct way to perform the free hand position and stroke. To master this important shaving skill requires regular practice.

1. **When to use the free hand stroke.** The free hand position and stroke is used in six of the fourteen shaving areas. See Numbers 1, 3, 4, 8, 11, 12 on the accompanying illustration shown in red.

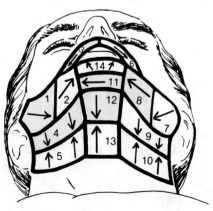

Diagram of shaving areas.

- 1. Free hand.
- 2. Back hand.
- 3. Free hand.
- 4. Free hand.
-    5. Reverse free hand.
-    6. Back hand.
-    7. Back hand.
- 8. Free hand.
-    9. Back hand.
-    10. Reverse free hand.
- 11. Free hand.
- 12. Free hand.
-    13. Reverse free hand.
-    14. Reverse free hand.

2. **How to hold the razor.** The position of the right hand is as follows:

a) Take the razor in right hand.

b) Hold handle of razor between third and fourth fingers, the small fingertip resting on the tang of the razor. Place tip of thumb on reverse side of the shank close to blade. Rest tips of fingers on the back of the shank.

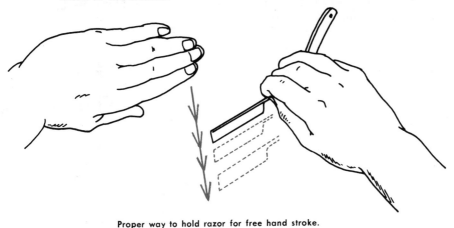

Proper way to hold razor for free hand stroke.

c) Raise elbow of the right arm nearly level with the shoulder. This is the position used in the arm movement. (*Note: Some practitioners prefer to use the wrist movement, in which case the elbow is not raised as high.*)

The position of the left hand is as follows:

a) Keep the fingers of the left hand dry in order to prevent them from slipping on the wet face.

b) Keep left hand back of razor in order to stretch skin tightly under razor.

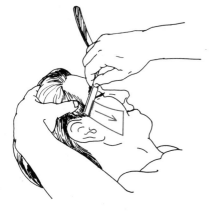

3. **How to stroke the razor.** The free hand stroke is performed in the following manner:

a) Use a gliding stroke towards you.

b) Direct the stroke towards the point of the razor in a forward sawing movement.

Free hand stroke.
Shaving area No. 1.

Exercise No. 2

BACK HAND POSITION AND STROKE

After the student has developed skill in performing the free hand position and stroke, he is ready to proceed with the back hand position and stroke.

1. **When to use the back hand stroke.** The back hand stroke is used in four of the fourteen basic shaving areas. See Numbers 2, 6, 7, 9 on the accompanying illustration shown in red.

1. Free hand.	8. Free hand.
• 2. Back hand.	• 9. Back hand.
3. Free hand.	10. Reverse free hand.
4. Free hand.	11. Free hand.
5. Reverse free hand.	12. Free hand.
• 6. Back hand.	13. Reverse free hand.
• 7. Back hand.	14. Reverse free hand.

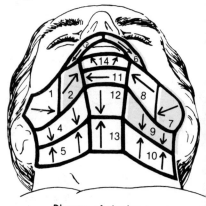

Diagram of shaving areas.

2. **How to hold the razor.** The position of the right hand is as follows:
   a) Hold the shank of the razor firmly with the handle slightly bent back.
   b) Rest the shank of the razor on the first two joints of the first three fingers. Hold thumb on the underside of the shank. Rest end of tang on inside of first joint of third finger as in Fig. 1. Little finger remains idle. For two other ways to hold razor, see Figs. 2 and 3.

Fig. 1. First 2 joints of the first 3 fingers.

Fig. 2. First 2 joints of the first 2 fingers.

Fig. 3. Fingers wrapped around handle.

   c) Turn the back of the hand away from you and bend the wrist slightly downward. Then raise the elbow so that you can move the arm freely. This is the position used for the back hand stroke with the arm movement. (*Note: Some practitioners prefer to use the wrist movement, in which case the arm is not held as high as for the arm movement.*)

The position of the left hand is as follows:

a) Keep the fingers of the left hand dry in order to prevent them from slipping.

b) Stretch the skin tightly under razor.

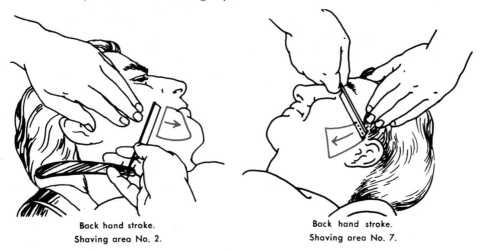

Back hand stroke.
Shaving area No. 2.

Back hand stroke.
Shaving area No. 7.

3. **How to stroke the razor.** The back hand stroke is performed in the following manner:

a) Use a gliding stroke away from you.

b) Direct stroke towards the point of the razor in a forward sawing movement.

Exercise No. 3

REVERSE FREE HAND POSITION AND STROKE

The reverse free hand stroke and the free hand stroke are similar in some respects, the main difference being that the movement is directed upwards in the reverse free hand stroke, while the palm of the hand faces the practitioner.

1. **When to use the reverse free hand stroke.** The reverse free hand stroke is used in four of the fourteen basic shaving areas. See Numbers 5, 10, 13, 14 on the accompanying illustration shown in red.

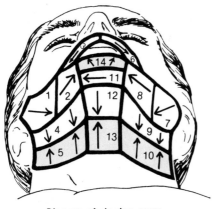

Diagram of shaving areas.

1. **Free hand.**
2. **Back hand.**
3. **Free hand.**
4. **Free hand.**
• 5. **Reverse free hand.**
6. **Back hand.**
7. **Back hand.**
8. **Free hand.**
9. **Back hand.**
•10. **Reverse free hand.**
11. **Free hand.**
12. **Free hand.**
•13. **Reverse free hand.**
•14. **Reverse free hand.**

2. **How to hold the razor.** The position of the right hand is as follows:

   a) Hold the razor firmly as in a free hand position, turn hand slightly towards you so that the razor edge is turned upward.

   The position of the left hand is as follows:

   a) Keep hand dry and use it to pull the skin tightly under razor.

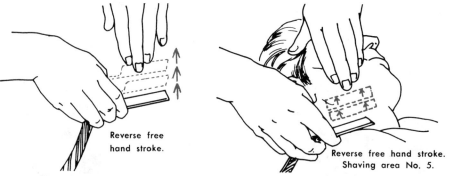

Reverse free hand stroke.

Reverse free hand stroke. Shaving area No. 5.

3. **How to stroke the razor.** The reverse free hand stroke is performed in the following manner:

   a) Use upward semi-arc stroke towards you.

   b) The movement is from the elbow to the hand with a slight twist of the wrist.

Exercise No. 4

REVERSE BACK HAND POSITION AND STROKE

The reverse back hand position and stroke, although not frequently used, must be practiced diligently in order to be mastered.

1. **When to use the reverse back hand stroke.** The reverse back hand stroke is used for making the left sideburn outline and for shaving the left side behind the ear while the patron is sitting in an upright position.

2. **How to hold the razor.** The position of the right hand is as follows:

   a) Hold the razor firmly as in the back hand position.

   b) Turn the palm of the hand to the right so that it faces upward.

   c) Drop the elbow close to the side.

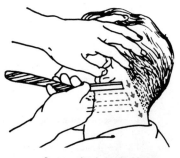

Reverse back hand stroke.
Shaving left side of neck below ear.

The position of the left hand is as follows:

   a) Raise the left arm and hand in order to draw the skin tightly under the razor.

3. **How to stroke the razor.** The reverse back hand stroke is performed in the following manner:

   a) Use a gliding stroke and direct the stroke downward towards the point of the razor in a sawing movement.

THE PROFESSIONAL SHAVE

While a professional shave is composed of many individual steps, they all come under three general classifications: preparation, shaving and finishing steps.

The following exercises explain these three classifications in detail.

Exercise No. 5

HOW TO PREPARE A CLIENT FOR SHAVING

The trained barber-stylist is a skilled professional artisan offering an important service to his clients.

The stylist's attitude in greeting a prospective client should be one of quiet dignity. The stylist should make the client feel welcome and completely at ease. The barber-stylist's approach should be relaxed and designed to impart complete confidence.

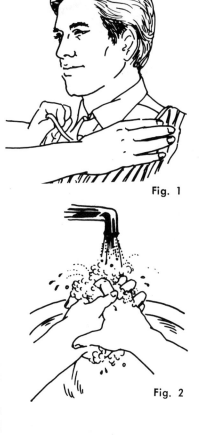

Fig. 1

1. Seat the client comfortably in the chair.
2. Grasp neck-pieces of chair cloth and bring it over front of client, as in Fig. 1.
3. Change paper cover on headrest and adjust the headrest to the proper height.
4. Lower, adjust and lock the chair to the proper height and level.
5. Wash hands with soap and warm water, and dry them thoroughly, as in Fig. 2.
6. Unfold a clean towel, and lay it diagonally across the client's chest.
7. Tuck in the left corner of the towel along the right side of the client's neck, the edge tucked inside the neck-band with a sliding movement of the forefinger of the left hand, as in Fig. 3. The lower end of the towel is crossed over to the other side of the client's neck and tucked under the neck-band, with a sliding movement of the forefinger of the right hand, as in Fig. 4.

Fig. 2

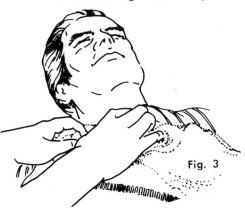

Fig. 3

Fig. 4

Exercise No. 6

HOW TO PREPARE THE FACE FOR SHAVING

Lathering and steaming the face are very important steps before shaving for the following reasons:

Lathering the face serves the following purposes:

1. Cleans the face by dislodging dirt and foreign matter.
2. Softens the hair and holds it in an upright position.
3. Affords a smooth, flat surface for the razor to glide over.

Steaming the face is helpful for the following reasons:

1. Softens the cuticle or outer layer of the hair.
2. Provides lubrication by stimulating the action of the oil glands.
3. Soothes and relaxes the client.

CAUTION. Do not use steam towel if the face is sensitive, irritated, chapped or blistered.

The face is prepared for shaving as follows:

1. The shaving lather is prepared in the latherizing unit. Transfer a quantity of lather into the hand and spread it evenly over the bearded parts of the face and neck.

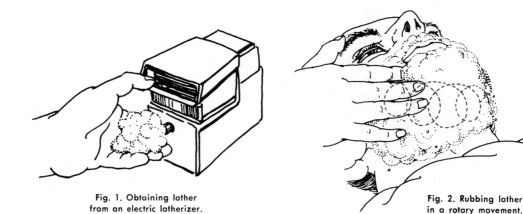

Fig. 1. Obtaining lather from an electric latherizer.

Fig. 2. Rubbing lather in a rotary movement.

2. Rub lather briskly into bearded area, using rotary movements, with the cushion tips of the right hand. Rub lather on right side of face. (Fig. 2.) Then gently turn the head with the left hand by lightly grasping the top of the head or the back of the head near the crown. Rub lather on the other side of face. Rubbing time is from one to two minutes, depending on the stiffness and density of the beard.

3. Take a clean towel, fold it once length-wise. (Fig. 3.) Then fold it again the short way by bringing together both ends of the towel. (Fig. 4.)

4. Place folded towel (Fig. 5) under stream of hot water, allowing it to become thoroughly saturated and heated. (Fig. 6.)

5. Wring out towel until fairly dry.

6. Bring the steam towel behind the client. Unfold it and hold each end. Place center of towel over client's mouth, under chin and lower part of neck. (Fig. 7.) Carefully wrap towel around face, leaving the nose exposed. Finally, fold the ends over each other on the forehead, covering the eyes. (Fig. 8.)

7. While the steam towel is on the client's face, strop the razor and immerse it into sanitizing solution. Then wipe the razor dry on a clean paper towel, and place it in a dry sanitizer until ready for use.

8. Remove steam towel and wipe lather off in one operation.

9. Re-lather the beard, then wipe the hands free of soap.

10. Take a position on the right side of the client, and place a clean tissue or paper on the client's chest for wiping lather from razor. Take the razor out of the dry sanitizer and proceed.

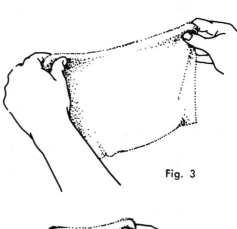

Fig. 3

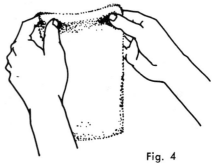

Fig. 4

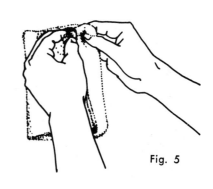

Fig. 5

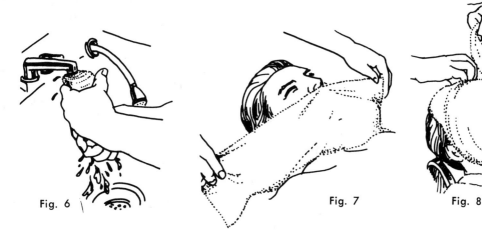

Fig. 6   Fig. 7   Fig. 8

POSITION AND STROKES IN SHAVING

The barber-stylist is now ready to begin shaving.

Shaving strokes should be given correctly and systematically over the face and neck.

Proper coordination of both hands makes for better and safer shaving. While the right hand holds and strokes the razor, the fingers of the left hand assist by stretching the skin tightly around the part being shaved. A tight skin has the advantage that it allows the beard to be cut more easily. To prevent slipping, use an alum block to help keep the fingers of the left hand dry at all times.

Loose skin on the face has a tendency to ruffle-up in front of the razor, thus resulting in cuts or nicks. However, if the skin is stretched too tight, it will be easily irritated in the shaving process. The skin must be held firmly, neither too loose nor too tight, to present a correct shaving surface for the razor.

SHAVING AREA No. 1

Free hand stroke. Barber-stylist stands on right side of chair. Gently turn client's face to the left. With second finger of left hand, remove lather from hairline. Hold razor as for a free hand stroke. Use long gliding diagonal strokes with the point of the razor in the lead. Beginning at hairline on right side, shave downward toward the jaw bone.

SHAVING AREA No. 2

Back hand stroke. Remaining in the same position, wipe razor clean on lather paper. Hold the razor as for a back hand stroke; use a diagonal stroke with the point of the razor in the lead. Shave all of the beard on the right side of the face.

SHAVING AREA No. 3

Free hand stroke. Keeping the same position, wipe razor clean. Hold razor as for a free hand stroke. Shave underneath the nostrils and over the right side of upper lip, using the fingers of the left hand to stretch the underlying skin. When shaving underneath the nostril, slightly lift the tip of the nose without interfering with the breathing. To stretch the upper lip, place fingers of left hand against nose while holding the thumb below the lower corner of the lip.

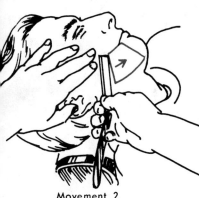

Movement 1

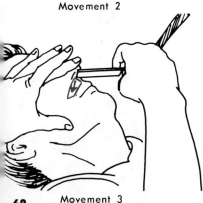

Movement 2

Movement 3

SHAVING AREA No. 4

Free hand stroke. Without wiping the razor, start at point of chin and shave all that portion below the jawbone down to the change in the grain of the beard. While shaving, hold the skin tightly between thumb and fingers of left hand.

Movement 4

SHAVING AREA No. 5

Reverse free hand stroke. Step to back of chair. Hold the razor as for a reverse free hand stroke. Shave the remainder of the beard upward with the grain. This movement completes shaving of the right side of the face.

Diagram of shaving areas for left side of face.

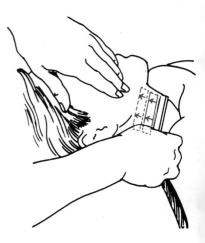

Movement 5

SHAVING AREA No. 6

Back hand stroke. Wipe razor clean and strop it. Stand on right side of client and turn client's face upward so that you can shave the left upper lip. Hold razor as for a back hand stroke. While gently pushing the tip of the nose to the right with thumb and fingers of left hand, shave the left side of upper lip.

Note: Some practitioners prefer to shave the upper lip after Step 8.

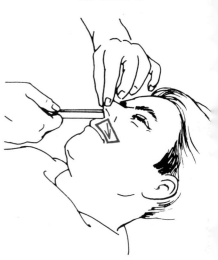

Movement 6

69

Movement 7

SHAVING AREA No. 7

Back hand stroke. Stand slightly back of client. Gently turn his face to the right. Re-lather left side of face. Clean lather from hairline. Stretching the skin with the fingers of the left hand, shave downward to the lower part of the ear and slightly forward on the face.

CAUTION. Be careful to stretch the skin well with the left hand as the razor may dig in along the ear.

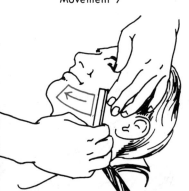

Movement 8

SHAVING AREA No. 8

Free hand stroke. Wipe off razor. Step to right side of client. Hold razor as for free hand stroke. Shave downward on left side of face towards jawbone and point of chin.

Note: Some practitioners prefer to shave the upper lip (see Step 6) at this time.

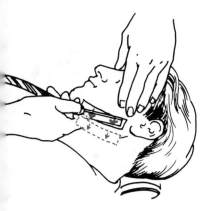

Movement 9

SHAVING AREA No. 9

Back hand stroke. Wipe off razor. Keeping the same position, hold razor as for back hand stroke. With the fingers of the left hand tightly stretching the skin, shave downward to where the grain of the beard changes on the neck.

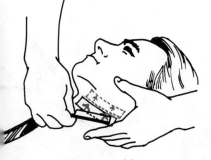

Movement 10

SHAVING AREA No. 10

Reverse free hand stroke. Wipe off razor. Stand slightly back of client. Hold razor as for reverse free hand stroke. Stretching the skin tightly with the left hand, shave the left side of the neck in an upward direction.

SHAVING AREA No. 11

Free hand stroke. Take your position at the side of the client and turn his head so the face is pointing upward. Hold razor as for free hand stroke, shave across upper part of the chin. Continue shaving across the chin until it has been shaved to a point below the jawbone. The skin is stretched with the left hand.

SHAVING AREA No. 12

Free hand stroke. Stretch the skin with the left hand and shave the area just below the chin until the change in the grain of the beard is reached.

Alternate method — some practitioners prefer to use the back-hand stroke as shown in illustration 12A.

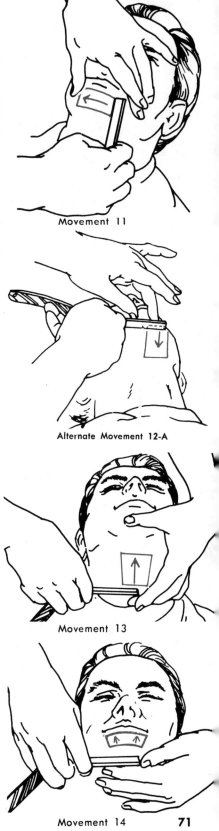

Movement 11

Alternate Movement 12-A

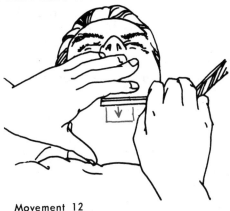

Movement 12

SHAVING AREA No. 13

Reverse free hand stroke. Change position to back of chair. Hold the razor as for reverse free hand stroke. Stretch the skin tightly and shave upward on the lower part of the neck.

CAUTION: Great care must be taken that the skin over the Adam's Apple is not cut.

Movement 13

SHAVING AREA No. 14

Reverse free hand stroke. Remain back of chair. Shave upward on lower lip with a few short reverse free hand strokes.

Wipe off razor again, and fold the lather paper in half.

During Movements 13 and 14 the practitioner should avoid breathing into the client's face as this is annoying and unhealthy to the client.

Movement 14

CLOSE SHAVING

The second time over is for the purpose of removing any rough or unshaven spots.

Remove all traces of lather with steam towel. Turn towel over and place it on the face.

Strop, sanitize and close the razor and place it on the work bench. Remove steam towel, pick up water bottle and sprinkle a little water in the cupped palm of the left hand. Moisten the bearded part of the face, place bottle on work stand, and proceed with the second time over. Use the free hand and reverse free hand strokes in shaving the second time over.

Stand a little in back of client. With a free hand stroke (see illustration), start to shave right side of face. Stroking the grain of the beard sideways, shave the upper lip and work downward to the lower jawbone. Shave lower part of neck with a reverse free hand strike and follow the grain of the beard.

Now, turn the client's face towards you. With a free hand stroke, start to shave left side of face. Stroking the grain of the beard sideways, shave from ear towards tip of nose. When finished, wipe off razor on lather paper and discard it into container.

Water Bottle

Right Side

"ONCE-OVER" SHAVE

If the client requests a "once-over" shave, the barber-stylist should be able to comply with his wishes. The "once-over" shave has the advantage in that it takes less time to give a complete and even shave. For a "once-over" shave, give a few more strokes across the grain when each shaving movement is completed. This will assure a complete and even shave with a single lathering.

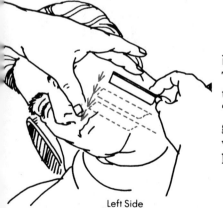

Left Side

SECOND TIME OVER

Close shaving is the practice of shaving the beard against the grain of the hair during the second time over. This shaving practice is undesirable because it irritates the skin and may cause an infection or ingrown hairs. For this reason, the barber-stylist should be cautious when giving a close shave.

ACCIDENTAL CUTS IN SHAVING

Consult Special Problems page of this chapter.

Exercise No. 8

FINAL STEPS IN FACE SHAVING

The final steps in face shaving require attention to a number of important details.

1. Apply face cream with massage movements.
2. Prepare steam towel and apply it over face.
   (Suggest facial treatment at this time.)
3. Remove steam towel from face.
4. Apply finishing lotion with several facial manipulations.
5. Pick up towel from client's chest.
6. Take your position behind the chair.
7. Spread towel over client's face and first dry the lower part and then the upper part of the face.
8. Take your position on the right side of the chair.
9. Wrap towel around hand as described in Exercise No. 9.

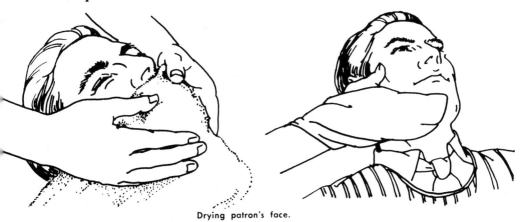

Drying patron's face.

10. Thoroughly dry the face.
11. Select a dry spot of towel and fold it around the hand.
12. Sprinkle talcum powder over dry towel.
13. Apply powder evenly to face.
14. Raise chair to an upright position.
15. Shave the neckline, if necessary, as described in Exercise No. 10.
16. Comb the hair neatly, as desired.
17. With neck towel, wipe off loose hair, lather or powder from face and clothing.
18. Remove linen.
19. Hand client a check for services rendered and courteously thank him.

Mustache trimming must be done before applying steam towel (Step 2) or after Step 17.

Exercise No. 9

WRAPPING A TOWEL AROUND THE HAND

A properly trained barber-stylist knows how to wrap a towel around the hand with ease and skill for the purpose of:

1. Cleansing and drying the face.
2. Applying powder to the face.
3. Removing all traces of powder, lather and any loose hair from face, neck and forehead.

The student should practice the following methods until he is able to wrap the towel around the hand with ease and skill.

Method No. 1

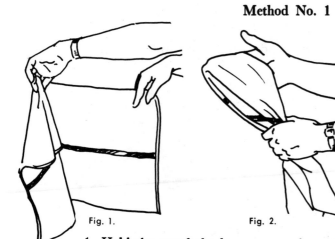 

Fig. 1.   Fig. 2.   Fig. 3.

1. Hold the towel the long way and grasp towel as in Fig. 1.
2. Hold the right hand in front of you, draw the upper edge of the towel across the palm of the right hand.
3. Then grasp the towel and draw it towards the right arm as in Fig. 2.
4. Holding the towel in this position, twist it around the outside of wrist and hold ends of towel to keep them from flapping in the client's face, as in Fig. 3.

Method No. 2

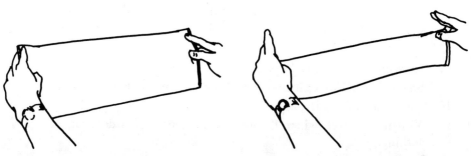

Fold in half.   Fold again in half.

Fold Linen Towel or Paper Towel

Use linen or paper towel, usually 16 x 24 inches. First, fold the towel in half lengthwise and then fold it again in half lengthwise, as shown in the above illustration.

Wrap Towel Around Hand

1. Grasp the towel between the index and middle fingers. (Fig. 1.)
2. Bring the towel around to cover the palm. (Fig. 2.)

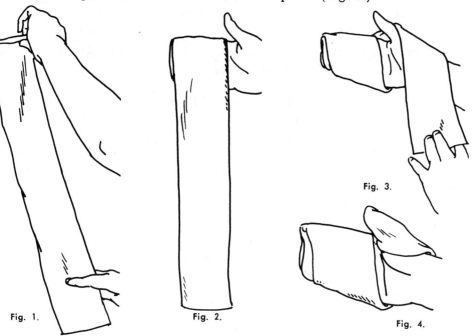

Fig. 1.

Fig. 2.

Fig. 3.

Fig. 4.

3. Bring the towel around the back of the hand and twist forward around the thumb. (Figs. 3 and 4.)
4. The towel is folded neatly and therefore the end will not flap in the client's **face.**

Exercise No. 10

NECK SHAVE

The neck shave, as part of the regular shave, involves shaving the neckline on both sides of the neck **below the ears.**

Raise the chair slowly to an upright position, tuck the towel around the back of the neck, and apply lather. Shave neckline, first at the right side using a free hand stroke and then at the left side using a reverse back hand stroke, as described in Exercise No. 4.

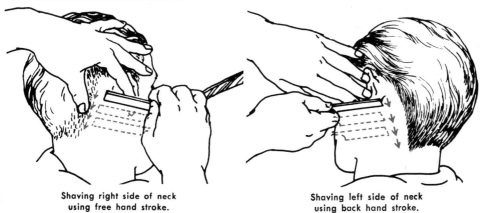

Shaving right side of neck
using free hand stroke.

Shaving left side of neck
using back hand stroke.

75

The lather from the razor may be transferred to the palm or base of left thumb, or to a strip of tissue, a corner of which is tucked under the towel.

Clean shaved part of neck with palm and fingers moistened with witch hazel, or antiseptic or warm water. Remove towel from around the neck and dry thoroughly. (This is the time to suggest a scalp treatment or hair tonic.)

Take your position behind the chair, replace towel around client's neck and comb or style the hair as desired by the client.

Releasing the Client

Take towel from the back of neck and fold it around the right hand. Remove all traces of powder and any loose hair.

Discard towel and remove chair cloth from client.

Make out price check and thank client as it is handed to him.

POINTS TO REMEMBER IN SHAVING

1. Always use a forward sawing movement with point of blade leading.
2. The experienced barber-stylist will observe the hair slope and shave with it—never against it.
3. A heavy growth of beard requires care in the lathering process and special technique in the use of the razor.
4. The lather should not be scattered carelessly all over the face.
5. The fingers of the left hand should be kept dry in order to grasp and stretch the skin and hold it firmly.
6. Hot towels should not be used on excessively sensitive skin, nor should they be used when the skin is chapped or blistered from cold or heat.
7. Take special precautions in shaving, especially beneath lower lip, lower part of neck, and around the Adam's apple, as these parts of the face and neck are usually the most tender and sensitive, and are easily irritated by very close shaving.

ELEVEN REASONS WHY A CLIENT MAY FIND FAULT WITH A SHAVE

1. Offensive body odor, foul breath or tobacco odor.
2. Dull or rough razors.
3. Unclean hands, towels or shaving cloth.
4. Cold fingers.
5. Heavy touch of hand.
6. Poorly-heated towels.
7. Lather which is either too cold or too hot.
8. Sticking your fingers in patron's mouth.
9. Glaring lights over head.
10. Unshaven hair patches.
11. Scraping the skin and close shaving.

SPECIAL PROBLEMS

TREATING SMALL CUTS

Whenever a slight cut or scratch drawing blood has occurred, pat the area dry with sterile cotton and apply styptic powder sparingly to the cut. After the powder has dried, dust off the area with sterile cotton or towel.

Never use a styptic pencil or any other astringent that will come in contact with more than one face, as there is great danger of infection.

BLACKHEADS OR COMEDONES

Blackheads, which make their appearance on the face and more particularly around the nose, may be removed by means of a blackhead extractor or by steaming.

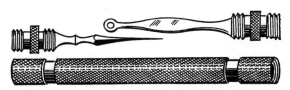

Blackhead (comedone) extractor

It is not wise to attempt to remove all the blackheads appearing on the surface at one time; they should be removed by a series of treatments extending over a period of time.

Facial massage and facial steaming help to dislodge and remove a number of blackheads. The comedone extractor may be used to remove blackheads. Place the round end of extractor with the hole over the blackhead and press gently until it comes out.

INGROWN OR WILD HAIR

An ingrown hair is one that has grown beneath the skin, causing a lump in which pus forms. This is usually caused by very close shaving or the rubbing of a shirt collar. People with curly hair are more prone to have ingrown hairs.

To remove a wild hair or dead hair, open the affected part with a sanitized needle, pull out the hair with a sanitized tweezer, then apply an antiseptic solution.

Tweezer with needle

QUESTIONS ON SHAVING

1. What three points should the barber-stylist know about the client's skin and hair when shaving?
2. What are nine requirements of a good shave?
3. How should the client be prepared for shaving?
4. How should the beard be prepared for shaving?
5. Which five sanitary precautions should be observed by the barber-stylist?
6. What is the most effective way to rub lather into the beard?
7. What action does the lather have on the beard?
8. What is the purpose of steaming the face?
9. When should a hot towel **not** be applied to the face?
10. Name the four standard positions and strokes used in shaving.
11. How should the razor be used to accomplish the free hand stroke?
12. How should the razor be used to accomplish the back hand stroke?
13. How should the razor be used to accomplish the reverse free hand stroke?
14. What should be the direction of the shaving strokes in respect to the grain of the hair?
15. When is the reverse back hand position and stroke usually used?
16. How many shaving areas are there in shaving the first time over?
17. Which side of the face is shaved first and which stroke is used first?
18. How is a "once-over" shave given?
19. What part of the neck is shaved with the standard or regular shave?
20. What are the final steps after shaving?
21. When should a facial be suggested to the client?
22. When should a hair tonic or scalp treatment be suggested to the client?
23. Give eleven reasons why a client may find fault with a shave?
24. What is an ingrown hair?
25. What is the cause of an ingrown hair?
26. What is the proper treatment for an ingrown hair?
27. How is a close shave produced?
28. Why is a close shave undesirable?

Chapter 7
MEN'S
HAIRCUTTING

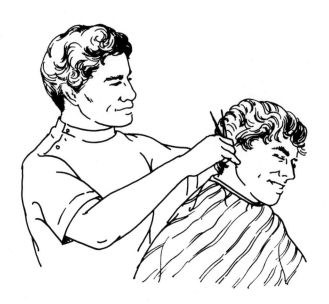

The art of haircutting involves the distinctive cutting and arranging of the hair to suit the individual requirements of a client. Each client presents a new problem which the barber-stylist cannot afford to neglect by careless or indifferent workmanship. Mistakes should be prevented rather than covered up or changed. Expert workmanship in haircutting can best be acquired by competent instruction and by patient practice.

FUNDAMENTALS IN HAIRCUTTING

It is essential that the barber-stylist acquire an easy, graceful position when cutting the hair. Avoid stooping, bending the knees or twisting the body into awkward positions. In haircutting, work to the right because this will give you a better view of your work. Learning correct habits in haircutting will help prevent fatigue and make your work more efficient.

IMPLEMENTS

The principal implements used in haircutting are: clippers, shears and combs.

IMPORTANT STEPS FOR A COMPLETE HAIRCUT

1. Preparation.
2. Clipper technique.
3. Shears and comb technique.
4. Arching technique.
5. (Optional) Thinning the hair.
6. Finger and shears technique.
7. Shaving neck and outline areas.
8. Final checkup and combing the hair.

Exercise No. 1

HOW TO PREPARE A CLIENT FOR A HAIRCUT

Before starting a haircut, the following preparation is required:

1. Have on hand all necessary linens, sanitized implements and supplies.
2. Lock chair and seat client comfortably, facing mirror.
3. Grasp neck-pieces of chair cloth and bring it over the front of client as in Fig. 1. (Some barber-stylists prefer the term "hair cloth.")
4. Remove or drop headrest.
5. Wash and dry hands.

 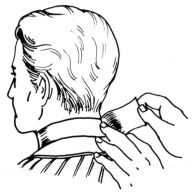

Fig. 1. Placing chair cloth over in front of client.

Fig. 2. Adjusting tissue neck-strip around neck of client.

Fig. 3. The extended portion of the neck-strip is folded over neck-pieces of chair cloth.

6. Adjust tissue neck-strip (neck-band) or towel protector under neck-pieces of chair cloth.

   a) If a tissue neck-strip is used, bring it completely around the client's neck with the ends overlapping in the back, as in Fig. 2. Over the tissue neck-strip, place the neck-pieces of the chair cloth and fasten them securely in the back. Extended portion of the tissue neck-strip is folded neatly over the neck-pieces of the chair cloth, as in Fig. 3.

   b) If a towel is used, spread it straight across the back of the client, the upper edge being tucked in at the neckline. Bring both ends of the towel around the client's neck, allowing one end to overlap the other under the chin. Place the neck-pieces of the chair cloth over the towel and fasten them securely. The extended portion of the towel is folded over the neck-pieces of the chair cloth to give a cuff-like effect.

7. (Optional)—Sprinkle talcum powder on a tissue and apply it over the back of the client's neck.

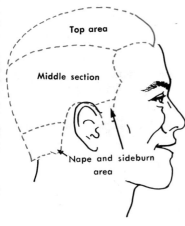

Top area

Middle section

Nape and sideburn area

HAIRCUTTING AREAS

In the styling of standard haircuts, the barber-stylist usually cuts the hair in the following order:

1. **Edging** — for sideburn and nape area.
2. **Siding** — for middle or contour part of head.
3. **Topping** — for top part of head.

The usual haircutting procedure is to first do the edging and then blend it with the middle and top sections of the head. However, exceptions to this procedure are made for:

1. **Reducing the sides.** Shaping the sides first prepares the way for edging.
2. Cutting a head of hair that is **irregular** or **bumpy.**
3. **A neglected head of hair.** In this instance, first do the top and sides before edging.

STANDARD TAPERED HAIRCUT

Exercise No. 2

CLIPPER TECHNIQUE

For the student, it is best to practice tapering with the blade guard of a disconnected electric clipper before cutting any hair from the head.

To learn the proper handling of the clipper the student should practice the following exercises diligently.

1. **How to hold clipper and comb.** The position of the right hand:
   a) Pick up the clipper with the right hand.
   b) Place thumb on the left side and fingers on the right side of electric clipper. Hold it lightly to permit freedom of wrist movement. (Fig. 1)

   The position of the left hand:
   a) With left hand comb hair down.
   b) With left hand steady the clipper. (Fig. 1)

Fig. 1. Tapering the hair with a clipper.
Steady clipper with left hand finger.

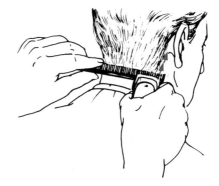

Fig. 2. Tapering the hair with clipper over the comb.

2. How to use clipper and comb.

a) Use clipper blade which gives longer cut before using clipper blade which gives shorter cut. (Fig. 2)

b) For a gradual even taper, tilt the blade as you clip so that the clipper rides on the heel of the bottom blade. See Fig. 3 for correct and incorrect tapering.

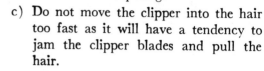

c) Do not move the clipper into the hair too fast as it will have a tendency to jam the clipper blades and pull the hair.

d) After tapering one strip of hair, comb down smooth and start tapering the next strip.

Fig. 3. Correct and incorrect methods of tapering the hair.

Haircut styles that require clipper tapering all around the head should begin at the left temple and continue around the head, finishing at the right temple. Haircut styles that require clipper tapering at the back of the neck only should begin at the left side of the neck, finishing at the right side of the neck.*

Some practitioners prefer to do clipper work from right sideburn to left sideburn, in which case the routine is reversed and is equally correct.

WHEN HAND CLIPPER IS USED

While the electric clipper is generally being used by most barber-stylists, it is advisable that they also learn how to handle and use the hand clipper. The hand clipper is a much slower cutting implement and perhaps the student should practice and perfect the clipper movement on this implement before turning to the faster electric clipper. A hand clipper should be available in the event that a breakdown of some sort prevents the use of the electric clipper.

The hand clipper can be used to taper the hair around the head in the same manner as the electric clipper.

Holding the clipper.

Using the index finger as a guide.

SHEAR AND COMB TECHNIQUE

Shear and comb technique is used to cut the ends of the hair and even up the clipper taper. It is usually employed after the clipper work is completed.

To learn shear and comb technique the student should practice the following exercises:

1. **How to hold shears and comb.**

   a) Pick up shears firmly with the right hand and insert thumb into thumb grip, place third finger into finger grip and leave little finger on finger-brace of shears.

   b) Pick up comb* with the left hand and place fingers on top of teeth with the thumb on the backbone of the comb. (Fig. 3)

Fig. 1. Proper way to hold shears for regular cutting.

   To comb hair downward turn comb towards client's head, as in turning a key, by using the thumb and the first two fingers. (Fig. 2)

Fig. 2. Turning the comb downward.

   The positions of both the right hand and left hand are as follows:

   a) Hold shears and comb slightly to your right front.

   b) Hold comb parallel with the still blade of the shears, as in Fig. 3.

2. **How to use shears and comb.** (Figs. 3 and 4)

   a) Keep one blade still while moving the other blade with the thumb. Master this technique before attempting to do a haircut.

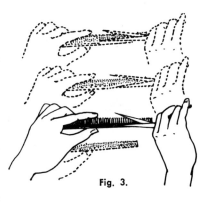

Fig. 3.

   b) While manipulating the shears move both shears and comb slowly upward at the same time.

   c) Turn teeth of comb downward when combing the hair downward. (See Fig. 2)

   d) Finish one vertical strip at a time before proceeding with the next strip to the left. Working from right to left gives a better view of the work.

For the student, start with the coarse teeth of the comb. After sufficient skill is developed, use the fine teeth of the comb.

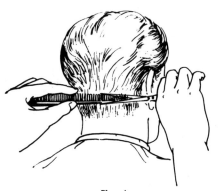

Fig. 4.

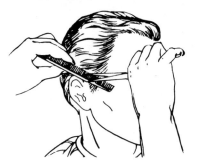

Fig. 1. Right sideburn.

Suggestions on the Use of the Shears and Comb

The procedures given here may be changed to conform with your instructor's routine which is equally correct.

Note—This exercise co-ordinates with Exercise No. 4 which follows.

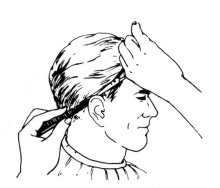

Fig. 2. Over and back of ear.

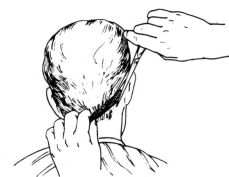

Fig. 3. Side of neck.

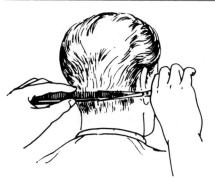

Fig. 4. From nape to as high as necessary.

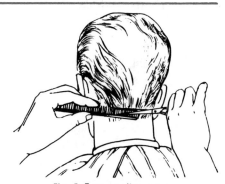

Fig. 5. Even up clipper taper.

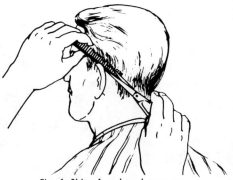

Fig. 6. Side of neck and over ear.

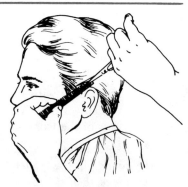

Fig. 7. Front of ear and left sideburn.

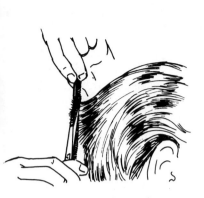

Fig. 8. Using comb and shear to blend hair at back of head.

Fig. 9. Up and over comb and shear technique on top of head.

SHEAR-POINT TAPERING

Shear-point tapering is a useful technique for thinning out difficult heads of hair caused by hollows, wrinkles and creases in the scalp and by whorls of hair on the scalp. Dark and ragged hair patches on the scalp can be minimized by this special technique.

The shear-point taper is performed with the cutting points of the shears. Only a few hairs are cut at a time and then combed out. Continue cutting around the objectionable spot until it becomes less noticeable and blends in with the surrounding outline of the haircut.

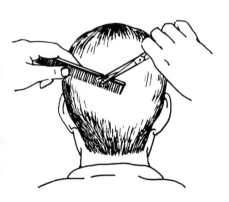

Shear-point tapering ragged or choppy areas.

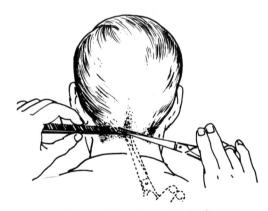

Shear-point tapering depression in nape.

CAUTION. Do not cut the hair close to the skin in the hollows or wrinkles, as it will cause unevenness and nicks to appear.

ARCHING TECHNIQUE

Fig. 1. Outlining in front of and over the ear.

Fig. 2. Outlining the right side of neck downward.

Fig. 3. Outlining the right side of neck upward.

Arching technique means marking the outer border of the haircut in front and over the ears and side of the neck. This outlining is accomplished with the points of the shears and is usually performed while doing the shears and comb work as described in Exercise No. 3.

To learn arching technique the student should practice the exercise diligently.

> *The following is one method of arching, your instructor's method is equally correct. Be guided by your instructor.*

1. How to hold shears with right hand.
  a) Pick up shears and insert thumb in thumb grip, place third finger into finger grip and little finger on brace of shears.
  b) Use the most convenient fingertip of left hand to steady point of shears. (Fig. 1)

2. How to arch the right side.
  a) Always make outline around ear as close to the natural hairline as possible.
  b) Start in front of ear and make a continuous outline around the ear and down the side of neck. (Figs. 1 and 2)
  c) Reverse the direction of arching back to starting point. (Fig. 3)
  d) Continue arching around ear until a definite outline is formed.
  e) Square off the length of the right sideburn. (Fig. 4)

Some barber-stylists prefer to square off the sideburn before arching the right side.

Fig. 4. Squaring off the right sideburn.

Fig. 5. Outlining the left side of neck downward.

Fig. 6. Outlining the left side of neck upward.

3. How to arch the left side.

Starting in front of the left ear, with the shears make a continuous outline over the left ear and down the side of neck (Fig. 5); then reverse the direction of the shears and return to the starting point. (Fig. 6 and 7) The squaring off of the left sideburn to match the right sideburn is done last. (Fig. 8)

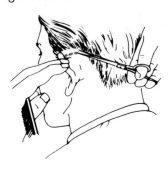

Fig. 7. Outlining over left ear.

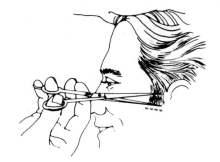

Fig. 8. Squaring off left sideburn.

SIX POPULAR LENGTHS OF SIDEBURNS

Use the corner of the eyes as a guideline to the length of sideburns.

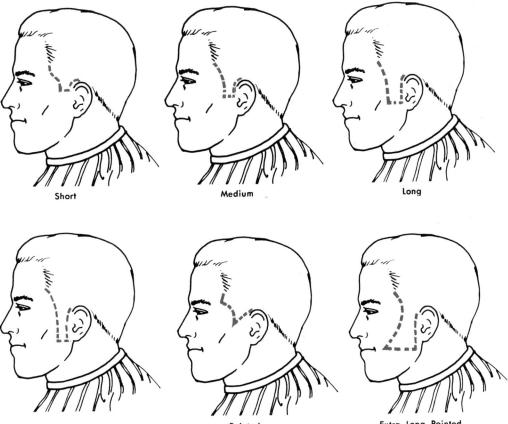

Short

Medium

Long

Extra Long

Pointed

Extra Long Pointed

Exercise No. 5

HAIR THINNING

Hair thinning is required to reduce the bulk of the hair wherever necessary. Thinning (serrated) shears or regular shears can be used for this purpose.

Plan of thinning the hair. The barber-stylist stands in back of the client, combs away the front hair which does not require thinning. The hair is then thinned on both sides of the head, strand by strand as required, and the loose cut hair is combed out. The top part is done last.

1. **Thinning with serrated shears.** The hair strand is combed, and the spread hair held between the index and middle fingers, as in Fig. 1. Then the hair is cut about one inch from the scalp. If another cut is necessary it should be made about one inch from the first cut. Do not cut twice in the same place. To shorten the hair the regular shears are used.

Fig. 1. Thinning hair with thinning shears—holding hair between index and middle finger.

Fig. 2. Thinning hair with thinning shears — holding hair with comb facing away from barber-stylist.

Fig. 3. Thinning hair with thinning shears — holding hair with comb facing barber-stylist.

2. **Thinning with serrated shears and comb.** Instead of the index and middle fingers, the comb may be used to hold the hair, as in Fig. 2 and 3. The thinning is done in the usual manner.

Fig. 4. Thinning hair — using regular shears.

CAUTION. Do not cut the hair too close to the scalp nor thin out too much hair, as it will cause short hair ends to protrude and light spots to appear.

Back-combing. Combing the short hair of the strand first, towards the scalp, guards against thinning out too much hair.

3. **Thinning with regular shears.** Hold a small strand of hair between the thumb and index finger, insert the strand in the shears, as in Fig. 4. Slide the shears up and down the strand, closing them slightly each time they are moved towards the scalp. Slither enough to allow the hair to lie close to the scalp wherever needed.

Exercise No. 6

FINGER AND SHEAR TECHNIQUE

In order to finish the haircut properly, any noticeable unevenness remaining after shear and comb work should be removed. If the top hair needs shortening it may be accomplished during the finger and shear technique.

─────── IMPORTANT REMINDER ───────
The following method is one way to perform finger and shear technique. Remember, your instructor's method is equally correct.

Procedure for Side Part

First, start finger and shear work on top of head. Then, proceed to right side and finish on left side. To perform finger technique on top, start at front part of head and work towards the crown.

To perform finger technique on **top and right side of head**, stand behind the client.

1. Hold shears and comb as follows:
   a) Hold shears by inserting third finger grip and place little finger on brace.
   b) Grasp comb with left hand.

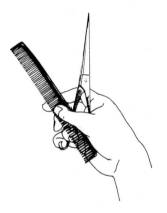

Fig. 1. Proper way to hold comb and shears.

2. Start just above the right temple, palm shears in right hand, transfer comb from left hand to right hand (Fig. 1) and comb a strand of hair two or three inches in width towards the back of the head.

3. Raise the comb sufficiently to permit first and second fingers of the left hand to grasp the hair underneath the comb. The fingers holding the hair should bend to conform with the shape of the head.

4. Place comb between thumb and index finger of left hand.

Fig. 2. Make cut over fingers.

5. Cut the hair the proper length to blend well with the shorter hair on side of head. (Fig. 2)

6. Hold on to the cut hair, palm the shears, transfer comb from left to right hand and comb through the hair held in the fingers of the left hand.

7. Release the fingers, sliding the comb and picking up underneath hair beyond the cut just made, and cut the hair.

8. Comb the hair at that point again and repeat the same cutting movements until the back of the head is reached. (Fig. 3)

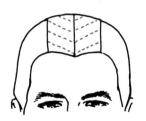

Fig. 3. Diagram for finger and shear technique.

9. Start again at the front of the head, continue to comb and cut until the back of the head is reached again.
10. Continue to comb and cut, going a little lower each time until the side of the head is reached. (Figs. 2 and 3)

RIGHT SIDE OF HEAD

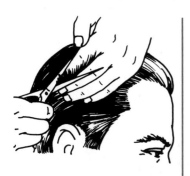

Fig. 4 Finger and shear technique on right side of head.

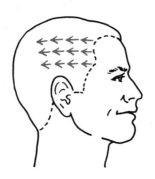

Fig. 5. Diagram for right side of head.

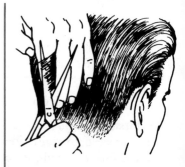

Fig. 6. Finger and shear technique on back part of head.

LEFT SIDE OF HEAD

To perform finger technique on the left side of head, stand on left side of the client.

1. The finger technique for the left side of head is done in the same manner as on the right side, with the exception that the barber-stylist stands on the side front of the client and the hair is combed away from him. (Fig. 7 and 8)

Fig. 7. Finger and shear technique on left side of head.

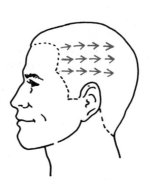

Fig. 8. Diagram for left side of head.

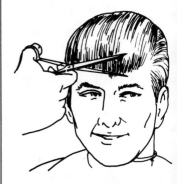

Fig. 9. If required, trim hair to desired length.

PROCEDURE FOR CENTER PART AND POMPADOUR

Center part. Do finger and shear work on the top right side first and then the left side. For a **pompadour hairstyle,** part hair in the center, then follow the same procedure for the center part.

Note—Some barber-stylists prefer to do the finger and shear work from the top to the sides, whereas others find it more convenient to work from the sides to the top. Follow your instructor's directions.

Exercise No. 7

SHAVING NECK AND OUTLINED AREAS

Preparation for a Neck Shave

The neck shave contributes to the appearance of the finished haircut. Shaving the outlined areas of the sideburns, around the ears and the sides of the neck below the ears gives the client a clean appearance. If the haircut requires a round or square outline at the nape of the neck, the free hand stroke should be used at the back of the neck.

To prepare for a neck shave follow these steps:

1. Remove all cut hair from around the head and neck with a clean towel, tissues or hair vacuum. (Fig. 1)
2. Loosen the chair cloth and neck-strip carefully, so that no cut hair will fall down the neck or shirt.
3. Discard the cut hair at the base of the chair in the following manner: Pick up the chair cloth at the lower edge and bring it up to the upper edge. Remove chair cloth carefully so that no cut hair will fall on the client. Drop upper edge of chair cloth, giving a slight shake to dislodge all cut hair. (Fig. 2)
4. Replace chair cloth as before. It should be left a few inches away from the neck so that it does not come in contact with the client's skin.

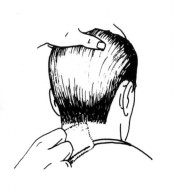

Fig. 1. Dusting neck.

Fig. 2. Removing chair cloth.

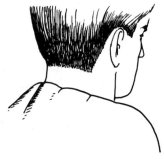

Fig. 3. Place towel across shoulders.

5. Spread a face or paper towel straight across the shoulders, then tuck it into the neck-band. (Fig. 3)

Applying Lather for Neck Shave

1. Prepare lather same as for the beard.
2. Lather both sides of the head and the back of the neck as follows: Give a light coat of lather at the hairline around and over the ears, sideburns and down the sides of the neck. If the back of the neck is to be shaved, apply lather to the back of the neck up to the hairline.
3. Rub the lather in lightly with the ball part of the fingertips or thumb.

Fig. 1. Shaving right sideburn
to proper length.

Shaving Outlined Areas

Shaving outlined areas is a follow-up to Exercise No. 4, on Arching Technique. The purpose of this exercise is to shave over the outlined areas of the ears, neck and sideburns.

1. Shaving right side.

a) Hold razor as in free hand stroke.

b) Place thumb of left hand on the scalp above the point of razor, and stretch scalp under razor.

Fig. 2. Shave over ear.

Fig. 3. Shave outline below ear.

Fig. 4. Clean neck below ear.

c) Shave sideburn to the proper length. (Fig. 1)

d) Shave around ear at hairline and straight down side of neck, using free hand stroke with the point of razor. Be careful not to shave into the hairline at the nape of the neck. (Figs. 2, 3 and 4)

2. Shaving left side.

a) Hold razor as in reverse hand stroke.

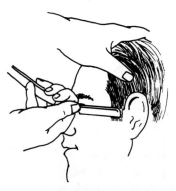

Fig. 5. Shave left sideburn to proper length using reverse back hand stroke.

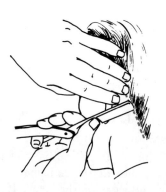

Fig. 6. Shave left side of neck using back hand stroke.

Fig. 7. To achieve a square or round shaped hair style, shaving is required

b) Place thumb of left hand on scalp above point of razor and stretch skin under razor.

c) Shave sideburn to proper length. (Fig. 5)

d) Shave around ear at hairline using free hand stroke.

e) Shave neck below ear, using the reverse back hand stroke with point of razor. (Fig. 6). Hold ear away with fingers of left hand. If the stroke is done with one continuous movement, a straight line will be formed down the side of the neck.

f) If necessary, shape nape area round, square or tapered. (Fig. 8, 9 and 10).

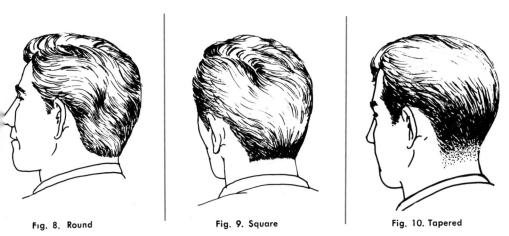

Fig. 8. Round   Fig. 9. Square   Fig. 10. Tapered

3. Provided the client does not specify otherwise, shave the neck outline straight down the sides of the neck behind the ears.

At the client's request, neckline may be rounded at the bottom edge on both sides, or may be shaved straight across the back of the neck, producing a square back. The square back can have either straight corners or rounded corners.

Clean Shaved Areas

After the neck shave has been completed, clean shaved parts with palms and fingers moistened with witch hazel, an antiseptic, or warm water. Dry and powder the neck thoroughly. Replace the towel across the client's shoulder and tuck it in neatly into the neck band for final checkup and combing of the hair.

SINGEING

Value of singeing. Present-day authorities claim that singeing is not beneficial to the hair and classify it as "quack" treatment. Therefore, singeing has been, for the most part, discontinued in this country.

FINAL CHECKUP AND COMBING OF THE HAIR

A checkup of the haircut and combing of the hair are the steps to complete a haircut. Here is a suggested routine to follow:

1. Retouch parts of the haircut with shears and comb.
2. Trim hair in ears, in nose, and on eyebrows. (Ask for the client's permission before trimming the eyebrows.)

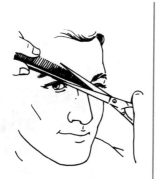
Trimming eyebrows.

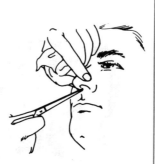
Trimming hair out of nose.

Trimming hair from ear.

ADDITIONAL SERVICES

EYEBROWS

The service generally rendered in a barber-styling shop is the shaving or plucking of hair that grows too thick between the brows.

TRIMMING HAIR FROM NOSTRILS

There are two ways in which to trim hair from the nostrils, as follows:

1. Rest the palm on the forehead, holding the nose firmly with the thumb and index finger. Carefully trim the protruding hair from the nostrils. Use tissue to remove cut hair from upper lip and shears.
2. Lay the back of the fingers on the face with the shears resting on the index finger. Carefully trim the protruding hair from each nostril.

TRIMMING PROTRUDING HAIR FROM EARS

To cut hair protruding from the ears, lay the last three fingers against the face with the shears on top of the middle finger. This is done to protect the client in the event he moves his head, as the practitioner's hand and shears move together without the danger of cutting the client's ear.

The tissue in the left hand is used to remove the hair as it is cut.

3. Massage the scalp for a few seconds. This is the time to suggest a shampoo, hair tonic or any other hair and scalp service.

4. If the client's answer is negative, then ask him if he wants his hair combed dry or damp.

5. Always comb or style the hair before releasing the client from the chair.

6. With the comb almost held flat, use the coarse teeth of comb. Do not dig into scalp. If client wears a part, comb hair as illustrated, or comb hair to desired hairstyle.

Comb hair forward, make part with coarse end of comb.

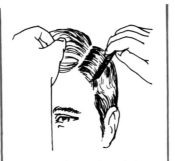

Comb side front hair downward.

Comb top hair to the hair style desired.

If a hair brush is allowed in your state, be sure that it is properly cleaned and sanitized before using it on the client.

Final Checkup

1. Go over the finished haircut to correct any uneven parts.

2. Allow client to see back view of haircut with the aid of a mirror.

3. Make corrections as requested by the client.

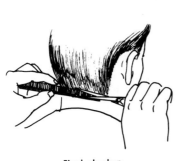

Final checkup.

Wiping away loose hair.

4. Remove all traces of loose hair from around the neck, forehead or nose with a clean towel wrapped around the right hand, or with tissues.

5. Remove chair cloth.

6. Adjust and lock chair in level position.

7. Make out check and thank patron when giving it to him.

8. Release client from chair.

BASIC STEPS OF A STANDARD HAIRCUT

PREPARATION

1. Arrange necessary implements and supplies.
2. Adjust chair cloth (hair cloth) over client.
3. Remove headrest.
4. Wash hands with soap and water, then dry.
5. Adjust neck-strip or towel around neck and fasten neck-pieces of chair cloth around it.
6. Comb hair and check for scalp sores or disorders.
7. Ask client how hair is to be cut and styled.

PROCEDURE

A. **Clipper work.**
  1. Taper hair evenly with clipper, working from left to right side of head. (Some barber-stylists prefer to work from the right to left side of the head.)

B. **Shear and comb work.**
  1. Even up hair taper at right side of head and square off right sideburns.
  2. Outline arch on right side of head.
  3. Taper and blend hair, working from right side to the left side of the head.
  4. Outline arch on left side of head and square off left sideburn to match with right sideburn.

C. **Thin out hair with regular shears or thinning shears, if necessary.**

D. **Shears and finger work.**
  1. Shorten or reduce any pronounced unevenness in the hair, on right top side of head.
  2. Shorten or reduce any pronounced unevenness in the hair, on left top side of head.
  3. Trim front outline, if necessary.
  4. Comb hair and note where further trimming is needed.
  5. Drum out loose hair with fingertips of both hands.
  6. Comb hair casually.
  7. Brush off loose hair from forehead, ears and neck with tissue.
  8. Loosen chair cloth, remove neck-strip and finish dusting off any loose hair or use hair vacuum.

E. **Neck shave.**
  1. Adjust towel around neck.
  2. Apply lather over outlined areas of sideburns, around ears and sides of neck.
  3. Shave right side outlined area of head first and then the left side.
  4. Clean shaved areas with palms and fingers moistened with witch hazel or warm water.

F. Final details.

1. Place towel around neck to protect clothing.
2. Retouch haircut wherever necessary, with shears and comb.
3. Trim undesirable hair from ears, nose and eyebrows, if necessary.
4. Give a few scalp manipulations and suggest a suitable hair tonic or scalp treatment.
5. If no hair tonic is to be used, ask client if he wishes the hair to remain dry or dampened with water.
6. Comb or dress hair as desired.

G. Releasing the client.

1. Wipe off loose hair with towel, tissue or hair vacuum.
2. Remove towel or tissue and chair cloth from client.
3. Make out check for client.
4. Thank client as you hand him his check.

REMINDERS

SANITARY MEASURES

After releasing the client, take care of the following sanitary measures:
1. Discard used towel and neck-strip.
2. Shake chair cloth at the base of chair, fold and place it on arm of chair.
3. Clean and sanitize used implements.
4. Place sanitized implements into dry (cabinet) sanitizer, or ultra-violet ray sanitizer.
5. Sweep hair from floor and place it into a closed container.
6. Have needed supplies in readiness for next client.
7. Wash hands.

TEN REASONS WHY A PATRON MAY FIND FAULT WITH A HAIRCUT

1. Offensive body odor, bad breath or tobacco odor.
2. Improper hairstyle.
3. Poor workmanship.
4. Cutting off too much or too little hair.
5. Irregular hairlines.
6. Unsanitary practices, such as unsanitized implements, unclean towels or chair cloths (hair cloths).
7. Allowing cut hairs to fall down client's back.
8. Pulling the hair with dull shears or clippers.
9. Blowing loose hair off client's neck.
10. Scratching the client's scalp when combing the hair.

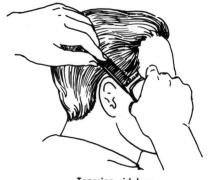

Tapering sideburn
and over ear.

Exercise No. 10

CLIPPER OVER COMB TECHNIQUE

These illustrations show one way in which clipper over comb technique is accomplished. Remember your instructor's method is equally correct.

Starting tapering at
base of neck.

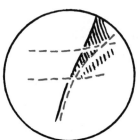

In tapering with a clipper be sure to tilt the comb away from the head in order to form a uniform taper for medium or longer cut.

The top of taper usually is no higher than the top of the ear.

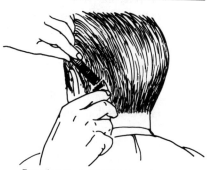

Tapering the left side to match
with the right side.

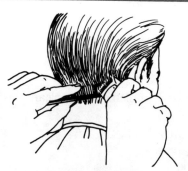

Clipping hair across the
teeth of comb.

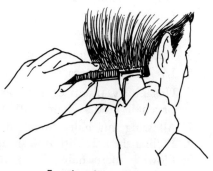

Tapering the nape area.

Exercise No. 11

ARCHING WITH A CLIPPER

Many barber-stylists prefer to use a specially constructed clipper with a small head having a fine cutting edge for squaring off sideburns and making the outline around the ears and sides of neck. This method of arching is much faster.

Suggestions

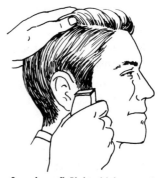

Squaring off Right sideburn and arching turn clipper over on its cutting edge.

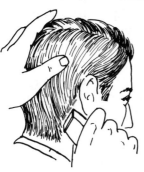

Outlining right side of neck.

Outlining left side of neck.

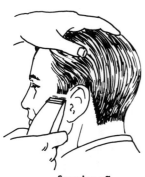

Squaring off left sideburn.

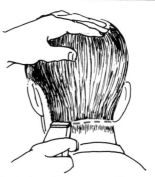

To produce a square nape line turn clipper over on its cutting edge.

FOUR BASIC PATTERNS FOR CUTTING SIDES AND BACK

To simplify haircutting procedures, the edging and siding phases of cutting has been divided into four basic patterns, namely: short, semi-short, medium length, trims and long haircuts.

A variation of hairstyles can be developed or created from these basic haircut patterns to suit the client's tastes and desires.

SHORT HAIRCUT STYLES

Short haircut styles are quite popular in the Armed Forces where neatness and uniformity are important.

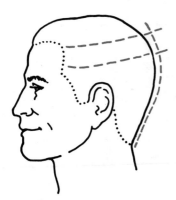

Starting with the coarse clipper blade at the left sideburn, proceed upwards to the hatband, then gradually tilt the heel of the clipper back as you proceed up the head until the heel of the clipper runs off the side of the head. Repeat this movement as you proceed towards the back of the head.

Note: It is important to remember that an even, gradual taper, giving a smooth blended appearance, is the objective to be achieved. There must not be any ridges (steps) left, either from the shears or clipper work.

Use the fine clipper blade to taper the left sideburn. Proceed in the same manner on the back and right side of the head.

Clipper taper for short cut.

To gradually blend the fine clipper taper with the coarse clipper taper, tilt the heel of the clipper.

SEMI-SHORT HAIRCUT STYLES

Semi-short haircut styles are similar to the short haircuts with the following exceptions:

1. The coarse clipper starts tilting back at the top of the ears instead of at the hatband, producing a slightly longer hairstyle.
2. The length of the hair on the back is left longer than on the sides. The coarse clipper goes up the head to about the top of the ears and then starts to taper out.
3. In using the fine clipper blade, remove only the sideburn lines. When going around the ears, remove about one-half inch from the hairline.

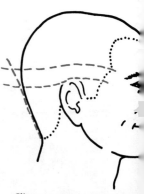

Clipper taper for semi-short haircut.

MEDIUM LENGTH HAIRCUT STYLES

Medium haircut styles do not give that scalped appearance.

The coarse clipper may be used on the sideburns; however, as soon as the teeth of the clipper start cutting into the hair, the clipper is tilted on its heel, ending the clipper taper about even with the top of the ears. The coarse clipper is not used around the ears. In this style the fine clipper blade is not used on sides at all.

On the back of the head, the coarse clipper proceeds up the head to a point at about the middle of the ears, then the clipper is tilted back as you proceed up and the taper ends by the time the top of the ears is reached.

The fine clipper blade is used to remove the hairline at the nape of the neck.

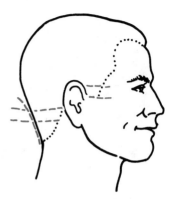

Clipper taper for medium haircut.

TRIM AND LONG HAIRCUT STYLES

Hair trims and long haircut styles require considerable skill and artistic sense to achieve satisfactory results.

Some professional barber-stylists refer to these haircut styles as "shear-trim" or "clippers in the nape area and shears on the side." When a client asks for a "trim," he usually means that he wants his hair cut the length that it grew from his last haircut.

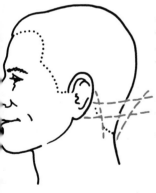

To achieve best results, the barber-stylist must give consideration to the color and texture of the hair, as well as the client's facial characteristics, to decide as to the closeness of shear work on the sides and at the back of the head.

With these styles the coarse clipper is started at the hairline of the nape and the clipper is tilted at the bottom of the ears. The rest is done with shears and comb.

The fine clipper blade is used to taper the hairline and also remove the fine hair at the nape below the ears.

For sideburns and over the ears, the hair is shortened with the shears and comb. The outline around the ears is kept to the natural hairline.

Clipper taper for long trim.

POPULAR HAIR TRIMS

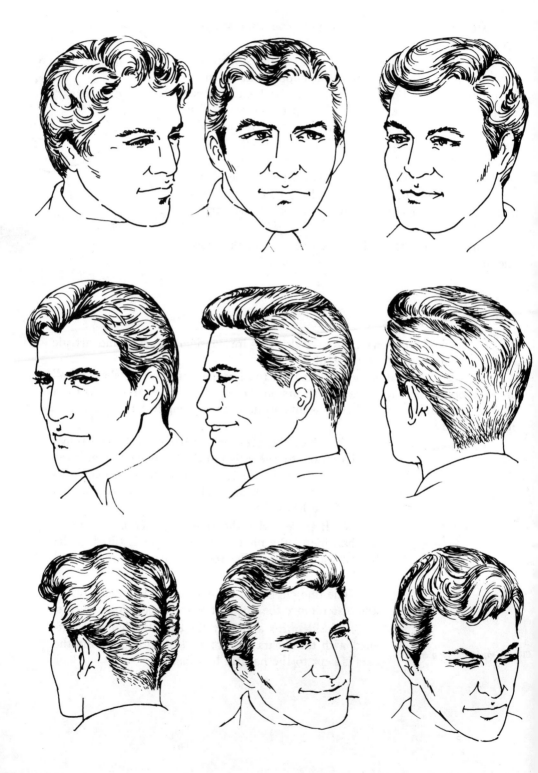

SHORT POMPADOUR OR BRUSH CUT

The short pompadour denotes a short hairstyle in which the hair is combed back without any parting.

Hair texture. Coarse hair is the most desirable for a short pompadour or brush cut. Fine hair is acceptable if it is thick enough and the patron has the proper shaped head. **Fine, thin hair is the least desirable.**

From the short pompadour have sprung such variations as the:

1. Crew cut.
2. Flat-top.
3. Butch cut.

Short pompadour.

CREW CUTS

Many barber-stylists refer to the crew cut as short pomp or brush cut.

The length of hair on the sides and back of the head usually determines the crew cut style, as follows:

1. Short sides and back — short crew cut.
2. Semi-short sides and back — medium crew cut.
3. Medium sides and back — long crew cut.

As a general rule, the edging and siding are done first and the top area is done last. However, the topping can be done with the clipper and then the shears and comb are used to smooth out any uneven spot or area.

The top hair should be graduated in length from the front hairline to the back part of the crown. The top hair, from side to side, should form a slight curve to conform with the general contour of the head.

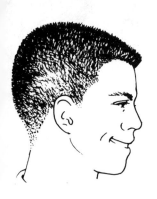

Short crew cut.

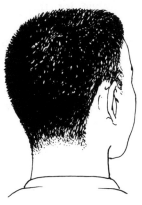

Back view of crew cut.

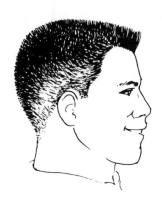

Long crew cut.

103

FLAT TOPS

The sides and back areas of the flat-top hairstyle are quite identical to that of a crew cut, with the following exceptions:

1. The top area — the emphasis is on flatness.
2. The sides at top — appearance is square.

Suggested Procedure

The barber-stylist stands behind the client, the hair at the crown is cut down flat to about one-quarter to one-half inch in length, one inch in depth and about two to three inches in width.

Standing in front of the client, the front center hair is cut down flat about two inches in length and one inch in depth, then straight across both sides.

It is important that the hair in the center and the sides are the same height. Ask the client if the front hair is the desired length. If it is not, then cut the hair to the desired height.

The clipper or shears and comb may be used in cutting the flat-top.

Standing in back using
shear and comb.

Standing in front
using shear and comb.

Standing in back using
clipper over comb.

BUTCH CUT

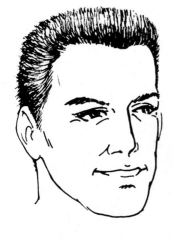

The Butch cut is popular with boys as it requires the least attention. Some men, too, desire this style for the same reason.

Procedure. The sides and back areas are cut as for the short crew cut. The top hair is cut the same length, about one-quarter to one-half inch all over the top, following the contour of the head.

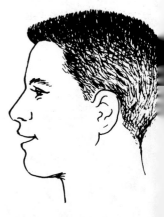

Butch cut for man.

Butch cut for boy.

BASIC PRINCIPLES OF MEN'S HAIRSTYLING

WHICH HAIRSTYLE SHALL IT BE?

Before cutting any hair, the barber-stylist studies the client's features and offers suggestions as to what kind of hairstyle is most suitable for him.

To be successful the barber-stylist must perfect the skill of haircutting. Each haircut should represent a work of art. Try to give the type of haircut that will emphasize the proper contour lines of the head.

Hairstyling has been defined as "the artistic cutting and dressing of hair to best fit the client's physical needs and personality."

MEN'S FACIAL TYPES

The facial type of each person is determined by the position and prominence of the facial bones. There are seven facial types: oval, round, square, oblong, pear shape, heart shape, and diamond.

To recognize each facial type and be able to give correct advice, the barber-stylist should be acquainted with the outstanding characteristics of each.

FACIAL TYPES

Select the right hairstyle for yourself and also for your clients. While no amount of exercise will change your facial shape, the right hairstyles can complement your facial shape in much the same way certain clothes flatter the body.

The following facial types are for your guidance in styling your client's hair.

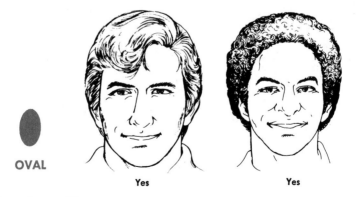

OVAL

Yes   Yes

The perfect face shape. You can wear any hairstyle. Try changing your part. Experiment — keeping in mind your lifestyle, what you feel comfortable with and can easily maintain.

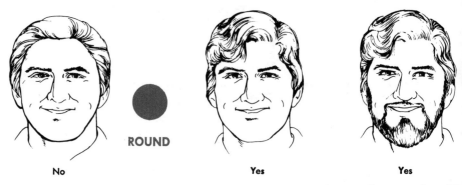

| No | ROUND | Yes | Yes |

The aim here is to slim the face. Don't wear hair too short or it will emphasize the fullness. An off-center part and some waves at eye-level will help give a less full appearance. If a beard is worn, style it so that it will make the face appear oval.

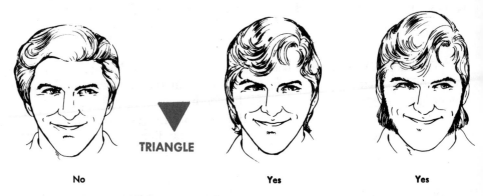

| No | TRIANGLE | Yes | Yes |

The potential problems with this facial shape are over wide cheekbones and a very narrow chin. Keep the hair close to the crown and temples and longer and fuller in back to de-emphasize these points. A full beard, or even "mutton chops" would also help fill out the narrow jaw.

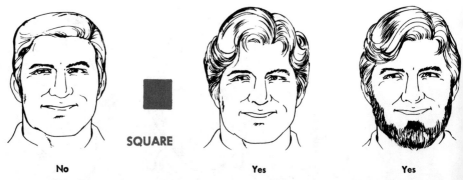

| No | SQUARE | Yes | Yes |

To minimize the angular features of the square facial type at the forehead, use wavy bangs that blend into the temples. This can soften the square forehead and draw attention to your strong, masculine jaw. If a beard is worn, style it to slenderize the face.

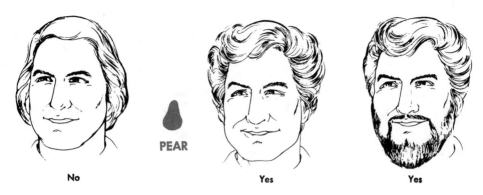

| No | Yes | Yes |

This shape is narrow at the top and wide on the bottom. You need volume and fullness at the crown and temples for balance. A short, full styles is best, ending no longer than just above the jawline. A good perm could be another good solution for assuring width at the top. If a beard is worn, it should be styled to slenderize the lower jaw.

| No | Yes | Yes |

The long face needs to be shortened, the angularity hidden, the hairline never exposed. Blown bangs can do it all at the same time. A layered cut is best. A mustache will help to shorten the appearance of a long face.

| No | Yes | Yes |

The idea here is to fill out your face at the temples and chin and keep hair close to the head at the widest points. Deep full bangs will give a broad appearance to the forehead and a one-length cut in the back will add width.

107

STRAIGHT

Usually all hairstyles are becoming to the straight or normal profile.

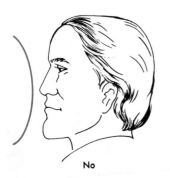

No

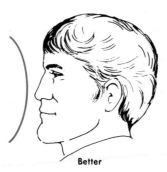

Better

CONCAVE

Requires close hair arrangement over the forehead to minimize the bulginess of the forehead.

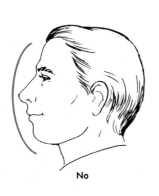

No

Better

CONVEX

To conceal the short receding forehead, arrange the top front hair over the forehead. To minimize the receding chin, a beard should be worn.

No

Better

ANGULAR

Draw hair forward to conceal a receding forehead. A short beard and mustache would help minimize a protruding chin.

NOSE

No

Better

PROMINENT NOSE

A hooked nose, a large nose or a pointed nose, all come under this classification. To minimize the prominence of the nose, bring the hair forward at the forehead and the hair back at the sides.

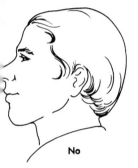

No

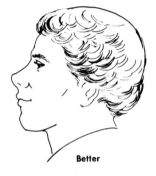

Better

TURNED-UP NOSE

Comb the hair down over the forehead and comb the hair back at the sides.

NECK

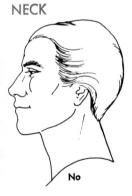

No

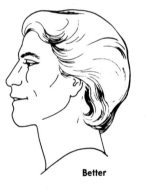

Better

LONG NECK

Leave the hair full or longer on the neck to minimize the length of the neck.

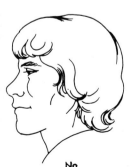

No

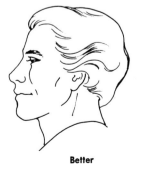

Better

SHORT NECK

Leave the neck exposed to create length to the neck.

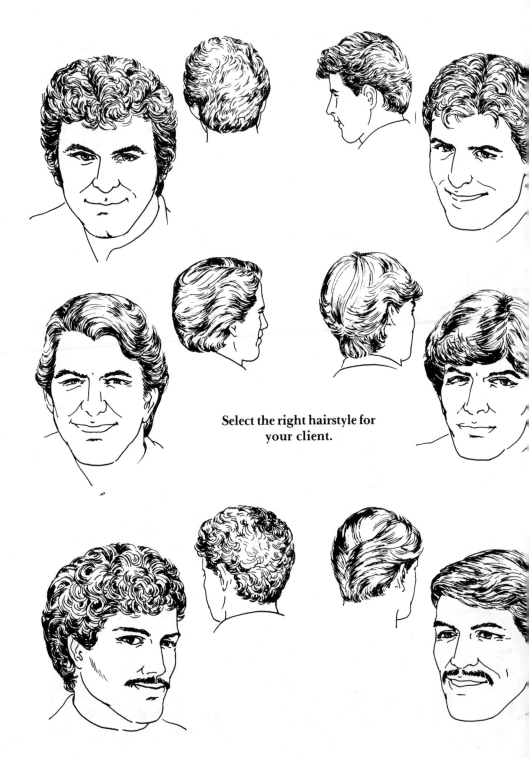

Select the right hairstyle for
your client.

ADDITIONAL HAIRSTYLES
FOR MEN AND BOYS

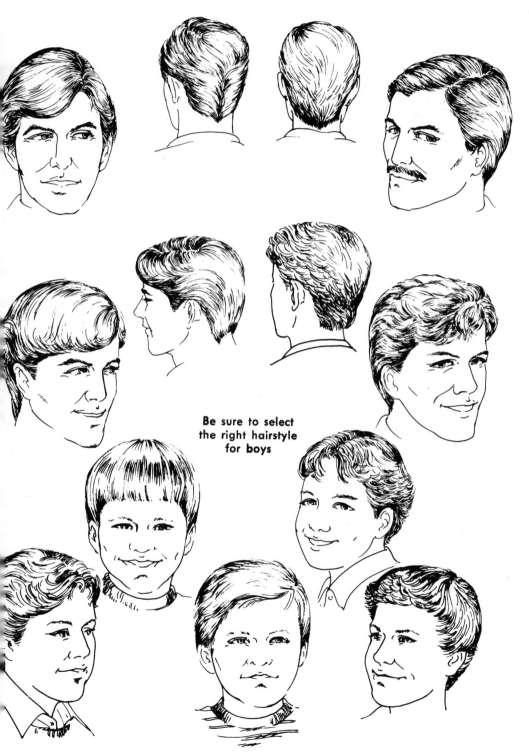

Be sure to select
the right hairstyle
for boys

QUESTIONS ON MEN'S HAIRCUTTING

1. What is meant by the art of haircutting?
2. What is meant by a hair trim?
3. How can the art of haircutting be acquired?
4. Which three head areas does the barber-stylist consider in modern haircutting?
5. Name three variations of the brush cut.
6. To get a better view of shears and comb work, what procedure should be followed?
7. Which sanitary precautions should be observed by the barber-stylist?
8. How should the client be prepared for a haircut?
9. Where is clipper work generally started and finished on the client's head?
10. Why do some barber-stylists prefer to start clipper work on the right side of the head?
11. How should the clipper be used in tapering the hair?
12. What is the proper position of the shears and comb in haircutting?
13. What is the purpose of finger work in haircutting?
14. What plan is followed in shaving the neckline?
15. Name the shaving strokes used: a) over the right side of the neck; b) left side of the neck.
16. Give ten reasons why a client may find fault with a haircut.

QUESTIONS ON BASIC PRINCIPLES OF MEN'S HAIRSTYLING

1. What preliminary facial analysis should the barber-stylist perform before cutting the hair?
2. Why is it important that the barber-stylist have an understanding of facial types?
3. How many facial types are there? Name them.
4. Which is considered the perfect facial type?
5. What is the styling objective when dealing with a round facial type?
6. What is the styling objective when dealing with the oblong (long) face?
7. What should be done with a convex profile to conceal the short, receding forehead?
8. How can we minimize the effect of a prominent nose?
9. What should be done to minimize a long neck?
10. What can be done to minimize a short neck?

Chapter 8

CUTTING AND STYLING CURLY AND OVER-CURLY HAIR

Learning how to artistically cut and groom curly and over-curly hair presents a challenge to the well-trained barber-stylist. To do the best possible work for clients calls for training and experience in this specialized art.

To adequately meet this challenge, the barber-stylist must know:

1. The structure, appearance, variety and qualities of curly and over-curly hair.
2. What haircutting implements are required.
3. Which haircuts and hairstyles are best for clients.
4. How to achieve a well-groomed appearance for clients.

Over-curly hair is present in all races to a greater or lesser degree. This type of hair presents peculiarities which the competent barber-stylist should be equipped to service.

The barber-stylist who is properly trained in this work becomes a valuable asset to the barber-styling shop where he or she is employed. Clients appreciate the practitioner who is able to render such a helpful service. The stylist's income naturally increases with success.

STRUCTURE OF CURLY OR OVER-CURLY HAIR

1. **In straight hair,** the follicles and the hair shaft are straight in appearance. The hair shaft projects from the skin at a slight angle. Each hair strand has a uniform thickness throughout its entire length.
2. **In curly and over-curly** hair, the follicles have a curved shape. As the hair emerges from the skin, it twists upon itself to form small loops.

113

Another difference is that the hair shaft is not uniform in thickness. Instead, there is frequent narrowing of its width. At these narrow or weak points, the hair can easily break off.

| STRAIGHT HAIR | WAVY HAIR | CURLY OR OVER-CURLY HAIR |

Shapes and cross-sections of different forms of hair.

Members of the black race have distinctive hair characteristics. As a general rule, the hair is short, thick, black and curly or kinky in appearance. Exceptions are found where the hair has a straight appearance or is naturally blonde or red in color. Hair texture among blacks, as with most other races, may vary from one person to another.

When a cross-section of curly or over-curly hair is examined under the microscope, it presents an almost flat shape, as shown in the above illustration. However, two other varieties common among the blacks are round (straight hair) and oval (wavy hair).

HYGIENE AND SANITATION

Personal hygiene and barber-styling shop sanitation are important subjects to the professional practitioner. For good appearance and for good health, both personal hygiene and shop sanitation should be followed at all times. The results will prove to be beneficial to both the practitioner and clients. The successful barber-stylist is always well-groomed.

For detailed information on this subject, read chapter 1 on **Hygiene and Good Grooming.**

BARBER-STYLING SHOP SANITATION

Barber-styling shop sanitation can best be maintained if the barber-stylist observes the following important rules:

1. Keep the hands clean by washing them with soap and warm water before and after serving each client.
2. Keep the hydraulic chair, work station and surrounding floor clean and free from hair.
3. Store sanitized implements in a clean container or dry sanitizer.
4. Keep all waste materials in closed containers.
5. Use only clean towels and fresh supplies on clients.

Also follow the rules and regulations issued by your State Board and the Department of Health.

For more information on this subject, read chapter 3 on **Sterilization and Sanitation.**

IMPLEMENTS

The principal implements used for cutting curly or over-curly hair are the clippers, shears and comb. The straight razor is usually used to shave the outlined areas to finish a haircut.

The sizes of clipper blades used most often for curly or over-curly hair are Numbers 0000, 000, 00, 1, 1A, 1½ and 2. These clipper blades may be used as suggested below:

1. The #0000 and #000 clipper blades are most suitable for the neck area, either before or after the haircut. The #00 blade is used primarily for a medium neckline clean-up.

2. The #1 blade is usually used with the clipper over comb technique. It can also be used in cutting the hair with or against the grain.

3. The #1A blade is best for the sides of the head.

4. The #1½ blade is used for long trims. It is generally used on the sides and back of the head against the grain. It is also used with the grain on top of the head.

5. The #2 blade can be used for long trims, either with or against the grain.

Shears give a polished look to the haircut. They serve mainly to smooth out clipper markings and smooth out uneven hair ends. Just as with the clippers, shears can be used over the comb.

Combs. Since the strands of curly and over-curly hair are usually hard to comb, a strong comb is recommended. The coarse comb with wide teeth is the preferred one.

Clippers. The **lever type clippers** can accomplish the same as the slip-on-blade type (detachable head). The sizes of fine or coarse cutting blades may be regulated by adjusting the lever controlling the lower or still blade.

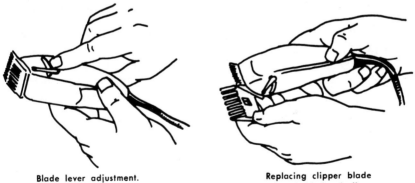

Blade lever adjustment.

Replacing clipper blade
on detachable-head clipper.

Detachable-head clippers (slip-on blade type). The blades in various sizes may be removed and re-inserted onto the head of the clipper as often as it is necessary.

Success comes to you if you study and work hard to become a Professional Barber-Stylist. The end result is that you become an asset to yourself, to your family and community. Your instructor will help you to achieve your goal.

Exercise No. 1

HOW TO PREPARE A CLIENT FOR A HAIRCUT

Before starting a haircut, the following preparation is required:

1. Have on hand all necessary linens, sanitized implements and supplies.

2. Lock the chair and seat client comfortably in the chair, facing mirror.

3. Grasp neck-pieces of chair cloth and bring it over the front of client. (Some practitioners prefer the term "hair cloth.")

4. Remove or drop headrest.

5. Wash and dry hands.

6. Adjust tissue neck-strip (neck-band) or towel protector under neck-pieces of chair cloth.

   a) If a tissue neck-strip is used, bring it completely around the client's neck with the ends overlapping in the back. Over the tissue neck-strip, place the neck-pieces of the chair cloth and fasten them securely in the back. Extending portion of the tissue neck-strip is folded neatly over the neck-pieces of the chair cloth.

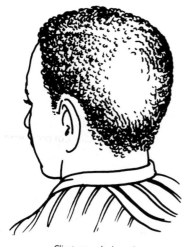

Client properly draped for haircutting.

   b) If a towel is used, spread it straight across the back of the client, the upper edge being tucked in at the neckline. Bring both ends of the towel around the client's neck, allowing one end to overlap the other under the chin. Place the neck-pieces of the chair cloth over the towel and fasten them securely, so that they will not interfere with the action of the clipper.

7. (Optional)—Sprinkle talcum powder on a tissue and apply it over the back of the client's neck.

116

CLIPPER HAIRCUTTING

For the beginner, it is best to practice tapering with the blade guard of a disconnected electric clipper before cutting any hair from the head.

To learn the proper handling of the clipper the student should practice the following exercises diligently.

1. **How to hold clipper and comb.** The position of the right hand:
   - a) Pick up the clipper with the right hand.
   - b) Place thumb on the clipper and fingers around the clipper.
     Hold it lightly to permit freedom of wrist movement. (Fig. 1)
   - c) Left hand: Use comb to guide clipper and to comb hair downward.

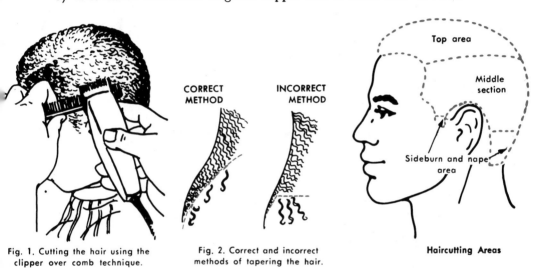

CORRECT METHOD   INCORRECT METHOD

Top area

Middle section

Sideburn and nape area

Fig. 1. Cutting the hair using the clipper over comb technique.

Fig. 2. Correct and incorrect methods of tapering the hair.

Haircutting Areas

2. **How to use clipper and comb.**

   a) For a gradual, even taper, tilt the blade as you clip so that the clipper rides on the heel of the bottom blade. See Fig. 2 for correct and incorrect tapering.

   b) Do not move the clipper into the hair too fast as it will have a tendency to jam the clipper blades and pull the hair.

3. After tapering one strip of hair, comb down smooth and start tapering the next strip. (See Fig. 1) Clipper tapering should begin at the left temple and continue around the head, finishing at the right temple.*

*Some practitioners prefer to do clipper work from right sideburn to left sideburn, in which case the routine is reversed and is equally correct.

Fig. 3. Outlining nape with #000 blade.

Cutting and tapering the hair with the clipper can be accomplished in the following ways:

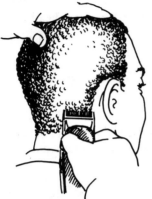

1. Clipper cutting **against** the grain is accomplished by cutting the hair in the opposite direction to which the hair grows. Tapering the hair is accomplished by gradually tilting the clipper until it rides on its heel.

1. Clipper cutting against the grain.

2. Clipper cutting **with** the grain means the cutting of the hair is in the same direction in which it grows.

When using a clipper on hair which has a tight curl formation, the practitioner should try to cut with the grain (in direction of hair growth). Cutting tight, curly hair against the grain clogs up the clipper blades and halts the action of the clipper.

2. Clipper cutting with the grain.

3. Clipper cutting **across** the grain. The hair is cut neither with the grain nor against the grain. It is usually done on the sides of the head.

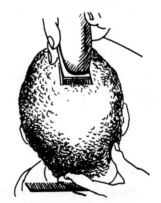

3. Clipper cutting across the grain.

4. DIFFICULT HAIR. Hair that grows in a whirlpool, taper against the grain in a circular movement.

5. Clipper cutting over the co...

4. Clipper cutting the hair in a **circular** motion. This type of cutting is advisable in whorl areas or in places where the hair does not grow in a uniform manner.

5. Clipper cutting **over a comb** is a method of cutting in which the hair may be cut with the minimum change of clipper blades.

Exercise No. 3

SHEARS AND COMB TECHNIQUE

Shears and comb technique is used to cut the ends of the hair and even up the clipper taper. It is usually employed after the clipper work is completed.

To learn shears and comb technique the student should practice the following exercises:

1. **How to hold shears and comb.**

   a) Pick up shears firmly with the right hand and insert thumb into thumb grip, place third finger into finger grip and leave little finger on finger brace of shears.

   b) Pick up comb* with the left hand and place fingers on top of teeth with the thumb on the backbone of the comb. (Fig. 3)

Fig. 1. Proper way to hold shears.

*For the student, start with the coarse teeth of the comb. After sufficient skill is developed, use the fine teeth of the comb.

Fig. 2. Turning the comb downward.

   To comb hair downward, turn comb toward client's head, as in turning a key, by using the thumb and the first two fingers. (Fig. 2)

   The position of both the right hand and left hand are as follows:

   a) Hold shears and comb slightly to your right front.

   b) Hold comb parallel with the still blade of the shears, as in Fig. 3.

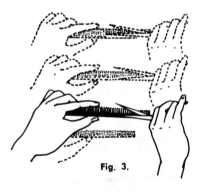

Fig. 3.

2. **How to use shears and comb.** (Figs. 3 and 4)

   a) Keep one blade still while moving the other blade with the thumb. Master this technique before attempting to do a haircut.

   b) While manipulating the shears move both shears and comb slowly upward at the same time.

   c) Turn teeth of comb downward when combing the hair downward. (See Fig. 2)

   d) Finish one vertical strip at a time before proceeding with the next strip to the left. Working from right to left gives a better view of the work.

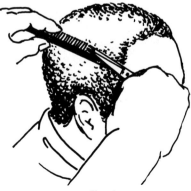

Fig. 4.

1. Right sideburn.

Suggestions on the Use of the Shears and Comb

The procedures given here may be changed to conform with your instructor's routine, which is equally correct.

Note — This exercise co-ordinates with Exercise No. 4, which follows.

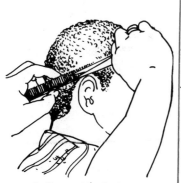

2. Over and back of ear.

3. Smooth out clipper taper.

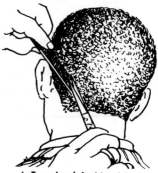

4. Tapering left side of neck.

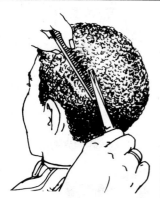

5. Blending side with top hair.

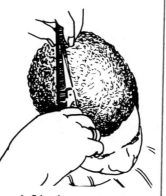

6. Trimming uneven hair.

7. Shear point cutting top hair.

Exercise No. 4

ARCHING TECHNIQUE

Arching technique means marking the outer border of the haircut in front and over the ears and side of the neck. This outlining is accomplished with the points of the shears and is usually performed while doing the shears and comb work as described in Exercise No. 3.

To learn arching technique the student should practice the following exercise diligently.

Fig. 1. Outlining in front of and over the ear.

1. **How to hold shears with right hand.**

   a) Pick up shears and insert thumb in thumb grip, place third finger into finger grip and leave the little finger on brace of shears.

   b) Place point of shears blade against scalp. The fingers holding the shears are on the bottom and the thumb on top. (Fig. 1)

   c) Use the most convenient fingertip of left hand to steady point of shears. (Fig. 1)

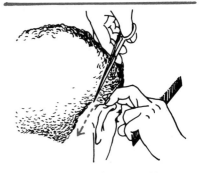

Fig. 2. Outlining the right side of neck downward.

2. **How to use shears — Arching the right side.**

   The proper way to use shears is as follows:

   a) Always make outline around ear as close to the natural hairline as possible.

   b) Start in front of ear and make a continuous outline around the ear and down the side of neck. (Figs. 1 and 2)

   c) Reverse the direction of arching back to starting point. (Fig. 3)

   d) Continue arching around ear until a definite outline is formed.

   e) Mark outline for length of sideburns. (Fig. 4)

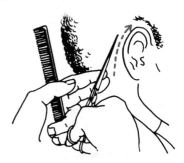

Fig. 3. Outlining the right side of neck upward.

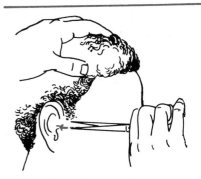

Fig. 4. Squaring off the right sideburn.

f) Arch the left side of the head. Start in front of the left ear with the shears, make a continuous outline over the left ear and down the side of neck; then reverse the direction of the shears, and return to the starting point. The squaring off of the left sideburn is done last. (Figs. 5, 6, 7 and 8)

Fig. 5. Outlining the left side of neck downward.

Fig. 6. Outlining the left side of neck upward.

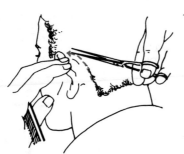

Fig. 7. Outlining over left ear.

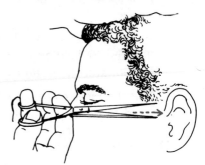

Fig. 8. Squaring off left sideburn.

SIX POPULAR LENGTHS OF SIDEBURNS

Use the corner of the eyes as a guideline to the length of sideburns.

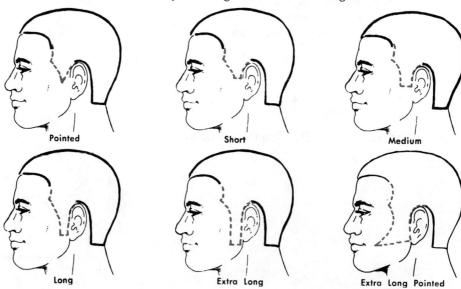

Pointed

Short

Medium

Long

Extra Long

Extra Long Pointed

122

Exercise No. 5

ARCHING WITH A CLIPPER

Many barber-stylists prefer to use a specially constructed clipper with a small head having a fine cutting edge for squaring off sideburns and making the outline around the ears and sides of neck. This method of arching is much faster.

Suggestions

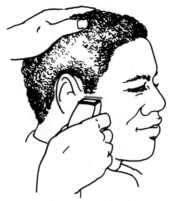

Squaring off right sideburn
Turn clipper on its cutting edge.

Outlining right side
of neck.

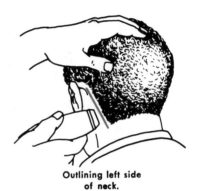

Outlining left side
of neck.

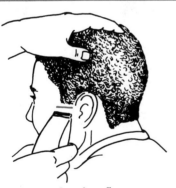

Squaring off
left sideburn.

To produce a square nape line
a clipper may be used.

Exercise No. 6

SHAVING NECK AND OUTLINED AREAS

Preparation for a Neck Shave

The neck shave contributes to the appearance of the finished haircut. Shaving the outlined areas of the sideburns, around the ears and the sides of the neck below the ears gives the client a clean appearance. If the haircut requires a round or square outline at the nape of the neck, the free hand stroke should be used at the back of the neck.

To prepare for a neck shave follow these steps:

1. Remove all cut hair from the head and neck with a clean towel, tissues or hair vacuum. (Fig. 1)

2. Loosen the chair cloth and neck-strip carefully, so that no cut hair will fall down the client's neck.

3. Discard the cut hair at the base of the chair in the following manner: Pick up the chair cloth at the lower edge and bring it up to the upper edge. Remove the chair cloth carefully so that no cut hair will fall on the client. Drop upper edge of chair cloth, giving a slight shake to dislodge all cut hair. (Fig. 2) Be careful that you check the surface before applying the shaving cream for concealed scars or lumps to avoid accidentally cutting the client.

4. Replace chair cloth as before. It should be left a few inches away from the neck so that it does not come in contact with the client's skin.

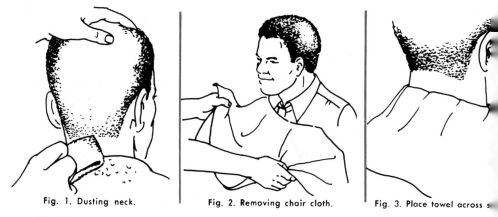

Fig. 1. Dusting neck.   Fig. 2. Removing chair cloth.   Fig. 3. Place towel across s

5. Spread a face towel straight across the shoulders, then tuck it into the neck-band. (Fig. 3)

Applying Lather for Neck Shave

1. Prepare lather same as for the beard.

2. Lather both sides of the head and the back of the neck as follows: Give a light coat of lather at the hairline around and over the ears, sideburns and down the sides of the neck. If round neck shave is to be given, apply lather to the back of the neck up to the hairline.

3. Rub the lather in lightly with the ball part of the fingertips or thumb.

124

Shaving Outlined Area

Shaving outlined areas is a follow-up to Exercise No. 4, on Arching Technique. The purpose of this exercise is to shave over the outlined areas of the ears, neck and sideburns.

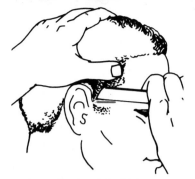

Fig. 1. Shaving right sideburn to proper length.

1. **Shaving right side.**

   The proper way to shave the outlined area is as follows:

   a) Hold razor as in free hand stroke.

   b) Place thumb of left hand on the scalp above the point of razor, and stretch scalp under razor.

   c) Shave sideburn to the proper length. (Fig. 1)

   d) Shave around ear at hairline and straight down side of neck, using a free hand stroke with the point of razor. Be careful not to shave into the hairline at the nape of the neck. (Figs. 2, 3 and 4)

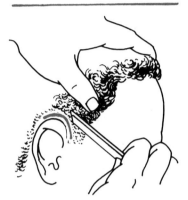

Fig. 2. Shave over ear.

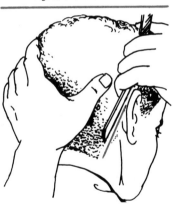

Fig. 3. Shave outline below ear.

2. **Shaving left side.**

   The proper way to shave the outlined area is as follows:

   a) Hold razor as in reverse hand stroke.

   b) Place thumb of left hand on scalp above point of razor and stretch skin under razor.

   c) Shave sideburn to the proper length. (Fig. 5)

   d) Shave around ear at hairline using a free hand stroke.

   e) Shave neck below ear, using the reverse back hand stroke with point of razor. (Fig. 6) Hold ear away with fingers of left hand. If the stroke is done with one continuous movement, a straight line will be formed down the side of the neck.

Fig. 4. Clean neck below ear.

125

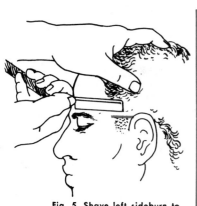

Fig. 5. Shave left sideburn to proper length using reverse back hand stroke.

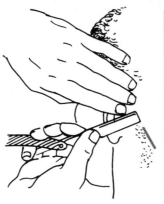

Fig. 6. Shave left side of neck using back hand stroke.

Fig. 7. To achieve a square or round shaped hair style, shaving is required.

f) If necessary, shave nape area round or square. (Figs. 8 and 9)

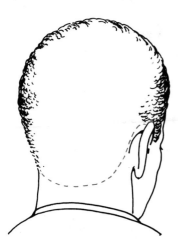

Fig. 8. Round.

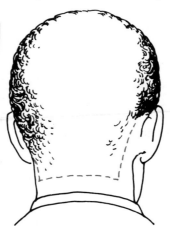

Fig. 9. Square.

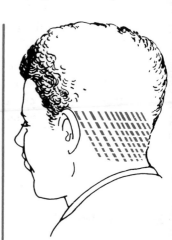

Fig. 10. Tapered.

3. Provided the client does not specify otherwise, shave the neck outline straight down the sides of the neck behind the ears. At the client's request, neckline may be rounded at the bottom edge on both sides, or may be shaved straight across the back of the neck, producing a square back. The square back can have either straight corners or rounded corners.

Clean Shaved Areas

After the neck shave has been completed, clean shaved parts with palms and fingers moistened with witch hazel or warm water. Dry and powder the neck thoroughly. Replace the towel across the client's shoulders and tuck it neatly into the neck-band for final checkup and combing of the hair.

--- REMINDER ---

For Sanitary Measures and Ten Reasons Why a Client May Find Fault with a Haircut, turn to page 97.

HAIRSTYLES FOR MEN AND BOYS

PROFESSIONAL BARBER-STYLISTS

It is the duty of every professional barber-stylist to give the client the style of haircut which will emphasize his good points and minimize his or her poor ones, such as bumps, hollows and scars.

Each halircut requires the practitioner's personal touch, keeping in mind the client's wishes and the style which is most becoming to his or her personality.

However, if the client asks for your professional advice, then suggest the style of haircut which best improves his or her appearance.

EACH HAIRCUT SHOULD REPRESENT A WORK OF ART

IMPORTANT REMINDER

Due to the fact that there are so many different textures and degrees of curliness in curly and over-curly hair, achieving proficiency in haircutting requires a great deal of practice. Follow your instructor's directions explicitly. His or her routine may be different from the one outlined in the following lessons, but **remember that your instructor's method is equally correct.**

Exercise No. 7

MEDIUM LENGTH HAIRCUT

A medium haircut requires considerable skill and artistic sense to achieve satisfactory results, as the hair is cut neither too short nor too long. Every phase of haircutting is employed in this style.

Before.

PROCEDURE

After.

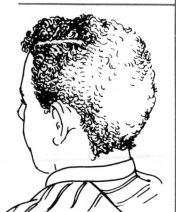

1. Prepare and drape patron for haircut.

2. Comb top hair forward in the direction in which it grows.

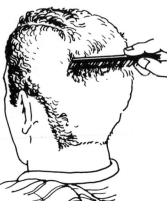

3. Comb back and side hair downward in the direction in which it grows.

Note—Some practitioners prefer to start clipper work on the left sideburn, while others prefer to start on the right sideburn. Either procedure is correct. Follow your instructor's directions.

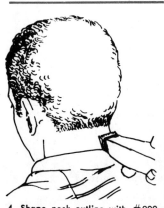

4. Shape neck outline with #000 clipper blade.

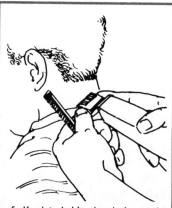

5. If detachable head is used, change to #1½ blade. If lever type is used, adjust lever to 1½ mark.

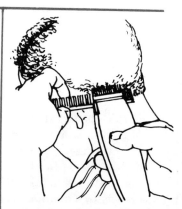

6. With clipper over comb technique cut hair about 1½ inches higher than previous line.

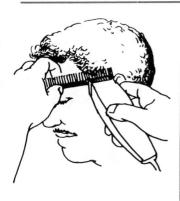

7. Continue with #1½ blade, cut left side of head 1½ inches above hair line. Do the same on right side.

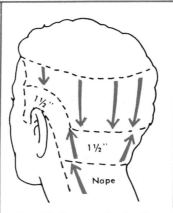
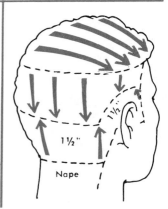

8. and 9. Diagrams showing the various steps for the medium cut.
Right side same as left.

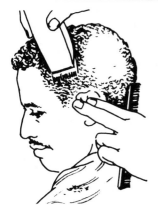

10. Change over to blade #1. Cut hair with the grain, going over area previously cut to taper uneven spots.

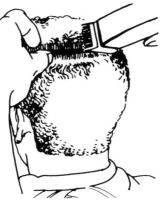

11. To avoid close cutting, change to #1½ blade and cut against the grain by using clipper over comb.

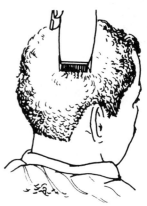

12. Using #1½ blade, taper both sides and back downward, starting in the crown area.

13. Using #1½ blade, cut top hair across grain.

14. Continue to top front part of head.

15. Change to #000 blade using clipper over comb method to blend nape outline into an even, gradual upward taper.

129

SHEARS AND COMB TECHNIQUE

Shears and comb technique is used after clipper cutting is completed. It is usually used to smooth out uneven areas. Arching is coordinated with the shears and comb phase of haircutting.

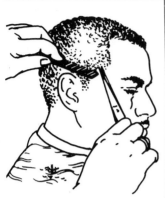

1. Retouch hair at right side of head, using points of shears.

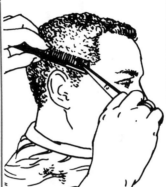

2. Use the coarse end of comb to avoid close cutting.

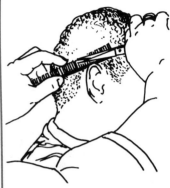

3. Continue towards the back; do the back and left side of head in the same manner.

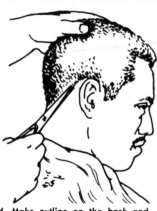

4. Make outline on the back and over the right ear with points of the shears.

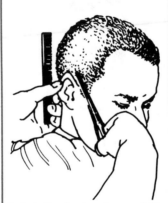

5. Arch the front and over right ear; also square off the right sideburn.

6. Continue to arch the left side of the head.

7. Square off left sideburn.

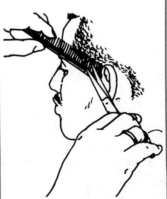

8. Retouch left side in the same manner as right side.

9. Use the coarse end of comb to avoid close cutting.

130

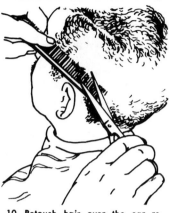

10. Retouch hair over the ear region.

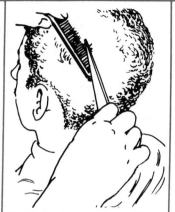

11. Blend the side hair with top area.

12. Cut top area to the desired length.

13. Cut the top front area to desired length.

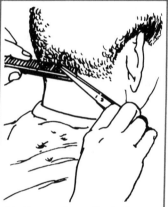

14. Remove clipper line in the nape area.

15. Shave the outlined areas on both sides of head.

SHEAR-POINT TAPERING

The shear-point technique is generally used for the following:

1. Hollows and creases.
2. Thinning out uneven dark hair patches.
3. Hair that grows in whorls on various parts of the head.

The shear-point taper is accomplished with the cutting points of the shears. Only a few hairs are cut at a time and then combed out. Continue cutting in or around the objectionable spot until it becomes less noticeable and blends in with the rest of the hair.

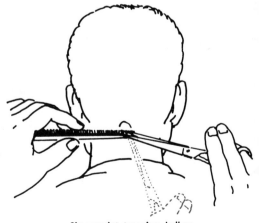

Shear-point tapering hollow spot in nape area.

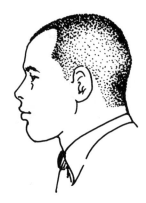

MAN'S QUO VADIS HAIRCUT

Quo Vadis is a popular haircut style which is suitable for over-curly hair.

The basic problem in this haircut is to achieve an even and smooth cut over the entire head. Since the hair grows close to the scalp, clipper lines and patches are readily noticeable; and therefore extra care must be exercised to avoid or eliminate such lines.

To avoid these irregularities, use a clipper over the entire head. Use the #000 clipper blade over the neck. The #1 clipper blade is best all over the head.

PROCEDURE

1. Use #000 clipper blade to outline neck area.

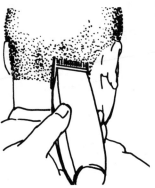

2. Change over to #1 blade and clip hair to crown in strips.

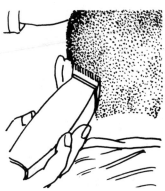

3. Shows the back of the head clipped to the crown. To avoid ridges or patches the clipper blade should overlap the cut strip.

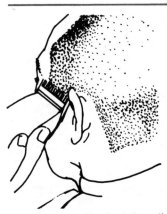

4. Continue to clip the hair until left side is reached.

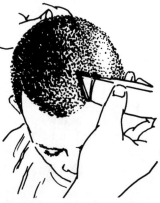

5. The crown is cut from the forehead to back part of head.

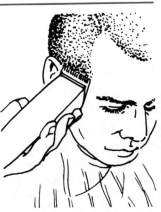

6. The right side is clipped to match the left side.

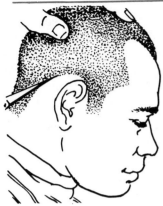

7. After the hair has been evenly cut all over the head, arch left and right sides of the head in the usual manner.

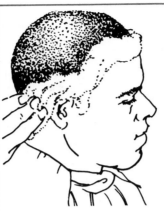

8. Prepare for shaving front hairline, around ears and sides of neck.

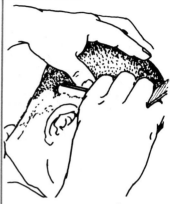

9. Shave right side outline.

10. Front hairline and left outline properly lathered.

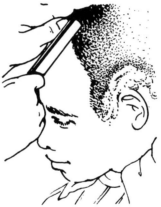

11. Shave the front hairline the Quo Vadis line and hair part. Shave the left outlined area.

12. Quo Vadis line—front view.

Before—Profile.

After—Three-quarter front view.

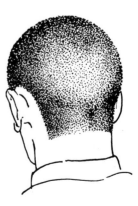

Back view.

Exercise No. 9
AFRO-NATURAL STYLES

FULL
MEDIUM
SHORT

Afro-Natural Hairstyles are popular today with many men of all ages, young men and boys with over-curly hair. It is to the professional barber-stylist's benefit to be able to style and satisfy those client's having over-curly hair.

Afro-hairstyles' theme is the **natural look** without resorting to any hair straightening treatments.

After the client has been prepared in the usual manner for a haircut, the hair is combed either with a wide tooth comb or hair lifter in order to bring the hair ends to the surface. After this is done, the hair is styled to the client's wishes, and to improve his appearance.

SPECIAL PROBLEMS
INGROWN HAIRS

An ingrown hair grows underneath the skin and thereby sets up a skin infection.

Among the common causes of ingrown hairs are:
1. Very close shaving, particularly during the second time over.
2. Close shaving in the nape area.
3. Wearing tight shirt collars which rub against the neck.

Corrective Procedure
1. Sterilize a needle and tweezers.
2. With the needle, gently pierce skin and lift the hair from under the skin.
3. With the tweezer, pull out the hair.
4. Apply antiseptic lotion such as hydrogen peroxide or tincture of iodine.

Prevention of Ingrown Hairs
To prevent ingrown hairs and their resultant infections, the barber-stylist should:
1. Avoid close shaving.
2. Advise client to wear a loose shirt collar.

In some instances, clients may discontinue shaving and cultivate a beard instead.

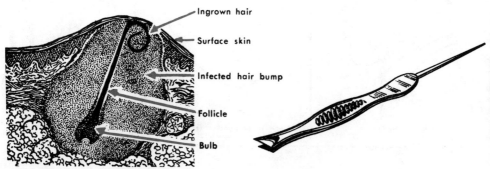

Ingrown hair
Surface skin
Infected hair bump
Follicle
Bulb

Ingrown hair growing under the skin

Tweezer with needle

Exercise No. 10

BOY'S HAIRCUT

Before.

After.

The professional barber-stylist needs special training and experience to become competent with children's haircuts. By catering to children, he can also bring parents to the barber-styling shop. Thus, the haircutting and hairstyling needs of the entire family can be better served.

Children's hair is usually unruly and difficult to cut. However, their hair texture is soft and wavy and therefore lends itself to appropriate styling. Avoid close cutting to prevent the scalp from showing through.

PROCEDURE

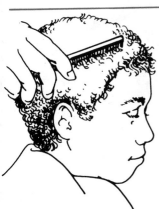

1. Comb top hair forward in the direction in which it grows.

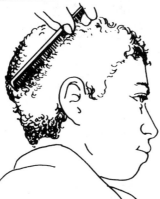

2. Comb sides and back hair downward in the direction in which it grows.

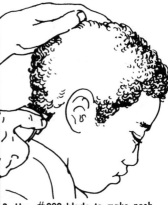

3. Use #000 blade to make neck outline.

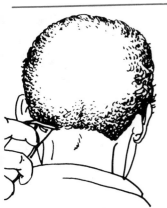

4. If necessary, turn over clipper to make an even straight line across neck.

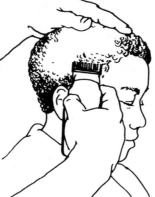

5. Change clipper blade to #1½, cut hair 1 inch above ear. To make taper, tilt clipper on its heel.

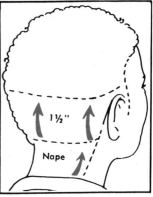

6. Diagram showing various steps.

135

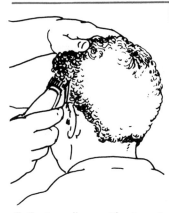

7. Continue clipper cutting towards the back of the head until the left temple is reached.

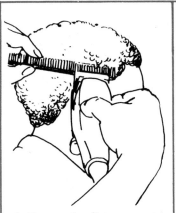

8. Now use the clipper over comb up to crown. Start at right temple and work around the head until the left temple is reached.

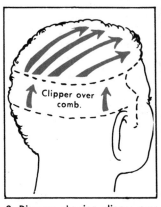

9. Diagram showing clipper over comb procedure.

(Clip hair with grain. See photo #10.)

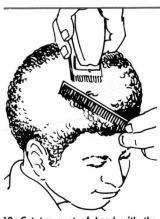

10. Cut top part of head with the grain while holding uncut hair with comb.

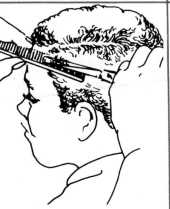

11. Smooth out with shears and comb any uneven spots, starting from right temple to back of head until the left temple is reached.

12. Cutting uneven hair at top of head.

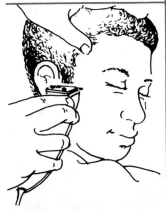

13. Cleaning the outlined areas with clipper turned over, as shaving is not recommended for young boys.

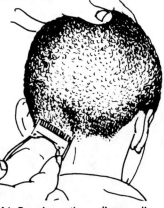

14. Tapering the clipper line smooth with #000 blade.

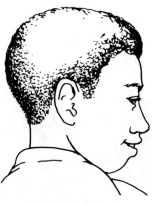

15. Finished hair cut.

QUO VADIS HAIRCUT FOR BOYS
PROCEDURE

The cutting of a boy's Quo Vadis line is the same as for the man's. However, the outlined areas (arching on the right and left sides of the head and front hairline) are accomplished with a special clipper designed especially for this purpose, called outliner or edger.

It is inadvisable to use a razor on young boys as they may move their heads and an accident may occur.

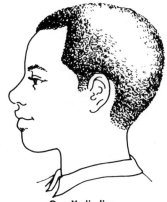

Quo Vadis line
without hair part.

REMINDER

Clipper work may be started on the right or left side of the head or neck. Either procedure is correct. Follow your instructor's directions.

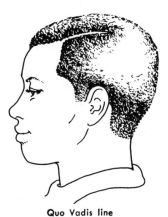

Quo Vadis line
with hair part.

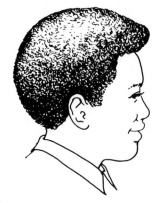

AFRO-NATURAL HAIRSTYLES FOR BOYS

Afro-Natural Hairstyles are also very popular with boys. Every barber-stylist should be able to offer the latest Afro-Natural Hairstyles to boys.

QUESTIONS ON CUTTING AND STYLING CURLY AND OVER-CURLY HAIR

1. What is meant by the art of haircutting?

2. How can the art of haircutting be acquired?

3. Which three head areas does the barber-stylist consider in modern haircutting?

4. Which sanitary precautions should be observed by the barber-stylist?

5. How should the client be prepared for a haircut?

6. Where is clipper work generally started and finished on the client's head?

7. How should the clipper be used in tapering the hair?

8. For upward tapering, what is the proper position of the shears and comb in haircutting?

9. To get a better view of shears and comb work what procedure should be followed?

10. What plan is followed in shaving the neck outline?

11. Name the shaving strokes used: a) over the right side of the neck; b) left side of the neck.

12. Give ten reasons why a client may find fault with a haircut.

13. List four important final steps after a haircut.

14. After releasing the client, list seven sanitary measures to be performed.

Chapter 9

MUSTACHES AND BEARDS

INTRODUCTION

To be considered a professional artisan, the barber-stylist must be prepared to perform many services in addition to cutting and styling hair. The stylist should be capable of offering clients all the services necessary for grooming the hair and skin. One service which should be offered in the shop is mustache and beard designing and trimming.

THE MUSTACHE

Mustaches have been worn by men from prehistoric times. They are worn throughout the world by men in every area of society.

Since the mustache is worn primarily for personal adornment and not for utility, the wearer is extremely concerned or particular about how it is designed, shaped and trimmed.

The barber-stylist who offers the service of mustache trimming should perform this technique carefully and artistically.

PROCEDURE FOR TRIMMING A MUSTACHE

1. Thin the mustache with comb and shears.

2. Trim mustache to desired length with shears.

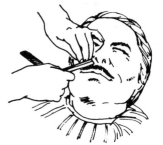

3. Shape mustache with razor.

Added services for mustaches are:

a) Waxing: Mustache ends
b) Penciling: Temporary color
c) Coloring: Suitable color

FIFTEEN CONTEMPORARY MUSTACHE STYLES

Each individual client has his own preference as to how his mustache should be trimmed. Therefore, mustache styles are endless in number. The barber-stylist who is prepared to perform the additional service of mustache designing, shaping and trimming will find that clients will really appreciate this service.

It is important that the professional barber-stylist know how to trim and shape mustaches. Of equal importance is his ability to understand and apply the principles involved in designing mustaches. The following are some of the items which must be considered in the proper designing of mustaches:

SUITABLE MUSTACHE DESIGNS

A mustache should be designed in accordance with the facial features of the wearer. While the client's personal taste must be considered, the most attractive and suitable mustaches are designed in accordance with the facial features. Basically, the size of the mustache should correspond to the size of the facial features, a large design for heavy facial features and a smaller design for fine, small, smooth facial features.

1. Large, coarse facial features — Heavy mustache
2. Prominent nose — Large mustache
3. Long, narrow face — Narrow, thin mustache
4. Extra large mouth — Pyramid shaped mustache
5. Extra small mouth — Narrow, short, thin mustache
6. Smallish regular features — Small, triangularly shaped mustache
7. Wide mouth with prominent upper lip — Heavy handlebar mustache or large, divided mustache
8. Round face with regular features — A semi-squarish mustache
9. Square face with prominent features — Heavy linear mustache with ends curving slightly downward
10. Important factors — (1) length of mouth; (2) size of nose; (3) upper lip area

BEARDS

There are a number of men who are wearing beards made popular during the sixteenth century by the great painter Van Dyke and now known as the Van Dyke beard.

Implements: Beard trimming, for the most part, is performed with the scissors and comb. Other instruments which may be employed in performing this service are the outliner (edger) and the razor.

IMPORTANT REMINDER

The procedure on the following page is one way to perform beard designing and trimming. Remember, your instructor's method is equally correct.

Drape the client as for a haircut. Client sits up so that he can observe his reflection in the mirror and so the barber-stylist can trim each side of the beard equally.

PROCEDURE

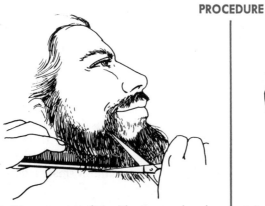

1. Trim away excess hair with scissors and comb, or clipper and comb.

2. Draw the desired beard design with a black eyebrow pencil.

3. Outline the upper part of the beard with outliner.

4. Outline the under part of the beard with outliner.

5. Apply and massage lather into beard to be shaved. Shave the unwanted part of the beard. Remove lather and penciled beard design. Apply after shave lotion.

6. Check and retouch the beard with scissors and comb or clipper and comb wherever necessary. Style hair as desired.

FINISHED BEARD DESIGNS

7. Beard with a mustache

8. Beard connecting with mustache

GOATEE

The purpose of a beard or a goatee is to balance facial features and to correlate face, head, and body proportions. A beard or a goatee should reflect desirable facial shapes.

It is customary to first shave the sides of the face and then trim the beard to the desired shape and length. The mustache is trimmed and dressed last in accordance with the patron's wishes.

GOATEE AND MUSTACHE TRIMMING

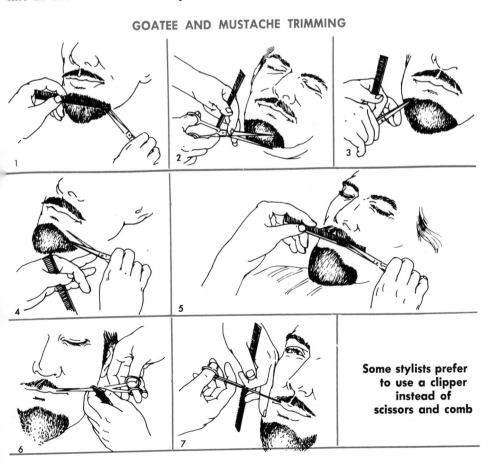

Some stylists prefer to use a clipper instead of scissors and comb

VARIOUS TYPES OF BEARDS

145

CONCLUSION

Beards have been worn by men since prehistoric times. In ancient times, they were worn as signs of manhood, strength, wisdom, and dignity. Poets, philosophers, and statesmen wore beards to lend dignity and distinction to their positions in society. In fact, throughout history the beard has played a vital role as an emblem of notability.

The reasons for beards run from necessity (to cover facial blemishes) to social demands, to religious edicts, and to tribal customs. Whatever the reason, beards are and have been part of the grooming habits of men throughout the ages.

As this chapter indicates, there is tremendous versatility in the designs of beards. The fact that the beard, in some form or another, has survived from the age of the caveman to the present day is absolute testimony of its acceptance by man as a permanent part of facial grooming.

QUESTIONS ON MUSTACHES AND BEARDS

1. What is the primary reason why a man wears a mustache?

2. How should a mustache be designed?

3. What is the basic consideration in determining the size of the mustache?

4. Why is a beard a necessity to some clients?

5. What form of beard was made popular in the sixteenth century?

Chapter 10

SHAMPOOING AND RINSING

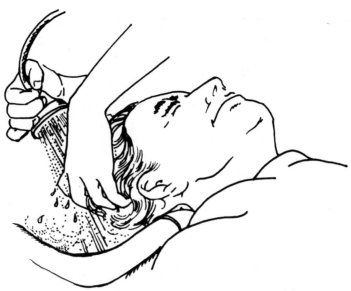

The primary purpose of shampooing is to maintain a clean and healthy condition of the scalp and hair. To be effective, a shampoo must remove all dirt, oil, perspiration and skin debris without adversely affecting either the scalp or the hair.

The hair is vulnerable to dust particles, natural oils from the sebaceous glands, perspiration and shed dead skin cells which accumulate on the scalp. This accumulation offers a breeding place for disease-producing bacteria which, in turn, can lead to scalp disorders. The hair and scalp should be thoroughly shampooed as frequently as required in order to keep them clean, healthy and free from bacteria.

FOUR REQUIREMENTS OF A SHAMPOO

1. It should cleanse the hair of oils, debris and dirt.
2. It should work efficiently in hard as well as soft water.
3. It should be non-irritating to the eyes and skin.
4. It should leave the hair and scalp in their natural condition.

WATER

Water is composed of hydrogen and oxygen.

For efficiency in shampooing, it is important that the barber-stylist know what type of water is available and it is important to know whether the water is hard or soft.

Soft water. Rain water or water that has been chemically softened contains very small amounts of minerals and therefore lathers freely. For this reason, it is preferred for soap shampooing.

Hard water contains certain minerals and as a result soap shampoo does not readily lather in this water. Depending on the kind of hard water available in your community, it usually can be softened by a chemical process and made suitable for shampooing.

WATER TEMPERATURE

The water should be comfortably warm for the client.

1. Cold water, in addition to being uncomfortable for the patron, tends to hamper maximum foaming.
2. Hot water causes a flaking and drying reaction on the scalp.
3. Comfortably warm water is not only comfortable and relaxing to the client, but reacts favorably in the foaming process.

CHOICE OF SHAMPOO

A shampoo service should be special for each client rather than a routine operation. This requires that the barber-stylist examine the client's hair and scalp, have an understanding of the various types of shampoos and whether they would do an effective job. The selection of the particular shampoo for individual clients is an important matter of judgment for the professional practitioner. Conditions which must be considered in the selection of a shampoo are:

1. Excessively Dry Hair — Use an oil shampoo or one with a neutral base.
2. Oily Condition — Green soap shampoo or plain shampoo.
3. Tender Scalp — Cream or egg shampoo.
4. Sensitive Scalp — Egg, oil or mild shampoo.
5. Normal Scalp — Plain shampoo.

PREPARATION

Adequate preparation is the first step in giving a good shampoo. Before starting, the barber-stylist should have on hand all necessary supplies and should wash his or her hands with soap and warm water. Following a definite procedure not only saves time, but also makes for greater efficiency.

The essential supplies needed for a shampoo are:

1. The shampoo selected.
2. Soft, warm water capable of producing an abundance of lather with the shampoo. (Remember, hard water will not produce lather unless softened by a boiling or chemical treatment.)
3. Shampoo bowl or tray, chair cloth, and towels.

HOW TO PREPARE CLIENT FOR SHAMPOO

1. Seat client in a comfortable and relaxed position.
2. Arrange chair cloth as follows:
   a) Grasp the ends of the neck of the chair cloth, one end in each hand.
   b) Place the chair cloth over the front of the client.
   c) Place towel around neck.
   d) Secure chair cloth at the back of the neck over the towel.
3. Unfold one face towel lengthwise and tuck it around the client's left side of neck from center of back to center of front, allowing remainder of towel to fall over left shoulder.
4. Unfold another face towel lengthwise and repeat on right side of neck.

After the client has been prepared and properly protected with the linen arrangement, it is advisable to examine the condition of client's hair and scalp. Briefly massage the scalp. This procedure serves to loosen the epidermal scales, debris and scalp tissues, and thus prepares the hair to receive the shampoo.

SHAMPOOING AT THE CHAIR

The shampoo may be applied while the client is sitting upright in the hydraulic chair or is seated at the shampoo bowl. The method employed is usually that preferred by the practitioner or by the facilities available.

APPLICATION OF SHAMPOO

The shampoo is applied by spreading sections of the hair apart with the thumb and fingers of the left hand and applying the shampoo directly on the scalp. Care must be taken to be sure that all parts of the scalp are covered. After sufficient shampoo has been applied, it should be completely massaged into the scalp. Warm water is gradually added from the regular water dispenser to help work up a rich, creamy lather over the entire scalp.

During the process of working up a lather and manipulating the scalp, great care must be exercised to be certain that the shampoo lather does not run onto the forehead or into the eyes or ears of the client.

All shampoo movements must be executed with the cushion tips of the fingers.

The scalp manipulations are repeated several times until the lather is completely worked into the hair and scalp. The excess lather is then removed by a sweep with the palm of the hand from the front to the back of the head. The lather is washed from the practitioner's hand at the shampoo bowl.

The client is now asked to move to the shampoo bowl in order to thoroughly rinse the remaining lather from the hair. If a second shampoo application is required, this may be done at the shampoo bowl.

TWO METHODS OF SHAMPOOING AND RINSING

There are two methods employed for shampooing and rinsing at the shampoo bowl. These are the **Inclined Method** and the **Reclined Method.**

THE INCLINED METHOD

While giving the shampoo or rinsing the head, the client's head is bent forward over the shampoo bowl.

The following procedure is necessary for the inclined position in shampooing:

1. Place clean towel over edge of shampoo bowl.
2. Have client sit on a stool close to shampoo bowl.
3. Massage scalp to loosen dandruff and to increase the blood circulation.
4. Follow Steps 1 to 8 for a plain shampoo as described on following page.

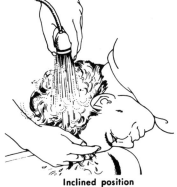

Inclined position

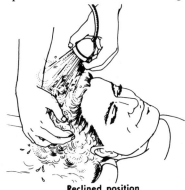

Reclined position

THE RECLINED METHOD

The reclined method requires that the entire shampooing and rinsing procedure is performed at the bowl. In this method, the hydraulic chair is reclined with the client's head lying upon a headrest of a shampoo tray or in the neckrest of the bowl. This method is favored by professional practitioners because it is more comfortable for the client and it permits greater speed and efficiency in the performance of the shampoo.

The following procedure is for the reclined position in shampooing:

1. Remove the headrest.
2. Massage scalp to loosen dandruff and to increase the blood circulation.
3. Turn the chair around with its back facing the shampoo bowl.
4. Place a folded towel in the groove of the shampoo bowl to support the client's neck or attach a shampoo tray to the bowl.
5. Recline the chair until the client's head rests comfortably in the groove of the shampoo bowl or on the tray.
6. Follow Steps 1 to 8 as for a plain shampoo as described below.

PROCEDURE FOR PLAIN SHAMPOO

1. Apply shampoo to all parts of the scalp.
2. Gradually apply enough warm water to make an abundance of lather over the entire scalp.
3. Massage scalp for several minutes as described below.
4. Rinse the hair thoroughly with warm water and repeat the lathering if necessary.
5. Hair may be rinsed with cool water.
6. Wipe face and ears thoroughly.
7. Dry the hair completely.
   (Suggest hair tonic or hair dressing at this time.)
8. Comb hair neatly.

Lathering the head

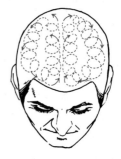

Scalp massage movements

MASSAGE MANIPULATIONS DURING SHAMPOO

The proper way to massage the scalp during a shampoo is as follows:

1. After lathering the scalp and hair, stand behind the client.
2. Place the fingertips at the back of the head just below the ears.
3. Apply rotary movements from the ears to the temples up to the forehead, then over the top of the head down to the neck.
4. Repeat these movements for several minutes.

SUPERIOR SHAMPOO SERVICE

If the barber-stylist is to develop a superior type of shampoo service, he or she must give individual attention to each client's needs. In addition to the selection of the shampoo best suited to the condition of the scalp, the effectiveness of the shampoo will depend on:

1. The way the shampoo is applied.
2. The way the scalp is massaged.
3. The way the shampoo is rinsed from the hair.

A good shampoo service not only removes dirt and dandruff from the scalp and hailr, but also helps to keep the scalp and hair in a healthy condition. The barber-stylist who gives the utmost care and attention to shampoo service will be performing an important service for each client.

COMMON FAULTS IN SHAMPOOING

A good barber-stylist makes every effort to please his or her clients. A dissatisfied client may find fault with a shampoo for any of the following reasons:

1. Improper selection of shampoo
2. Insufficient scalp massage.
3. Insufficient rinsing of hair.
4. Water too cold or too hot.
5. Allowing shampoo or water to run down the client's forehead, or into his eyes or ears.
6. Wetting or soiling the client's clothing.
7. Scraping or scratching the client's scalp with fingernails.
8. Improper drying of the hair.
9. Not getting the scalp and hair clean.

TYPES OF SHAMPOOS

PLAIN SHAMPOOS

Plain shampoos are usually clear and transparent and may have a natural amber shade, or be colored a greenish yellow. They may contain a plain liquid soap or a detergent-based product. These shampoos seldom have lanolin or other special agents used to leave a gloss on the hair.

A plain shampoo may be used on hair that is in **good** condition. It should **never be** used on hair that has been colored as it will strip or fade the color of the hair.

LIQUID CREAM SHAMPOOS

Liquid cream shampoos are usually semi-heavy white liquids. As a rule, they contain soap or sometimes soap jelly. **Magnesium stearate** is also used as a whitening agent. They often contain oily compounds, to make the hair feel silky and softer. Use this type of shampoo as directed by your instructor or manufacturer.

LIQUID DRY SHAMPOOS

Liquid dry shampoos are cosmetic products used for cleansing the scalp and hair when the client is prevented by illness from having a regular shampoo.

Caution: Be sure the shop is well ventilated when using liquid dry shampoo.

Procedure for Liquid Dry Shampoo

1. Brush hair thoroughly—comb lightly.
2. Part hair into small sections.
3. Saturate a piece of cotton with the liquid, squeeze out lightly, then rub it over the scalp briskly along each part. Follow by rubbing with a towel swiftly along the part. Repeat all over the head in this manner. Next, apply liquid with cotton pledget down length of hair strands.
4. Rub the hair strands with the towel to remove soil.
5. Re-moisten hair lightly with liquid, and comb hair to desired style.

Such a dry shampoo will freshen the hair and tone the scalp without endangering the client. (When using any type shampoo, carefully read and follow the manufacturer's directions.)

POWDER DRY SHAMPOO

A powder dry shampoo is usually given when the client's health will not permit the giving of a wet shampoo.

A commercial powder dry shampoo containing orris root powder is freely sprinkled into the hair and worked in, one section at a time. This powder, which takes up the oil in the hair, is then brushed out of the hair with a long-bristled brush.

Brush the hair, strand by strand, until every trace of powder has been removed. Between strokes, the brush should be wiped on a clean towel to remove the dust and dirt.

OTHER SHAMPOOS

For dry or damaged hair, use either:

1. **Egg shampoo.** Apply a mixture of one or two whole eggs to the hair and scalp in the same manner as for a regular shampoo. Use only tepid water, as hot water will congeal the egg on the hair.
2. A commercial shampoo containing a **small amount of egg.** Apply as directed by the manufacturer.
3. Any other commercial shampoo which contains ingredients helpful to dry scalp and hair.

Castile and olive oil shampoos. Contain coconut oil soap solution, dissolved flakes of castile soap and a small amount of olive oil to prevent the excessive drying produced by the high alkali content of the soap. It is neutral and mild in action, provided it contains a **high grade** castile soap. Be guided by your instructor.

Tincture of green soap. Cleanses, but it contains a large amount of alcohol which often dries the hair and scalp excessively after prolonged use. This effect can be avoided by gently massaging a small amount of warm olive oil into the scalp.

Medicated shampoos. These are usually liquid or jelly type shampoos which contain some medicinal agent, such as sulphur, tar, cresol, a small percentage of phenol or some other antiseptic agent.

Therapeutic medicated shampoos. Contain special chemicals or drugs which are very effective in reducing excessive dandruff. They must be used only with a physician's prescription and instructions.

Hot oil shampoo. Very seldom used today as it is being replaced by improved shampoos capable of cleansing and correcting a dry condition of the scalp and hair.

Acid-balanced (non-strip) shampoos are formulated to prevent the stripping of hair color from the hair. They are mild in action, contain certain conditioners and are low in alkaline content. They are also recommended for brittle, dry or damaged hair. Follow the manufacturer's directions.

SPECIAL SHAMPOOS

There are a number of shampoo mixtures available for professional use. At times, the barber-stylist may be uncertain as to which shampoo to use. To avoid making mistakes, carefully read the label and literature accompanying the shampoo. Such information will reveal the principal ingredients of the shampoo and the advantages claimed for the product.

One way to test a particular brand of shampoo is to give it a fair trial for a period of time. Make sure to follow the manufacturer's instructions. Keeping a written record of the shampoo used and the results obtained on clients will eliminate guesswork as to its effectiveness. In this way, the actual merits of the shampoo may be demonstrated to the barber-stylist's satisfaction. In addition, the patron will benefit from this experience.

HAIR RINSES

The barber-stylist is engaged in the business of selling services. The more services the stylist has to offer, the better the stylist can satisfy clients and meet competition. Hair rinses are a profitable service which can be easily learned and applied.

A hair rinse is an agent which can cleanse the hair and scalp, bring out the luster of the hair, condition the hair and scalp or add highlights and color to the hair.

Rinses are divided into four main groups, as follows:

1. Water rinse.   2. Acid rinse.   3. Dandruff rinse.   4. Bluing rinse.

Water rinse. A tepid, soft water rinse is generally used after a shampoo. The object is to remove any residue present on the hair.

An acid rinse eliminates curd formation and adds luster to the hair. This rinse is advisable in areas that are serviced by hard water.

The vinegar rinse, containing acetic acid, is used as follows:

1. After rinsing the shampoo from the hair, towel dry.
2. Add two tablespoons of white vinegar to one pint of tepid water.
3. Pour this solution over the hair several times, catching it in another bowl.
4. Rinse the hair with tepid water and towel dry.
5. Comb hair to desired style.

A **dandruff rinse** is a commercial product applied following a shampoo. It removes and controls dandruff. Many such rinses, of good quality, are on the market. Some rinses are used in a prepared form while others are diluted with water. Always follow the manufacturer's directions.

Bluing rinse, a prepared product, is used to neutralize yellow tinge in grey hair and brighten black hair by giving a blue-black appearance. For application, follow the manufacturer's directions.

RINSES IN CONNECTION WITH HAIR COLORING

Acid-balanced (non-strip) rinse is formulated to prevent the stripping of a hair coloring treatment. Most manufacturers formulate this type of rinse for use in connection with their particular tint product.

Reconditioning rinse may be used following a hair coloring treatment. Follow the manufacturer's directions.

Color rinses are prepared rinses used to highlight or add temporary color to the hair. These rinses remain on the hair until the next shampoo. For application, follow the manufacturer's directions.

QUESTIONS ON SHAMPOOING AND RINSING

SHAMPOOING

1. What is the purpose of a plain shampoo?
2. How often should the hair be shampooed?
3. What kind of soap should be used in a shampoo?
4. Outline the important steps in giving a shampoo.
5. What kind of water should be used to shampoo the hair? Why?
6. Which supplies are needed to give a shampoo?
7. How should the barber-stylist prepare for a shampoo?
8. How should the client be prepared for a shampoo?
9. Why should the scalp be massaged before giving a shampoo?
10. Briefly outline the procedure for giving a plain shampoo.
11. Briefly outline the massage manipulations applied to the scalp during a shampoo.

HAIR RINSES

1. What value does a rinse have on the hair?
2. Name four types of hair rinses.
3. What is the active ingredient of a vinegar rinse?
4. Which hair rinse is best for hard water areas?
5. What benefits are received from a bluing rinse?

Chapter 11
SCALP AND HAIR TREATMENTS — HAIR TONICS

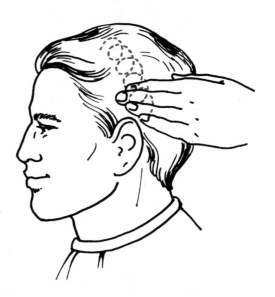

The purpose of scalp and hair treatments is to preserve the health and appearance of the hair and scalp. These treatments also assist in preventing and combating disorders of the scalp, such as dandruff, loss of hair, dryness or oiliness.

CLEANLINESS ESSENTIAL

A basic requirement for a healthy scalp is constant cleanliness. The scalp and hair should be kept clean by frequent treatment and shampooing. A clean scalp will resist a wide variety of disorders.

Because the scalp and hair are vitally related, many scalp disorders need correction in order to keep the hair healthy. **A healthy scalp will usually produce healthy hair.**

Even the healthy person should have scalp treatments to preserve the natural health of the hair. While shampooing will keep the hair clean, it will not prevent the hair from becoming dry and brittle.

PREVENTIVE TREATMENTS

Scalp treatments should be preventive rather than used as a means of effecting a cure. When a thin area appears in the hair, it is an indication that the condition causing the loss of hair has already reached an advanced stage. The condition has often reached a stage where it is too late to bring the hair follicle and papilla back to normal.

Scalp treatments are most valuable, therefore, as preventive measures. Properly and regularly administered, they are of vital importance in keeping the hair and scalp normal and healthy.

The professional barber-stylist should be capable of giving scientific scalp and hair treatments. Acquiring the ability to give professional advice and treatment to clients will pay dividends to qualified practitioners.

A scalp and/or hair treatment may be given either as a separate treatment or in connection with other services. Depending on the client's needs, the treatment may include:

1. Cleansing by means of a suitable shampoo.
2. Massage by means of the hands or electrical appliance.
3. Use of electrical appliances, such as electric steamer, infra-red lamp, ultra-violet lamp, high-frequency current or dermal lamp.
4. The application of cosmetic preparations, such as hair tonics, astringents, antiseptics, etc.

Do not suggest a scalp treatment if there are scalp abrasions or a scalp disease present.

Advise clients to consult a physician for serious or contagious scalp ailments. However, conditions caused by neglect, such as tight scalp, overactive or underactive oil glands and tense nerves, can be corrected by proper scalp treatments.

SCALP MASSAGE (MANIPULATIONS)

Scalp manipulations. Since the same manipulations are given with all scalp treatments, the barber-stylist should learn to give them with a continuous, even motion, which will achieve stimulating and soothing effects upon the client. Scalp massage is best applied as a series of treatments, once a week for normal scalp and more frequent treatments for scalp disorders under the direction of a dermatologist.

A thorough scalp massage is beneficial in the following ways:

1. The blood and lymph (limf) flow are increased.
2. Nerves are rested and soothed.
3. Scalp muscles are stimulated.
4. The scalp is made more flexible.
5. Hair growth is promoted and the hair is made lustrous.

Anatomy. Knowing the muscles and location of blood vessels and nerve points of the scalp and neck will help guide the barber-stylist to those areas in which massage movements are to be directed.

Preparation of patron for scalp treatment. As in any other treatment, the barber-stylist must gather all the necessary equipment needed for the scalp treatment that is about to be given. Prepare client as for a shampoo.

With each movement described below, the hands are placed **under** the hair. Thus, the length of the fingers, the balls of the fingertips and the cushions of the palms stimulate the muscles, nerves and blood vessels in the scalp area.

PROCEDURE FOR A SCALP MASSAGE

In scalp massage apply firm pressure on upward strokes. Firm rotary movements are given to loosen the scalp tissues. These movements improve the health of hair and scalp by increasing the circulation of the blood to the scalp and hair papillae. When giving a scalp massage, care should be taken to give the manipulations slowly without pulling the hair in any way.

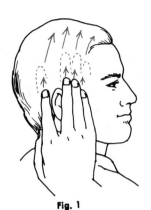

Fig. 1

NOTE. The following procedure is one way to give a scalp massage. However, your instructor may have developed his own routine which is equally correct. Be guided by your instructor.

Position: Place the fingertips of each hand at the hairline on each side of the client's head, hands pointing upward. (Fig. 1.)

Movement: Slide the fingers firmly upward, spreading the fingertips. Continue until the fingers meet at the center or top of the scalp. Repeat three or four times.

Position: Place the fingers of each hand on the sides of the head behind the ears. (Fig. 2.)

Movement: Use the thumbs to massage from behind the ears towards the crown. Repeat four or five times. Move the fingers until both thumbs meet at the hairline at the back of neck. Rotate the thumbs upward towards the crown.

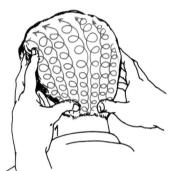

Fig. 2

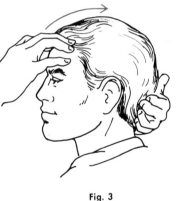

Fig. 3

Position: Step to the right side of the client. Place the left hand back of the head. Place the thumb and fingers of the right hand against and over the forehead, just above the eyebrows. (Fig. 3.)

Movement: With the cushion tips of the thumb and fingers of the right hand, massage slowly and firmly in an upward direction towards the crown while keeping the left hand in a fixed position at the back of the head. Repeat four or five times.

Position: Step to the back of the client. Place the hands on each side of his head, at the front hairline. (Fig. 4.)

Movement: Rotate the fingertips three times. On the fourth rotation, apply a quick, upward twist, firm enough to move the scalp. Continue this movement on the sides and top of the scalp. Repeat three or four times.

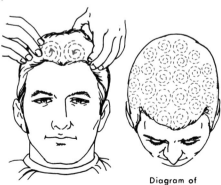

Fig. 4

Diagram of rotary movements of the scalp.

157

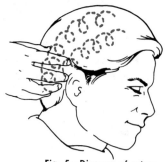

Fig. 5—Diagram of rotary movements of the scalp

Position: Place the fingers of each hand below the back of each ear. (Fig. 5.)

Movement: Rotate the fingers upward from behind the ears to the crown. Repeat three or four times. Move the fingers toward the back of the head and repeat movement with both hands. Apply rotary movements in an upward direction toward the crown.

Fig. 6

Position: Place both hands at the sides of the head. Keep fingers close together and hold index finger at hairline above the ears. (Fig. 6.)

Movement: Firmly move the hands directly upward to the top of the head. Repeat four times. Move hands to above ears and repeat movement. Move hands again to back of ears and repeat movement.

MASSAGE AND ITS INFLUENCE ON THE SCALP

Massage Movements	Muscles	Nerves	Arteries
Fig. 1	Auricularis superior	Posterior auricular	Frontal Parietal
Fig. 2	Auricularis posterior Occipitalis	Greater occipital	Occipital
Fig. 3	Frontalis	Supra-orbital	Frontal
Fig. 4	Frontalis	Supra-orbital	Frontal Parietal
Fig. 5	Auricularis posterior Occipitalis	Greater occipital	Posterior auricular Parietal
Fig. 6	Auricularis anterior and superior	Temporal auricular	Frontal Parietal

WHEN TO RECOMMEND SCALP TREATMENTS

The barber-stylist may employ scalp treatments in his work for any of the following reasons:

1. To keep the scalp clean and healthy.
2. To promote the growth of hair.
3. To try to prevent the excessive loss of hair.

When advising clients to take scalp treatments, always explain that regular, systematic treatments are necessary in order to assure lasting improvement. In mild cases, at least one scalp treatment a week is required. For severe cases, the frequency of treatment is increased to two or three times a week. Scalp treatments may be given less frequently if any improvement is noted.

No barber-stylist should undertake to treat any scalp disease. If the client has any abnormal scalp condition, it is safest and best to refer the client to a private doctor. To assist recovery, the doctor may suggest that the patient receive supplementary scalp treatments by the barber-stylist. Cooperating with the doctor is in the best interests of the client.

TREATMENT FOR NORMAL SCALP AND HAIR

The purpose of a general scalp treatment is to keep the scalp and hair in a clean and healthy condition. Regular scalp treatments are also beneficial in preventing baldness.

PROCEDURE AFTER A SHAMPOO

1. Dry the hair and scalp thoroughly.
2. Part the hair and apply a scalp ointment directly to the scalp.
3. Place both thumbs about three-quarters of an inch apart on each side of the parted hair.

Applying scalp ointment
with a swab

4. Rotate thumbs in a circular manner, pressing firmly against scalp.
5. Make another hair part about 1" away from the first one. Apply ointment and massage.
6. Repeat Steps 2 to 5 and continue until the entire scalp has been treated.
7. Adjust the infra-red lamp.
8. Expose scalp to red dermal light or infra-red lamp for three to five minutes, parting the hair to permit maximum exposure.
9. Stimulate scalp with high-frequency current for two to three minutes.
10. Apply suitable hair tonic and work it well into the scalp.

Applying heat
with infra-red lamp

11. Comb hair to desired style.

159

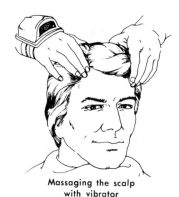

Massaging the scalp
with vibrator

SCALP TREATMENT WITH VIBRATOR

A vibrator (vī'brā-tor) is an effective mechanical aid in giving a stimulating scalp massage.

Before using, adjust the vibrator on the back of the hand, leaving the thumb and fingers free. Then turn on the current. The vibrations are transmitted through the cushions of the fingertips. The same movements are followed as for a regular hand scalp massage.

When using the vibrator on the scalp, be careful to regulate the intensity and duration of the vibrations, as well as the pressure applied.

SCALP STEAM

A scalp steam is used to stimulate the blood supply to the scalp. For procedure, see page 167.

DRY SCALP AND HAIR TREATMENT

Inactivity of the oil glands or the excessive removal of natural oil from the hair and scalp may produce a dry condition of the hair and scalp. Among the contributory causes of dry hair and scalp are leading an indoor life, frequent washing of the hair with strong soaps or alcoholic shampoos, and the continued use of drying tonics or lotions.

Avoid the use of strong soaps, preparations containing a mineral oil or sulfonated oil base, or greasy preparations and lotions with a high alcoholic content.

PROCEDURE

1. Massage and stimulate the scalp for three to five minutes.

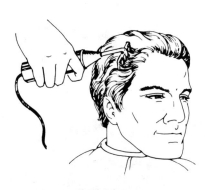

Applying
High-Frequency Current.

2. Apply the scalp preparation for this condition. If a vegetable oil is used, work gently but thoroughly into the scalp.
3. Steam the scalp with hot towels or scalp steamer for seven to ten minutes.
4. Give a shampoo suitable for dry scalp.
5. Towel dry the hair, making sure the scalp is thoroughly dried.
6. Apply scalp cream sparingly with a rotary, frictional motion.
7. Apply a red dermal or infra-red lamp over the scalp for three to five minutes.
8. Stimulate scalp with direct high-frequency current, using glass rake electrode, for about five minutes.
9. Comb hair to desired style.

OILY SCALP TREATMENT

The main cause of an oily scalp is excessive intake of fatty foods in the diet and the resultant over-activity of the oil glands.

PROCEDURE

1. Gently massage the scalp.
2. Shampoo the scalp and hair with a shampoo suitable for an oily scalp.
3. Towel dry the hair, leaving it in a damp condition.
4. Part the hair and apply medicated lotion or ointment to the scalp only.
5. Steam the scalp with hot towels or scalp steamer.
6. Towel dry excessive moisture from hair.
7. Expose scalp to infra-red lamp for about five minutes.
8. Apply an astringent or alcoholic scalp lotion.
9. Dress hair to desired style.

Applying heat
with infra-red lamp

CAUTION. Creams or ointment can be applied **before** using high-frequency current. Hair tonics or lotions with alcoholic content may be applied only after the application of high-frequency current.

DANDRUFF TREATMENT

The principal signs of dandruff are the appearance of white scales on the hair and scalp and the accompanying itching of the scalp. Dandruff may be associated with either a dry or oily condition of the scalp. The more common causes of dandruff are poor circulation of blood to the scalp, improper diet, neglect of cleanliness, and infection.

CAUTION. To prevent the spread of dandruff in the shop, the barber-stylist must sanitize all implements and avoid the use in common of combs, brushes and scalp applicators.

Applying scalp lotion with
cotton pledget.

PROCEDURE

1. Shampoo according to the condition of the scalp (dry or oily dandruff).
2. Dry the hair thoroughly.
3. Apply dandruff or antiseptic lotion to scalp with cotton pledget.
4. Apply four or five steam towels or use scalp steamer over the scalp.
5. Dry the hair thoroughly.

6. Both the barber-stylist and the client put on tinted safety eye goggles.
7. Expose scalp to ultra-violet rays for five to eight minutes (see illustration below), parting the hair every half inch.
8. Apply regular scalp manipulations for five minutes.
9. Apply dandruff ointment to the scalp and retain it until the next shampoo.
10. Expose scalp to red dermal light or infra-red lamp for five minutes. **Alternate Step.** In place of Step 10, high-frequency current may be applied for three to five minutes.
11. Comb hair to desired style.

TREATMENT FOR ALOPECIA

Alopecia (al-o-pe 'she-ah) refers to a condition of premature baldness or excessive hair loss. The chief causes responsible for alopecia are heredity, poor circulation, lack of proper stimulation, improper nourishment, certain infectious skin diseases such as ringworm, or constitutional disorders. The treatment for alopecia is directed at stimulating the blood supply and reviving the hair papillae (pa-pil 'e) involved in hair growth.

PROCEDURE

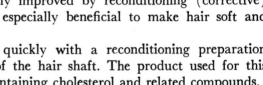

1. Apply regular scalp manipulations.
2. Shampoo the hair and scalp as required (dry or oily).
3. Dry the scalp thoroughly.
4. Protect client's and barber-stylist's eyes with goggles.
5. Expose the scalp to ultra-violet rays for about five minutes.
6. Apply scalp ointment or lotion.
7. Apply indirect high-frequency current for about five minutes.
8. Comb hair to desired style.

Applying
Ultra-Violet Rays.

CORRECTIVE HAIR TREATMENT

A corrective hair treatment deals with the hair shaft, not the scalp. Dry and damaged hair can be greatly improved by reconditioning (corrective) treatments. Hair treatments are especially beneficial to make hair soft and pliable.

Dry hair may be softened quickly with a reconditioning preparation applied directly on the outside of the hair shaft. The product used for this purpose is usually an emulsion containing cholesterol and related compounds.

PROCEDURE

1. Prepare the client as for a normal scalp treatment.
2. Massage and stimulate the scalp for three to five minutes.
3. Apply a mild shampoo.
4. Blot the hair with a towel.
5. Apply reconditioning agent according to the manufacturer's directions.
6. Dry the hair with hand dryer.
7. Comb hair to desired style.

DIFFERENT TYPES OF HAIR LOSS

Beginning baldness in
men from 30 to 40
Scalp treatments are
most beneficial at this
stage

Partial baldness in
men from 40 to 50
Scalp treatments are
worth trying at this
stage

Extensive baldness in
men from 50 to 60
Too late for scalp
treatments

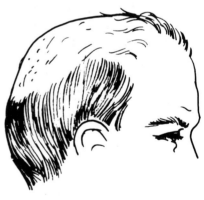

Extensive baldness in
men from 61 and over
Too late for scalp
treatments

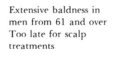

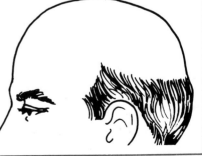

CONDITIONERS

The professional treatment of hair requires the use of many chemicals. Some chemicals remove excess amounts of natural oils and moisture from the hair, causing it to become dry and brittle. As a result, hair conditioners are required to help restore some of the natural oils and moisture and make the hair ready to accept other hair services. Clients with naturally dry, brittle hair also will benefit from regular conditioning treatments.

Conditioners are primarily designed to coat and give body to damaged hair. They are available in cream and liquid forms. The formulation of the product varies with the manufacturer. It may contain lanolin, cholesterol, moisturizers, sufonated oil, vegetable oils, proteins, or various combinations of these. For the best results, it is important that each product be applied exactly as indicated by manufacturer. Most conditioners are applied to hair that has been shampooed and towel dried.

There are four general groups of hair conditioners available. The selection of the type to be used depends on the texture and condition of the hair and the results to be achieved.

1. **Timed conditioners,** are applied to hair, allowed to stay on from 1-5 minutes, and then rinsed out. The hair is then styled. These conditioners usually have an acid pH; they do not penetrate into the hair shaft, but add natural oils and moisture to the hair.

2. **Conditioners combined with styling lotions** (usually for longer hair). Protein or resin based conditioners are incorporated into the setting lotion and applied as part of the hairstyling process. A little water, added during the hairsetting procedure, helps to facilitate setting by keeping hair soft and manageable. This type of conditioner is designed to slightly increase hair diameter by a **coating action,** which gives it body. It is available in several strengths to accommodate the texture, condition, and quality of the hair.

3. **Protein penetrating conditioners** utilize hydrolized protein (very small fragments) and are designed to **pass through the cuticle,** penetrate into the cortex, and replace the keratin that has been lost from the hair. They improve texture, equalize porosity, and increase elasticity. The excess conditioner must be rinsed from the hair before styling.

4. **Neutralizing conditioners** are used to neutralize a highly alkaline condition caused by chemical (permanent) waving and chemical hair relaxing. These conditioners have an acid pH and are designed to prevent damage to the hair and alleviate scalp irritation caused by strongly alkaline products.

Note: Regardless of the type of conditioner used, it is important that the barber-stylist follow manufacturer's directions at all times.

HAIR CONDITIONERS

REVIEW QUESTIONS ON HAIR CONDITIONING

A discussion of hair conditioners and of hair conditioning appears in various areas in the textbook. However, in order to facilitate the study of this important subject, the following review questions are presented as a complete and cohesive subject.

1. What type of hair requires reconditioning treatments?
2. What can be done to restore some of the natural oils to hair after a coloring treatment?
3. With what part of the hair does a corrective treatment deal?
4. How can strength and body be restored to damaged hair?
5. What purpose is served by a conditioner applied to chemically processed hair?
6. What should be done with damaged hair before attempting to give a tinting treatment?
7. In addition to lanolin, what chemical substances are usually contained in reconditioning agents?
8. For what purpose are reconditioning treatments given to human hairpieces?
9. After a chemical (permanent) wave, what should be done to keep the hair healthy?
10. What should be done with hair after it has received a chemical relaxing treatment?
11. Why are hair conditioning treatments especially beneficial?
12. How can hair be made and kept soft and pliable?
13. Cholesterol is an important ingredient of what cosmetic emulsion?
14. When should a reconditioning treatment be applied to chemically treated hair?
15. Why is it undesirable to apply reconditioning treatments requiring massage or heat just before a permanent wave or hair relaxer?
16. Before applying a permanent wave lotion, what preparation should be used to recondition overporous or damaged hair?
17. What preparations are employed to revitalize, recondition, or correct abused, bleached, tinted, or damaged hair?
18. What are the two general classifications of fillers?
19. How should hairpieces that have become dull and lifeless be treated?

HAIR TONICS

The term "hair tonic" is employed to indicate almost any type of cosmetic solution which is used to stimulate the scalp, help to correct a scalp condition or to groom the hair.

Since there are numerous hair tonics available, the barber-stylist should have an understanding of the ingredients and actions of the various types and the specific use of each. The practitioner should be prepared to advise clients concerning the use of tonics and the specific purpose of each.

While hair tonics are essentially cosmetic solutions which are used primarily on the hair, the scalp also receives a number of benefits from their application.

In order that the client receive the maximum benefits from a tonic application, his scalp should be prepared with a series of scalp manipulations. These manipulations should be applied with the cushion tips of the fingers. The fingers should be worked through the hair to the surface of the scalp and then manipulated to move the skin with firm, upward pressure.

PURPOSES OF HAIR TONICS

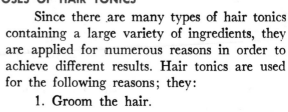

Since there are many types of hair tonics containing a large variety of ingredients, they are applied for numerous reasons in order to achieve different results. Hair tonics are used for the following reasons; they:

1. Groom the hair.
2. Help correct an oily dandruff condition.
3. Help correct a dry dandruff condition.
4. Stimulate the scalp.
5. Offset an itching scalp.
6. Maintain a normal healthy scalp.

Types of Hair Tonics

1. **Non-alcoholic.** This type is usually an antiseptic with hair grooming ingredients added.
2. **Alcoholic.** This type usually contains an antiseptic and alcohol which act as a mild astringent.
3. **Cream.** This type is an emulsion containing lanolin and mineral oils.
4. **Oil mixture.** This type contains a considerable amount of alcohol with a small portion of oil floating on the top. Used as a grooming agent.

SCALP STEAM

Along with a hair tonic, the barber-stylist may use:
1. Steam applications (scalp steamer or steaming towels).
2. Electric vibrator.
3. Scalp manipulations.

Steam applications relax the pores, soften the scalp and hair and increase the blood circulation.

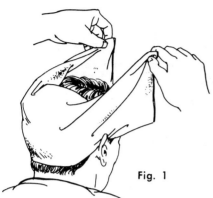

Fig. 1

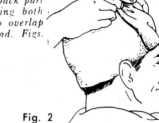

Fig. 2

METHOD 1
Place the center of towel on the patron's back part of head and bring both ends of towel to overlap over the forehead. Figs. 1 and 2.

METHOD 2
Place the center of towel along left side of head and wrap it so that the ends will overlap on the right side of head. Fig. 3.

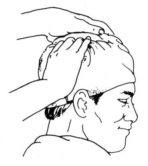

Fig. 3

The **scalp steamer** is a helpful piece of equipment. It assures a constant and controlled source of steam. When ready to be used, fill the container with water, fit the hood over the client's head and turn on the electricity. Many hoods have openings on the side for the hands to be inserted in order to give a scalp massage together with the scalp steam.

Steaming towels are used in the absence of a scalp steamer. They are prepared, one at a time, by soaking the towel in steaming water. The excess water is wrung out and the steaming towel is wrapped around the client's head. As the towel cools, another one is applied in its place.

PROCEDURE FOR A SCALP STEAM

1. Apply regular scalp manipulations to increase the circulation of the blood.
2. Steam the scalp with two hot towels or scalp steamer.
3. Apply the hair tonic carefully and massage it well into the scalp.
4. Comb hair to the desired style.

PROCEDURE FOR HAIR TONIC TREATMENT

1. Wash hands.
2. Arrange linen and supplies.
3. Massage scalp with hands or vibrator.
4. Apply steam towel twice on scalp, or use scalp steamer.
5. Apply suitable tonic directly to scalp.
6. Massage scalp with hands or vibrator.
7. Comb hair to desired style.

QUESTIONS ON SCALP AND HAIR TREATMENTS
— HAIR TONICS

SCALP TREATMENTS

1. What is the purpose of scalp massage?
2. In what ways does scalp massage benefit the blood and nerves?
3. What is the purpose of general scalp treatments?
4. What is accomplished by using a scalp steam?
5. When is a dry scalp treatment recommended?
6. What are some of the common causes of a dry scalp?
7. What is the main cause of an oily scalp?
8. What are the principal signs of dandruff?
9. What are the common causes of dandruff?
10. What are the chief causes of alopecia?
11. What is the aim in treating alopecia?
12. Give the four steps for applying a scalp steam.

HAIR TONICS

1. What are hair tonics?
2. Why should the barber-stylist know the various kinds of hair tonics?
3. What is a scalp steam?
4. What are six purposes of a hair tonic?
5. What are the five steps for applying a hair tonic?

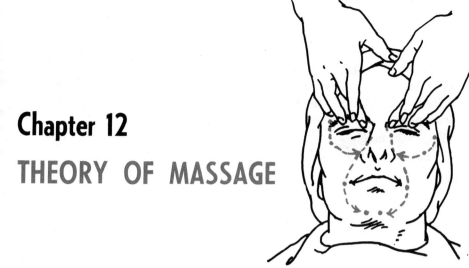

Chapter 12
THEORY OF MASSAGE

Most clients enjoy a properly administered facial or scalp massage for its stimulating and relaxing effects. It produces a glow in the cheeks, a tingling feeling in the scalp and helps to relieve that "tired feeling." It is important for professional success that the barber-stylist understand the principles of massaging and acquires a skillful touch in the application of massage movements.

It is not enough to know how to mechanically execute the massage movements. To properly administer a professional massage, the barber-stylist must have some basic knowledge of nerve points, the structure of the skin, muscles and blood circulation.

Massage involves the application of external manipulations to the face or any other part of the body. This is accomplished by means of the hands or with the aid of electrical appliances, such as a vibrator. Each massage movement is applied in a definite way to accomplish a definite result.

The beneficial effects produced by massage depend upon the type, intensity and extent of the manipulations employed. Massaging must be performed systematically. It should never be a casual or irregular process. Consideration must be given to the condition of the skin and the general physical condition of the client.

A normal skin condition may receive soothing, mildly stimulating or strongly stimulating massage treatments, depending upon the type, intensity and duration of the manipulations. However, a sensitive, inflamed skin condition could be further damaged by massage manipulations. Under such conditions, if massaging is desired, the manipulations must be gentle and soothing to the skin. Massaging should always be employed with judgment and moderation.

Massaging should never be recommended or employed when the following conditions are present:

1. Inflammation of the skin — Massage would intensify the condition.
2. Severe skin lesions — Massage would aggravate the condition.
3. Pus containing pimples — Massage could spread infection.
4. Client has high blood pressure — Massage could increase the pressure.
5. Skin infection — Massage could aggravate and spread infection.

The primary rule in the application of massage manipulations is: "When massaging any part of the head, face or neck, all pressure should be applied in an upward direction." This rule should be followed in all massaging services, whether they are intended to stimulate, relax or soothe the skin. When applying rotary manipulations, the same rule applies because the pressure should be applied on the upward swing of the movement.

The **basic manipulations** used in massage are as follows:

1. **Effleurage** (ef-loo-razh') (stroking movement). This is a light, continuous movement applied in a slow and rhythmic manner over the skin. No pressure is employed. Over large surfaces, the palm is used; while over small surfaces, the fingertips are employed. Effleurage is frequently applied to the forehead, face and scalp for its soothing and relaxing effects.

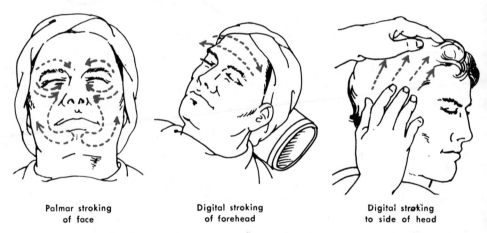

Palmar stroking
of face

Digital stroking
of forehead

Digital stroking
to side of head

2. **Petrissage** (pe'tri-sazh) (kneading movement). In this movement, the skin and flesh are grasped between the thumb and fingers. As the tissues are lifted from their underlying structures, they are squeezed, rolled or pinched with a light, firm pressure. This movement exerts an invigorating effect on the part being treated.

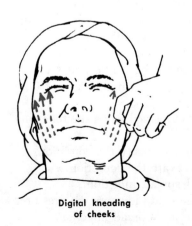

Massage movements
are directed towards
the origin of muscles
to avoid damage to
muscular tissues.

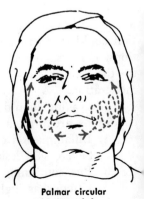

Digital kneading
of cheeks

Palmar circular
friction of face

3. **Friction** (deep rubbing movement). This movement requires pressure on the skin while it is being moved over the underlying structures. The fingers or palms are employed in this movement. Friction has a marked influence on the circulation and glandular activity of the skin.

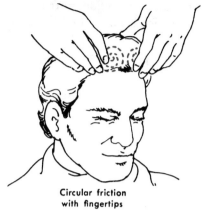

Circular friction
with fingertips

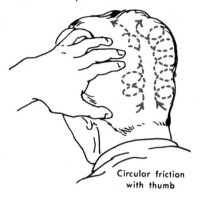

Circular friction
with thumb

4. **Percussion** or **tapotement** (ta-pot-mahn') (tapping, slapping and hacking movements). This form of massage is the most stimulating. It should be applied with care and discretion. Tapping movements are more gentle than slapping movements. Percussion movements tone the muscles and impart a healthy glow to the part being massaged.

In tapping, the fingertips are brought down against the skin in rapid succession, whereas in slapping, the whole palm is used to strike the skin. Hacking movement employs the outer ulnar borders of the hands which are struck against the skin in alternate succession.

Digital tapping
of face

In facial massage, only **light** digital (dij'i-tal) tapping is used.

5. **Vibration** (shaking movement). The fingertips or vibrator are used to transmit a trembling movement to the skin and its underlying structures. To prevent over-stimulation, this movement should be used sparingly and should never exceed a few seconds duration on any one spot.

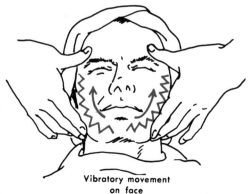

Vibratory movement
on face

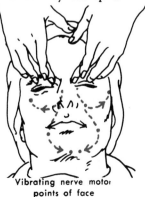

Vibrating nerve motor
points of face

171

Skillfully applied massage influences the structures and functions of the body, either directly or indirectly. The immediate effect of massage is first noticed on the skin. The part being massaged responds by increasing its functional activities, as noticed by a more active circulation, secretion, nutrition and excretion. There is scarcely an organ of the body which is not favorably affected by scientific massage treatments.

Beneficial results may be obtained by proper facial and scalp massage, as follows:

1. The skin and all its structures are nourished.
2. The muscle fiber is stimulated and strengthened.
3. Fat cells are reduced.
4. The circulation of the blood is increased.
5. The activity of the skin and scalp glands is stimulated.
6. The skin is rendered soft and pliable.
7. The nerves are soothed and rested.
8. Pain is sometimes relieved.

Electrical appliances most commonly used in giving facial and scalp massage are as follows:

1. Vibrators.
2. High-frequency applicators.
3. Therapeutic lamps, such as infra-red lamp, ultra-violet lamp and white or colored bulbs.

QUESTIONS ON THEORY OF MASSAGE

1. What is massage?
2. What parts of the body are usually massaged by the barber-stylist?
3. Name five basic movements used in massage.
4. What are the effects of massage on the skin?
5. What is the effect of massage on the blood circulation?
6. What are the effects of massage on the nerves?
7. What are the effects of massage on the muscles?

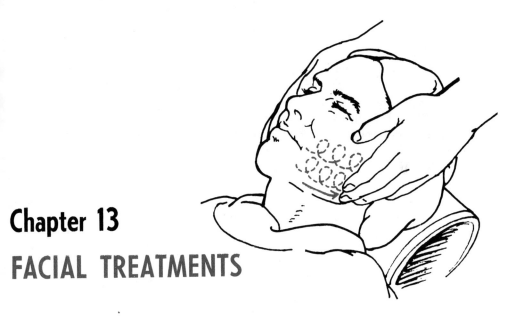

Chapter 13
FACIAL TREATMENTS

A facial treatment is probably the most relaxing and restful service offered in the barber-styling shop. The client really enjoys the relaxation and stimulation from properly administered massage movements and feels both soothed and rejuvenated.

The barber-stylist does not treat skin diseases. However, the professional practitioner is capable of recognizing various skin ailments and knows which can be serviced in the barber-styling shop and which should be referred to a physician.

Facial treatments in the barber-styling shop come under two categories:

1. **Preservative** — to maintain the health of the facial skin by correct cleansing methods, increased circulation, relaxation of the nerves, activation of the skin glands and increased metabolism.

2. **Corrective** — to correct some facial skin conditions, such as dryness, oiliness, blackheads, aging lines and minor conditions of acne.

Facial treatments can be developed into profitable services which will keep clients coming back for additional services. Discriminating men seek facials for their soothing and refreshing benefits. **Special facials** are available for particular conditions of the skin. A tactfully directed sales talk can materially help to stimulate revenue from facial business.

To be competent with facials, the barber-stylist should know how to **analyze** the condition of the client's skin and recommend the most effective treatment. To accomplish this scientifically requires a **knowledge** of the anatomy of the head, face and neck in connection with facial massage.

Quiet, orderly surroundings are essential for giving facials. A quiet manner on the part of the practitioner is conducive to the client's relaxation. Clients appreciate clean, scientific and comfortable facial service.

173

Facial treatments are **beneficial** for the following reasons:

1. They cleanse the skin.
2. They increase circulation.
3. They activate glandular activity.
4. They relax tense nerves.
5. They maintain muscle tone.
6. They strengthen weak muscle tissue.
7. They correct certain skin disorders.
8. They help prevent the formation of wrinkles and aging lines.
9. They improve skin texture and complexion.
10. They help to reduce fatty tissues.

To give the various types of facial treatments, the barber-stylist requires hot and cold water, towels, vibrator, therapeutic lamp and various preparations, such as facial creams, ointments, lotions, oils, packs, masks and powders.

SCIENTIFIC REST FACIAL

The scientific rest facial is a general treatment, beneficial for its cleansing and stimulating action on the skin. It also exercises as well as relaxes the facial muscles.

The five causes of wrinkles are:

1. Loosening of the elastic skin fibers because of the abnormal tension or relaxation of the facial muscles.
2. Shrinking of the skin tissue because of advancing years.
3. Excessive dryness or oiliness of the skin.
4. Facial expressions which continually crease and fold the skin.
5. Improper hygienic care of the skin.

PREPARATION

In preparing the client for a scientific rest facial, the barber-stylist should pay attention to the following points:

1. Arrange all necessary supplies in their proper place.
2. Adjust chair, linens and towels.
3. Protect client's hair by fastening a towel around his head.
4. Recline the hydraulic chair.
5. Wash hands with soap and warm water.

All creams and other products should be removed from their containers with a sanitized spatula. Do not dip the fingers into any of the products used.

PROCEDURE

The following steps may be employed in giving a scientific rest facial. However, your instructor's routine is equally correct.

1. Apply cleansing cream over the face, using stroking and rotary movements.
2. Remove cleansing cream with a smooth, warm damp towel.
3. Steam face mildly with three towels.
4. Apply tissue cream with fingertips to the skin.
5. Gently massage the face, using continuous and rhythmic movements. (See "Facial Massage Movements" in this chapter.)

6. Wipe off excess cream with a hot towel.
7. Steam the face with hot towels.
8. Remove hot towel and follow with a cool towel.
9. Pat astringent or face lotion over the face and dry.
10. Apply powder over the face and remove excess powder.
11. Raise the hydraulic chair.
12. Comb hair to desired style.

CLEAN-UP

1. Discard all disposable supplies and materials.
2. Close containers tightly, clean them and put them in their proper places.
3. Sanitize implements.
4. Wash and sanitize your hands.

POINTS TO REMEMBER IN FACIAL MASSAGING

1. Have client thoroughly relaxed.
2. Provide quiet atmosphere.
3. Maintain a clean, orderly arrangement of supplies.
4. Follow systematic procedure.
5. Give facial massage properly.

TWELVE REASONS WHY A CLIENT MAY FIND FAULT WITH A FACIAL

1. Offensive body odor, foul breath or tobacco odor.
2. Harming or scratching the skin.
3. Excessive or rough massage.
4. Getting facial cream into eyes.
5. Using towels that are too hot.
6. Breathing into the client's face.
7. Not being careful or sanitary.
8. Not showing interest in the client's skin problems.
9. Carelessness in removing cream, leaving a greasy film behind the ears, under the chin or in other areas.
10. Not permitting the client to relax, either by talking or being tense while giving facial manipulations.
11. Leaving chair to obtain materials or supplies.
12. Heavy, rough or cold hands.

FACIAL MANIPULATIONS

In giving facial manipulations, you must remember that an even tempo or rhythm induces relaxation. Do not remove the hands from the face once the manipulations have been started. Should it become necessary to remove the hands, they should be feathered off and likewise very gently replaced with feather-like movements.

FOLLOW YOUR INSTRUCTOR'S ROUTINE

Each instructor may have developed a particular routine in giving manipulations. The following illustrations merely show the different movements that may be used on the various parts of the face and neck. Follow your instructor's routine.

MOTOR POINTS OF THE FACE

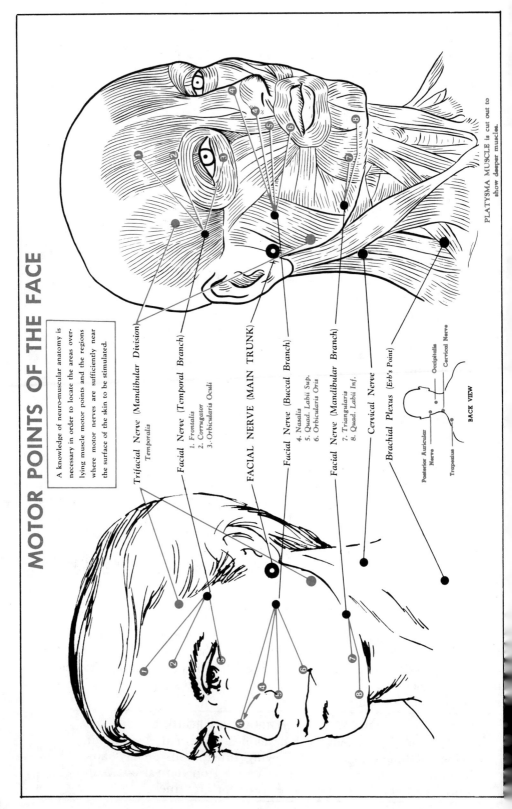

A knowledge of neuro-muscular anatomy is necessary in order to locate the areas overlying muscle motor points and the regions where motor nerves are sufficiently near the surface of the skin to be stimulated.

Trifacial Nerve (Mandibular Division)
Temporalis

Facial Nerve (Temporal Branch)
1. Frontalis
2. Corrugator
3. Orbicularis Oculi

FACIAL NERVE (MAIN TRUNK)

Facial Nerve (Buccal Branch)
4. Nasalis
5. Quad. Labii Sup.
6. Orbicularis Oris

Facial Nerve (Mandibular Branch)
7. Triangularis
8. Quad. Labii Inf.

Cervical Nerve

Brachial Plexus (Erb's Point)

PLATYSMA MUSCLE is cut out to show deeper muscles.

Posterior Auricular Nerve

Occipitalis

Cervical Nerve

Trapezius

BACK VIEW

176

FACIAL MASSAGE MOVEMENTS USING HANDS

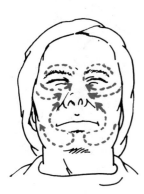

Fig. 1

1. Apply cleansing cream lightly over the face with stroking, spreading and circular movements. (Fig. 1).

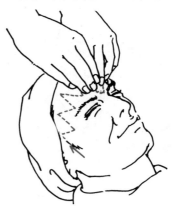

Fig. 2

2. Stroke fingers across forehead with up and down movements. (Fig. 2).

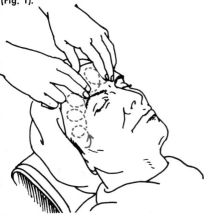

Fig. 3

3. Manipulate fingers across forehead with a circular movement. (Fig. 3).

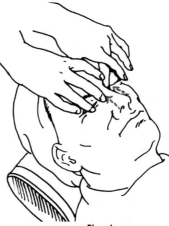

Fig. 4

4. Stroke fingers upward along side of nose. (Fig. 4).

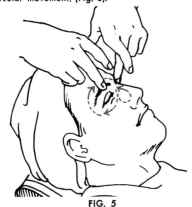

FIG. 5

5. Apply a circular movement over side of nose and use a light, stroking movement around the eyes. (Fig. 5).

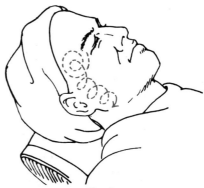

Fig. 6

6. Manipulate the temples with a wide circular movement. (Fig. 6).

7. Manipulate the front and back of the ears with a circular movement. (Fig. 6).

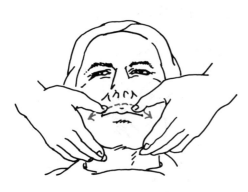

Fig. 7

8. Gently stroke both thumbs across upper lip. (Fig. 7).

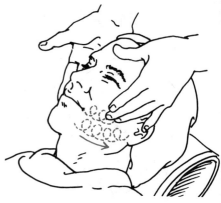

Fig. 8

9. Manipulate fingers from corners of mouth to cheeks and temples with a circular movement. (Fig. 8).

10. Manipulate fingers along lower jaw bone from tip of chin to ear with a circular movement. (Fig. 8).

11. Stroke fingers above and below along lower jaw bone from tip of chin to ear. (Fig. 8).

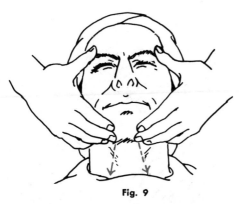

Fig. 9

12. Manipulate fingers from under chin and neck to back of ears, and up to temples. (Fig. 9, 10).

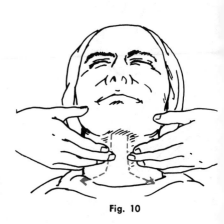

Fig. 10

Repeat all massage movements three to six times.

VIBRATORY FACIAL

The procedure for a **vibratory facial** is similar to the **scientific rest facial** with minor variations. Again we emphasize that the following procedure may be changed to conform with your instructor's routine, which is equally correct.

PROCEDURE

1. Prepare the client and steam his face with warm towels.
2. Apply massage cream.
3. Give massage movements, using the vibrator.
4. Apply a little cold cream with light hand manipulations.
5. Remove all the cream with a warm towel and follow with a mild witch hazel steam.
6. Apply one or two cool towels, followed by a face lotion.
7. Dry thoroughly and powder.

MASSAGE MOVEMENTS USING VIBRATOR

1. Adjust the vibrator on right hand and place fingertips on left nostril. Vibrate left side of face as follows:
2. Vibrate a few light up and down movements on the left side of nose.
3. Gently slide fingers around eyes and then direct them toward center of forehead.
4. Vibrate rotary movement towards the left temple. Pause for a moment.
5. Continue the rotary movements down along the jawline toward the tip of chin.
6. Vibrate from the chin towards the cheek, using wider, firmer movements.

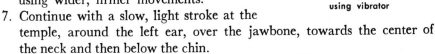

Facial massage movements
using vibrator

7. Continue with a slow, light stroke at the temple, around the left ear, over the jawbone, towards the center of the neck and then below the chin.
8. Vibrate rotary movements over the neck, behind the ear, up to the temple and then towards the center of the forehead.
9. Repeat Steps 2 to 8 on the right side of the face.
10. Repeat Steps 2 to 8 on the left side and then on the right side of the face.

RULES TO FOLLOW IN USING VIBRATOR

1. Regulate the number of vibrations to avoid over-stimulation.
2. Do not use the vibrator too long in any one spot.
3. Vary the amount of pressure in accordance with the results desired.
4. Do not use vibrator over the upper lip, as the vibrations may cause discomfort.
5. For soothing and relaxing effects, give very slow, light vibrations for a very short time.
6. For stimulating effects, give light vibrations of moderate speed and time.
7. For reducing fatty tissues, give moderate, fast vibrations with firm pressure.

Electric vibrator

ROLLING CREAM FACIAL

The facial massage formerly identified with the barber-styling shop is the rolling cream facial. For many years, this was the only type of facial service available in the barber-styling shop. However, with the development of new products and new techniques, new and more efficient facial services have been introduced and are now available. It is advisable, however, to understand the rolling cream facial, its purpose and its basic procedure.

The rolling cream facial is designed to cleanse and stimulate the skin. Due to the drying qualities of the rolling cream and the procedure of application, this type of facial should be recommended only to clients with (a) normal skin, (b) oily skin, or (c) thick skin. It should not be recommended to clients with (a) very dry skin, (b) skin with acne (c) tender, sensitive skin, (d) thin skin, or (e) rough or pimpled skin.

The rolling massage cream is pink in color. It becomes dry and flakes off as it is being massaged over the skin.

Note: The following is one of several methods for performing this service. Your instructor may have his own technique which is equally correct.

Procedure

1. Prepare patron as for a scientific rest facial.
2. Moderately steam face with 2 or 3 warm towels.
3. Apply dabs of rolling cream to chin, cheeks and forehead. Dampen the fingertips of both hands with water and spread cream evenly over face and neck with smooth stroking movement.
4. Massage the face and neck with uniform, rotary, stroking and rubbing movements with the cushion tips of the fingers until most of the cream has rolled off.
   CAUTION. Care should be taken not to use rough movements over the skin or permit particles of the cream to get into patron's eyes.
5. Apply small portion of cold cream to face and neck, using lighter manipulations. Remove cream with a warm towel.
6. Apply witch hazel steam to face and neck with one or more hot towels, following with one or two cold towels to close pores.
7. Apply astringent lotion. Dry and powder face and neck.
8. Finish as for a scientific rest facial.

SPECIAL PROBLEMS

DRY SKIN FACIAL

A dry skin is caused by an insufficient flow of sebum (oil) from the sebaceous glands. This type of facial assists in correcting the dry condition of the skin. It may be given with or without an electrical current. For more effective results, the use of electrical current is recommended.

Procedure

1. Prepare client as for a scientific rest facial.
2. Apply cleansing cream over the face.
3. Remove the cream with a soft, dry towel.

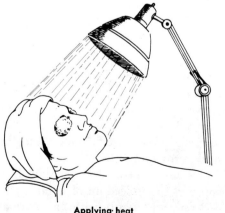

Applying heat
with infra-red lamp

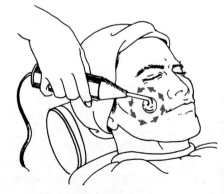

Applying high-frequency
current

4. Swab face with cotton pads dipped in witch hazel.
5. Steam the face moderately with three or four warm towels.
6. Massage a tissue cream containing lanolin gently into the skin, using stroking and rotary movements.
7. Expose the skin to a red dermal light or infra-red lamp for three to six minutes.
8. Knead the skin between the fingertips and thumb by gently twisting it to the right and then to the left.
9. Apply the high-frequency current with a glass electrode for three to four minutes.
10. Wipe excess cream with three or four warm towels, followed by a cold towel.
11. Dry the face thoroughly with a soft towel.
12. Gently rub several drops of muscle oil into the skin.
13. Apply powder.

OILY SKIN FACIAL

An excessively oily skin or any skin showing signs of enlarged pores or blackheads will benefit from this special facial treatment. This condition may be due to excessive use of starchy or oily foods, and may also be due to faulty hygienic habits.

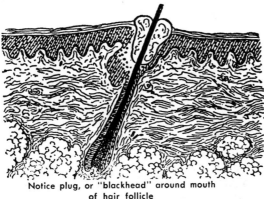

Notice plug, or "blackhead" around mouth of hair follicle

Procedure
1. Prepare client as for a scientific rest facial.
2. Cleanse the skin either with cleansing cream or soap and warm water.
3. Steam the skin with three hot towels.
4. Press out blackheads with a sanitized comedone extractor.
5. Pat the face with an astringent lotion and then apply an astringent cream.
6. Apply regular hand manipulations for about five minutes.

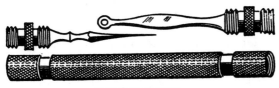

Comedone extractor

7. Apply the mild high-frequency current for three to four minutes.
8. Apply warm towels to remove astringent cream.
9. Sponge the face with a soda solution (one tablespoon of baking soda to one quart of water).
10. Dip several layers of cheesecloth or a piece of linen into astringent lotion and spread it over the face for a few minutes.
11. Remove covering and apply one or two cold towels.
12. Apply an astringent lotion, dry and powder the face.

ACNE FACIAL

Upon the advice of a physician, local treatments may be helpful in correcting acne and in clearing up the skin. Cleanliness and sanitation rules must be strictly observed in treating any form of acne.

Pimples

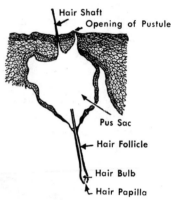

Formation of acne pustule
and enlargement of
sebaceous gland with pus

Procedure

1. Cleanse the skin with cleansing cream.
2. Steam the face with three moderately hot towels, and remove the cream with the last towel
3. Press out blackheads with a sanitized comedone extractor.
4. Sponge the skin well with an antiseptic acne lotion.
5. Rub an acne cream gently into the skin.
6. Cover the eyes with cotton pads moistened with witch hazel.
7. Expose the face to the red dermal light or infra-red lamp from five to ten minutes.
8. Apply high-frequency current for five minutes. Do not spark.
9. Wipe off excess cream with two or three warm towels.
10. Sponge the skin with an astringent lotion.
11. Apply one or two cool twels, followed by an application of witch hazel.
12. Dry and powder the face

PACKS AND MASKS

Facial packs and masks are popular in the barber-styling shop. They can be used as part of a facial or applied as a separate treatment.

Face packs and masks differ in their composition and usage. **Packs** are usually applied directly to the skin. On the other hand, **masks** are applied to the skin with the aid of gauze layers.

When applied to the skin, good quality packs and masks should feel comfortable and produce slight tingling and tightening sensations. Whatever product is used, follow the manufacturer's directions as to preparation, application and removal from the skin. It is important that at all times the skin be cleansed before applying a pack or mask.

Depending on their composition, packs can cleanse, soften, smooth, stimulate and refresh the facial skin. The results obtained, however, are temporary in nature.

CLAY PACK

The clay pack is suitable for all types of skin except a dry skin condition. It has a mild tonic effect which prevents undue wrinkling of the skin.

Procedure

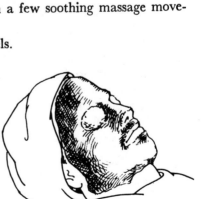

1. Prepare a warm clay pack according to the manufaturer's directions.
2. Prepare the client by arranging the linen and fastening a towel around his head to protect the hair.
3. Steam the skin with three moderately hot towels.
4. Spread the warm clay pack over the warm skin, using continuous stroking and rotary movements.

Clay pack

5. Cover the eyes with cotton pads moistened with witch hazel.
6. Dry the pack on the skin by exposure to a red dermal lamp.
7. Remove the pack with warm, damp steam towels.
8. (Optional.) Expose the face to the soothing blue light for a few minutes.
9. Apply cold cream or tissue cream with a few soothing massage movements.
10. Remove cream, and apply two cold towels.
11. Apply a mild lotion, dry and powder.

HOT OIL MASK

The hot oil mask is recommended for extremely dry, parched and scaly skin, prevalent during dry, hot or windy weather. It is used to soften, smooth and stimulate the skin tissues.

Formula for Hot Oil Mask

2 tablespoons of olive oil.
1 tablespoon of castor oil (refined grade).
1/4 teaspoon of glycerine.
Mix the oils in a small container and warm.

Hot oil mask

Procedure

1. Prepare client as for a scientific rest facial.
2. Prepare mask. Saturate cotton pads (4x4 inches) or an 18-inch square of gauze with warm oil mixture.
3. Follow Steps 1 to 5 as in scientific rest facial.
4. After the manipulations, do not remove cream, but place the cotton pads or gauze over the face.
5. Adjust eye pads.
6. Use red dermal light or infra-red lamp from eight to ten minutes.
7. Remove mask and cream.
8. Finish the facial as in a scientific rest facial.

Commercial Facial Packs and Masks

Available for use in the Barber-styling shop are various types of commercial facial packs and masks, such as milk and honey pack, egg white pack and witch hazel pack. For proper use, the barber-stylist should first read the manufacturer's claims and directions. Judge the merits of the pack or mask before recommending it to a patron.

QUESTIONS ON FACIAL TREATMENTS

1. What are ten benefits of facial treatments?
2. Name five causes of wrinkles.
3. Which supplies and equipment are required for facial treatments?
4. Why should the barber-stylist know the histology of the skin and the anatomy of the head, face and neck before giving a facial massage?
5. Why should the barber-stylist know the composition and action of various creams applied to the skin?

SCIENTIFIC REST FACIAL

1. In giving a plain facial, what attention should the barber-stylist show toward a client?
2. Why should the barber-stylist never lean over the client's face?
3. How should the client be protected from offensive tobacco odor?
4. What preparation should be made before giving a plain facial?
5. Briefly outline the procedure for giving a plain facial.
6. What are five important points to remember in giving a plain facial?
7. Give 12 reasons why a client may find fault with a facial.

SPECIAL PROBLEMS

1. What is the purpose of a dry skin facial?
2. What are the principal causes of an oily skin?
3. What implement is used to press out blackheads and whiteheads?
4. What is the action of a clay pack on the skin?
5. Which facial treatment requires the guidance of a physician?
6. In which facial treatments should the eyes be covered with cotton pads?
7. In which facial treatments should an astringent lotion or cream be applied?
8. For what skin condition should a hot oil mask be recommended?

Chapter 14
MEN'S
RAZOR HAIRCUTTING

INTRODUCTION

Razor haircutting gives the barber-stylist a wide range in which to express his or her artistic and professional talents. It provides an additional technique for helping to achieve the ultimate haircutting objective of designing a hairstyle which enhances the appearance of the client. It helps to develop a foundation for greater versatility in hairstyling

Competency in razor haircutting is developed only after thorough training, complete dedication and long practice. It is not a skill which is easily or quickly acquired. It demands painstaking care, careful concentration and constant effort. The technique of handling a razor should be completely mastered before attempting to use it to cut or style a client's hair.

Properly performed, razor cutting gives the barber-stylist a distinct advantage in cutting and styling hair. Razor haircutting is especially suitable in order to achieve one or more of the following:

1. Thin and shorten the hair
2. Taper and blend the hair
3. Help make resistant hair more manageable

In order to achieve satisfactory results when razor haircutting, the barber-stylist must give careful consideration to the following:

1. The client's styling wishes
2. The client's features, head shape and facial contour
3. The texture of the client's hair

BASIC PRINCIPLES OF HAIRSTYLING

Before razor cutting, the barber-stylist studies the client's features and offers suggestions as to what kind of hairstyle is most suitable for him.

Each hairstyle should represent a work of art. It is of utmost importance that the barber-stylist emphasize the best features of the client in order to make the client look most attractive considering age, weight and height.

185

IMPLEMENTS USED IN RAZOR HAIRCUTTING

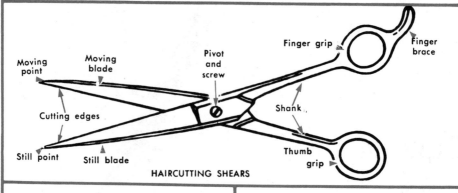

HAIRCUTTING SHEARS

Moving point, Moving blade, Pivot and screw, Finger grip, Finger brace, Cutting edges, Shank, Still point, Still blade, Thumb grip

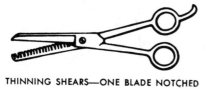

THINNING SHEARS—ONE BLADE NOTCHED

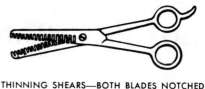

THINNING SHEARS—BOTH BLADES NOTCHED

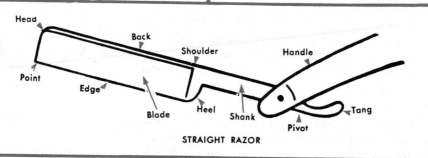

STRAIGHT RAZOR

Head, Back, Shoulder, Handle, Point, Edge, Blade, Heel, Shank, Pivot, Tang

SINGLE EDGE RAZOR WITH SAFETY GUARD

DOUBLE EDGE RAZOR WITH SAFETY GUARD

POPULAR COMBS

LARGE-TOOTH COMB

TAIL (RAT-TAIL) COMB

ALL PURPOSE COMB

HAIRCUTTING COMB

HAIR ANALYSIS

Knowing the quality, texture and elasticity of hair helps the artisan to decide what he or she expects to achieve with each individual client. The following hair analysis should be of some assistance:

1. **Coarse hair with good and moderate porosity** is the ideal type of hair. It has bulk and is porous so that the hair can be shaped to any hairstyle to satisfy the client.

2. **Medium (average) hair with good and moderate porosity.** This type of hair creates no problem in razor haircutting.

3. **Fine hair** does not have the bulk necessary to razor cut. However, many barber-stylists prefer to use the razor instead of the scissors and clippers even to cut and style fine hair. Extreme caution should be exercised when razor cutting fine hair.

Problem Hair

4. **Wiry (resistant) hair.** Occasionally the barber-stylist is confronted with wiry type hair. This type hair is unruly and difficult to cut even with the conventional scissors and clippers.

   Wiry hair can be razor cut by first preparing it with a softening treatment. This can be accomplished by either one of the following ways:

   a) Give a creme shampoo with warm water.

   b) After a regular shampoo, apply a product made for softening the hair and apply hot towels over the head. A steamer may be used instead of hot towels.

5. **Over-curly hair.** It is advisable to first straighten this hair with a chemical hair straightener before razor cutting.

TYPES OF RAZORS

Two main types of razors are used by barber-stylists in haircutting.

1. The guarded razor.
2. The straight open-blade razor.

The **guarded razor** is generally used by the beginning barber-stylist. It provides safety and prevents the blade from cutting too deeply. Another advantage is that the guarded blade can be easily and inexpensively replaced when it becomes dull. No honing or stropping of the blade is required.

The **straight open-blade razor** is widely used, especially by the experienced barber-stylist. With this kind of razor, cut hair does not accumulate at the cutting edge. Some artisans prefer to use the straight razor unstropped. **The wedge type of razor is also used by some barber-stylists.**

Razor with safety guard.

Straight razor.

HOLDING THE RAZOR

Holding the razor properly makes it easier to execute the various strokes used in razor haircutting. The two basic positions used in holding the razor are:

1. **The free hand position.** Permits the barber-stylist to do exact haircutting, particularly on difficult parts of the head (Figs. 1 and 2).

2. **The straight handle position.** Precision stroking is made possible. Can also be used for cutting the hair on the top, back and sides of the head (Fig. 3).

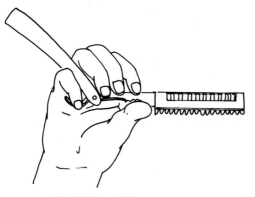

Fig. 1. Free hand position.
Place three fingers over the shank, the thumb in the groove of the shank and the little finger resting in the hollow part of the tang.

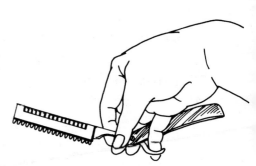

Fig. 2. Free hand position.
The safety guard must face the barber.

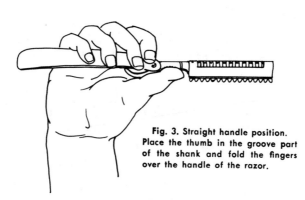

Fig. 3. Straight handle position.
Place the thumb in the groove part of the shank and fold the fingers over the handle of the razor.

RAZOR AND COMB TECHNIQUES

RAZOR STROKING AND COMBING

Proper stroking of the razor and combing during the tapering process are of utmost importance in razor haircutting. It is better to taper a little at a time than to taper too much. You must remember, after the hair is cut it cannot be replaced.

Arm and Hand Movements

Some barber-stylists prefer the arm movement. The razor stroking and combing is done with stiff arms, using the elbows as a hinge. Some barber-stylists use both wrist and arm movements. This is a matter of preference.

The barber-stylist should develop a technique which best suits the stylist and which gives the maximum results without excessive tiring.

RAZOR TAPER-BLENDING

Razor cutting is the best technique to use for taper-blending of the hair. The cutting action of the razor permits a **smoother blend** than that usually accomplished with the scissors and/or clippers.

A) **Light taper-blending.** The razor is held almost flat against the surface of the hair. Note the small amount of hair that is cut when the blade is only slightly tilted (Fig. A). Very little pressure is used.

B) **Heavier taper-blending.** The razor is held up to 45 degrees from the surface of the hair strand. As the razor is tilted higher, the depth of the cut increases (Fig. B). Usually a little more pressure is used than in light tapering.

C) **Terminal blending.** The angle of the razor blade is increased to almost 90 degrees (Fig. C). Short sawing strokes are used. Other terms used for terminal blending are hair-end tapering and blunt cutting.

RAZOR AND COMB COORDINATION

Razor stroking and combing are done in a continuous movement. The razor tapers while the comb removes the cut hair and recombs the hair for the next stroke or strokes.

One razor stroke and comb coordination.

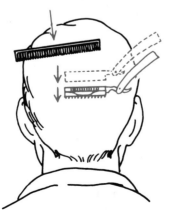

Two razor strokes and comb coordination.

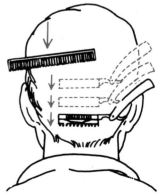

Three razor strokes and cor coordination.

For the beginner, the use of a razor with a safety guard is recommended until he or she has gained proficiency; then the beginner may use a razor without the safety guard, under the guidance of the instructor.

More strokes and heavier tapering are required for coarse, thick hair. The first strip of hair is usually combed first, followed by three razor strokes and followed again with the comb. The comb removes the cut hair and recombs the hair. This allows you to see how much hair has been cut and also gives you a guide to use for tapering the next strip.

Guide For Coarse, Thick Hair

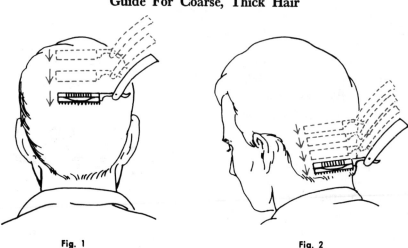

Fig. 1   Fig. 2

Crown area. Three long strokes are to be used (Fig. 1).
Nape area. Four short strokes should be used (Fig. 2).
Left and right sides of head. Three strokes may be used (Fig. 3).

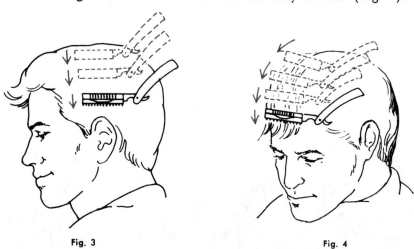

Fig. 3   Fig. 4

Top area. Consideration must be given to the hairstyle to be created. The stroking and the pressure of the razor depend largely upon the amount of hair to be removed to achieve the finished hairstyle (Fig. 4).

Front hair. To equalize the length of long and uneven front hair, pick up the hair with the comb in the right hand (Fig. 5). Hold the hair straight out between the middle and index fingers of the left hand. Transfer the comb to the left hand as shown in Fig. 6. Hold the razor at an angle, and with short sawing strokes cut the hair to the desired length.

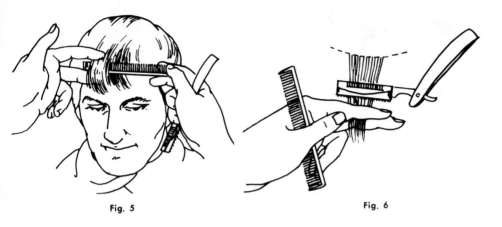

Fig. 5   Fig. 6

TAPERING NORMAL TEXTURE (AVERAGE) HAIR

Hair of normal texture — neither coarse nor fine — is considered to be average hair. Razor stroking this type hair requires fewer strokes and lighter pressure than coarse, thick (bulky) hair.

Guide For Normal Texture Hair

Crown area. Two long strokes are used (Fig. 1).
Nape area. Three short strokes are used (Fig. 2).

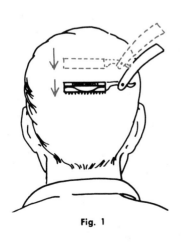
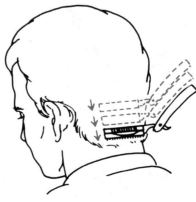

Fig. 1   Fig. 2

Left and right sides of head. Two short strokes may be used (Fig. 3).

Top of head. The stroking and pressure of the razor in this area are the same as for the sides and back areas (Fig. 4).

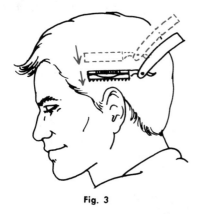

Fig. 3

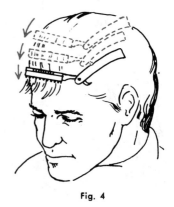

Fig. 4

FINE HAIR

With this type hair, there is usually no bulk to remove. However, the razor may be used to blend the hair ends to achieve a particular hairstyle.

Stroking of the razor is usually lighter than for normal (average) hair.

HAIR SECTIONING

Short hair or hair that is cut regularly every few weeks usually does not require any sectioning. However, sectioning the head in razor haircutting is usually necessary.

There are several good ways to section the head. Your instructor's method may be equally correct.

Depending on the barber's preference, the head may be sectioned in any of the following ways:

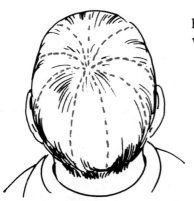

Fig. 1. Umbrella effect.

1. **Umbrella effect.** Before sectioning the hair, it is advisable to comb the hair first in an umbrella effect. Starting at the crown, comb the hair in all natural directions, similar to the spokes of a wheel (Fig. 1).

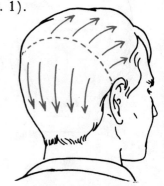

2. **Two sections.** First, part the hair from ear to ear across the crown. All hair in front of the part is combed forward. All hair behind or below the part is combed downward (Fig. 2).

Fig. 2. Two sections.

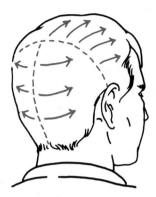

Fig. 3. Three sections.

3. **Three sections.** First, part the hair from ear to ear across the crown. All top and side hair is combed forward. Then, make a vertical part from the crown to the nape. Each of these subsections is combed toward the sides. In the nape area where there is no part, comb the hair downward (Fig. 3).

4. **Four sections.** Add one more section to the previous three sections. Make a top center part. On each side comb the hair downward (Fig. 4).

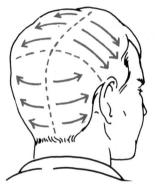

Fig. 4. Four sections.

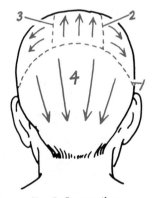

Fig. 5. Four sections.

5. **Four sections.** First, part the hair from ear to ear across the crown. Second, section right side from center of right eyebrow to crown and comb down. Make another section on the left side from center of left eyebrow to crown and comb down. Comb all back hair downward (Fig. 5).

6. **Five sections.** The same as Number 5 with the exception that the back section is divided in two (Fig. 6) and combed as indicated by arrows.

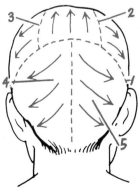

Fig. 6. Five sections.

BASIC STEPS OF A STANDARD RAZOR HAIRCUT

PREPARATION

1. Arrange necessary sanitized implements and supplies.
2. Adjust chair cloth (hair cloth) over client.

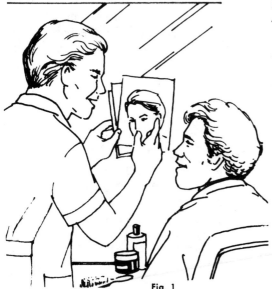

Fig. 1

3. Remove headrest.
4. Wash hands with soap and water, then dry.
5. Adjust neck-strip or towel around client's neck in the usual manner.
6. Fasten neck pieces of chair cloth over neck-strip or towel.
7. Analyze the client's facial and head shape (Fig. 1).

WHICH STYLE SHALL IT BE?

Before cutting any hair, the barber-stylist studies the client's features and offers suggestions as to what kind of hairstyle is most suitable.

Appearance before haircut.

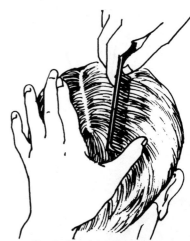

Fig. 2. Examining the scalp.

8. Examine the client's scalp for the presence of scars, growths, thinning areas or any disorders (Fig. 2).
9. Determine the condition of the client's hair (texture, quality, length and degree of bulkiness).
10. Ask client what kind of a haircut he or she desires and recommend a suitable style that will improve the client's appearance.

NECK CLEAN-UP, TAPERING AND ARCHING

Give a basic trim, using clippers and scissors. Outline around the neckline, over and front of ears.

1. The neckline should be cut low with very little tapering with scissors (Fig. 3) and clippers (Fig. 4). This is considered a "clean-up" of the neck area.

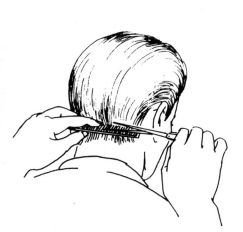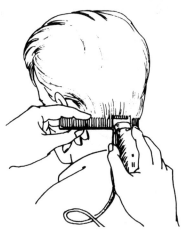

Fig. 3. Neck tapering with scissors and comb.

Fig. 4. Neck tapering using clipper over comb.

2. The arch around the ears should be as close to the ears as possible. The hair should appear neat but expose as little skin as possible (Fig. 5). Follow natural growth on the sides of neckline (Fig. 6). **It is inadvisable to shave around the ears, unless requested by the client.** Shaving on the sides of the neck is not necessary, unless the areas below the ears require it.

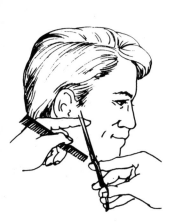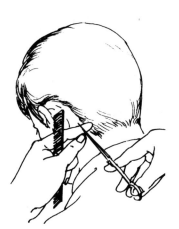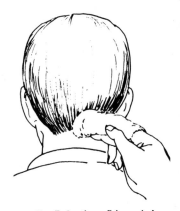

Fig. 5. Arching the right side in the usual manner.

Fig. 6. Arching the left side in the usual manner.

Fig. 7. Dusting off loose hair.

3. Remove loose hair from the neck and around ears (Fig. 7).

SHAMPOOING THE HAIR

A shampoo should be given in conjunction with a razor haircut. A shampoo removes dirt, dandruff (epidermic scales), accumulated oils and perspiration. In addition, it conditions the hair (makes hair soft) for razor haircutting. Hair properly conditioned for razor haircutting permits the razor to taper the hair into a smooth, even cutting. Unclean hair, especially when sprays or oils have been applied to the hair, may cause unevenness or choppiness in the tapering or cutting process.

TOWEL DRYING HAIR

Fig. 8. Towel drying the hair.

1. Prepare client for a shampoo, remove hair cloth, neck-strip or towel and prepare him as for a regular shampoo.

   a. After the final rinse, dry client's face and ears with ends of towel.

   b. Drape client's head with towel.

   c. Massage scalp with both hands in a circular motion until the hair is partially dry (Fig. 8). For razor cutting, the hair must be in a damp condition.

2. For the client who shampoos his or her own hair and does not desire a shampoo, the hair should be conditioned for razor haircutting, as follows:

a) If the hair is soft, wet the hair with warm water; towel dry. Leave hair damp.

b) If the hair is wiry or resistant, it must be treated. This is accomplished by first wetting the hair with warm water, removing excess water, and giving a scalp steam with hot towels. Change the towels several times.

   If a scalp steamer is available, this may be used instead of the hot towels.

SECTIONING THE HAIR

Combing the hair into sections is recommended when cutting hair that has grown long and also in virgin hairstyling. Since the hairstyle illustrated here is long enough to be sectioned, be guided by the following rules:

Fig. 9. The hair combed into an umbrella effect.

1. **Comb hair into an umbrella effect.** Stand behind the client. Use the pivot (whorl) area at the crown as a guide. Comb the top hair forward, around left and right sides and then down the back of the head (Fig. 9).

2. **Subdivide the hair into four sections** as shown in Fig. 10, as follows:

   a) A horizontal part across the crown, from ear to ear.

   b) A side part on both sides of the head. Comb side hair downward as indicated by arrows.

   c) Back area. Comb hair downward as illustrated by arrows.

Athough the hair may be divided in various ways, the four section method has been selected for this particular lesson.

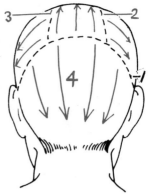

Fig. 10. The hair subdivided into four sections.

PROCEDURE FOR A BASIC RAZOR HAIRCUT

The method of razor haircutting should follow a basic plan which can be varied for each different hairstyle. No two artists will follow the same definite procedure. In this text, one basic plan is followed. However, your instructor's procedure may be different, but equally correct. Two plans are outlined here: one followed in this text, and an alternate plan.

PATTERN 1 — USED IN THIS TEXT	**PATTERN 2 — ALTERNATE METHOD**
1. Back part of head a) Downward b) Top right to left-downward c) Top left to right-downward	1. Right side of head a) Downward b) Towards the back c) Towards the face
2. Right side of head a) Downward b) Towards the back c) Towards the face	2. Left side of head a) Downward b) Towards the back c) Towards the face
3. Left side of head a) Downward b) Towards the back c) Towards the face	3. Back part of head a) Downward b) Top right to left-downward c) Top left to right-downward
4. Top hair a) Crown to forehead b) Top left side c) Top right side	4. Top hair a) Top left side b) Top right side c) Crown to forehead

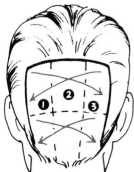

Fig. 1. Back

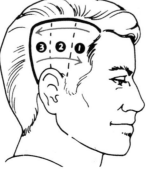

Fig. 2. Sides

Fig. 3. Top

RAZOR CUTTING FOR BACK OF HEAD

Some barber-stylists prefer to razor cut the back of the head first and then do the sides of the head. This is a matter of preference.

1. Section hair into three vertical partings or subsections (Fig. 1).
2. Taper hair one strip at a time in a downward direction, blending it with hair previously trimmed (Fig. 2). Use short, even strokes with the razor.

Fig. 1. Back area subdivided into three strips.

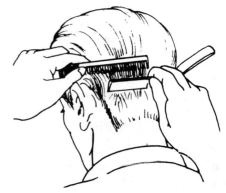

Fig. 2. Taper to blend with nape hair.

Be careful to avoid ridges, lines or any appearance of unevenness (choppiness).

a) **First strip.** Start at the upper left side, below the crown (pivot area) and taper downward.

b) **Second strip.** Start below the crown (pivot area) and taper downward towards the center of the nape.

c) **Third strip.** Start at the upper right side below the crown, and taper downward.

3. Comb hair from top-right side toward left-downward (Fig. 3). Taper the hair into two sections.

a) **Top section.** Taper lightly from right to left (Fig. 4).

b) **Lower section.** Taper to blend with nape hair from right to left side (Fig. 5).

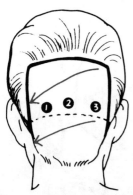

Fig. 3. Comb back hair from right top towards left-downward.

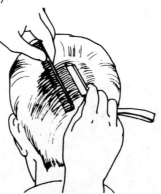

Fig. 4. Top section. Taper lightly from right top downward towards the left.

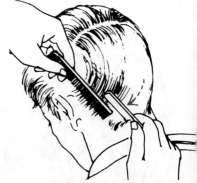

Fig. 5. Lower section. Blend with nape hair, right to left.

4. Comb hair from top-left side toward right-downward (Fig. 6).
   a) Taper the **upper** and **lower sections** downward towards the right in the same manner as previously explained (Figs. 7 and 8).

Fig. 6. Comb hair from top-left to right-downward.

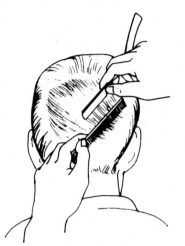

Fig. 7. Upper section. Start at the top left and taper towards right-downward.

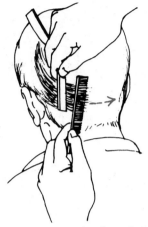

Fig. 8. Lower section. Taper the lower back section towards the right.

IMPORTANT REMINDER

For best results in razor cutting the barber-stylist must:

1. Avoid tapering too close to the hair part.
2. Avoid thinning hair too close to the scalp.
3. Avoid over-tapering the hair. It is better to cut less hair than too much. Cut hair cannot be replaced.

Some barber-stylists prefer to start razor cutting on the right side of the head while others prefer to start on the left side. This is a matter of preference; either way is correct.

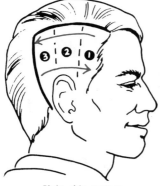

Right side pattern.

Pattern For Right Side

1. Comb hair downward and subdivide into three vertical partings.
2. Taper downward, Sections 1, 2 and 3.
3. Comb hair towards the back.
4. Taper lightly towards the back.
5. Comb hair towards the face.
6. Taper lightly towards the face.

1. **Downward Direction.**
   a) **Vertical partings.** With comb in right hand and with index finger of the left hand, section the hair into three vertical partings (Fig. 1).
   b) **Section 1.** Start about ¾ of an inch from the part and taper downward (Fig. 2). Cut off uneven hair ends (Fig. 3).

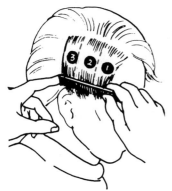

Fig. 1. Part the hair into three vertical sections.

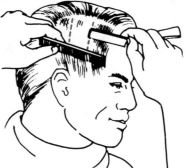

Fig. 2. Taper the first section.

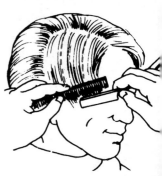

Fig. 3. Remove uneven hair ends.

   c) **Section 2.** Repeat the same tapering procedure as for Section 1.
   d) **Section 3.** Repeat the same tapering procedure as for Section 1.

   CAUTION. Be sure to protect the ear with the comb.

2. **Toward the Back.**
   a) **Comb hair** from face toward the back of the head (Fig. 4).
   b) **Taper hair.** Start tapering slightly back from the hairline (Fig. 5) and continue to taper lightly toward the back of the head.

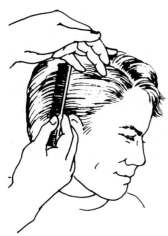

Fig. 4. Comb hair towards the back.

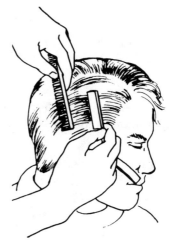

Fig. 5. Taper towards the back.

3. **Toward the Face.**

   a) **Comb hair** forward-downward toward the face (Fig. 6).

   b) **Taper hair,** starting at the upper back corner (Fig. 7).

   c) Continue to taper toward the front hairline.

   d) If necessary, cut off extra long hair at the hairline.

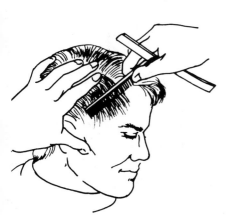

Fig. 6. Comb hair towards face.

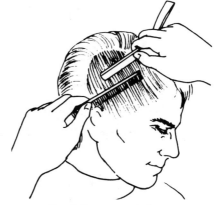

Fig. 7. Taper towards face.

RAZOR CUTTING FOR LEFT SIDE

Follow exactly the same procedure as that outlined for the right side of the head.

1. Comb hair downward and subdivide left side into three vertical sections.

2. Taper Sections 1, 2 and 3 downward.

3. Comb and taper hair lightly toward the back.

4. Comb and taper hair lightly toward the face.

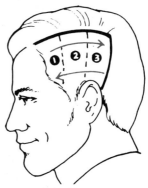

Left side pattern.

In razor cutting, the top part of the head is of utmost importance, as this area is usually where creative skill is required to achieve the hairstyle desired. How much to taper depends on the ultimate style desired and the amount of hair the client has. The order in which tapering is done is a matter of preference. In this particular style, a definite pattern is followed; however, your instructor's routine is equally correct.

Procedure

1. **Top hair forward.** Usually this step in razor cutting is done first. Comb the hair forward evenly (Fig. 1).

   a) **Top right side.** Start to taper just forward of the crown and proceed toward the forehead (Fig. 2). How much to taper depends upon the ultimate hairstyle you want to achieve.

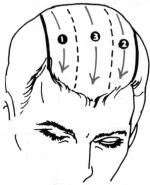 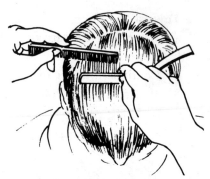

Fig. 1. Comb hair forward.

Fig. 2. Taper top right side toward forehead.

   b) **Top left side.** Repeat on the left top side in the same manner.

   c) **Top center** is usually done last. Be careful not to taper too much hair.

   d) **Front section.** Insert comb in hair to pick up left half of front section; hold the hair firmly between the middle and index fingers.

   1) Taper the hair (Fig. 3). Comb the hair forward again and remove any unevenness.

Fig. 3. After tapering top left side, taper front hair.

   2) Repeat this procedure until all front hair has been tapered.

2. **Top left side.** Comb and distribute top hair evenly to the **left side** of the head (Fig. 4).

   a) **Start at top front.** Lightly taper top hair downward to blend with the side hair. If necessary trim uneven hair along the hairline (Fig. 5).

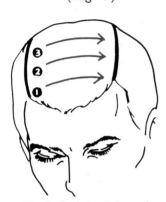

Fig. 4. Comb top hair evenly to left side.

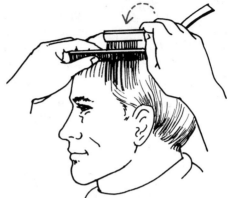

Fig. 5. Taper the right side from front towards back to blend with previously tapered hair.

   b) **Middle top area.** Proceed in the same manner as above.

   c) **Back top area.** Continue to taper in the same manner. It is of utmost importance that the hair over the ear blends with the back hair.

   CAUTION. Be sure that the ear is protected with the comb when tapering in this area.

Fig. 6. Comb top hair evenly to right side.

Fig. 7. Taper top front hair to blend with previously tapered hair.

3. **Top right side.** After the left side is completed, comb and distribute the hair to the **right side** of the head (Fig. 6).

   a) **Start at top front.** Follow the same procedure for tapering right side of the head as that outlined for the left side of the head (Fig. 7).

CAUTION. The same precaution must be taken to protect the ear from injury by protecting it with the comb, and extreme caution must be taken that the hair blends with the back hair.

203

Hair styled with air-waver.

COMPLETION

Shave neckline and under the ears if required. Be sure to cut very low without attempting any further tapering.

If the client expresses a wish to have the arch shaved around the ears do so, but remember to keep as close to the ears as possible.

Clean up around neck and ears. If special styling such as air-waving, etc., is desired, it should be done at this time. Otherwise the client's haircut has been completed.

Part and comb the hair in the desired hairstyle.

Before razor cut.

Hair combed with side part.

Hair combed after a permanent wave.

Wipe off loose hair with towel, tissue or hair vacuum.

Remove towel or neck-strip and chair cloth, and release client in the usual manner.

Clean-up. Put everything in proper order and place used implements in container to be sanitized. Wash hands.

SAFETY PRECAUTIONS AND REMINDERS
RAZOR HAIRCUTTING

1. **Wash hands** before and after working on a client.
2. **Examine client's scalp** and hair before razor cutting. Look for unusual conditions or disorders, such as growths, depressions, rashes, abrasions or balding spots.
3. **Analyze the client's head shape**, facial contour, neckline and hair texture.
4. Buy and use only **good quality** haircutting implements.
5. Scissors and razors must be kept in a **sharpened condition** at all times. Have implements sharpened when necessary. A dull cutting edge will not cut well and may cause pain or discomfort to your client.

CAUTION. Do not test sharpness of implements with your fingers.

6. **Handling scissors.** Extend scissors (handles first) to persons receiving them. Protect the skin by guiding the scissor blades with fingertips of left hand or with comb. Avoid nipping the skin or digging points of scissors into client's neck or scalp.

7. **Razor sharpness and handling.** Replace or resharpen razor blades when dull. Place discarded blades into a closed container. A dull razor will pull the hair and cause pain or discomfort to the client. To avoid injury, use a **razor with a guard** until you are proficient in razor cutting.

8. **Section the hair** before virgin hairstyling or before cutting long hair.

9. **Wet hair** before using a razor to cut, taper or thin hair.

10. **Hair thinning and tapering.**
    a) Avoid tapering the hair too close to the hair part, since coarse or medium textured hair ends may stand up and make the part look ragged.
    b) Avoid thinning coarse hair too close to the scalp because short, stubby hair ends will protrude through the top layer.
    c) Avoid over-tapering the hair; it is impossible to correct a haircut after too much hair has been removed.

11. **Caring for haircutting implements.**
    a) Do not leave implements exposed. Avoid dropping them to the floor, since this may cause damage to cutting surfaces, or knock implements out of line which may cause injury.
    b) Clean and sanitize implements after each use. Store them in a dry sanitizer until they are to be used again.
    c) Protect implements after each use. Place scissors in case and keep razor closed.

12. **Hard rubber combs.** Combs made of hard rubber are the most durable and are popular with barber-stylists. A variety of sanitized combs must be available to perform the various phases of haircutting. **Combs must be cleaned and sanitized** after each use.

13. **Clippers.** Keep clippers clean and lubricated. Hair must be removed from the clippers, and clipper blades must be cleaned and sanitized after eash use. Avoid dropping the detachable clipper blades to the floor, since this may cause damage to the cutting surface and/or may cause injury.

14. **To avoid injury,** do not annoy or distract anyone while he is in the process of cutting hair.

QUESTIONS ON MEN'S RAZOR HAIRCUTTING

1. What should be considered before giving the client a razor haircut?
2. For what three purposes can the barber-stylist use a razor haircut?
3. List five types of men's hair which the barber-stylist may encounter in his work.
4. Name two types of razors used in haircutting.
5. Which type of razor is best suited for a beginning barber-stylist?
6. Which two hand positions can be used in holding the razor for haircutting?
7. Name three ways to taper-blend the hair with a razor.
8. Which method of taper-blending requires the least amount of pressure with the razor?
9. How should the barber-stylist coordinate razor and comb movements?
10. What kind of stroke and pressure is employed to taper: a) coarse bulky hair; b) normal (average) hair texture?
11. What type of hair does not require sectioning?
12. What are two good reasons for shampooing the hair before a razor cut?
13. Why should the client's scalp and hair be examined before razor cutting?
14. Should the client's hair be in a dry or damp condition before it is cut with a razor?
15. For best results, what should the barber-stylist avoid when giving a razor cut?
16. To prevent accidents, what three precautions should be followed by the barber-stylist?

Chapter 15

WOMEN'S SHEARS AND RAZOR HAIRCUTTING

The art of women's haircutting requires thorough training and practice in the proper way to shape the hair with shears, thinning shears, and razor. Molding the hair properly with a good haircut serves as a foundation for modern hairstyles. The barber-stylist's professional education is not complete until he or she has acquired the artistic skill and judgment required for successful women's haircutting.

Many of the same fundamental principles of haircutting apply to the servicing of both men and women. The same techniques are employed in the process of cutting, shaping, thinning, tapering and blending hair of both men and women. In general, women's haircut styles and designs tend to be more loose and casual than men's.

Modern hairstyles are developed to emphasize a woman's individuality and to accentuate her good points while minimizing her poor features. However, the barber-stylist must be guided by the client's wishes in addition to what he or she considers best for her personality. In selecting the proper style of haircut, he or she must take into consideration the client's head shape, facial features, neckline and the texture of her hair.

VARIOUS SHAPES OF HEADS

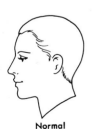

Normal

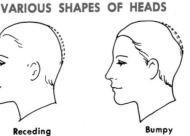

Receding   **Bumpy**

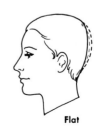

Flat

207

SECTIONING THE HAIR FOR CUTTING

There are several correct ways to section the head for cutting. The following are two accepted methods. Your instructor's method is equally correct.

FOUR (4) SECTION PARTING

The hair should be sectioned as shown in Fig. 1. Pin up, as in Fig. 2, leaving nape hair to use as guide length.

Fig. 1

Fig. 2

FIVE (5) SECTION PARTING

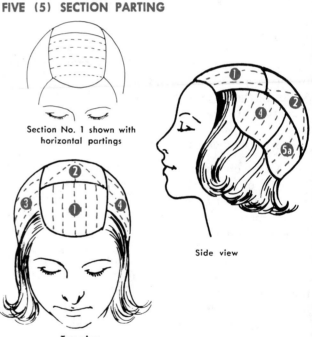

Section No. 1 shown with horizontal partings

Back view

Side view

Top view
Section No. 1 shown with vertical partings

Five (5) section parting, with sub-parting panels. Section and pin up hair in the order shown in illustrations.

The back section (No. 5) may be divided into Sections No.5a and No. 5b for easier handling.

Top section (No. 1) may be sub-parted in two ways, as shown in the above illustrations, with partings running in either a horizontal or vertical direction.

HAIR THINNING

The purpose of thinning the hair is to remove excess bulk without shortening its length.

The **hair texture** determines the point where thinning should start on the hair strand. As a rule, **fine hair** may be thinned **closer** to the scalp than coarse hair. Why? Because if coarse hair is thinned too close to the scalp, the short stubby ends will protrude through the top layer. Fine hair, on the other hand, is softer and more pliable and when cut very short will lay flatter on the head.

How much to thin depends on the particular hairstyle to be created. As a guide, start thinning different textures of hair as follows:

1. Fine hair — from ½ to 1 inch from the scalp.
2. Medium hair — from 1 to 1½ inches from the scalp.
3. Coarse hair — from 1½ to 2 inches from the scalp.

HAIR THINNING AREAS

There are several areas where it is not advisable to thin the hair.

1. Hairline at nape of neck (ear to ear).
2. Area at side of head, above ears.
3. Around facial hairline. Usually hair is not heavy at hairlines.
4. In the hair part. The cut ends would be seen in the finished hairstyle.

Hair in shaded areas does not require thinning

METHODS OF HAIR THINNING
THINNING WITH THINNING SHEARS

When using the thinning shears, grip the hair firmly by overlapping the middle finger a trifle over the index finger, as shown in the illustration.

Thinning the hair. Pick up a strand of hair from ½ to 1 inch wide by 2 to 3 inches long, depending on the texture of the hair, holding it straight out between the middle and index fingers. Place thinning shears 1 to 2 inches from the scalp (depending on the hair texture) and cut into the hair. Move out another 1½ inches and cut again.

CAUTION. When using the thinning shears, it is advisable to avoid thinning the top layer of strand.

Thinning with thinning shears

THINNING OR SHAPING WITH SHEARS

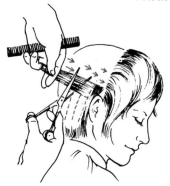

Thinning with Scissors (Shears)

When using regular shears to thin the hair, smaller sections of hair are picked up than when using the thinning shears. The technique is also changed. This process of thinning is known as **slithering.**

Slithering. Hold a strand of hair straight out between the middle and index fingers. Place the hair in the shears so that only the underneath hair will be cut. Slide the shears up and down the strand, closing them slightly each time the shears is moved toward the scalp. Repeat this procedure twice on each strand.

Alternate method of holding the hair is with the thumb and index finger.

Back-Combing. The short hair may be back combed as shown in illustration, and then slithered as explained above. It is advisable to hold the end of the strand with the thumb and index finger.

Never thin the hair near the ends of a strand; to do so will render the hair shapeless.

Back-Combing the Shortest Hair (Ruffing or Teasing)

Slithering the Hair After Back-Combing

WET OR DRY HAIRCUTTING WITH SHEARS
THE BASIC HAIRCUT

The art of cutting women's hair is important in the development of the professional barber-stylist. As in any other exercise of personal skill, there exists differences of opinion with reference to the proper procedure to be followed in the performance of this technique. Each barber-stylist is especially interested in developing the skill required to give a basic haircut to women.

A basic haircut means many different things to different people. However, this term is primarily used to describe an all-purpose haircut. A basic haircut is one that can easily be shaped or molded into a wide variety of finished hairstyles.

The techniques described in this chapter present only one method of performance. Your instructor may have another method which may be equally correct.

Shear cutting may be done on either dry or wet hair.

1. **Dry cutting.** If the hair is cut while dry, then it may be shampooed after the cutting is completed.
2. **Wet cutting.** The hair may be cut immediately after it has been shampooed.

PREPARATION

Dry cutting. The client is draped in the usual manner.

Wet cutting. Adjust neck strip or towel around neck. Use plastic cape to protect client's clothing. Shampoo or wet the hair for wet cutting.

1. Examine head shape, facial features and hair texture.
2. Comb and brush hair free of tangles.
3. Divide hair into four or five main sections.

Procedure

The procedure for both dry cutting and wet cutting is the same.

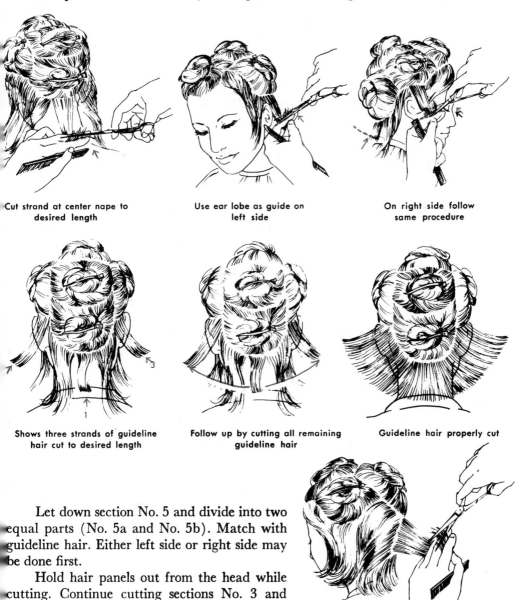

Cut strand at center nape to desired length

Use ear lobe as guide on left side

On right side follow same procedure

Shows three strands of guideline hair cut to desired length

Follow up by cutting all remaining guideline hair

Guideline hair properly cut

Let down section No. 5 and divide into two equal parts (No. 5a and No. 5b). Match with guideline hair. Either left side or right side may be done first.

Hold hair panels out from the head while cutting. Continue cutting sections No. 3 and No. 4 in the same manner.

Cutting section No. 5b

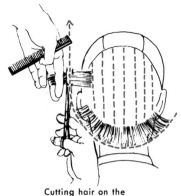

Cutting hair on the back side of hand

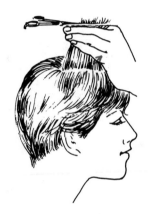

Head completely cut

Crown section No. 2. Hold pre-cut strands out from the head, match length by picking up strands from section already cut. Continue around the head, matching length with sides and back hair.

Divide section No. 1 into two parts. Pick up hair from the middle of the section, using previously cut hair as a guide. Maintain the hand movements in the 45° arc. Proceed to cut both parts of section No. 1 in the prescribed manner.

If **bangs** are to be cut, move from side of patron to directly in front for even cutting. Test hair for bounce (elasticity) then determine desired length. If bangs are to be short, use bridge of nose as a guide. If style is to be long, shape strands to blend into length of the sides.

Thinning. To complete the shaping of the hair, excess bulk should be removed by thinning with thinning shears or regular shears. It is recommended that all hair be checked for proper length.

Hair completely cut. Hair that has been correctly cut and tapered is easily adaptable to many different styles.

COMPLETION

Remove neck strip or towel and hair cloth or plastic cape. Thoroughly remove all hair clippings from hair cloth or cape, client's clothing and from work area. Release client or proceed with the next professional service she may desire.

HELPFUL HINTS ON SHINGLING

Regardless of the prevailing hair fashion, there will always be a number of clients who want their hair cut or molded short. To satisfy these clients you must know how to shingle the hair. The following illustrations show how shingling is accomplished by using the regular shears and comb.

Note—In shingling, the blade of the shears is held parallel with the comb; only the top blade moves and does the cutting.

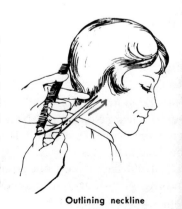

Outlining neckline

Shingling procedure. Start at the nape line, shingling the hair upward in a graduated effect. After reaching the top of the section being cut, turn the comb downward and comb the hair. Proceed, section by section, until the entire back of the head is shingled in a smooth uniform manner.

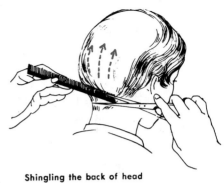

Shingling the back of head

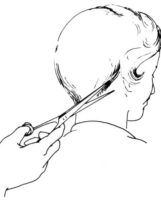

Cleaning neck with clippers   Cleaning neck with points of shears

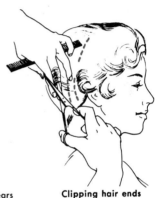

Clipping hair ends

STYLE CUTTING

Style cutting is the art of cutting the hair to facilitate the development of waves. The technique employed is one of tapering or shaping the hair to conform with the formation of a wave. The hair would be cut a little deeper in the trough or indentation of the wave and a little less in the crest of the wave. This method of haircutting acts to facilitate the formation and durability of a hair wave.

The Use of Clippers

There is a mistaken idea that the use of the clippers to clean the neck line has a tendency to make the hair grow in thicker at the neck. This is not true, as the amount of human hair can only be as great as the number of hair follicles, and these are not increased in number by the use of the clippers or any other implement.

CORRECTING SPLIT HAIR ENDS

Trichoptilosis (tri-kop-ti-lo'sis) is the technical term for split hair ends. When the hair becomes dry and brittle, due to various causes, the hair ends frequently split. Temporary relief for this condition may be obtained by clipping the hair ends.

RAZOR HAIRCUTTING

INTRODUCTION

Haircutting with a razor differs from other methods due to the fact that a sharp razor is used for cutting hair which is first dampened with water. This method of cutting the hair has found favor with both barber-stylists and clients. It is a technique which requires great care and skill in order to be performed in a satisfactory manner.

After the hair has been thoroughly dampened, combed and sectioned, it is ready for the razor cut. As the hair strand is drawn toward the barber-stylist, the razor is placed upon it, flat, not erect, about one inch from the scalp. Using short, steady, downward strokes toward the end, the hair is tapered to the desired thickness and length. Many practitioners prefer to taper both the top and the bottom of each strand.

Thinning Hair With Razor

Hold a strand of hair straight out between the middle and index fingers. Place the razor flat, **not erect,** about 1 to 2 inches from the scalp (depending on the hair texture), with **pressure on the back of** the razor, **not the edge.** Use short, steady strokes toward the hair ends.

Thinning with razor.

Tapering hair ends after back-combing

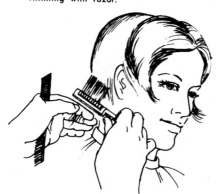

Razor cutting uneven ends.

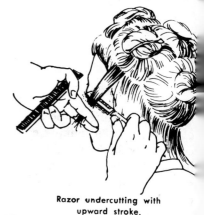

Razor undercutting with upward stroke.

BASIC HAIRCUT

To be proficient in razor cutting, the barber-stylist must have handy everything that is required. Nothing is more disturbing to the client than to have the practitioner leave the chair to get something he or she has forgotten.

PREPARATION

1. Seat client, adjust neck strip and plastic cape.
2. Examine head shape, facial features and hair texture.
3. Comb and brush hair free of tangles.
4. Shampoo or wet the hair.
5. Divide hair into four or five main sections.

Blunt cut a strand at center nape for desired hair length.

On the left side, use ear lobe as a guide for measuring desired length.

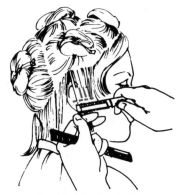

On the right side, follow same procedure as for the left side.

Placement of cut guideline strands.

Guideline hair. Cut guideline hair from center to left, matching length of previously cut strands.

Continue to cut and blend the remainder of hair on the left side.

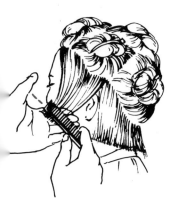

Left side guideline completed—length evenly matched.

The same procedure used on the left side is continued on the right side.

Guideline hair completely cut.

Divide section No. 5 into two parts. (Sections No. 5a and No. 5b.) From center of section No. 5a, pick up horizontal strands. Pick up guideline strand for length. When guideline hair falls away, cut hair—moving hands out and upward into a 45° arc. Proceed to cut to the left into section No. 4 in the same manner. Return to section No. 5b and cut this section, moving to the right into section No. 3, always lifting hands in an upward 45° arc as the hair is cut. **Measure carefully with guideline.** Next, proceed to cut section No. 2 (crown) using previously cut hair as a guide.

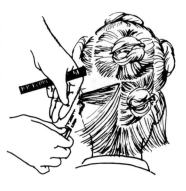

Shaping section No. 5a.

TOP SECTION

Divide section No. 1 into two parts. Pick up hair from the middle of the section, using previously cut hair as a guide. Maintain the hand movements in the 45° arc. Proceed to cut both parts of section No. 1 in the prescribed manner.

Shaping top section.

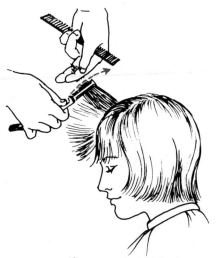

Alternate method of shaping top section.

If **bangs** are to be cut, move from side of client to directly in front for even cutting. Test hair for bounce (elasticity); then determine desired length. If bangs are to be short, use bridge of nose as a guide. If style is to be long, shape strands to blend into length of the sides.

Thinning. To complete the shaping of the hair, excess bulk should be removed by thinning with a razor, thinning shears or scissors. It is recommended that all hair be checked for proper length.

HAIR PROPERLY RAZOR CUT

The barber-stylist should strive to become proficient in women's razor cutting. If the hair is cut uniformly all over the head, the client will have no problem in combing and styling her hair.

On the other hand, if the hair is cut so that it has different lengths, the client will encounter difficulty in combing and styling it.

Satisfied clients require artistic and creative hairstyling. The barber-stylist who is capable of satisfying clients brings in added revenue to the shop and also improves his or her own earning power.

Correct uniform razor cutting.

Completed razor cutting with bang effect and/or off-face style.

Hair razor cut for a straight back style.

COMPLETION

Remove neck strip and plastic cape. Thoroughly clean all hair clippings from cape, client's clothing and from work area. You may then proceed with the next professional service desired by the client.

HELPFUL HINTS IN LADIES' HAIRCUTTING

There are as many ways to cut women's hair as there are practitioners performing this service. The following are several suggestions which will help to achieve special results in cutting women's hair:

1. To develop a soft pompadour effect, hair is parted parallel to the hairline and directed off the face for cutting. This technique positions the hair properly for cutting underneath at the ends, giving lift and softness to the hair.
2. To develop a side angled bang, direct the hair parallel to the forehead. Shorten the hair to a point that is approximately level with the outer ends of the eyebrow.
3. To develop an off-the-face style, direct the hair back from the hairline in vertical partings. Start cutting the hair about three inches from the hairline at the face and shorten as previously planned.
4. To develop a lifted nape effect, section the hair vertically across the crown downward. The lengths are graduated in a blended taper from about three inches to two inches at the nape.

One of the important objectives in hairstyling is to minimize and draw attention away from the client's less attractive features. This objective can be attained by either partially concealing less attractive features or counteracting them by arranging some effect which draws attention away from them. The helpful hints described above should be of assistance in planning a haircut which contributes greatly to this effort.

POPULAR STYLES FOR WOMEN

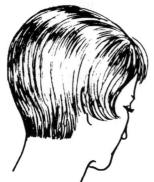

Bangs with short or square napeline.

Bangs with shingled back and "V" shaped nape.

Off-the-face hair style requires natural wavy hair and fuller neckline.

Parted with side bang. Sides smoothly combed back. Nape may be natural, round or short.

LEARN HOW TO HANDLE CHILDREN

Special consideration should be given to children and teenagers. Barber-stylists who know how to handle children will usually attract the mothers to the same shop for their own haircuts.

Popular hair styles for young girls.

TRIMMING AND SHAPING OVER-CURLY HAIR

Over-curly hair has its own particular characteristics, as have the other types of hair, which require special techniques for cutting and styling. Of prime importance to the barber-stylist is the ability to create a hairstyle that will enhance the appearance of the client and to visualize how the finished hairstyle will look. Knowing the correct styling techniques and using common sense in their application are the marks of the trained barber-stylist.

The steps outlined below represent one method of styling over-curly hair for men and women. Where your instructor's methods differ, follow his or her techniques.

Combing hair upward with hair lifter.

1. Drape client in the usual manner for haircutting.

2. Shampoo and dry hair thoroughly.

3. Apply an emollient product lightly to the scalp and hair to replace lost oil.

4. Using a wide-tooth comb, or a hair lifter, comb the hair upward and slightly forward, making the hair as long as possible. Start at the crown and continue until all hair has been combed out from the scalp and distributed evenly around the head. By combing in a circular pattern, splits are usually avoided.

5. Visualize the style and length of hair desired. Start by tapering the sides, and cut in the direction hair will be combed.

6. Taper the back part of the head to blend with the sides.

7. Trim the extreme hair ends of the crown and top areas to desired length.

8. For an off-the-face hairstyle, comb hair up and backward. For forward movement, comb hair up and forward.

9. Blend side hair with the top, crown and back hair.

10. Outline the hairstyle at sides, around the ears and nape area, using either scissors or hairliner (special type clipper).

Trimming hair to desired length.

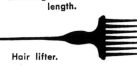

Hair lifter.

11. Give finishing touch. Fluff slightly with hair lifter, wherever needed. Lightly spray the hair to give it a natural, lustrous sheen.

219

TERMS USED IN CONNECTION WITH HAIRCUTTING

Basic haircut—Cutting the hair to a length which is not too long nor too short in order that it properly fit many different hairstyles.

Guideline—A strand of hair, at the nape or sides of the head, cut to a precise length. This cut strand establishes a guideline to be followed in cutting the balance of the head and helps to establish the general cutting pattern.

Shingling—Cutting the hair close to the nape of the neck, leaving the hair gradually longer toward the crown, without showing a definite line.

Thinning—Decreasing the thickness of the hair where it is too heavy.

Tapering—Shortening the hair in a graduated effect.

Feathering—Another term for tapering.

Slithering—The process used in thinning and tapering the hair at the same time with scissors.

Shredding—Another term for slithering.

Effileing—A French term for slithering.

Blunt or club cutting—Cutting the hair straight off, without tapering.

Layer cutting—Tapering and thinning the hair by dividing it into many thin layers.

Natural hairline—Where no artificial hairline is created in short hairstyles, the hair at the nape of the neck is left in its natural hairline.

Featheredge—When the hair at the nape of the neck is shingled in a graceful upward effect, and the neck is cleaned with shears, razor or clipper.

Back-combing—Combing the short hairs of a strand towards the scalp. Other terms used for back-combing are: teasing, ruffing and French lacing.

QUESTIONS ON WOMEN'S HAIRCUTTING

1. Why is mastery of the art and technique of hair cutting so important to the student?
2. Name the main implements used in hair cutting.
3. What purpose is served by thinning the hair?
4. Why may fine hair be cut closer to the scalp than coarse hair?
5. About how close to the scalp should: a) fine hair; b) medium hair; c) coarse hair be thinned?
6. In which areas is it advisable not to thin the hair?
7. Why is it not advisable to thin hair in the hair part?
8. Why should you avoid removing too much hair during the thinning process?
9. What is shingling?
10. Why should the hair be damp for razor shaping?
11. What does the barber-stylist use as a guide when he wants to create short bangs?
12. What is meant by back-combing?
13. What is meant by slithering the hair?
14. What is meant by the term "tapering"?
15. Prior to cutting over-curly hair, what is used to comb the hair? Why?

Chapter 16
FINGER WAVING MEN'S HAIR

INTRODUCTION

Finger waving is the technique of creating hairstyles with the aid of the fingers, comb, waving (styling) lotion, hairpins or clips, and a styling hair net (trainer). Proficiency in the art of finger waving gives the barber-stylist a very important additional service which he or she can offer to clients.

The best results in developing soft, natural waves are obtained in hair that has a natural wave or has been permanently waved. It is more difficult to properly finger wave hair which is straight. A pleasing finger wave should harmonize with the shape of the client's head, as well as with the client's facial features.

STYLING LOTION AND COMB

The use of a good styling lotion is an aid to better finger waving, as it makes the hair pliable and keeps it in place.

The proper choice of styling lotion should be governed by the texture and condition of the client's hair. A good styling lotion is harmless to the hair; it should not flake after it has dried.

Hard rubber combs with both fine and coarse teeth are recommended for finger waving.

FINGER WAVING

PREPARATION

The practitioner washes his or her hands and has available all necessary sanitized implements and clean supplies. Prepare client by properly draping him or her with clean towel and a shampoo cape.

After the client's hair is shampooed, towel-blot the hair.

The hair is parted, combed smooth, and arranged to conform to the ultimate hairstyle. Styling lotion is applied with an applicator or pump-sprayed on to the hair and distributed through the hair with the comb. Avoid the use of an excessive amount of styling lotion.

To locate the direction of natural hair growth, comb hair away from the face and push it forward with the palm of your hand.

The finger wave may be started on either side of the head. In this presentation, however, the work begins on the right top side.

SHAPING THE TOP AREA

Shape the top hair with a comb, using a circular movement, starting at the front hairline and working towards the back, until the crown has been reached. (Fig. 1)

FORMING THE FIRST RIDGE

The index finger of the left hand is placed directly above the position for the first ridge.

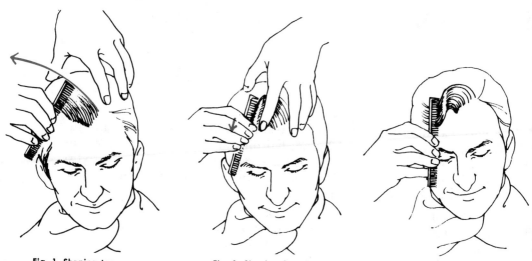

Fig. 1. Shaping top area.   Fig. 2. Shaping first ridge.   Fig. 3. Flatten comb against head.

With the teeth of the comb pointing slightly upward, the comb is inserted directly under the index finger. Draw the comb forward about one inch along the fingertip. (Fig. 2)

With the teeth still inserted in the ridge, comb is flattened against the head in order to hold the ridge in place (Fig. 3). (The left hand is not shown so that you may see the ridge and position of the comb.)

Remove the left hand from the head and place the middle finger above the ridge and the index finger on the teeth of the comb. Emphasize the ridge by closing the two fingers and applying pressure to the head. (Fig. 4)

CAUTION. Do not try to increase the height of the ridge by pushing or lifting it up with the fingers. Such movement will distort and move the ridge formation off its base.

Without removing the comb, the teeth are turned downward and the hair combed in a right semi-circular effect to form a dip in the hollow part of the wave. (Fig. 5) This procedure is followed section by section until the crown has been reached. (Fig. 6)

Fig. 4. Emphasize first ridge of the wave.

Fig. 5. Hair is combed in a semi-circular effect to form first wave.

Fig. 6. Completing the first ridge at the crown.

The ridge and wave of each section should match evenly without showing separations in the ridge and hollow part of the wave.

FORMING THE SECOND RIDGE

The formation of the second ridge is begun at the crown area. (Fig. 7) The movements are the reverse of those followed in forming the first ridge. The comb is drawn **back** from the fingertip, thus directing the formation of the second ridge. All movements are followed in a reverse pattern until the hairline is reached, thus completing the second ridge. (Fig. 8)

Third ridge. If an additional ridge is required, the movements are the same as for the first ridge.

Fig. 7. Beginning of the second ridge.

COMPLETING THE FINGER WAVE

1. Place net over hair, and if a pedestal dryer is used, safeguard client's forehead and ears with cotton gauze or paper protectors.
2. Adjust the dryer to medium heat and allow hair to dry thoroughly; otherwise the wave will comb out.

Fig. 8. First and second ridges completed.

3. After the client's hair is completely dried, remove hair net. Remove clips and pins from hair.
4. Comb hair into natural waves.

SHADOW WAVING

Shadow waving is recommended for the sides (and sometimes the back) of the head. The wave is made in exactly the same manner as in finger waving, except that the ridges are kept low.

REMINDERS AND HINTS ON FINGER WAVING

1. Avoid the use of an excessive amount of styling lotion.

2. Before finger waving, locate the position of the natural wave in the hair.

3. To emphasize the ridges of a finger wave, press and close the fingers holding the ridge against the head.

4. To have a longer lasting finger wave, mold the waves in the direction of the natural hair growth.

5. Before combing out, the hair should be thoroughly dried.

6. A styling hair net is placed over the hair to protect the setting while the hair is being dried.

7. To hold the finger wave in place longer, apply a hair spray lightly.

8. Lightened or tinted hair that tangles or snarls is easier to comb if a cream rinse is used.

QUESTIONS ON FINGER WAVING MEN'S HAIR

1. Define finger waving.
2. How do you protect the client's clothing?
3. How should the hair be protected while being dried?
4. What type of hair is the easiest to finger wave?
5. Give two main points in judging a good finger-waved hairstyle.
6. Why are styling (waving) lotions not harmful to the hair?
7. Prior to drying the hair, why are cotton, gauze or paper protectors placed over the client's ears and forehead?

Chapter 17
AIR-WAVING AND CURLING

AIR-WAVING

The introduction of air-waving has enabled the barber-stylist to achieve new heights in men's hairstyling. The use of air-waving techniques has permitted the modern barber-stylist to create many new styles for the improvement of the appearance of the client. At the same time, air-waving makes the hairstyle last long enough to be practical for everyday wear.

Air-waving contributes the finishing touch to a natural, attractive looking hairstyle. It can also be used to good advantage for the control of problem hair, such as cowlicks, thin hair and hair that is too wavy.

Air-waving may be defined as the temporary reshaping of the patron's hair with the aid of a styling dryer, comb, brush and special cosmetics. Air-waving is also called blow-waving, wind-waving and air-jet styling.

To master the skills of air-waving, the barber-stylist must know:
1. The basic elements of hairstyling and finger waving.
2. How to select the right hairstyle for each client.
3. How to properly merchandise air-waving to clients.

The barber-stylist who learns how to efficiently utilize the art of air-waving will find his or her services to be in great demand. The experienced barber-stylist is bound to be rewarded for his or her efforts, both through creative achievement and financial gain.

AIR-WAVING EQUIPMENT AND SUPPLIES

For air-waving, the barber-stylist will need the following:
1. **Equipment and Implements.**
   a) **Air-wavers** (styling dryers) without attachments or with comb and brush attachments.
   b) **Combs.** Whether metal and/or hard rubber combs is a matter of personal preference.
   c) **Styling brushes.**

225

2. **Supplies.**
   a) Shampoo.
   b) Styling lotion.
   c) Styling gel.
   d) Conditioner.
   e) Hair spray.
   f) Hair dressing (non-greasy).

3. **Accessories.**
   a) Shampoo cape.
   b) Towels and neck-strips.
   c) Styling hair nets (trainers).
   d) Chair cloth (hair cloth).

AIR-WAVER (STYLING DRYER)

The **air-waver without attachments** is an electrical device especially designed for the barber-stylist. Its main parts are a handle, a small fan, a heating element, a slotted nozzle, and controls. When in operation it produces a steady stream of warm air, hot air or cool air. The controls permit the barber-stylist to make necessary adjustments in the operation of the air-waver (styling dryer). For instance, less heat is needed for fine hair, whereas a higher temperature is required for coarse hair.

The **air-waver with attachments** consists of several replaceable attachments, such as a comb with fine teeth, a comb with coarse teeth, and a styling brush.

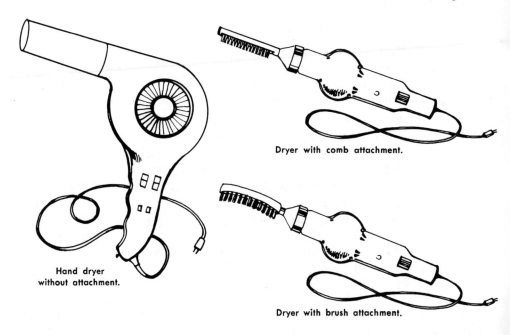

Dryer with comb attachment.

Hand dryer without attachment.

Dryer with brush attachment.

CAUTION. **When using the air-waver, the following precautions must be observed:**

1. Do not immerse air-waver in water.
2. Direct the stream of hot air away from the scalp.
3. Spray the hot air back and forth; avoid holding slotted nozzle of the dryer too long in one place.
4. Avoid having the comb attachment of the air-waver touch the scalp, as it may cause scalp burns.

COMBS AND BRUSHES

Both **metal combs** and those made of **hard rubber** are recommended for air-waving; it is a matter of preference. However, some artisans prefer metal combs, as they retain and transmit heat so that the hair can be reshaped in the shortest possible time. Styling combs are available with coarse teeth, and coarse and fine teeth.

Metal comb.

Hard rubber comb.

Styling brush.

Special **narrow styling hair brushes** are also used in air-waving. It is easier for the barber-stylist to brush the hair into the desired style with a narrow brush.

COSMETICS USED IN AIR-WAVING

The principal cosmetics used in air-waving include styling lotions, styling gels, hair and scalp conditioners, hair sprays and hair dressings.

IMPORTANT REMINDER

Manufacturers are constantly developing new products and improving existing cosmetics. Since these cosmetics vary both in composition and action on the hair, be guided by the manufacturer's directions or your instructor as to proper usage on client's hair and scalp.

Styling lotion.

Styling lotions. These cosmetics are applied after shampooing for the purpose of making the hair more manageable in air-waving. Having the consistency of a dense liquid, they may be applied with a plastic squeeze bottle or trigger (pump) action bottle.

Styling gels. Available as a semi-solid cosmetic, they are packaged in tubes and jars. Recommended for controlling and styling unruly hair.

Hair conditioners. Used either independently or as part of corrective treatment for dry and brittle hair.

Hair sprays. Applied from an aerosol or pressurized container to keep the finished hairstyle in place.

Hair dressings. Available as a liquid or gel in tubes or jars. Have the appearance of a non-greasy, milky white emulsion, and serve to dress the hair.

227

BASIC STEPS FOR AIR-WAVING
AIR-WAVER AND COMB TECHNIQUES

Preparation. To be proficient in air-waving, the barber-stylist must have handy everything that is required, such as supplies and equipment. Nothing is more disturbing to the client than to have the practitioner leave the chair to get something he or she has forgotten during preparations.

Styling of the hair with air-waver with **comb attachment** and a hand comb is usually done after the hair has been cut, shampooed and towel dried. The hair is left damp or moist.

Redraping client. It is customary to remove the wet towels and shampoo cape, and then redrape patron by adjusting the neck-strip and chair cloth (hair cloth) in the usual manner as for a regular haircut.

SIDE PART WITH A WAVY POMPADOUR

Instructions for a side part with a wavy pompadour follow:

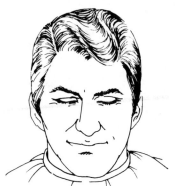

Side part with
wavy pompadour.

Procedure

1. **Styling lotion.** After the shampoo, the hair is towel dried and is left damp. A styling lotion is then lightly sprayed on and distributed evenly throughout the hair with the comb.

    Styling gel. If the hair is unruly and difficult to style, the styling gel is used instead of styling lotion. Place a small amount of the styling gel in the palm of the left hand, rub palms together, then smooth the gel on the hair with both palms. Comb gel through the hair until evenly distributed.

2. **Locate natural wave formation.** Comb hair in the direction of wave desired, then push edge of left hand towards the comb, adjust hair, then comb to determine best wave formation (Fig. 1).

3. **First ridge of first section.** Re-comb hair in the direction of the ultimate hairstyle (Fig. 2).

    Insert hand comb into the hair, **away** from the forehead, then insert teeth of the air-waver directly over the hand comb **towards** the forehead (Fig. 3). Draw hand comb to the left and air-waver to the right simultaneously, forming a ridge (Arrows in Fig. 3). Hold hair locked in this position for a short while until the **ridge** is definitely formed.

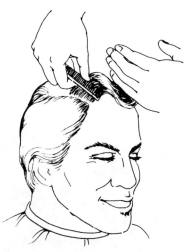

Fig. 1. Locating natural wave.

4. **Second section of first ridge.** Proceed with next section toward crown along the hair part. Insert the hand comb into second section of the hair (Fig. 4).

Insert the teeth of the air-waver directly over the teeth of the hand comb and draw the hand comb to the left and air-waver to the right simultaneously. Retain this position until the ridge is definitely formed (Fig. 5).

CAUTION. Care must be taken that this section of the ridge joins the first section without a break.

Fig. 2

5. **Second ridge of first section.** The hand comb and air-waver movement is just the **opposite** to that of the first ridge.

Insert hand comb into the hair away from the forehead (Fig. 6) and insert the teeth of the air-waver towards the forehead over the hand comb. Draw the hand comb towards the **right** and the air-waver towards the **left** (Fig 7), thus forming a ridge. Keep the implements in this position until the ridge is definitely formed.

Fig. 3

Fig. 4

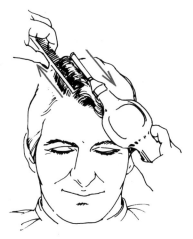

Fig. 5

Fig. 6

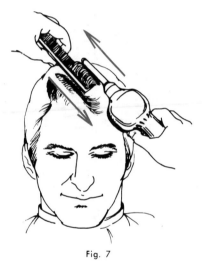

Fig. 7

6. **Second section of second ridge.** (Figs. 8 and 9). Repeat procedure outlined in Step 5 (Figs. 6 and 7).

    CAUTION. Care must be taken that this ridge joins the first section without a break in the ridge (Figs. 8 and 9). This completes the first and second ridges, thus completing the first complete wave. (Fig. 10, next page.)

7. **Third ridge.** If additional ridges and/or waves are required, repeat instructions outlined in Steps 3-6.

8. **Sides and back hair.** Comb hair neatly as desired.

9. **Final drying of hair.** Adjust the styling hair net (trainer) over the hair.

    The styling hair net protects the hair from being disarranged during the drying process. The drying may be done either with the regular hand dryer (Fig. 11) or with a pedestal or hood type dryer.

10. **Completion.** Remove the styling hair net, re-comb hair so that it will look natural and touch-up wherever necessary, as you would for a regular haircut.

11. **Clean-up.** Clean up work area. It is essential that all implements used are sanitized and everything is put back in its proper place.

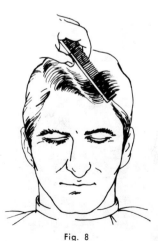

Fig. 8

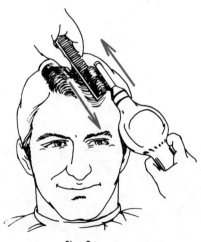

Fig. 9

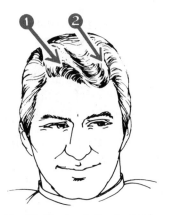

Fig. 10. Showing first and second
ridges of the completed wave.

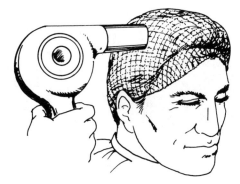

Fig. 11. Drying the hair
with hand dryer.

METHOD OF TYING KNOT IN HAIR NET (TRAINER)

1. Pick up center of longest edge of hair net.
2. Start knot about 5 inches from top for good form.
3. Wind strand loosely around tip of index finger.
4. Pull tip of net through loop, slip off finger and tighten knot.
5. Place or drape hair net around head, tie the two loose ends into a knot at nape. Loose end of knot at forehead is tucked **under** hair net.

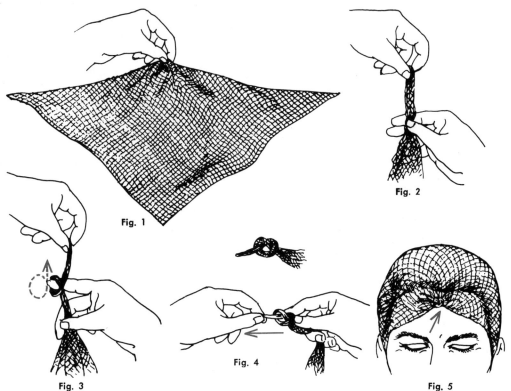

Fig. 1

Fig. 2

Fig. 3

Fig. 4

Fig. 5

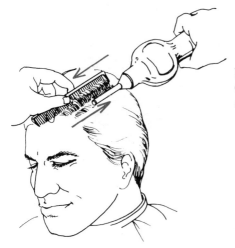

CREATING FULLNESS WITH COMB AND AIR-WAVER

To achieve hair lifts or fullness to various parts of the head, the hair must be slightly damp. Apply a light spray of styling lotion to assist in creating the desired hairstyle.

Lifting Hair Above Part With Comb

1. **Left side part.** Starting at the front section of the head, the hand comb is inserted into the hair about an inch and one-half from the part. Draw it towards the part a little to one side, insert the air-waver over the comb and draw the comb in opposite direction to form a ridge. Hold the comb in this position until a firm ridge has been formed. Continue towards the crown until the entire length of the part is completed.

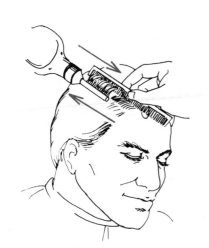

2. **Right side part.** The procedure is exactly the same as that for the left side part, with the exception that the hand comb is held in the right hand and the air-waver is controlled by the left hand. However, the waving should start at the crown and worked forward towards the face.

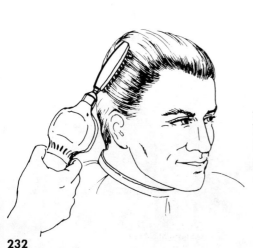

BLOWER WITH BRUSH ATTACHMENT

Brush attachment to the blower may be used to **smooth down stubborn hair** at the sides, back and crown areas of the head. Brush the hair slowly and firmly in the direction of the style desired. Repeat this movement as many times as necessary to achieve the desired results.

To control unruly hair a styling gel should be applied prior to using the blower with brush attachment.

COMB AND BLOWER (DRYER) TECHNIQUE

Comb and blower technique is another method of air-waving.

After the hair has been shampooed and left damp, a styling lotion is applied and combed through the hair. The following procedure may be used:

1. **Lift along left hair part.** To create a lift or a little height along the left hair part, start at the front of the head and work towards the crown.

    Insert the hand comb about an inch and one-half from the part and draw the comb a little to the back and towards the part simultaneously. This will create a ridge (Fig. 1). Adjust the blower to hot and spray the hot air back and forth until a soft ridge has been formed.

    CAUTION. Direct the hot air to the ridge and not to the scalp, as it may cause discomfort to the patron.
    a) **Second and third sections.** Repeat the instructions outlined above.

2. **High forward front.** Insert the hand comb from one-half to two inches, depending upon the height of the front hair desired. Draw comb a little to one side and toward the forehead to create a high ridge (Fig. 2). Spray hot air from the blower back and forth along the forehead until a high soft ridge has been created.

3. **Lift along right hair part.** To create a lift along the right hair part, it is advisable to hold the hand comb with the right hand and the blower with the left hand. The procedure is the same as previously outlined for creating a **lift for the left side part.**

4. **Final steps.** After the hair has been brushed and combed into desired style, follow the same procedure as previously outlined in **Air-waver and Comb Techniques.**

Fig. 1. Lift for height along left side part.

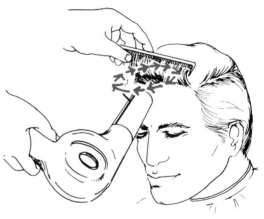

Fig. 2. Create a high front.

Fig. 3. Lift for height along right side part.

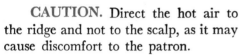

233

SHADOW WAVE WITH COMB AND BLOWER

A **shadow wave** is the same as a regular wave with low ridges. To accomplish a shadow wave, a hand comb and blower may be used.

Hair that has a natural wave will more readily respond to shadow **waving** than hair that is straight.

Shadow waving is recommended for the front and sides of the head.

PROCEDURE

1. Shampoo, towel dry and comb hair in the direction of the ultimate hairstyle. Apply a small amount of styling lotion; add more as needed. Warm water may be used instead of styling lotion.

Fig. 1. Shadow waving—
creating a shallow wave.

2. Insert hand comb about two to two and one-half inches from the hairline and draw the comb forward, a little to one side, so that the hair will form a shallow wave (Fig. 1). If necessary, when the wave does not form readily, the hair can be guided into a wave effect by pressing with the index finger or middle finger of the right hand. After the wave has been formed, apply hot air from the blower in a rotating motion. Maintain this position until the wave has formed.

3. After the waving has been done, adjust styling hair net, dry and finish the hairstyle in the usual manner.

BRUSH AND BLOWER TECHNIQUE

The use of a narrow brush and a blower is another method of styling the hair. To be truly a professional, the barber-stylist must know how to use all the implements available. Many times the stylist will prefer the use of a brush rather than a comb in order to achieve a certain effect.

CREATE FULLNESS

In areas where fullness is desired, or to give contour to the head, the hair is first lifted with a brush, hot air from the blower is sprayed to the lifted hair and then softly molded into the hairstyle desired with the comb and brush.

Fullness—Top side of part.

Before styling is started, the hair is shampooed and towel dried, leaving the hair damp. Then apply styling lotion, comb through hair and proceed with the styling.

Fullness at Top Side of Part

Brush top hair away from part, then with a twist of the wrist draw brush slightly toward part, creating a slight ridge or height. Blow hot air along the ridge, moving the blower back and forth. Avoid blowing hot air to the scalp. Repeat section by section, working from front to back of the head.

Fullness on Right and Left Side of Head

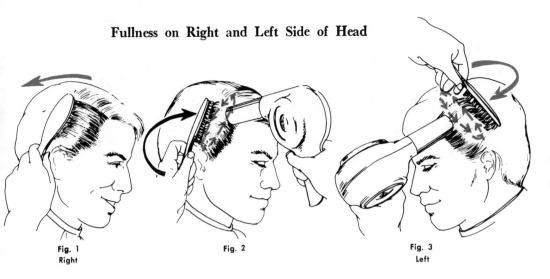

Fig. 1
Right

Fig. 2

Fig. 3
Left

Right side. To create fullness at the right side of the head, brush hair towards the back slightly (Fig. 1) and then with a twist of the wrist, turn and push the brush forward, creating a lift (Fig. 2). Blow hot air to the area for a few moments or until the hair is set in position.

Left side. Repeat same procedure as for right side of head (Fig. 3).

Fullness for the Front Hair

A brush may be used to create a high lift at the front hairline. Draw the brush underneath the hair, and with a quick turn of the wrist turn the brush upward. Spray hot air with the blower in a back and forth movement until the hair is partially dry. Remove brush by drawing it outward. The hair is then combed with the hair ends blending with the rest of the hairstyle. A shadow wave may be created with the hair ends behind the lifted hair.

Fullness—for front hair.

CROWN SWIRL

First, comb the crown hair in a swirl effect, with the grain or in the direction of hairstyle desired. Then brush hair slightly forward in the same direction as previously done with the comb. While brushing, twist the wrist inward and draw hair slightly in reverse, thus creating fullness in the area. (Fig. 1 next page.) Blow hot air to the area with a rotating movement, until the desired fullness has been achieved. Direct the hot air through the hair, avoiding hot air application directly to the scalp.

Repeat this procedure on various parts of the crown until the swirl effect has been achieved.

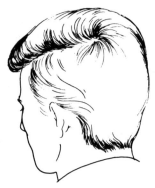

Fig. 1. Swirl fullness in the crown area.

Fig. 2. Swirl effects on the top and front areas.

To achieve swirl effects on top and front areas of the head (Fig. 2), the same procedure may be followed.

AIR-WAVING WOMEN'S HAIR

It is performed in the same manner as finger-waving, using an electric air-waver comb and styling comb.

The hair is styled after it has been cut, shampooed, and towel dried.

To achieve ridges and waves on various parts of the head, the hair must be slightly damp. Apply a light spray of styling lotion to assist in creating the desired hairstyle.

It is important to locate the natural wave formation in the hair. Comb the hair in the direction of the wave desired. This will help to establish the natural hair growth pattern (Fig. 1). Comb the hair in the direction of the planned hairstyle. Comb the hair with air-waver until it is dry enough to hold a wave.

Fig. 1. Combing hair in direction of wave desired.

SHAPING HAIR WITH COMB

1. **Right side part.** Starting at the front of the head, insert the styling comb into the hair about 1½″ from the part. Draw the styling comb towards the back. Insert the air-waver under the comb and draw the air-waver comb towards the face to form a ridge. Hold both combs in this position until a firm ridge has been formed (Fig. 2). Continue towards the crown until the entire length of the ridge is completed.

Fig. 2. Forming ridge.

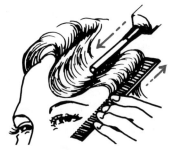

Fig. 3. Forming second ridge.

Fig. 4. Finished style.

Form the second ridge by starting at the crown and work towards the the front. The ridge and shaping is made just the reverse of the first ridge (Fig. 3).

Support the completed ridgeline with the styling comb while the air-waver comb lifts and designs the pattern.

2. **Left side part.** The procedure is exactly the same as that for the right side part, with the exception that the hand comb is held in the right hand and the air-waver is controlled by the left hand. However, the waving should start at the crown and work forward towards the face.

A finished wave is formed with the air-waver comb and styling comb, taking advantage of the natural waving pattern of the hair (Fig. 4).

AIR-CURLING

Air-Curling with Round Brush

Air-curling is most successful on hair that is naturally curly or has received a permanent wave. The basis for all successful air-curling styling is carefully planned hair cutting. In order to properly receive an air-curling service, hair should be cut with tapered ends. Successful air-curling is extremely difficult on hair with blunt-cut hair ends.

DRYER (BLOWER) AND BRUSHES

Hand dryer

Large round brush.

Narrow rounded-shoulder brush.

Narrow round brush.

Wide rounded-shoulder brush.

The following technique is offered as one method of creating a natural-looking, easy-to-wear, informal style with a brush and blower. (Your instructor's methods are equally correct.)

PROCEDURE

1. Shampoo and towel dry the hair.
2. Properly cut the hair, leaving tapered ends.
3. Apply styling lotion and/or conditioner.
4. Pre-plan the style. Start at the crown or top of the head, as desired. Section the hair, pick up a wide strand, and comb through (Fig. 1).
5. Bring the comb out to the hair ends and insert the brush. Brush through the strand, bringing the brush out to the ends.
6. Roll the hair with the brush, making a complete downward turn, away from the face, until the brush rests on the scalp. Maintain this position and start the blower. Direct the blower very slowly through the curl in a back-and-forth movement (Fig. 2). When the hair section is completely dry, release the brush with a rounded movement.

    Use clippies to secure each curl as it is completed and to hold it in place until it is cooled off.

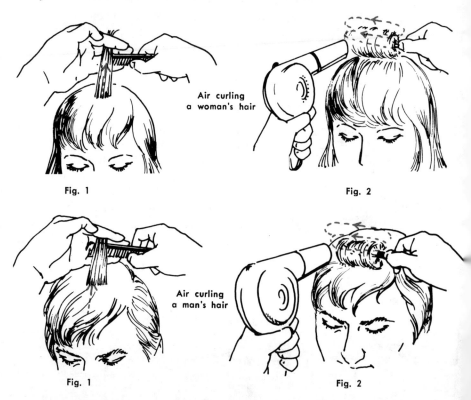

Air curling a woman's hair

Fig. 1   Fig. 2

Air curling a man's hair

Fig. 1   Fig. 2

7. Continue making curls in the same manner across the crown and back of the head. Clip each curl as completed.

    Shape the neckline curls with a comb, or make pin curls on the nape for a finished, close-to-the-head look.

In air-curling it is essential that when the hairstyle is completed the scalp be thoroughly dry. The hairstyle will not hold if the scalp is damp.

Complete the styling with a light application of lacquer to give shine and holding power to the hair.

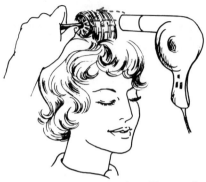

To give the crown hair a slight lift, a small round brush is used. The dryer is kept on the move from side to side along the curl. Secure each curl with clippies as it is completed.

PAGE BOY EFFECT.
Curl hair under.

Front hair.

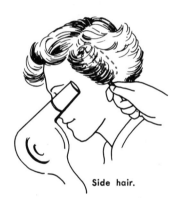

Side hair.

SMOOTH TOP WITH FLIP.
To create a smooth top with flip, the hair ends are lifted by placing brush close to scalp. Rotate brush. As the brush rotates, the hot air is directed to the base within the cupped area.

POPULAR AIR-CURLING STYLES

SAFETY PRECAUTIONS AND REMINDERS

1. **Styling dryer.** Move moderately hot air back and forth on the hair and away from the scalp. Avoid holding the dryer too long in one place.
2. **Metal comb.** To avoid scalp burns, keep teeth of heated metal comb away from the scalp.
3. **Combs.** Depending on the barber-stylist's preference, use either hard rubber or metal combs.
4. **Implements.** After they are used, keep implements clean and sanitized.
5. **Supplies.** Clean up work bench. Put everything back in its proper place.
6. For best results, patron's hair should be from two to three inches in length.
7. Shampoo hair and leave it slightly damp.
8. If desired, apply a styling gel, lotion or very warm water before, and sometimes during, the waving.
9. The hair must be thoroughly cooled before it is combed out. This may be accomplished by switching the dryer to cold and cooling the hair that has been dried.
10. Make sure that the blow dryer is perfectly clean and free of dirt, grease and hair, before using.
11. The air intake at the back of the dryer must be kept clear at all times.

QUESTIONS ON AIR-WAVING

1. What is air-waving?
2. By what other names is air-waving known?
3. List the equipment and implements used in air-waving.
4. Name two kinds of electrical styling dryers.
5. How does the barber-stylist control the air temperature of the styling dryer?
6. What three steps usually precede air-waving?
7. When towel drying the hair, in what condition is it to be left for air-waving?
8. In air-waving styling, what is generally used to make the hair more manageable?
9. In air-waving, what is used to control unruly hair?
10. In creating a ridge, to what area is the hot air directed?
11. In creating a ridge and wave that require more than one section, what should be their final appearance?
12. How is the fullness created at the sides of the head?
13. When and why is hair spray used in air-waving?
14. For what type of hair is a conditioner recommended?
15. How is a styling dryer blowing hot air used?
16. When using a metal comb, why must it be kept away from the scalp?

Chapter 18
CURLING IRON TECHNIQUES

INTRODUCTION

The barber-stylist who hopes to be successful in the modern, style-conscious world of hair grooming must maintain a knowledge and understanding of all methods employed in hairstyling. The art or technique of styling hair with the aid of curling irons, requiring no setting or styling creams or lotions, is in great demand in the modern shop. The mastery of this art or technique is a basic requirement for success as a barber-stylist.

IMPLEMENTS

Thermal curling iron styling requires the use of three implements in addition to the regular barber-styling tools: (1) a metal comb; (2) an electric dryer, and (3) electric curling irons.

1. Metal combs are preferred because they can withstand and retain heat.
2. The hand dryer is used to prepare the shampooed hair for styling and, in conjunction with a styling brush or comb, can help form the base design of a style very quickly. Curling irons and combs are then used to complete the style.
3. The curling irons must be made of the best quality steel in order that they hold an even temperature during the curling, styling process. The curling or styling portion of the iron is composed of two parts: (a) the rod (prong), and (b) the shell (groove or bowl).
   a) The rod is a solid steel, perfectly round rod.
   b) The shell is perfectly round with the inside grooved so that the rod can rest in it when the irons are closed.

HEAT TESTING IRONS

Before discussing the manipulative techniques, a word of caution must be offered. Always heat test the irons before applying to the hair.

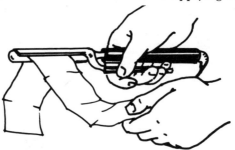

Clamp the heated iron over a tissue neck strip and hold for five seconds. If the paper scorches or turns brown, the iron is too hot. Decrease the temperature before using. It should be noted that fine, lightened or badly damaged hair can withstand less heat than normal hair.

CURLING IRON MANIPULATIONS

The following is a series of basic manipulative movements for using heated curling irons. Most other movements employed when using curling irons in hairstyling are adaptations or derivations of these basic movements.

The method of holding the iron is a matter of the personal preference of the artisan. The technique used should be the one which gives the practitioner the greatest ease, comfort and facility of movement. The following series shows a grip with only the little finger used for opening the clamp. Some barber-stylists prefer to use the little finger plus the ring finger for this purpose. Either method is equally correct.

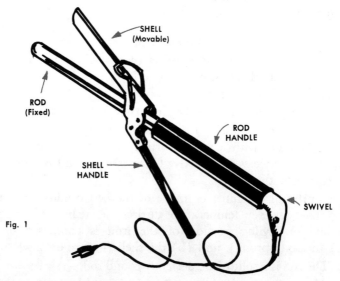

Fig. 1

Fig. 1— An electric curling iron with the various parts indicated.

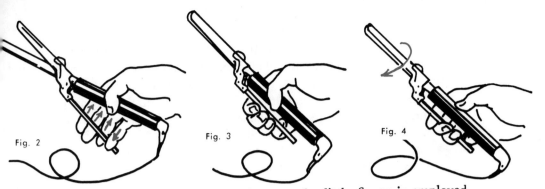

Fig. 2—When holding the curling iron for use, the little finger is employed
      to open the clamp.

Fig. 3—Three forefingers are used to close clamp and manipulate iron.

Fig. 4—Thumb has been shifted to aid in turning and manipulating iron.

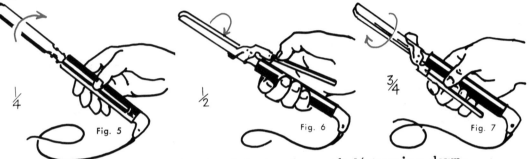

Fig. 5--The clamp has been closed and the iron has made ¼ turn in a down-
      ward direction. A swivel at the base of the shaft handle permits the
      iron to turn without twisting the electric cord.

Fig. 6--The iron has now made a ½ downward turn and the thumb has been
      employed to ease open the clamp and relax the tension on the hair.

Fig. 7--The thumb is now used to continue to turn the iron to ¾ of the
      complete rotation.

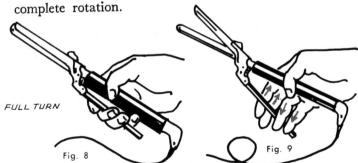

Fig. 8--The iron has made a full turn and the fingers have been brought back
      to their original position.

Fig. 9--An alternate method of holding the iron, with the little finger and the
      ring finger used to open the clamp.

    Note: Those barber-stylists who wish to use the stove-heated curling irons
will find that the techniques of performance are very similar to those presented
here for electric curling irons.

CONSTANT PRACTICE REQUIRED

Constant practice in manipulating curling irons is required in order to develop any degree of efficiency. Three exercises must be performed over and over until perfected.

1. Since it is most important to develop a smooth rotating action, constantly practice turning the iron while opening and closing it at regular intervals. Dexterity must be developed in rotating the irons in both directions: a) downward (toward the practitioner) and b) upward (away from the practitioner). Fig. 1.

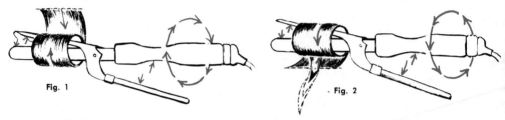

Fig. 1   Fig. 2

2. It is important to practice releasing the hair to prevent binding. Practice opening and closing the irons in a quick clicking action to prevent binding.

3. Practice guiding the hair strand into the center of the curl as you rotate the iron. This exercise results in the end of the strand being firmly in the center of the curl. Fig.2.

THERMAL-IRON CURLING TECHNIQUES ON SHORT HAIR

The method set forth should be used in iron curling short hair only.

The base of each curl is formed by sectioning and parting to conform with the size of the curl desired. It is important to consider hair length, density and texture. The base is usually about 1½-2 inches in width and approximately ½ inch in depth.

After the base is sectioned off the hair in the curl section must be combed smoothly straight out from the scalp. The hair must be combed smoothly in order that the heat and tension be the same for all hairs in the section. Loose hairs may result in an uneven and ragged curl.

1. Insert the iron with the rod down, close the shell and hold it at the base for approximately 5 seconds to heat the hair. Slide iron up approximately one inch from the scalp. Fig. 1.

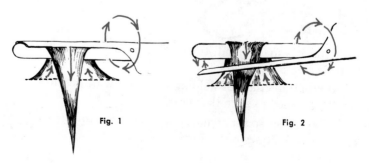

Fig. 1   Fig. 2

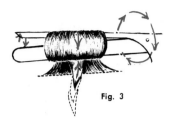

Fig. 3

Fig. 4

2. Hold the ends of the hair strand with the thumb and two fingers of one hand, with a medium degree of tension. Turn the iron downward (toward the practitioner) with the other hand. Fig. 2.

3. Open and close the iron rapidly, as you turn, to prevent binding and creases in the hair caused by the shell. Guide the ends of the strand into the center of the curl as you rotate the iron. Fig. 3.

4. The result of this procedure will be a smooth, finished curl with the ends firmly fixed in the center. Fig. 4.

THERMAL-IRON CURLING — MEDIUM HAIR

Section and form the base of the curl as described earlier.

1. The hair is inserted into the open iron at the scalp, the hair is pulled over the rod in the direction of the curl and the shell is closed. Hold in this position for about 5 seconds to heat the hair, and then slide the iron up about one inch from the scalp. The shell must be on top. Fig. 1.

2. The iron is rotated downward, ½ revolution, pull the end of the strand over the rod to the left and direct it toward center of the curl. Fig. 2.

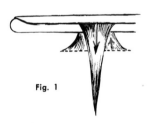

Fig. 1

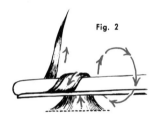

Fig. 2

3. Complete the revolution of the iron and continue directing the ends toward the center. Fig. 3.

4. Make another complete revolution of the iron. The entire strand has been curled with the exception of the end. Enlarge the curl by opening the shell. Insert the end of the curl in the opening created between the shell and the rod. Fig. 4.

5. Close the shell and slide the iron toward the handle. This technique will move ends of strand into center of the curl. Rotate iron several times to even out the distribution of the hair in the curl. Fig. 5.

Fig. 3

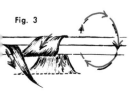

Fig. 4

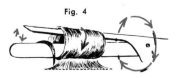

Fig. 5

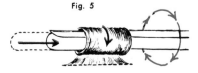

245

REMOVING THE CURL FROM THE IRON

During the curling process the comb is employed to protect the client's scalp from possible burns.

When the curl is formed and the ends are freed from between the rod and the shell, one complete revolution of the iron is made inside the curl. This final revolution is made to smooth the ends and to loosen the hair away from the

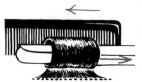

iron. The comb is then employed in conjunction with the iron to remove the curl from the iron. The iron is drawn slowly in one direction while the comb holds the curl steady and slowly and carefully draws in the opposite direction. Thus the curl is removed from the iron.

VOLUME THERMAL-IRON CURLS

In order to create volume or lift in the finished hairstyle, the barber-stylist develops volume curls. The degree of lift desired will determine the type of volume curls being used.

Volume Base Curls

This type of curl is developed to provide maximum life or volume since the curl is placed very high on its base.

Section off the base in the manner previously described. Hold the curl strand up at a 135° angle. Slide the iron over the strand about ½ inch from the scalp. Wrap the strand over the rod with medium tension. Maintain in this position approximately 5 seconds to heat the strand and set the base. Roll the curl in the usual manner and place it firmly, **forward and high on its base.**

Full Base Curls—designed to provide strong curls with full lift.

Section off the base as described. Hold the hair strand up at a 125° angle. Slide the iron over the hair strand about ½ inch from the scalp. Wrap the strand over the rod with medium tension. Maintain in this position about 5 seconds to heat strand and set the base. Roll the curl in the usual manner and place it firmly in **the center of its base.**

Full Base	One-Half Off Base	Off Base

Half Base Curls—designed to provide strong curls with moderate lift.

Section off the base as described. Hold the hair at a 90° angle. Slide the iron over the hair strand about ½ inch from the scalp. Wrap the strand over the rod with medium tension. Maintain in this position about 5 seconds to heat strand and set base. Roll the curl in the usual manner and place it **half off its base.**

Off Base Curls—designed to provide strong curls with only slight lift.

Section off the base as described. Hold the hair at a 70° angle. Slide the iron over the hair strand about ½ inch from the scalp. Wrap the strand over the rod with medium tension. Maintain in this position for about 5 seconds to heat strand and set base. Roll the curl in the usual manner and place it **completely off its base.**

HELPFUL HINTS ON IRON CURL STYLING

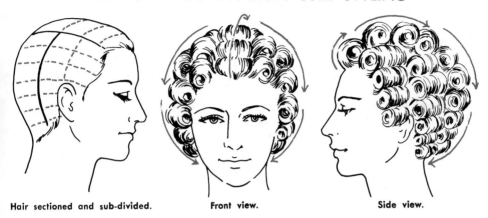

Hair sectioned and sub-divided.

Front view.

Side view.

Head completely curled with thermal roller curls, also called "style" curls.

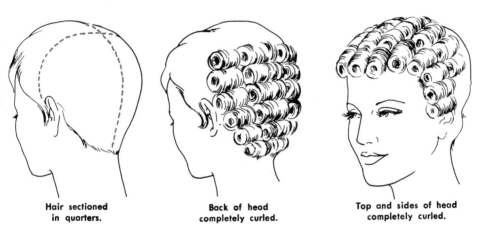

Hair sectioned in quarters.

Back of head completely curled.

Top and sides of head completely curled.

ARRANGING THE HAIR IN A SUITABLE HAIRSTYLE

To style the hair into a suitable hairstyle, brush the hair, working up from the neckline. Push the waves and curls into place as you progress over the entire head.

If the hairstyle is to be finished with curls, do the bottom curls last.

REVIEW QUESTIONS

CURLING IRON TECHNIQUES

1. What is thermal waving and curling?
2. What are the two parts of the styling portion of the irons?
3. What degree of heat should be used on lightened, fine, or badly damaged hair?
4. How are the irons tested for desirable temperature?
5. In what position should the irons be held?
6. What type of combs must be used in iron curling?
7. What are volume iron curls used for?

Chapter 19

PERMANENT (CHEMICAL) WAVING FOR MEN

INTRODUCTION

Men's hair fashions and techniques have undergone drastic changes in recent years. Men have become more hair fashion and style conscious. They have become more and more interested in getting away from the flat, "plastered down" look and have become interested in individualized styling. Longer hair, waves, color and directed lines have become important elements in modern hair grooming.

With many men it is necessary that curls or waves be imparted to the hair in order that it be properly fashioned. These curls and waves are developed by the relatively inexpensive but very effective process of chemical permanent waving.

Permanent waving for men is not concerned with large curls or high styling. Rather, it is employed to remove flatness and to give or add body or fullness to the hair and help to develop a personalized "contoured" look.

PRINCIPAL ACTIONS IN PERMANENT WAVING

The procedure of permanent waving involves two major actions on the hair, namely:

1. Physical action
   a) The wrapping of hair around rods
2. Chemical action
   a) Processing—softening the hair
   b) Neutralizing—rehardening the hair into its new shape

Knowing just what takes place as the hair is wrapped around the rods, the chemical action of the waving solution when applied to the hair, and how the neutralizer rehardens the hair in its newly formed position, is vital to successful permanent waving.

PHYSICAL ACTION

Wrapping. This physical action consists of wrapping the hair around the rods without stretching and with an absolute minimum of tension. By being so wrapped, the hair can expand when completely saturated by the chemical solution during processing.

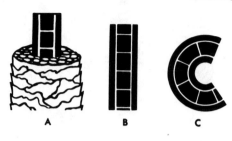

A. Each hair strand is composed of many poly-peptide chains. This series of illustrations shows the behavior of one such chain.

B. Hair before processing. Chemical bonds (links) give hair its strength and firmness.

C. Hair wound on rod. The hair bends to the curvature and size of the rod.

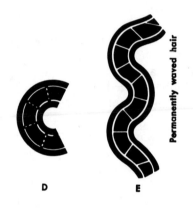

D. During processing, waving solution breaks the chemical bonds (links), permitting the hair to adjust to the curvature of the rod while in this softened condition.

E. The neutralizer re-forms the chemical bonds (links) and rehardens the hair, thus creating the permanent wave.

Hair develops and maintains its natural form by means of physical and chemical cross-bonds in the cortical layer, which hold the hair fibers in position and give the hair its strength and firmness. These physical (hydrogen) and chemical (sulfur) bonds must be broken before the shape or contour of the hair can be changed.

Processing. The physical bonds are much the weaker of the two types of bonds and are easily broken by the shampooing and rinsing process. However, the chemical action of the permanent waving solution is required in order to break the chemical bonds and thus soften the hair. This chemical action permits rearrangement of the inner structure of the hair so that it can assume the form of the curlers around which it is wound.

Neutralizing. After the hair has assumed the desired shape, it must be chemically neutralized so that the hydrogen and sulfur cross-bonds in the cortical layer are re-formed. This action also rehardens the hair into its newly curved form. When this action is completed, the hair is unwrapped from the rods and assumes its newly curled formation.

SCALP AND HAIR ANALYSIS

A very important step before giving a permanent wave is to make a **correct** and **careful analysis** of the client's scalp and hair condition. The intelligent and professional approach is to learn all the possible facts about the client, such as:

1. Scalp condition
2. Hair porosity
3. Hair texture
4. Hair elasticity
5. Hair density
6. Hair length

SCALP CONDITION

Scalp examination. The scalp should be examined very carefully. Abrasions on the scalp can make permanent waving dangerous to a client. An irritated scalp and badly damaged hair are both signs that a permanent wave should be postponed until the condition has been corrected.

HAIR POROSITY

Porosity of the hair is its ability to absorb fluids or liquids. Since water changes some of the qualities of the hair, this analysis should be made before the shampoo, when the hair is dry.

The ability of hair to absorb is very closely related to the speed with which hair can accept any fluid. This speed of absorption determines the degree of hair porosity. When analyzed properly, porosity can be a measure for determining the strength of waving solution required. Unless pre-permanent analysis is closely observed, damaged hair may result.

The **processing time** for any permanent wave depends much more on **hair porosity** than on any other factor. The more porous the hair, the less processing time it takes, and a milder waving solution is required. **The degree at which hair absorbs the permanent waving solution is related to its porosity, regardless of texture.**

Hair porosity is **affected** by such factors as the client's health, climate, altitude, humidity, excessive exposure to sun and wind, and the continued use of harsh shampoos and other products.

Porosity classified. Before giving a permanent wave, determine the degree of porosity. The various degrees of porosity are discussed in the chapter on hair.

Porosity test. In order to test accurately for porosity, use three different areas: front hairline, in front of ears and near the crown.

Grasp a small strand of dry hair and comb smoothly. Hold the ends firmly with the thumb and index finger of one hand and slide the fingers of the other hand from the ends toward the scalp. If the fingers do not slide easily or if the hair ruffles up as your fingers slide down the strand, **the hair is porous.**

Testing for hair porosity

The more ruffles formed, the more porous is the hair. The less ruffles formed, the less porous is the hair.

If the fingers slide easily and no ruffles are formed, the cuticle layer lays close to the hair shaft. This type of hair is least porous, is most **resistant** and will require a **longer processing time.**

HAIR TEXTURE

Hair texture refers to the individual size of the hair strand and its degree of coarseness or fineness. **The texture and porosity are judged together in determining the processing time.** Although porosity is the most important of the two, texture does have a part in judging processing time. However, when coarse hair is very porous, it will process faster than fine hair that is **not** porous.

COARSE

MEDIUM

FINE

Hair texture should also be considered in deciding the size of the **wave pattern.** The texture of the client's hair must be taken into consideration when planning a hairstyle.

Variations in hair texture are due to:

1. **Diameter of the hair shaft:** coarse, medium, fine or very fine
2. **Feel of the hair:** harsh, soft or wiry

HAIR ELASTICITY

Hair elasticity is a very important factor to consider when giving a permanent wave. Elasticity is the ability of the hair to stretch and contract. All hair is elastic, but its elasticity ranges from very good to poor. Without elasticity, there will be **no curl in the hair.** The greater the degree of elasticity, the longer the wave will remain in the hair, because less relaxation of the hair occurs.

The elastic qualities of hair will determine the success of a permanent wave.

1. Hair with **very good elasticity** will produce a resilient curl or firm wave.
2. Hair with **good elasticity** will produce a curl with average resilience.
3. Hair with **fairly good elasticity** will produce a slightly less resilient curl.
4. Hair with **poor elasticity,** also known as **limp** hair, will result in a very small amount of resiliency in the curl.

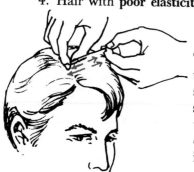

A simple test for elastic qualities of the hair. Take a single dry hair and hold it between the thumb and forefinger of each hand. **Slowly** stretch it between them. The further it can be stretched without breaking, the more elastic is the hair. If the elasticity is good, the hair slowly contracts after stretching. Hair with **poor** elasticity will break quickly and easily when stretched.

Testing for elasticity

Normal dry hair is capable of being stretched about one-fifth its length, and will spring back when released. However, wet hair can be stretched 40% to 50% of its length. Porous hair will stretch more than hair with poor porosity.

Poor elasticity. Signs of poor elasticity are: limpness, sponginess and hair that tangles easily.

Limp hair will **not** develop a firm, strong wave. However, there are special waving solutions available for this type of hair. Limp hair requires a **smaller** diameter rod than hair having good elasticity.

HAIR DENSITY

The density of the hair is the number of hairs per square inch on the scalp. Density has nothing to do with the hair's texture. **Smaller blockings** (subsections) and **larger rods** are often required for thickly growing hair. However, if the **hair is thin** per square inch, **smaller blockings** and **smaller (thinner) rods** are required in order to form a good wave pattern close to the head.

Avoid large blockings on a thin hair growth, as the strain may cause breakage.

HAIR LENGTH

Hair length is another important factor that must be considered. Waving hair of average length presents no real problem. However, if the client wears his hair six inches or longer, a number of waving and wrapping problems may be created. Because of its excessive length, the hair cannot be wrapped close enough to develop a good, strong wave pattern near the scalp. In addition, the extra pull of the excessive hair weight may pull the wave out of the hair very quickly. Therefore, in selecting a hairstyle it is very important to carefully consider hair length, in addition to its texture, elasticity and density.

CURLING RODS

Proper selection of curling rods is essential for successful permanent waving.

The **size of the rods** controls the shape of the hair during the waving process. Rods are made of a canvas and plastic composition, and they vary in diameter, length and design.

Curling rods are available in various **lengths:** long, medium and short (3½" to 1¾" in length).

They also come in varying **thicknesses.** These range in diameter size from large to very thin (size ¾" to ⅛").

All rods must have some means of securing the hair and the rod into the desired position to prevent the curl from unwinding.

TYPES OF RODS

There are two types of rods in general use: straight and concave.

Straight rods are made so that their circumference and diameter are almost the same throughout their entire length. They may, however, taper very slightly toward the center.

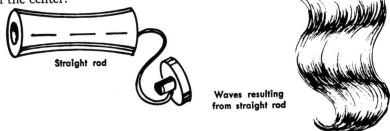

Straight rod

Waves resulting from straight rod

This type of rod usually creates the same size wave throughout the entire hair strand and length of the rod.

Large, straight rods are usually employed to give a "body wave". They permit the formation of a strong permanent with a large enough wave to be dressed into any hairstyle desired. The "body wave" is usually the type of permanent wave desired by most men as a foundation for continued styling.

Concave rods are usually thinner in diameter than the straight rods. They are formed with a smaller circumference in the center area, which gradually increases to their largest circumference at both ends.

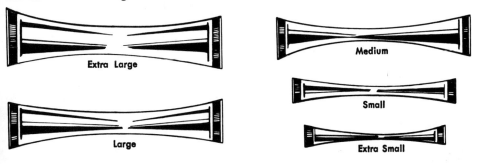

Extra Large

Medium

Large

Small

Extra Small

Concave rods are used when a definite wave pattern, close to the head, is desired.

When hair is wound on a rod, the outside hair of the winding forms a larger wave than the hair next to the rod. This creates a tighter wave at the hair ends, which gradually becomes slightly wider as it nears the scalp.

Waves resulting from concave rod

CHEMICAL SOLUTIONS

For success in permanent waving, it is absolutely essential that the curling rods and lotion be properly selected. The chemical compounds contained within the waving lotion will have an important influence on the procedure to be followed in the waving process.

WAVING SOLUTIONS

Permanent waving solutions in general use today have as their basic ingredient ammonium thioglycolate (commonly referred to as "Thio") that permanently changes the structure of the hair. This compound is prepared by combining ammonia and thioglycolic acid. Other ingredients included in the waving solution may be lanolin and its derivatives, wetting agents, protein and conditioners. Excess ammonia is added to make the solution alkaline.

Preconditioning. Over-porous or damaged hair may require a preconditioning treatment before the application of waving lotion. Special fillers that contain protein are now available which condition the hair and equalize its porosity. Some fillers also contain lanolin and cholesterol, which may help to protect the hair against the harshness of the waving solution.

Conditioners. The alkaline permanent waving solution has a tendency to remove natural oils from the hair, causing it to dry out rapidly through loss of moisture. Mineral oils, lanolin or lanolin derivatives are added to the waving lotion, or may be used in a separate application, to replace natural oils. The moisture content is somewhat preserved and the feel and appearance of the hair are improved by permitting the conditioner to remain in the hair after the solution has been rinsed out.

Strengths of waving solutions. The strength of the waving solution can be adjusted by either increasing its pH (alkalinity) or by increasing the amount of active ingredient (ammonium thioglycolate). To adjust the pH of the solution, the ammonia content is either increased or decreased. However, it should not be increased to exceed pH 9.6, which is a strong solution.

Most manufacturers of permanent waving products market three or more strengths, such as the following:

1. **Weak or mild strength**—damaged or porous hair
2. **Average strength**—normal hair (having good porosity)
3. **Stronger strength**—resistant hair (less porosity)

Important reminder. Manufacturers of permanent waving products are constantly improving their formulas. It is advisable to follow their directions explicitly.

NEUTRALIZERS

Neutralizers contain peroxide, lanolin and other special ingredients. They come in various forms, such as liquids, powders and crystals. Depending on the method of application, they may have a thick consistency and may have to be diluted. **Conditioners** are often incorporated in the prepared liquid neutralizer to give some protection to the hair.

SECTIONING AND BLOCKING

Sectioning is dividing the head into uniform working panels.

Blocking (sub-sectioning) is the subdividing of panels into uniform individual rectangular rod sections. Uniform wave patterns depend on the following:

1. Uniformly arranged sections
2. Equally subdivided sections (blockings)
3. Clean and uniform partings (length and width)

The size of the blockings is determined by the diameter of the rods, in addition to the density and texture of the hair.

Depending on the pattern used in hair sectioning, the number of hair blockings may vary with each patron.

The **average blocking** for a standard wave should match the diameter (size) of the rod being used. However, the length of the blocking can be a little bit shorter but not longer than the length of the rod. If the rod is shorter than the length of the blocking, the hair will tend to slip off the ends of the rod during winding.

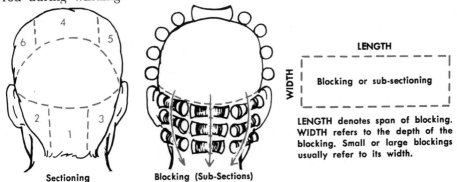

Sectioning   Blocking (Sub-Sections)

LENGTH denotes span of blocking. WIDTH refers to the depth of the blocking. Small or large blockings usually refer to its width.

Wave formation. The **size of the rods and blockings** determines the size of the wave formation. **Processing time** has no bearing on the size of the wave pattern. Thicker hair with good elasticity gives a deeper wave formation. Thinner hair, usually fine in texture, gives a more shallow wave. The loss or increase of elasticity also affects the depth of the wave pattern.

SUGGESTED BLOCKINGS AND ROD SIZES

Although the hair elasticity and texture must both be considered in the choice of rods, the texture should be the determining factor.

Coarse hair—good elasticity. Thickly growing hair requires smaller (narrower) blockings and larger rods to permit better arrangements for a definite wave pattern.

Medium hair—average elasticity. Medium or average textured hair requires smaller blockings and medium size rods.

255

Fine hair—poor elasticity. Thin hair requires smaller blockings and smaller (thinner) rods to prevent strain or breakage, and to form a good wave pattern close to the head.

Damaged hair—very poor elasticity. Use smaller hair sections and larger rods. If the damaged hair is fine in texture, use smaller hair blockings and medium rods.

Hair in nape area. Use smaller blockings and smaller rods.

Long hair. To permanently wave hair longer than six inches, wrap it smoothly and close to the scalp in smaller blockings. Making smaller blockings permits the waving solution and neutralizer to penetrate more thoroughly.

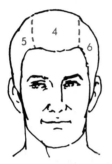

If you know the texture, elasticity, porosity and condition of the client's hair, you are better able to judge how the hair is to be sectioned, how it is to be blocked, which rods to use, and where the application of waving solution should begin. (**Be guided by your instructor.**)

REMINDER. The size of the rods and blockings determines the size of the curl or wave pattern. Processing time has no bearing on the size of the wave pattern.

Regular sectioning diagram

WINDING OR WRAPPING THE HAIR

To form a uniform wave with a strong ridge, hair must be wrapped smoothly and neatly on each rod without stretching. Hair is not stretched because the penetration of waving solution causes the hair to expand. Tight wrapping or stretching interferes with this expansion and prevents penetration of the waving solution and neutralizer, which may cause hair breakage.

END PAPERS

Porous end papers are very important aids in the proper wrapping or winding of the hair around curling rods. Properly used end papers may help in the formation of smooth and even waves. They help to eliminate the possibility of "fishhooks" and minimize the danger of breakage of the hair ends. They are especially important in helping to smooth out the wrapping of uneven hair lengths.

There are three methods of end paper application in general use in the practice of permanent waving. Each method may be equally effective, if properly used.

1. The book end paper wrap
2. The single end paper wrap
3. The double end paper wrap

BOOK END PAPER WRAP

Hair should be moistened (not saturated) with a weaker strength of the waving solution, starting one-half inch from the scalp and up to one inch from the hair ends. However, water should be used instead of waving solution until the student has become proficient in the technique of winding or wrapping the hair.

Procedure

Step-by-step procedure is illustrated by placing end papers, wrapping and fastening curls, using book end paper wrap method. (**Note:** The blocking should not be longer than the rod. If it is, the hair will not wave evenly.)

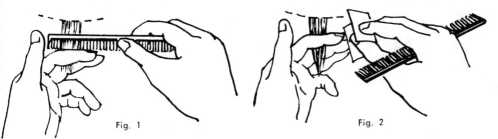

Fig. 1   Fig. 2

1. Part and comb sub-section up and out until all hair is evenly directed and distributed. 2. Hold strand between the index and middle fingers; fold and place the end paper over the strand, forming an envelope.

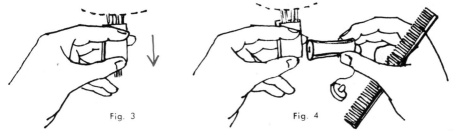

Fig. 3   Fig. 4

3. Hold the strand smoothly and evenly; slide the paper envelope a small fraction beyond the hair ends. 4. With the right hand, pick up rod.

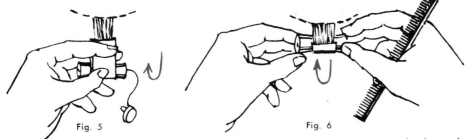

Fig. 5   Fig. 6

5. Place the rod under the folded end paper, parallel with the parting; draw end paper and rod towards hair ends until they are visible above the rod, and start winding end paper and hair under, toward the scalp. 6. Wind the hair smoothly (without tension) on the rod.

CAUTION. When wrapping hair, always avoid bulkiness on the rod. Bulkiness prevents the formation of a good curl because the hair cannot conform to the shape of the rod.

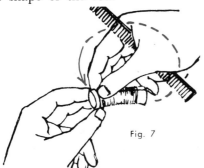

Fig. 7

7. Fasten the rod band evenly across the wound hair at the top of the rod.

CAUTION. The band should not cut into the hair nor be twisted against the curl, to prevent breakage.

257

Placement of Curl in Blocking

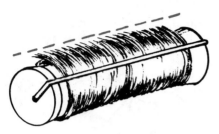

Regardless of the type or size of rod used, it should be placed slightly off its base in order to give a close to the head permanent and to leave the hair easy to handle. Placing the rod slightly off its base helps to prevent the creation of excessive tension and hair breakage.

SINGLE END PAPER WRAP

Hair preparation is the same as for the Book End Paper Wrap.

Fig. 1   Fig. 2   Fig. 3

Place the end paper on top of strand and hold it flat to prevent bunching. Fig. 1.

Place rod under the strand, holding it parallel with the parting; then draw the end paper and rod downward until hair ends are covered. Fig. 2.

Roll the end paper and strand under, using the thumb of each hand to keep the strand smooth. Fig. 3. Wind strand on the rod to the scalp without tension.

Fasten band at top of rod in the same manner as for Book End Paper Wrap.

DOUBLE END PAPER WRAP

Hair preparation—same as for Book End Paper Wrap.

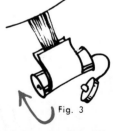

Fig. 1   Fig. 2   Fig. 3

Place one end paper beneath the hair strand and the other on top. Fig. 1.

Place rod under double end papers, parallel with hair part. Draw both towards hair ends. Fig. 2.

Wind the strand smoothly on the rod to the scalp without tension. Fig. 3. Then fasten band at top of rod as for Book End Paper Wrap.

PRE-PERMANENT WAVE SHAMPOO

In order to help assure success, it is necessary that the hair be shampooed prior to permanent waving.

Dust, hairdressing, sebum and various particles tend to accumulate in the hair between shampoos. Unless these are removed and the hair and scalp thoroughly cleansed, it will be extremely difficult to give a successful permanent.

The proper and even penetration of the waving solution and the neutralizer are essential to successful permanent waving. If the waving solution penetrates the hair evenly, the resulting curls and waves will be more uniform and manageable. Uneven or spottily curled hair is quite difficult to control and style. Even, longer-lasting waves can only be attained in clean hair.

TEST CURLS

Test curls help to determine in advance how the client's hair will react to the permanent waving process. A **test curl** gives you the information on how to protect the client's hair and how to obtain the best possible results.

Regular testing enables the artisan to observe the following aspects of the hair:

a) Speed of wave formation
b) Overall picture of wave formation
c) Exact time when peak of wave formation has been reached
d) Resistant areas

Test curls may be given **before** or **while waving** the entire head.

APPLICATION OF WAVING SOLUTION

SAFETY MEASURES

Safety measures protect the skin and scalp against chemical injury.

Always wear **protective gloves** or use protective cream to cover your hands.

For the **patron's safety,** apply protective cream around the hairline and neck, and cover with a strip of cotton or neutralizing band. Use dry cotton pledgets or neutralizing band between curls to absorb any excess waving solution. If cotton strips or bands become wet with solution, remove, blot and replace with dry material. If the solution drips on the skin or scalp, absorb with cotton pledgets saturated with cold water or neutralizer.

PROTECT CLIENT'S EYES. If the waving solution gets into the client's eye, rinse immediately with cold water or preparation recommended by your instructor and then take client to a doctor.

CAUTION. Be careful not to disturb the wrapping by dragging the nozzle over the curls. Do not leave the patron alone while processing the hair. Do not interrupt the rewet or saturation step. Complete it as quickly as possible.

PROCESSING TIME

Processing time is the length of time required for the hair strands to absorb the waving solution and complete the total rearrangement of the chemical bonds in the hair around the rod. The ability of the hair to absorb moisture may vary from time to time on the same individual, even while using the same solutions and procedures. **A record** of the previous processing time is desirable to use as a guide. It is usually safe to anticipate the processing time to be less than that suggested by the manufacturer or a client's previous record card.

The factors affecting processing time are the strength of the solution, texture, porosity, length and condition of the hair; atmospheric conditions, client's body heat and the working speed of the artisan.

Resaturation step during the processing time. Often, it is necessary to **rewet** all the rods a second time during the processing time. This may be due to:

1. Evaporation of the solution or dryness of the hair.
2. Hair poorly saturated.
3. Improper selection of solution strength for client's hair.
4. Failure to follow manufacturer's directions for a specific formula.

A reapplication of the solution will hasten processing. Watch the **wave** development closely, since **negligence may result in hair damage.**

Wave Pattern Formation

As the hair is processing, the wave forms a deep-ridged pattern. The wave has reached its peak when it forms a firm letter "S".

Unwinding hair without pulling or stretching. Processed strand opens up into an "S" formation.

The "S" pattern reaches a desirable peak only once. Shortly after the "S" is well formed, unless processing is stopped, the hair could become "frizzy." This indicates that the processing time has reached its absolute maximum. Beyond this point the hair becomes **over-processed** and **damaged.**

Different conditions and textures of hair will form different qualities of wave patterns. Hair of **good** texture will show a firm, **strong** pattern, whereas hair that is **weak** or **fine** will **not** produce a firm pattern.

Over-Processing

Any solution that can properly process the hair can also over-process it. Solution left on the hair too long, beyond the best wave formation point, results in over-processing. **Another cause of over-processing** is that test curls were not made frequently enough or were improperly judged. **If neutralizer is used too sparingly,** the hair may continue to process, also causing over-processing.

Over-processed hair is easily detected. It is **very curly when wet, completely** frizzy **when dry** and **refuses to be combed into a suitable wave pattern.** The elasticity of the hair has been excessively damaged and the hair is unable to contract into the wave formation. The hair feels harsh after being dried. **Reconditioning treatments should begin immediately.**

1. A good permanent wave looks like this. — 2. Under-processed curl. RESULT: Little or no wave. — 3. Over-processed curl. RESULT: Narrow waves when wet, no waves when dry. — 4. Porous ends over-processed. RESULT: Frizzy ends. — 5. Improper winding when hair ends are wound too tight. RESULT: No wave or curl at hair ends.

Under-Processing

Under-processing results in a limp or weak wave formation. The ridges are not well defined and the hair retains little or no wave formation. Under-processing may be corrected by giving one or two reconditioning treatments. After these treatments, rewrap the hair and apply a milder waving lotion, since the hair has already received some softening. Watch the wave formation closely.

NEUTRALIZATION OF THE HAIR

The waving solution produces the wave formation by rearranging the chemical bonds (links) in the cortex of the hair shaft into a new alignment. The rods hold the hair in this formation until it is "rehardened" or "fixed" by neutralization. The neutralizer stops the action of the waving solution, re-forms the chemical bonds and rehardens the hair in its new curled position.

PREPARATION FOR NEUTRALIZATION

Prior to the application of the neutralizer, most manufacturers require thorough rinsing with warm water to remove excess waving solution, followed by careful towel blotting of each curl to remove excess moisture. To obtain the best results from towel blotting, carefully press the towel with the fingers between each curl.

CAUTION. Do not rock or roll the rods while blotting. The hair is in a softened state and such movement may cause hair breakage.

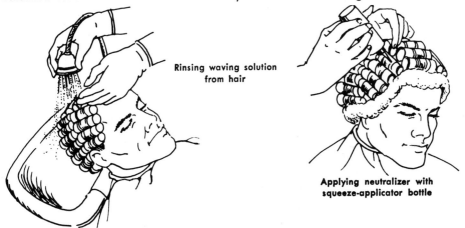

Rinsing waving solution
from hair

Applying neutralizer with
squeeze-applicator bottle

METHODS OF NEUTRALIZATION

Neutralizers are packaged in the form of powders, liquids or crystals and must be prepared immediately before their use, as directed by manufacturer.

There are two methods of neutralizer application in general use: the **Direct** or **On-the-Rod Method** and the **Conventional** or **Splash-On Method.**

Direct or **On-the-Rod Method** is also referred to as the **Applicator** or **Instant Method.** The neutralizer comes in two forms: ready for use and to be mixed.

1. **Ready for use neutralizer:** snip off tip of squeeze-applicator bottle and apply.
2. **Neutralizer to be prepared:** mix it according to manufacturer's directions, pour into the squeeze-applicator bottle and apply.

Procedure. Apply neutralizer directly to each curl in the same order as that followed in the application of the waving lotion. Start in the top center of the curl and apply in either direction then apply at the bottom of the curl, making sure that each curl is thoroughly saturated. Repeat if necessary. (Removing neutralizer, see* below.)

Note: A cotton pad saturated with neutralizer may be placed at the nape of the neck on the rim of the shampoo bowl, to assure that the neckline curls are in constant contact with the neutralizer.

Conventional or Splash-On Method. Mix neutralizer with water, following manufacturer's directions. Position client at shampoo bowl in the same manner as for a shampoo.

Procedure. Using glass or plastic measuring cup, pour one-half of the neutralizer carefully over the curls, thoroughly saturating each curl. The neutralizer is caught in a plastic basin or pocket in the neutralizing bib attached to the client's neck.

Using large pads of cotton or sponge, reapply neutralizer, thoroughly saturating each curl. Repeat 2 or 3 times. (Removing neutralizer, see* below.)

*REMOVING NEUTRALIZER

There are two general methods for removing neutralizers from the hair, regardless of the method used to apply it. (Manufacturer's directions must be followed at all times.)

Method 1. After the neutralizer is thoroughly applied, allow it to remain in the hair for five to eight minutes. Rinse the hair with tepid water and follow with a cool water rinse to reharden the hair. Lightly towel-blot the hair. Remove the rods carefully and proceed to set and/or style the hair.

Method 2. After the neutralizer is thoroughly applied, allow it to set for five to eight minutes. Carefully remove the rods without stretching the hair and apply the balance of the neutralizer to the hair. Permit an additional minute of neutralizing time and then rinse with cool water. Proceed with setting and/or styling the hair.

UNLESS THE HAIR IS THOROUGHLY AND CORRECTLY NEUTRALIZED, THE PERMANENT WAVE WILL NOT BE SUCCESSFUL AND ALL THE WORK DONE WILL BE WASTED. IN ADDITION, THE HAIR MAY BE DAMAGED.

PERMANENT WAVING METHODS

There are two types of permanent waving methods: cold waving (alkaline) and neutral (acid balanced) which is heat activated (page 264).

COLD WAVING (ALKALINE) METHOD

A correct analysis for permanent waving results should include:

1. Strength of waving solution
2. Proper size rods
3. Blocking and winding the hair
4. Test curl-wave formation
5. Processing time
6. Neutralization

There are different methods of giving a permanent wave. The suggested outline below is one of several ways that may be used. However, it may be changed to meet the requirements of the instructor or permanent wave manufacturer.

IMPLEMENTS AND SUPPLIES

1. Applicators
2. Porous end papers
3. Permanent waving solution
4. Neutralizer
5. Neutralizing bib
6. Shampoo cape
7. Curling rods
8. Protective cream
9. Cotton or neutralizing bands
10. Mild liquid shampoo
11. Neutral or cream rinse
12. Neck strips and towels
13. Combs
14. Hair clips
15. Shears (scissors)
16. Razor
17. Protective gloves
18. Record card

If the neutralizer is to be applied by the splash or pour-over method, rinse pan, measuring cup and quart jar are also needed.

PREPARATION

1. Select and arrange required materials.
2. Wash and sanitize hands.
3. Seat patron comfortably at the shampoo bowl.
4. Adjust towels and shampoo cape.
5. Carefully examine condition of scalp and hair.

DRAPE PATRON

There are several ways in which a client may be draped for a permanent wave. The comfort of the client and adequate protection of his or her person and clothing are important during the entire procedure. One way to drape a client is to place a small folded towel around the neck, fasten the shampoo cape over it and then place another towel over the cape. Fasten the towel securely.

PROCEDURE

1. If hair is long, cut before or after shampoo. If hair is short cut after permanent, if required.
2. Shampoo and **thoroughly** rinse hair. Towel dry and moisten the hair with waving solution as recommended by manufacturer.
3. Section and block (sub-section) the hair. Start wrapping in the nape area, or be guided by your instructor.
4. Apply protective cream and cotton strips around client's hairline. Artisan must wear protective gloves.
5. Apply permanent waving solution as recommended by manufacturer.
6. **Test curl-wave formation immediately** after saturating hair with waving solution. Take frequent test curls on different areas of the head.
7. Process hair for the required time. If rewetting the curls is necessary, apply the solution in the same order followed originally. Protect client with fresh protective cotton strips around hairline and neck.
8. When the curls have processed sufficiently, rinse out waving solution thoroughly. Use gentle water pressure, having a tepid temperature, or follow manufacturer's directions.
9. Blot excess moisture from hair wound on rods. **Do not** rock or roll the rods while blotting. The hair being in a softened state, any such movement may cause hair breakage.
10. Thoroughly apply neutralizer and retain for required time.

11. Unwind rods and remove carefully.
12. Apply neutralizer again, if required.
13. Rinse hair again, if required.
14. Towel dry and set and/or style hair.

A neutral or cream rinse, or hair cream, may be applied to protect the permanent and to facilitate the styling of the hair. If the manufacturer has included a special rinse with the product, its use will prevent excessive stretching while combing and will counteract any alkaline residue. Styling gel, if used, should be of a light consistency. **Avoid excess tension in styling the hair.**

COMPLETION
1. Check for scalp abrasions.
2. Set, dry and style hair.

CAUTION. Do not use extreme heat when drying the hair. In handling soft, fine, limp or damaged hair, it is of utmost importance to use as little tension as possible.

CLEAN-UP
1. Discard used supplies.
2. Cleanse and sanitize equipment.
3. Wash and sanitize hands.
4. Complete permanent wave record card.

NEUTRAL (ACID-BALANCED) HEAT PERMANENT WAVING

"Thio" permanent wave solutions must be highly alkaline if they are to be effective. As a result of this alkalinity, it has been found that permanent waving is harmful to lightened, tinted and damaged hair.

In an effort to develop a solution which will permit lightened, tinted and damaged hair to receive a permanent wave with the least risk, manufacturers have introduced the neutral or acid-balanced permanent wave.

Neutral (acid-balanced) permanent wave solutions use different chemical compounds than the "thio" type solutions. These products have a pH of 5.5 to 7; thus they are either neutral or slightly acid.

Neutral or acid solutions are very slow in penetrating the hair and, therefore, the processing speed is greatly reduced. To overcome this problem and make the products suitable for professional use, **heat must be applied.**

There are two methods in use today to speed up the processing time:
1. The heated clamp method
2. The hair dryer method

Pre-heated clamps with permanent wave machine

In both methods, processing does not effectively begin until heat is applied to the solution-dampened hair.

The techniques used for neutral and acid solution permanent waving are generally similar to those used for the alkaline method. However, manufacturers' directions vary somewhat with different products.

With the heated clamp method, clamps are pre-heated and then placed over the rods upon which hair has been wound and waving lotion applied.

When using the hair dryer method, wind the hair on the rods, apply lotion, and place a thin plastic cap over the hair. The client is then placed under a hair dryer.

Because each manufacturer has its own formula and special features related to its product, it is essential that the manufacturer's instructions be followed carefully.

Pre-heated dryer method

SPECIAL PROBLEMS

RECONDITIONING TREATMENTS

Dry, brittle, damaged or over-porous hair should be given reconditioning treatments. However, avoid any treatment requiring massage or heat just prior to a permanent wave. Such treatment could create a sensitive scalp.

SPECIAL PERMANENT WAVE FILLERS

Over-porous or damaged hair must be preconditioned before the application of waving solution. Special fillers that contain **protein** are now available, which recondition the hair and equalize its porosity. Some fillers also contain lanolin and cholesterol, which may help to protect the hair against the harshness of the permanent waving solution.

AFTER CARE

Reconditioning treatments for clients also have a place in the **after care** of a permanent wave and between permanent waves.

The after care of the client's permanent wave helps to keep the hair in the best possible condition. It includes regular hair care, as follows:
1. Shampoo hair weekly with mild shampoo and rinse.
2. Use appropriate hair conditioner as directed by manufacturer.
3. Comb and brush the hair daily. Use type of brush best suited to the hair. Avoid excessive brushing or combing in the opposite direction.
4. Suggest patron have hair trimmed and styled at regular intervals in order to make the hairstyle more serviceable.

TO TINT OR WAVE

If a client requests both a permanent wave and a hair tint on the same day, **advise against it.** Give the following reasons to the client:
1. If the tint is given first, the application of waving solution will lighten hair and often cause an uneven color.
2. If the permanent wave is given first, the application of a tint will distort and weaken the wave pattern.
3. The combination of two chemical treatments on the same day may cause scalp irritation and/or hair breakage.

First give the permanent wave and postpone the tint treatment for a few days to avoid distorting the wave pattern. Suggest a reconditioning treatment before the tint application.

Do not give a color rinse immediately after a permanent wave. It is also likely to disturb the wave pattern. If required, use a color rinse having a weak strength.

If the hair is to be lightened after the permanent wave, it should be reconditioned and the lightening treatment given at a later date.

WAVING TINTED OR LIGHTENED HAIR

Special precautions are recommended when waving tinted or lightened hair, such as:

1. Shampoo hair with a mild shampoo before waving.
2. Wrap the hair with a special conditioner, as required for damaged hair.
3. Use a special permanent waving solution according to directions.
4. Give test curls, using a mild waving solution and a shorter processing time than is employed for normal hair.

HAIR TINTED WITH METALLIC DYE

Hair tinted with a metallic dye must first be treated with a dye remover to avoid hair discoloration or breakage. **Do not** wave the hair if the test curls break or discolor. This type of discoloration is very difficult to remove.

CURL REDUCTION

Sometimes a client is unhappy with his hair after a permanent wave because the hair appears to be too curly. If the hair is fine in texture, do not suggest curl reduction until after two or three shampoos. This type of hair relaxes to a greater extent than normal or coarse hair. Usually, after the second shampoo, the hair has relaxed enough to be satisfactory.

If the hair has a normal or coarse texture, curl reduction may be given either immediately following neutralization or after a few days.

Permanent waving solution may be used to relax the curl, where required. Carefully comb it through the hair to widen and loosen the wave. When sufficiently relaxed, the hair is rinsed, towel blotted and neutralized.

If curl analysis and proper application have not been determined, hair could be damaged and breakage could occur. **Be guided by your instructor.**

CAUTION. Do not attempt curl reduction in hair which has been overprocessed. Such treatment will further damage the hair.

PERMANENT WAVING HAIR WITH PARTIAL PERMANENT

Previously permanently waved hair should be given a reconditioning treatment. Leave the conditioning agent over the old permanent and cover this hair with two or three end papers. Then proceed with the usual permanent wave routine.

This is only one suggestion for permanent waving this type of hair. Your instructor's method is equally correct.

ITEMS TO CONSIDER

Air conditioning. Because of its cooling effect, air conditioning may slow down the action of the permanent waving solution. Additional time **may be** required.

Long hair. Because of its excess length, long hair may require smaller blockings to assure thorough saturation of the waving lotion and neutralizer.

RELEASE STATEMENT

A release statement is used for permanent waving, hair relaxing, or any other type of chemical treatment. It relieves the salon owner, to some extent, from responsibility for accidents or damages.

——— RELEASE FORM ———

Client's Name .... **Address** ....

Condition of Hair ....

Permanent Wave: Kind .... **Given by** ....

I fully understand that the permanent wave treatment which I have requested and am about to receive is ordinarily harmless to normal hair, but may damage my hair because of its present condition.

In view of this, I accept full responsibility for any possible damage that may result, directly or indirectly, to my hair.

Signature of Client ....

Witnessed by .... **Date** ....

PERMANENT WAVE RECORDS

A record of each permanent wave must be kept for each client. It is referred to each time the client takes a permanent. It contains all essential information. It eliminates guesswork. The following is a typical form of Permanent Wave Card.

——— PERMANENT WAVE RECORD ———

Name .... Tel. ....

Address .... City ....

DESCRIPTION OF HAIR

Texture	Form	Length	Porosity	
coarse soft	straight	short	very porous	less porous
medium silky	wavy	medium	moderately porous	least porous
fine wiry	curly	long	normal	resistant

Condition:

☐ virgin ☐ rewave ☐ dry ☐ oily lotion .... strength...........................

If tinted or lightened, use: ☐ double end wrap ☐ water ☐ protein filler

previously waved with .... system

☐ original sample of hair enclosed ☐ not enclosed

TYPE OF PERMANENT WAVE

☐ regular ☐ body wave ☐ other .... lotion .... strength ....

Curls — Roller sizes: Top .... sides .... crown .... nape ....

Results: ☐ good ☐ poor ☐ too tight ☐ too loose
☐ sample of finished P.W. enclosed ☐ sample not enclosed

Date	Artisan	Price	Date	Artisan	Price

QUESTIONS ON PERMANENT WAVING FOR MEN

1. What is permanent waving?
2. The physical action involves the wrapping of the hair around ....
3. The chemical action requires processing with a permanent waving solution, followed by ....
4. Name two types of chemical solutions used in permanent waving.
5. What is the main action of a permanent waving solution?
6. What is the main action of the neutralizer?
7. What is the most important step before giving a permanent wave?
8. List six factors which a scalp and hair analysis should include.
9. What determines the choice of rods in permanent waving?
10. Why should hair be wrapped smoothly and without tension on each rod?
11. To achieve best results, what should guide the student?
12. What determines the size of the wave formation in permanent waving?
13. Why is it necessary to give test curl-wave formation?
14. At what three points should curl-wave development be tested?
15. When does the wave pattern reach its peak of complete wave formation?
16. What kind of hair texture will not form a firm wave pattern?
17. Why should safety rules be observed in permanent waving?
18. How is over-processed hair detected?
19. Why should a hair coloring treatment and a permanent wave not be given the same day?
20. Why should a color rinse not be given immediately following a permanent wave?
21. What determines the strength of waving solution used?
22. When may a permanent waving solution cause irritation to a healthy skin or scalp?
23. What must be done if the waving solution accidentally gets on the skin or scalp?
24. How may a permanent wave be relaxed, if it is too curly?
25. What strength waving solution is always recommended for tinted or lightened hair?
26. Why are special hair conditioners recommended for wrapping the hair?
27. In permanent waving, what determines the size of the blocking (subsectioning)?
28. What determines the length of rods used?
29. Which two hair factors determine the processing time during a permanent wave?
30. Why is hair elasticity so important in relation to permanent waving?

Chapter 20

CHEMICAL HAIR RELAXING, CHEMICAL BLOW-OUT & SOFT CURL PERMANENT

INTRODUCTION

The problem of dealing with over-curly, unruly hair has been plaguing both the barber-stylist and his or her clients for many years. Barber-stylists have found it to be very difficult to style this type of hair in a manner that would enhance the appearance of the client or to create a well-groomed appearance.

The answer to this problem has been found in the very lucrative service of chemical hair processing (hair straightening). When performed professionally, this service leaves the hair straight and in satisfactory condition to be combed and styled into almost any suitable fashion. It is essential to the barber-stylist that he or she be able to perform this service in order to take care of clients properly, and that he or she not allow this very profitable service to go by the wayside.

The technique of chemical hair processing or hair relaxing is not difficult but requires care and know-how. To attain proficiency in chemical hair processing, the barber-stylist must acquire a thorough technical knowledge and expert manipulative skills in this area.

Note—In the art of men's chemical hair processing (hair straightening), the chemical applied is called a chemical processing cream. Since the hair must be completely relaxed as part of the straightening procedure, this cream is called a "processor" or a "relaxer." In this text, it is primarily referred to as "processor."

ACTION OF CHEMICAL PRODUCTS

Two basic products are used in chemical hair processing, namely: chemical hair processor (pros'e-sor) and stabilizer (sta'bi-lī-zer) or fixative (fiks'a-tiv).

1. The two general classifications of hair processors are:
   a) Sodium hydroxide (caustic soda) products.
   b) Ammonium thioglycolate (thio) products.

   Sodium hydroxide (sō'dē-um hī-drok'sīd) has a softening and swelling action. As the processor penetrates into the chemical cross-bonds of the hair, they are unlocked and rearranged into a relaxed or straightened condition.

269

Ammonium thioglycolate (thī-ō-glī'kō-lat) softens and makes over-curly hair straight by changing its cystine (sis'tēn) linkage.

2. The **stabilizer** or **fixative.** When the hair is sufficiently straightened, the stabilizer is applied. This stops the action of the chemical processor and, at the same time, the cystine links are permanently reunited and the hair is rehardened into its new form.

It is important that the barber-stylist have a thorough understanding of the product being used and its action on the hair. **The manufacturer's directions should be followed explicitly.**

BASIC STEPS

Chemical hair processing involves three basic steps: processing, stabilizing and conditioning.

Processing. As soon as the chemical processor is applied, the hair begins to soften and to lose its tight curl.

Stabilizing. As soon as the hair has been sufficiently processed, the chemical processor is thoroughly rinsed out with warm water, followed by either:
1. A built-in shampoo stabilizer (fixative), or
2. A prescribed shampoo and stabilizer (fixative).

Conditioning. Depending upon the client's needs, the conditioner may be part of a series of hair treatments or it may be applied to the hair before or after the processing treatment. Conditioning is often necessary to give strength and body to damaged hair and to protect it against possible breakage.

Fine, wooly hair. It is not advisable to use a **strong** processor on fine, wooly hair, as it is too weak and fragile to withstand the softening agent in the processor. However, a **weak** or **mild** processor is permissible.

ANALYSIS OF CLIENT'S HAIR

It is essential that the barber-stylist have a working knowledge of human hair, particularly in the case of over-curly hair. Recognition of the qualities of hair is made possible by means of visible inspection, feel and by special tests. Before attempting to give a processing treatment to over-curly hair, the barber-stylist must judge its texture, porosity, elasticity and the extent, if any, of the damage to the hair.

CLIENT'S HAIR HISTORY

To help assure satisfactory results, records should be kept of each chemical processing treatment. These records should include the client's hair history and the client's release statement.

Release statement is used to protect the barber-stylist, to some extent, from responsibility for accidents or damages.

Before starting to process the hair, he must be certain of how the client will react to the processor. Therefore, the client must receive:
1. A thorough scalp examination and
2. A hair strand test.

Scalp examination. Inspect the scalp carefully for the presence or absence of eruptions, scratches or abrasions. To obtain a clearer view of the scalp, part the hair into half-inch sections. Hair parting may be done with the index and middle fingers or a comb. In either case the barber-stylist must exercise great care not to injure the scalp. **Such injuries may become seriously infected when aggravated by the chemicals in the processor.**

If any **scalp eruptions** or **abrasions** are present, do not apply the chemical hair processor until the scalp is again in a healthy condition.

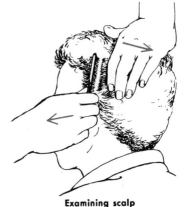

Examining scalp

STRAND TEST

Three strand tests are employed, as follows:

1. **Finger test** determines the degree of porosity in the hair. Grasp a single strand of hair and "run" it between thumb and index finger of the right hand, from the end toward the scalp. If it ruffles or feels bumpy, the hair is porous and can absorb moisture.

2. **Pull test** determines the degree of elasticity in the hair. Normally, curly, dry hair will stretch about one-fifth its normal length without breaking. Grasp half a dozen strands from the crown area, and pull them gently. If the hair appears to stretch or pull, it has elasticity and can withstand the processor. If not, conditioning treatments are recommended prior to a chemical processing treatment.

3. **Relaxer test.** Application of the processor to a **hair strand** will indicate the ultimate results of the complete treatment. Take a small section of hair and thread through a hole cut in a piece of wax paper or aluminum foil. Apply processor to the hair. **Do not use a base or cream.** Allow it to remain on the hair for required time and then remove with a piece of dry cotton. If the test is satisfactory, proceed with the treatment.

IMPLEMENTS AND SUPPLIES

Chemical processor	Hair conditioner	Spatula
Stabilizer (fixative)	Protective gloves	Timer
Shampoo	Towels	Absorbent cotton
Petroleum base	Comb and brush	Neck strip

CHEMICAL HAIR PROCESSING

Note—The following procedure is based primarily on products containing **sodium hydroxide.** For this or any other kind of product, follow the manufacturer's directions and be guided by your instructor.

PREPARATION

1. Select and arrange the required implements and supplies.
2. The practitioner washes and sanitizes his hands.
3. Prepare and drape the client as for a shampoo.
4. Examine and evaluate test results.
5. If necessary, trim damaged hair ends. **Do not shampoo.**

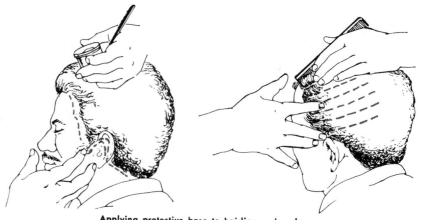

Applying protective base to hairline and scalp

PROCEDURE FOR SODIUM HYDROXIDE PROCESSOR

1. **Hair dried.** If moisture or perspiration is present on scalp, dry the client's hair and scalp.

2. **Application of protective base.** Most processors require the use of a petroleum base to protect the scalp from the active agents in the cream. The base is applied freely to the entire scalp with the fingers. The hairline around the forehead, nape of the neck, and over and around the ears must be completely covered. The base is actually "laid" on the scalp; it is not to be spread or rubbed on. Good coverage is important to protect the scalp and hairline from irritation. Any area which may come in contact with the processor must be protected.

3. **Use of conditioner** (if recommended). In many cases it is necessary to apply a conditioner to the hair before applying the processor. Over-curly hair which has been damaged or weakened may break at the ends. The conditioner is used to strengthen the damaged and weakened hair and to give protection against breakage.

4. **Applying the processor.** Use protective gloves. The processor must be applied with great caution. It is laid on the hair; **it must not be spread or rubbed on.** The processor is laid on the hair shaft starting at the thickest part of the hair, for the action will take a little longer here. Extreme care must be taken not to let any processor touch the ears, the scalp or the skin. The amount of cream used will vary, according

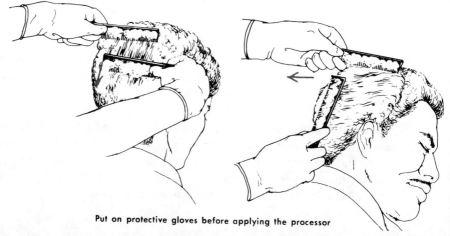

Put on protective gloves before applying the processor

to the head being worked on and the thickness and length of the hair. The processor is applied to the entire scalp area and to the hair shaft, but **not to the ends.** The ends are the weakest part of the hair and therefore should receive the processor after the spreading-out procedure is completed.

5. **Spreading out the processor.** The spreading-out procedure follows the same pattern as that followed in applying the processor. There are three specific reasons for this procedure, as follows:

a) To be sure the hair is completely covered from the scalp.

b) To be sure the hair is completely processed from the scalp.

c) To be able to determine how fast the hair is being processed.

After spreading out the processor over the entire scalp area and hair shaft, it is laid on the ends and then applied to the front hairline.

Use of combs in spreading. The processor may be spread over and through the hair by using two wide-tooth combs as follows:

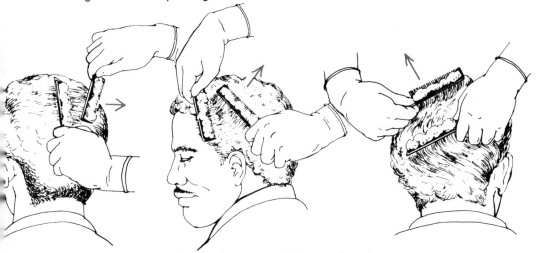

Spreading out the processor with large-tooth comb

a) Use the back of the combs to spread the processor over the entire head.

b) Begin combing with wide-tooth combs.

c) Comb in all directions, using hand-over-hand method.

d) Comb first to one side, then to the other.

e) Comb upwards from the temples.

f) By combing against the direction of hair growth, complete coverage will be obtained.

g) The underneath hairs will be covered and straightened by combing away from the direction of natural growth.

6. **Testing.** In spreading the processor, the barber-stylist inspects the action by stretching the strands to see how fast the natural curls are being removed. If the action is too fast in any area, the client should be taken to the shampoo bowl immediately and the processor washed from that particular section. The spreading procedure can be continued over the rest of the head, and finally to the hair ends.

7. **Rinsing out the processor.** When the processor has reached its maximum action, it must be **rinsed out rapidly and thoroughly.** The water must be warm but not hot. If the water is too hot, it may scald the patron

Processor ready to be rinsed

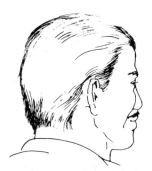

After the hair has been shampooed and combed

or cause the processed hair to revert. If the water is too cold, it will not remove the processor sufficiently. Unless the processor is completely removed, the chemical action continues on the hair.

CAUTION. Do not get processor or rinse water into the eyes or on the unprotected skin of the client. (If this should happen, rinse thoroughly with warm water.) In the rinsing process the stream of water must never be directed toward the scalp, but **out** from the scalp.

8. **Shampooing the hair.** The shampoo (cream shampoo recommended) is **gently** worked into the hair. The hair is very fragile at this point and tangled ends can be broken easily. Use **tepid** water and **avoid firm manipulations,** rubbing or tangling the hair. Most processed hair requires at least three shampooings.

9. **Applying stabilizer.** After the hair has been shampooed, a stabilizer is recommended. This helps to keep the hair in a processed state. The hair is completely saturated with the stabilizer and is then combed through with a wide-tooth comb. The comb is used to:
   a) Keep the hair straight.
   b) Completely saturate the hair with the fixative.
   c) Remove any tangles without too much pulling.

10. **Applying color rinse.** To remove a reddish cast caused by the processor, a color rinse may be applied. A color rinse may follow a stabilizer or a shampoo. Towel dry the hair and apply color rinse.

   Note: If the reddish cast is not evident until the hair has been dried, the color rinse may be applied to the dried hair.

11. **Applying conditioner.** Some manufacturers recommend the use of a conditioner to the scalp and hair to restore some of the natural oils which have been removed by the chemical hair processor. Before applying the conditioner, the hair and scalp is usually towel dried.

12. Style hair as desired.

13. If necessary, adjust hair net (trainer) and thoroughly dry hair with warm air, **not hot.**

14. Carefully remove hair net and recomb hair into a natural looking hairstyle.

Before: Unruly hair

After: Hair processed and styled

FINAL CLEAN-UP

1. Discard used supplies.

2. Cleanse and sanitize implements and equipment.

3. Wash and sanitize hands.

4. Complete hair processing record card.

Note— Different products used for processing the hair necessitate different methods of handling the hair during the processing and stabilizing period. Always follow the manufacturer's directions and be guided by your instructor.

RETOUCHING

Follow all steps for a regular chemical hair processing treatment, with the exception that the **processor is applied only to the new growth.**

VERY IMPORTANT REMINDER

Before proceeding with any chemical processing treatment, it is essential that strand tests be taken to determine the ability of the patron's hair to withstand the effects of the chemicals.

AMMONIUM THIOGLYCOLATE PROCESSOR

(Thio Processor)

The procedure is somewhat different when using an ammonium thioglycolate product, commonly known as **thio processor.**

PROCEDURE FOR THIO PROCESSOR

1. Preparation of the client is the same as previously described.
2. Shampoo the hair with a neutral shampoo. (Be careful not to irritate the scalp.)
3. Towel dry the hair, leaving it slightly damp.
4. If necessary, or if recommended by manufacturer, apply hair conditioner as previously described for sodium hydroxide products.
5. Prepare stabilizer before applying processor.
6. Use protective gloves or cream on the hands. Apply processor as previously described.
7. The spreading-out and testing procedure is the same as that followed for sodium hydroxide products.
8. When the hair has been sufficiently processed, the processor is rinsed out in a three-step process.
   a) Rinse about 50% of the processor from the hair with warm water.
   b) Comb the hair smooth and straight with the remaining processor left in the hair, continuing this combing for about five minutes to change cystine linkage into a straight position.
   c) The remaining processor is thoroughly rinsed from the hair with warm water, keeping the hair smooth and straight while rinsing.
9. After the processor is completely rinsed from the hair, apply stabilizer as previously described, and proceed in the same manner as outlined for sodium hydroxide treatment.

Completion. Final clean-up as previously described.

RETOUCHING

Follow all steps for a regular chemical hair processing treatment, with the exception that the **processor is applied only to the new growth.**

THE CHEMICAL BLOW-OUT

Over-curly hair has its own characteristics which require rather special techniques for styling. Of prime importance to the barber-stylist is the skill to create hairstyles which will enhance the appearance of the client. Knowing the correct styling techniques, having the ability to visualize what he or she is trying to achieve and using common sense are all indications of the trained professional.

A **chemical blow-out** is a combination of chemical hair straightening and hairstyling which creates a well-groomed style in the Afro-Natural tradition.

The chemical blow-out may be performed with either the "Thio" Hair relaxer or the sodium hydroxide straightener. The very important consideration with either method is not to over-relax the hair to the point where the blow-out process becomes impossible to perform.

Since the "Thio" chemical is not extremely strong and will not completely straighten over-curly hair it may be used for almost its entire recommended procedure.

The sodium-hydroxide chemical, however, is extremely potent and may very quickly process the hair to the point where it is unserviceable for a blow-out. When using sodium-hydroxide, timing becomes very important. Extreme care must be taken to control the amount of processing and the chemical should not be kept on the hair for more than 40% of the recommended processing time.

The procedures for both the "Thio" method of hair relaxing and the sodium hydroxide method have been thoroughly explained in this chapter. After all chemicals have been rinsed out of the hair, the stabilizer (neutralizer) applied to stop the chemical process, and then rinsed out, a good conditioner must be applied to the hair. Failure to thoroughly condition this weakened hair, prior to the blow-out procedure, could result in hair breakage when it is being subjected to processing with the Afro-Comb, hair lifter or pick. The conditioner will help to minimize possible damage or breakage and enable the hair to withstand the necessary combing.

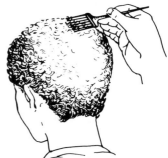

Using an Afro-Comb, hair lifter or pick, comb the hair upward and slightly forward, making the hair as long as possible. The hair closest to the scalp gives direction to the hair; therefore this hair must be picked upward and outward. Start at the crown and continue until all of the hair has been combed out from the scalp and distributed evenly around the head. By combing in a circular pattern splits are usually avoided.

The client is now placed under the dryer and the hair allowed to dry. The time permitted for drying depends on the length and thickness of the client's hair.

The dried hair is ready for shaping. Evenness is very important at this point. The hair length is checked in order that the shortest hair be used as the guide for the balance of the head. The barber-stylist must visualize the style and the length of hair he or she has planned for the blow-out.

The cutting should be started at the sides. The hair is evened out around the head with an electric clippers or scissors, while, at the same time, the picking of the hair outward from the scalp continues. The hair should be cut in the direction in which it is to be combed. The object is to achieve a smooth, even cut which is properly contoured. The final cutting should be done only with the scissors, just to even out loose or rugged ends.

Outline the hairstyle at the sides, around the ears and in the nape area, using either the scissors or the outliner. After the hair is cut to the desired style the finishing touches are applied. Fluff the hair slightly with the lifter, where required, and spray lightly. The lifter or pick is used to improve the smoothness of the style.

SOFT CURL PERMANENT

Soft curl permanent waving is a method of permanently waving over-curly hair. It is known by various names given by the manufacturers of the products being used.

PRECAUTIONS: The product used contains ammonium thioglycolate ("thio").

1. Do not use it on bleached, tinted or damaged hair, or on hair that has been colored with metallic dye or compound henna.
2. Do not use it on hair that has been relaxed with sodium hydroxide.
3. If permanent waving lotion or neutralizer accidentally gets into the client's eye, flush the eye immediately with water and refer the client to a doctor.

VERY IMPORTANT: To achieve a soft curl permanent, it is important to follow the manufacturer's or your instructor's directions explicitly. Doing otherwise may not give you good results and may cause damage to client's hair and skin.

The procedure below can be used for both men and women.

PROCEDURE

1. Examine the client's scalp. Do not use permanent waving gel or cream if the scalp shows signs of abrasions or lesions, or if the client has experienced an allergic reaction to a previous perm.

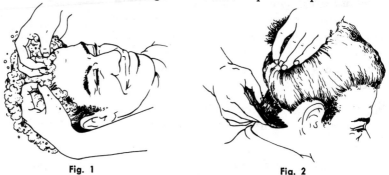

Fig. 1   Fig. 2

2. Shampoo and rinse hair thoroughly. Towel dry, leaving hair damp (Fig. 1).
3. Remove tangles with a large-tooth comb (Fig. 2).

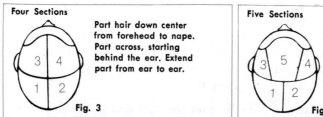

Four Sections

Part hair down center from forehead to nape. Part across, starting behind the ear. Extend part from ear to ear.

Fig. 3

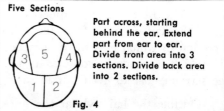

Five Sections

Part across, starting behind the ear. Extend part from ear to ear. Divide front area into 3 sections. Divide back area into 2 sections.

Fig. 4

4. Part hair into 4-5 sections, as recommended by your instructor (Figs 3 and 4).

(If manufacturer requires it, put a protective cream on the entire scalp including around the hairline.)

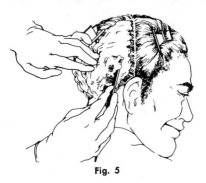

Fig. 5

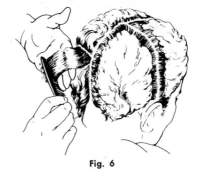

Fig. 6

5. Put on protective gloves.

6. Apply "thio" gel or cream to one section at a time, using a hair-coloring brush, fingers, or the back of a comb. Use the rat-tail of comb or brush to part hair and begin the application of "thio" gel or cream to the hair nearest the scalp, preferably starting at the nape area. Work the "thio" gel or cream to the ends of the hair (Fig. 5).

7. Comb the "thio" gel or cream through the entire head, first with a wide-tooth comb, then with a smaller tooth comb (Fig. 6).

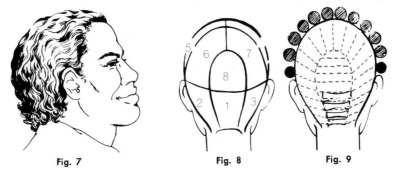

Fig. 7   Fig. 8   Fig. 9

8. When the hair becomes supple and flexible (Fig. 7), rinse with tepid water and towel dry. Do not tangle the hair.

9. Section the hair into nine sections (Fig. 8). Sub-section as you wrap the hair (Fig. 9).

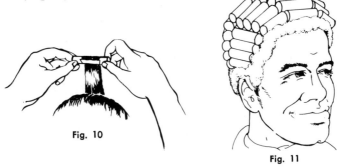

Fig. 10

Fig. 11

10. Wrap hair on desired size of curling rods (Fig 10). Use small (thin) curling rods for tighter curls and larger ones for looser curls. If the hair is short, use short rods since they make it easier to wrap and control short, curly hairs.

11. After the wrapping has been completed, protect client's skin by placing cotton around the hairline and neck (Fig. 11).

279

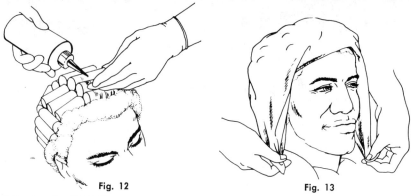

Fig. 12

Fig. 13

12. Apply "thio" gel or cream to all the curls until they are thoroughly saturated (Fig. 12).

13. Cover the client's head with a plastic cap (Fig. 13).

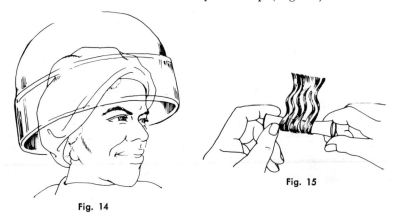

Fig. 15

Fig. 14

14. Have client sit under a pre-heated dryer for 15-25 minutes, or as recommended by the manufacturer (Fig. 14).

15. Take a test curl (Fig. 15), and if the desired curl pattern has not developed, have the client sit under the dryer for another 10 minutes or until a curl pattern develops.

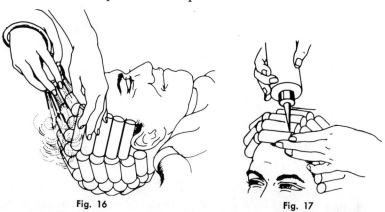

Fig. 16

Fig. 17

16. When the desired curl pattern has been reached, rinse the hair thoroughly with warm (not hot) water (Fig. 16). Blot each curl with a towel.

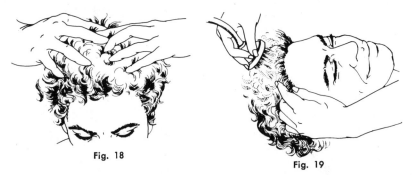

Fig. 18

Fig. 19

17. Use a prepared neutralizer, or mix neutralizer as directed by the manufacturer, and saturate each curl twice (Fig. 17). Allow neutralizer to remain on the curls for 5-10 minutes, or as directed by the manufacturer.

18. Carefully remove rods and apply balance of neutralizer to the hair. Work neutralizer through with fingers for thorough distribution (Fig. 18), and allow to remain on the hair for another 5 minutes.

19. Rinse hair thoroughly with cool water and towel blot (Fig. 19).

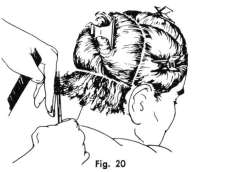

Fig. 20

Fig. 21

20. Trim uneven hair ends (Fig. 20).

21. Apply conditioner as directed by the manufacturer.

22. Air dry hair or style as desired (Fig. 21).

Fig. 22

Fig. 22 illustrates hairstyle BEFORE and Fig. 23 illustrates hairstyle AFTER a "Soft Curl Permanent" was given.

Fig. 23

281

Steps 1 - 7 are the same.

Step 8: When the hair has become supple and flexible (do not rinse), section and wrap in the usual manner (steps 9 and 10).

(Use small curling rods for tighter curls and larger ones for looser curls.)

REMINDER: To protect client's skin, place cotton around the head and neck (step 11).

Apply thio permanent wave lotion to each curl as directed by the manufacturer (Fig. 12). Steps 13 - 21 are the same.

AFTERCARE

1. Do not comb or brush the curls when wet; use a lifting pick instead.
2. Shampoo about once a week using a mild shampoo.
3. Conditioner or curl activator should be used daily to maintain flexibility, sheen, and proper moisture balance of the hair.

SAFETY PRECAUTIONS AND REMINDERS
CHEMICAL PROCESSING

1. Know the texture of the hair to be treated.
2. Check the elasticity of the hair for its ability to stretch and return to its normal length without breaking.
3. Check the porosity of the hair and its ability to absorb moisture.
4. Do not relax damaged hair. Suggest a series of reconditioning treatments.
5. Always read and follow the manufacturer's instructions before giving a processing treatment.
6. Have all implements and materials ready before you start the treatment.
7. Never give a chemical hair processing treatment to hair which has recently been straightened by a hot pressing comb.
8. Do not use a hot comb after a processing treatment. To do so will damage the hair.
9. Avoid rubbing the processor on the hair. Lay it on the hair shaft.
10. Do not give a processing treatment if the client suffers from nausea or if redness and irritation appear within or around the skin test area.
11. Strand test to be sure the processing treatment can be safely given.
12. Examine the scalp for abrasions; if any are present, do not give a processing treatment.
13. Apply a petroleum base to protect the scalp from the active agents in the processor (if required by the manufacturer).
14. If a base is used, after the application check carefully to see that the scalp has been completely and thoroughly covered. Failure to cover the scalp carefully can result in a burn or irritation by the chemicals being used.

15. Always use great care and caution when applying the processor.

16. Never leave the client alone while the processor is on the hair.

17. Wear protective gloves when giving a processing treatment.

18. Use extreme care when applying the processor to avoid spilling it on the ears, scalp or skin.

19. When rinsing the processor from the hair, great care should be taken that the water is not too hot. If hot water is used, the hair will revert to its natural curly shape and the entire process will be in vain.

20. Be sure to thoroughly shampoo and rinse the processor from the hair. Failure to do so will cause the processor to continue to act, resulting in hair damage.

21. When rinsing the shampoo from the hair, always work the fingers from the scalp to the ends, following the water stream to prevent tangling of the hair.

22. The application of a stabilizer to the hair following the shampoo is important to keep the hair in a relaxed or straight form.

23. Use a wide-tooth comb and avoid pulling when combing the hair.

24. To help restore some of the natural oils which have been removed by the chemicals, apply a conditioner after the hair and scalp are towel dried and before combing.

25. When retouching the new growth, do not allow the processor to overlap onto the already relaxed hair.

26. Avoid scratching the scalp with comb or fingernails.

27. Avoid leaving the chemical processor on the hair any longer than is necessary to straighten it.

28. Avoid harsh or rough handling of the scalp and the hair.

29. To avoid hair damage, do not use hot irons on processed hair.

30. Avoid getting chemicals or rinse water into the eyes.

31. Do not give a vigorous shampoo.

32. Do not use a strong processor on fine hair.

33. If hair ends are in a damaged condition trim the hair before a processing treatment is given.

34. Test the action of the processing agent frequently to determine how fast the natural curl can be removed.

35. When drying the hair, extreme heat from the dryer should be avoided to prevent damage to the hair and irritation to the scalp.

36. To remove a reddish cast caused by the processor, apply a color rinse to the hair.

37. Always fill out a record card at the completion of each treatment.

QUESTIONS ON CHEMICAL PROCESSING, CHEMICAL BLOW-OUT AND SOFT CURL PERMANENT

1. What is the action of a chemical hair processor?
2. What is the purpose of analyzing the client's hair prior to applying a chemical processor?
3. List four hair conditions to consider in a hair analysis.
4. What chemical compound is required in addition to the chemical processing agent? By what other term is it known?
5. What test should be given the client before he or she receives a chemical processing treatment?
6. If a client's hair has been receiving hot comb treatments, when can a chemical processing treatment be given to his hair?
7. What are three purposes of strand testing in the chemical processing procedure?
8. Why is a scalp examination especially important prior to a chemical hair processing treatment?
9. What is the purpose of the client's record card?
10. Why is it necessary to have the client sign a release?
11. What hair condition should prevent treatment with a chemical hair processor?
12. What is the purpose of the base which is applied to the entire scalp and surrounding areas?
13. Why use protective gloves when applying the chemical processor?
14. After the hair has been treated with sodium hydroxide processor, why should the hair be thoroughly rinsed prior to the application of a shampoo?
15. Why should the hair be carefully combed without touching the scalp before applying the processor?
16. Why is a cream shampoo preferred in giving a shampoo to chemically processed hair?
17. Why is it important to keep chemically processed hair from tangling during a shampoo?
18. Why should the hair have at least three shampoo applications after being treated with a sodium hydroxide hair processor?
19. What is the action of the stabilizer in the chemical hair processing procedure?
20. When should the hair be combed after a chemical processing treatment?
21. How is a chemical processing retouch given?
22. When should the hair be shampooed in giving a "thio" processing treatment?
23. How is the "thio" cream removed from the hair?
24. How are the underneath hairs covered in comb spreading?
25. What are some of the advantages of using combs in spreading the processor?
26. What type of combs are used in spreading the processor?
27. After a processing treatment, why is an application of a conditioner to the scalp and hair recommended?
28. What may be used if the hair develops a reddish cast after a processing treatment?
29. Why are hot irons not to be used over the hair after a processing treatment?
30. Why must a processing treatment not be given to hair that has received a hot comb treatment?
31. Define soft curl permanent.

Chapter 21
HAIR COLORING

THE SCIENCE OF COLOR VISION

Hair coloring (tinting) is the science and art of changing the color of the hair. **Hair coloring** involves the addition of an artificial color to the natural pigment in the hair, or the addition of color to bleached hair. The resultant color may duplicate a natural shade or produce an entirely new shade of hair. **Hair bleaching** is a partial or total removal of the natural pigment or artificial color from the hair.

(**Notes:** 1. The terms "tinting" and "coloring" are used interchangeably in this text. 2. Some barber-stylists prefer to use the term "lighten" in place of "bleach." 3. Consult page 529 for information on The Theory of Color.)

Hair tinting is another profitable source of income in the barber-styling shop, as it is a **repeat business.** The client who starts to have his or her hair tinted or lightened, usually keeps on having his or her hair retouched at regular intervals. Satisfactory service will encourage the client to return for additional services.

CLASSIFICATIONS OF HAIR COLORING

Temporary Hair Coloring

1. **Color rinses** are prepared rinses used to highlight the color or add color to the hair. These rinses contain certified colors and remain on the hair until the next shampoo.
2. **Highlighting color shampoos** combine the action of a color rinse with that of a shampoo. These shampoos generally contain certified colors, give highlights and impart color tones to the hair.
3. **Crayons** are sticks of coloring in all shades, compounded with soaps or synthetic waxes, sometimes used to color grey or white hair between hair tint retouches. Crayons are often used by men as a temporary coloring for **mustaches.** They come in several colors: blonde; light, medium and dark brown; black and auburn.

Semi-Permanent Hair Coloring

Tints that are formulated for four to six weeks duration are semi-permanent hair coloring agents. They are self-penetrating and are applied without peroxide. They do not change the basic structure of the hair.

Semi-permanent tints are designed:

1. To cover or blend partially grey hair without affecting the natural color of the hair.
2. To enhance the beauty of grey hair without changing its color.
3. To highlight and bring out the natural color of the hair.

Permanent Hair Coloring

1. **Aniline derivative tints** are also called **penetrating tints.** (Consult "Permanent Hair Colorings" in this chapter.)
2. **Pure vegetable tints (Egyptian henna).** Egyptian henna is still being used for professional hair coloring. While it is basically a harmless product, Egyptian henna has very little popularity for the following reasons:
   a) It takes too much time to work with.
   b) It is messy to work with.
   c) It produces off-shades of red.
   d) It gives an orange color tone to grey or white hair.
3. **Metallic** or **mineral dyes,** such as lead acetate or silver nitrate, are the **progressive type** or **color restorers.** They form a metallic coating over the hair shaft, and render the hair unsatisfactory for hair coloring. Applications are made successively until the proper shade has developed.
4. **Compound dyes,** such as compound henna, are combinations of vegetable dyes with certain metallic salts and other dyestuffs. The metallic salts fix the color. Compound dyes coat the hair shaft in the same manner as metallic dyes and render the hair unfit for coloring.

METALLIC (COATING) DYES

Metallic dyes and compound dyes are never used professionally. However, men do buy and apply such products to their hair. Therefore, the barber-stylist must be able to recognize and understand their effects on the hair. Such coloring agents must be removed and the hair reconditioned, before the application of penetrating tint or bleaches is possible.

Hair treated with either a metallic dye, compound dye or color restorer type of dye will appear to be dull with no highlights. It is generally harsh and brittle to the touch. These colorings usually fade into peculiar or unnatural shades. **Silver** dyes have a **greenish** cast; **lead dyes** have a **purple** color, and those containing **copper** dyes turn red.

The professional barber-stylist should know how each type of metallic dye acts on the hair.

Removal of Coating Dyes

Preparations are available for the removal of metallic (coating) dyes. In removing coating dyes, never guarantee the results, for complete success is not certain. For removing coating dyes, be guided by the manufacturer's directions.

PREPARATION FOR HAIR COLORING
WHAT TO CONSIDER IN COLOR SELECTION

Always consult the client and consider his or her color preference before starting to apply a tint or toner to the hair. For this purpose, make use of a well-lighted room, providing either a strong natural light or incandescent lighting. Fluorescent lighting is not suitable for judging hair colors.

When talking to the client, find out whether he or she knows what color suits his or her age and **skin tones.** You must consider that skin tones change with age. The natural color of the client's hair, which harmonized with his or her skin coloring at the age of twenty or thirty, may be harsh and unbecoming at the age of forty or fifty. For clients in this age group, keep to the lighter shades of color.

ALLERGY TO ANILINE DERIVATIVE TINTS
(Semi-Permanent and Permanent Tints)

Allergy is an unpredictable condition. Some clients may be sensitive to aniline derivative tints while others are not. To identify such individuals, **a skin or patch test** is required for all clients prior to applying a semi-permanent or permanent tint or toner. A person who has been free of an allergy may suddenly develop it. To be sure, give a patch test to find out if the client has become sensitive since his or her last tinting treatment.

The **U.S. Federal Food, Drug and Cosmetic Act** prescribes that a **patch test** or **predisposition test** must be given before each application of an aniline derivative tint, whether on a **virgin** (hair that has not been tinted) head or for a **retouch.** This test is required to protect the client, as well as yourself and the entire barber-styling profession.

CAUTION. Aniline derivative tints must **never** be used on the eyebrows or eyelashes. **To do so may cause blindness.** It is also advisable not to **color mustaches** with aniline derivative tints due to the sensitivity of the mucous membranes of the nostrils and lips.

EXAMINING SCALP AND HAIR

The scalp and hair are carefully examined to determine if it is safe to use an aniline derivative tint and whether any special hair tinting problems exist.

An aniline derivative tint **should not be used** if the following conditions are present:

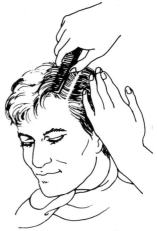

1. Signs of a positive skin test, such as redness, swelling, itching and blisters.
2. Scalp sores or eruptions.
3. Contagious scalp or hair disease.
4. Presence of metallic or compound dyes.

If the scalp and hair are in a healthy condition, carefully observe and record data relative to:

Examining the scalp.

1. **Type of hair.** Degree of porosity: either very receptive, moderately receptive, very resistant or moderately resistant.
2. **Texture of hair.** Coarse, medium, fine or wiry.
3. **Color of hair.** Natural or colored and the percentage of grey hair.

PATCH TEST

The patch test must be given 24 hours before each aniline derivative tinting or toner treatment. The tint used for the skin test must be of the same shade and mixture as the tint intended to be used for the hair tinting treatment.

Procedure

1. Select test area, either behind the ear extending partly into hairline or on the inner fold of the elbow.
2. Wash test area, about the size of a quarter, with mild soap and water.
3. Dry test area by patting with absorbent cotton or clean towel.
4. Prepare test solution by mixing one capful of tint and one capful of 20-volume peroxide, or as directed by the manufacturer.
5. Apply enough test solution with cotton-tipped applicator to cover the area previously cleansed.
6. Allow test area to dry. Leave uncovered and undisturbed for 24 hours.
7. Examine test area for either negative or positive reactions.

PATCH TEST FOR PERMANENT TINTS

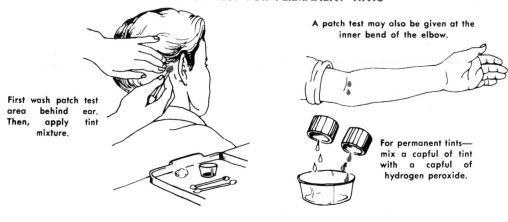

First wash patch test area behind ear. Then, apply tint mixture.

A patch test may also be given at the inner bend of the elbow.

For permanent tints—mix a capful of tint with a capful of hydrogen peroxide.

PATCH TEST FOR SEMI-PERMANENT TINTS

Measure one capful of full strength tint.

In giving a client a patch test for a semi-permanent tint, it is applied in the same manner as for a permanent tint, except that the semi-permanent tint is not mixed with hydrogen peroxide. Apply the tint full strength to the test area with a cotton-tipped applicator.

A **negative skin test** will show no signs of inflammation; hence, an aniline derivative tint or semi-permanent tint may be applied.

A **positive skin test** is recognized by the presence of redness, swelling, burning, itching, blisters or eruptions. The patron may also suffer from a headache and vomiting. A patron showing such symptoms is allergic to aniline derivative tint, and **under no circumstances should this particular kind of tint be used.** The patron **must** get immediate medical attention; otherwise, complications may set **in.**

HOW TO GIVE STRAND TESTS

A strand test is given **prior** to any complete color application to determine the actual color and the condition of the hair.

Strand Test for Semi-Permanent Tints

Semi-permanent tints do not require the addition of hydrogen peroxide to the coloring material. Give strand test in the following manner:

1. Gently shake the container of the tint.
2. Pour a small quantity of tint (about 1 teaspoon) into a glass or plastic bowl.
3. Apply the tint with a brush to the full length of a hair strand. Retain it on the hair until the desired shade has developed.
4. Remove excess color with a piece of wet towel or cotton, dry and examine the hair strand. If the results are satisfactory, proceed with the tint application.

Should the color produced in the test strand be different from the color desired, select another shade and strand test again.

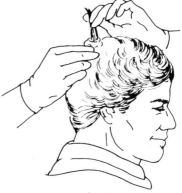

Strand testing.

Strand Test for Permanent Tints

Single application tints, double application tints and toners require the addition of 20-volume hydrogen peroxide to the coloring material. For these tints, give strand test in the following manner:

1. Mix ½ teaspoon or one bottle cap of the selected color with equal amount of 20-volume hydrogen peroxide. (Use plastic spoon.)
2. Apply mixture with a brush on both sides to the full length of a hair strand. Retain it on the hair until the desired shade has developed.
3. Remove excess color with a piece of wet cotton, dry and examine the hair strand. If the results are satisfactory, proceed with tint application.

Should the color produced on the strand be different from the color desired, select another shade and **strand test** again.

CAUTION: In strand testing for semi-permanent and **permanent** tints, if they show discoloration which might indicate the presence of a metallic dye, **corrective steps** must be taken before tint application.

HOW TO REMOVE TINT STAINS FROM SKIN

As a rule, soap and water will remove most tint stains. However, use one of the following methods for difficult stain removal!

a) Wet a piece of cotton with the left-over tint. With a rotary movement cover the stain areas; follow with a damp towel. Apply a small amount of face cream and wipe clean.

b) Use a prepared "tint stain remover."

Removing tint stains.

TEMPORARY COLOR RINSES

Because men, as a rule, are hesitant about accepting a hair color change, the temporary color rinses containing certified colors, may be used as successful devices in presenting to them a preview of some hair color change.

Temporary color rinses are satisfactory for clients who want to highlight the color of their hair or add slight color to grey hair. These rinses wash out with soap and water, but as a rule remain color-true from shampoo to shampoo. They come in various color shades: blonde, brown, black, red, silver and slate. These rinses are easily and quickly applied and are valuable as an introduction to semi-permanent or permanent hair coloring.

They can be used as follows:
1. To bring out highlights in hair of any shade.
2. To temporarily restore faded hair to its natural shade.
3. To neutralize the yellowish tinge of white or grey hair.
4. To tone down over-lightened hair.

TESTING FOR COLOR SELECTION

Before applying a color rinse to the hair give a preliminary strand test, which will indicate:
1. Whether the proper color selection was made.
2. The correct length of time to leave the color rinse on the hair.

HOW TO GIVE A STRAND TEST

1. Mix a small amount of the color rinse selected with warm water.
2. Apply the mixture to a full hair strand. Retain it on the hair as directed by the manufacturer.
3. Rinse, dry and examine the hair strand. If the results are satisfactory, proceed with the color rinse treatment.

Should the color produced on the test strand be different from the color desired, select another and **strand test** again.

DRAPING OF A CLIENT

Protect the client's clothing. Place a small turkish towel around his neck. After the plastic shampoo cape is fastened, turn a fold of the towel over the outside neck-band of the cape.

Another method of draping a client is shown in the following illustrations.

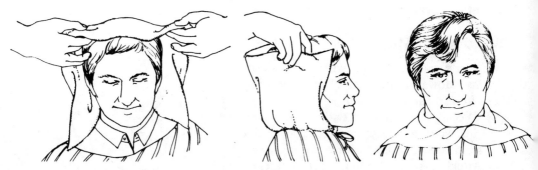

HELPFUL SUGGESTIONS IN HAIR COLORING

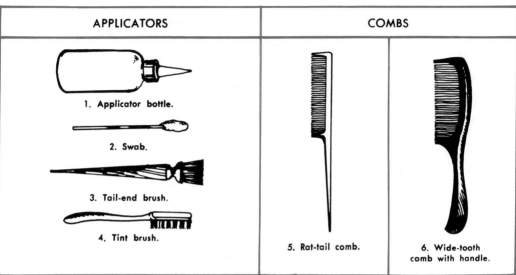

APPLICATORS	COMBS	
1. Applicator bottle.		
2. Swab.		
3. Tail-end brush.		
4. Tint brush.	5. Rat-tail comb.	6. Wide-tooth comb with handle.

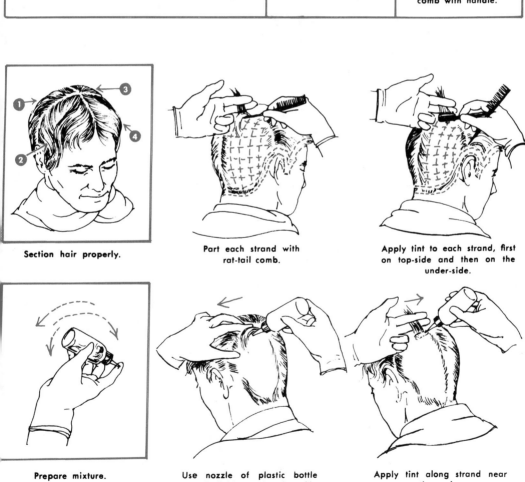

Section hair properly.

Part each strand with rat-tail comb.

Apply tint to each strand, first on top-side and then on the under-side.

Prepare mixture. Shake gently back and forth.

Use nozzle of plastic bottle to sub-divide section into ¼-inch strands.

Apply tint along strand near the scalp.

Glass or plastic bowls	Plastic cape and towels	Neck strip
Applicators —	Timer	Comb
Brush	Cotton	Protective gloves
Swab stick	Shampoo	Temporary rinse
Plastic bottle	Color rinse	Record card

IMPORTANT REMINDER

The procedures which follow represent two methods of applying a color rinse to the client's hair. Your instructor may have developed his or her own techniques which are equally correct.

PREPARATION

The client is usually given a haircut prior to a "color rinse" application.
1. Assemble all necessary supplies.
2. Prepare client. Protect his or her clothing with plastic cape and a towel.
3. Examine client's scalp and hair.
4. Select the desired shade of color rinse.
5. Prepare color rinse.
6. Give color strand test.

PROCEDURE FOR COLOR RINSE APPLICATIONS

1. Shampoo, rinse and towel blot the hair. (Excess moisture must be removed to prevent diluting the color.)
2. Prepare color rinse.

There are many kinds of temporary color rinses. For easy application they are usually prepared in a liquid form. To prepare a correct mixture the manufacturer's directions must be followed.

3. A plastic applicator bottle, or a glass, plastic or porcelain bowl may be used to contain the mixture.
4. The rinse may be applied by using any one of the following methods:

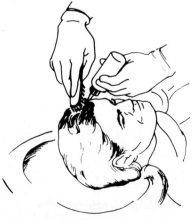

Applying color rinse around front hairline.

Brush-on Method

1. With a small brush apply the mixture around the front hairline. Manipulate the brush in short, rotary movements over the temple areas to lock the color in. This area is usually resistant.
2. Continue the application, working from the side areas toward the front.
3. Apply around the nape line and work upward to the crown area.
4. Brush the color rinse throughout the hair.
5. Check for complete coverage.
6. Leave rinse on for the desired length of time.
7. Follow manufacturer's directions for either rinsing or towel blotting.

8. Style the hair.
9. Fill out record card.
10. Clean up work area. Discard used material and return unused material and supplies to their proper places.

Applicator Method

The applicator method is very similar to the brush-on method. The only difference is that the tint mixture is applied with the applicator bottle and worked in with the cushion tips of the fingers.

RELEASE STATEMENT

A release statement is used for hair tinting or bleaching or any other treatment that may require the barber-stylist's or shop owner's release from responsibility for accidents or damages.

SAMPLE RELEASE

Client's Name .... Address ....

Condition of Hair: ....

Hair Coloring: Kind .... Given by ....

I fully understand that the hair coloring treatment which I have requested and am about to receive is ordinarily harmless to normal hair, but may damage my hair because of its present condition.

In view of this, I accept full responsibility for any possible damage that may result, directly or indirectly, to my hair.

Signature of Client ....

Witnessed by .... Date ....

SEMI-PERMANENT TINTS

Semi-permanent tints offer a form of hair coloring suitable for the client who has previously been reluctant toward hair color change.

The semi-permanent tint is a formulated coloring material which fills a gap between a temporary color rinse and a permanent hair color tint without in any way taking the place of either.

Naturally-colored hair which is drab or dull may be improved in color tone by the use of semi-permanent tints, since there is no bleaching action on the hair.

Semi-permanent tints depend on the original color and texture of the hair, the shade used and length of development time for successful results.

There is a wide range of colors available and the results obtained will depend mainly on the original color, and, to a lesser degree, on the texture of the client's hair.

The various shades may be blended to create individual color tones.

There are specifically designed blue-grey or silver-grey shades for hair ranging from the 10% to 100% grey.

CHARACTERISTICS OF SEMI-PERMANENT TINTS

1. Semi-permanent tints do not require the addition of hydrogen peroxide.
2. The color is self-penetrating.
3. The color is applied the same way each time.
4. Retouching is eliminated.
5. Color does not rub off, because it has slightly penetrated the hair shaft.
6. Hair will return to its natural color in four to six weeks, provided a mild, non-stripping shampoo is used.

Semi-permanent tints require a 24-hour patch test. Some semi-permanent hair colorings require pre-shampooing, others do not.

CAUTION: Be guided by your instructor and manufacturer's directions.

TYPES OF SEMI-PERMANENT TINTS

1. Semi-permanent tints which cover grey completely but do not affect the remaining pigmented hair.
2. Semi-permanent tints which make grey hair more beautifully grey without changing the natural pigment.
3. Semi-permanent tints which add color and highlights to hair without grey.

SELECTING COLOR SHADES FOR SEMI-PERMANENT TINTS

1. If the client's hair is slightly sprinkled with grey select a shade which matches his or her natural hair color.
2. If the hair is 50% or more grey select **one shade darker.**

MATERIALS AND SUPPLIES

Timer	Towels	Mild shampoo
Cotton	Tint cape for patron	Protective gloves
Comb	Applicators:	Selected semi-permanent tint
Color chart	Tint brushes	Acid or normalizing rinse
Glass or plastic bowls	Swab sticks	Record card
Clips	Plastic bottles	Talcum powder

PRELIMINARY STEPS

1. Give preliminary patch test 24 hours before tinting.
2. If the patch test is negative, then you can proceed with the tinting.
3. Examine client's scalp for irritation or abrasion.
4. Give strand test.

PREPARATION

The client is usually given a haircut prior to a hair coloring application.

1. Assemble all necessary supplies.
2. Prepare client. Protect his or her clothing with a towel and tint cape.
3. Re-examine client's scalp.
4. If required, give a mild shampoo.
5. Towel dry hair.
6. Put on protective gloves.
7. Give color strand test.

> IMPORTANT REMINDER: The procedure herein described is one way to apply a semi-permanent hair coloring. However, your instructor may have developed a particular technique which is equally correct.

PROCEDURE

The semi-permanent tint is applied with an applicator bottle to sectioned hair, or applied at the shampoo bowl with a brush or applicator bottle.

Since the manufacturers' directions vary, be guided by their directions or by your instructor.

1. Apply tint to the temples and sideburn areas.
2. Apply tint to the hair throughout the scalp area.

Applying tint to sideburn.

Use plastic cap covering, if recommended.

Rinse with warm water and work up a lather.

3. With fingers, gently work color through the hair until it is thoroughly saturated. (Do not massage into the scalp.)
4. If hair is longer than usual, pile it loosely on the top of the head.
5. During color development, be guided by your instructor or manufacturer's directions whether to use or omit a plastic cap covering.
6. Strand test for color.
7. When color has developed, wet hair with warm water, and work up a lather.
8. Rinse with warm water until water runs clear.
9. Give an acid or normalizing rinse.

CAUTION: Client should be seated in a **reclining position** to avoid getting tint in the eyes. If **inclined position** is used, then the client must hold a towel over the forehead and eyes to protect the eyes from the tint.

10. Remove stains if necessary.
11. Complete service in the usual manner.
12. Fill out record card.
13. Clean up. Discard used material and return unused material and supplies to their proper places.

SPECIAL PROBLEM

Some semi-permanent hair colorings have a tendency to build up color on the hair shaft with repeated applications. If this should occur follow this procedure for coloring the new growth.

1. Apply the color to only the new growth.
2. Retain until the desired color shade develops.
3. When the color has developed, wet the hair with warm water and blend the color through the hair with a large-toothed comb.

KEEPING HAIR TINT RECORDS

It is of the utmost importance to keep an accurate record of each hair coloring treatment, so that any difficulties encountered in one treatment may be avoided in subsequent ones. A complete record should be made of information, such as "dries out rapidly," "tint does not develop fast enough," or any other data connected with that particular head.

HAIR TINT RECORD

Name .... Tel. ....

Address .... City ....

Patch Test: Negative ☐   Positive ☐   Date ....

DESCRIPTION OF HAIR

Form	Length	Texture	Porosity	
straight	short	coarse	very porous	resistant
wavy	medium	medium	porous	very resistant
curly	long	fine	normal	perm. waved

Condition:

☐ Normal   ☐ dry   ☐ oily   ☐ faded   ☐ streaked   ....% grey

Previously lightened with .... for ....(time)

Previously tinted with .... for ....(time)

☐ original sample enclosed   ☐ not enclosed

CORRECTIVE TREATMENTS

Color filler used ....Corrective treatments with ....

HAIR TINTING PROCESS

whole head .... retouch .... inches   shade desired ....

Formula: Color .... Lightener ....

Results: ☐ good   ☐ poor   ☐ too light   ☐ too dark   ☐ streaked

Date	Barber-Stylist	Price	Date	Barber-Stylist	Price

HIGHLIGHTING SHAMPOO TINTS

(Single Application)

Highlighting shampoo tints are preparations containing aniline derivative tints combined with hydrogen peroxide and a neutral shampoo base. They are used when a **very slight change** in hair shade is desired. A 24-hour patch test is required.

These tints serve to cleanse the hair and highlight its natural color in a single operation.

Method of application. The hair is cut before the mixture is evenly distributed over the entire head at the shampoo bowl. Retain from 8 to 15 minutes. Rinse thoroughly.

PERMANENT HAIR COLORINGS

PENETRATING TINTS

Practically all professional permanent hair coloring is done with the use of oxidizing-penetrating tints containing an aniline derivative (a coal tar product).

Penetrating tints may be referred to as:

1. Single application tints, also called one process or one-step tints.

2. Double application tints, also called two process or two-step tints.

Single application tints (cream or liquid) perform two activities: they lighten and add color to the hair in a single application.

Double application tints (cream or liquid) perform only one activity at a time. For a complete color change or when a toner is desired, they require two separate and distinct applications to the hair:

a) **First**—the application of a lightener (bleach) or softener.

b) **Second**—the application of a tint or toner.

Both the single application and double application tints penetrate through the cuticle of the hair into the cortical layer. Here they are oxidized by the peroxide (which has been added) into color pigments which are distributed throughout the hair in much the same manner as the natural pigment.

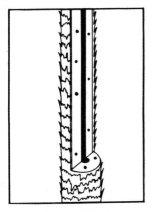

Gray untinted hair.

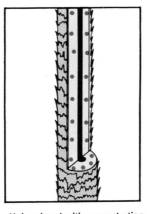

Hair colored with a penetrating aniline derivative tint.

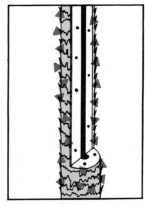

Hair colored with metallic (coating) dye.

When the developer (hydrogen peroxide) is mixed with the tint, a chemical reaction, known as **oxidation**, begins. For this reason, the tint mixture must be applied immediately to the hair. After the mixture is applied to the hair, the oxidation continues until the color has developed to the desired shade.

Timing the development of the applied tint requires a **thorough study** of the product being used.

Hydrogen Peroxide

For the uses of **hydrogen peroxide** and its availability, consult the **Hair Lightening** section of this chapter.

SINGLE APPLICATION TINTS

(Cream or Liquid Tints)

Single application tints represent a simplified method of hair coloring. In one application, the hair can be colored permanently **without** requiring pre-shampooing, pre-softening or pre-bleaching.

In most instances, the single application tints contain a lightening agent and a shampoo with an oil base combined with an aniline derivative tint. When ready for use, 20-volume hydrogen peroxide is added in fixed proportions, according to the manufacturer's directions.

A single application tint is applied on **dry hair only.** If the hair is in an extremely soiled condition and a shampoo is necessary, the hair must be thoroughly dried before applying the tint. The choice of shade varies from deepest black to lightest blonde.

The advantages of single application tints:
1. Save time by eliminating pre-shampooing or pre-lightening.
2. Leave no line of demarcation.
3. Color the hair lighter or darker than the client's natural color.
4. Blend in grey or white hair to match client's natural hair shade.
5. Tone down streaks, off-shades, discoloration and faded hair ends.

COLOR SELECTION

Some General Rules For Single Application Color Selection
1. To match the natural color of hair and to cover grey hair, select the color closest to the natural shade.
2. To brighten or lighten the hair color and to cover grey hair, select a shade lighter than the natural color. The selected tint must contain enough color to produce the desired shade on grey hair.
3. To darken the hair and cover grey hair, select a color darker than the natural hair color.
4. Study the manufacturer's color chart for correct color selections.

PRECAUTION: The color chart used for a color selection must be from the same manufacturer as the tint product. Each manufacturer's color chart is formulated to conform with his particular tint products.

IMPORTANT REMINDER. The procedure herein described is one way to apply a permanent hair coloring. However, your instructor may have developed his own technique which is equally correct.

SINGLE APPLICATION FOR VIRGIN HAIR

PRELIMINARY

1. Give 24-hour patch test before tinting.
2. If the patch test is negative and the scalp is normal, without irritation or abrasions, proceed with the color application.
3. Give a strand test.

MATERIALS AND SUPPLIES

Materials and supplies are the same as previously listed for semi-permanent tints with the following exception: include permanent tint and 20-volume hydrogen peroxide.

When is the best time to give a haircut? Before or after a permanent hair coloring application? The choice depends mainly on the length of hair and the instructor's preference.

If the hair is quite long, give the haircut first. However, if the hair is short, give the haircut after the tint application.

In either event, be guided by your instructor.

PREPARATION

1. Assemble all necessary supplies.
2. Prepare client. Protect his or her clothing with a towel and tint cape, since tint can permanently discolor clothing.
3. Re-examine client's scalp.
4. Select the desired shade of color.
5. Give color strand test.
6. Prepare formula.
7. Put on protective gloves.

Section hair into four quarters.

PROCEDURE

1. Men, as a rule, wear their hair rather short. If the hair is long enough, it may be sectioned into the four standard partings for tint application. If the hair is short, it may be parted by lifting the hair with the nozzle of the applicator bottle or with the comb.
2. Apply tint to the greyest parts first, such as temples, sideburns and nape area, since these areas are usually more resistant to color.
3. Apply tint to the scalp area by making 1/4-inch partings. The hair may be lifted with the nozzle tip of the applicator bottle. Except when tinting longer hair, the tint is applied about 1/2 inch from the scalp to the ends. After the head has been completely covered additional tint is applied to the scalp area. Since the scalp area receives the benefit of body heat, the tint in this area processes faster.
4. After the scalp area is completely covered, gently comb or work tint through the hair shaft until it is thoroughly saturated. **Do not massage.**
5. Check for complete coverage. Apply additional tint to areas, if needed.
6. Strand test for color.
7. Retain tint on hair for the required time as indicated by the strand test.
8. When the desired color has developed, rinse with warm water.

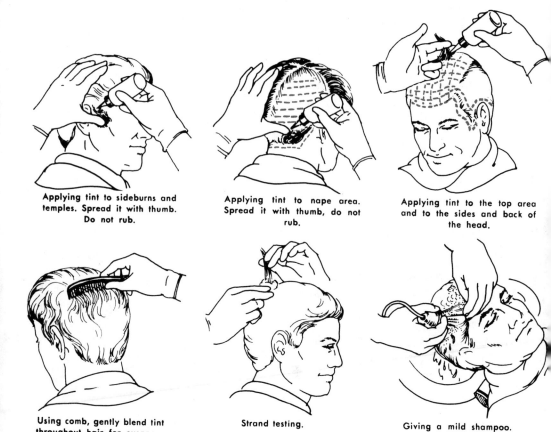

Applying tint to sideburns and temples. Spread it with thumb. Do not rub.

Applying tint to nape area. Spread it with thumb, do not rub.

Applying tint to the top area and to the sides and back of the head.

Using comb, gently blend tint throughout hair for evenness.

Strand testing.

Giving a mild shampoo.

9. Give a mild shampoo.
10. Rinse thoroughly with lukewarm water to remove excess color and shampoo.
11. Remove color stains, if necessary.
12. Dry and comb or style hair as desired.
13. Fill out record card.
14. Clean up. Discard used material and return unused material and supplies to their proper places.

SINGLE APPLICATION TINT RETOUCH

For a satisfactory retouch, the barber-stylist requires a high degree of skill and a uniform method of application. If the retouch is performed incorrectly, light and dark streaks may appear over the entire head.

PROCEDURE

To retouch the new growth, follow the same preparation as for coloring virgin hair. Refer to record card for correct color selection and other data.

1. Apply tint to **new growth** at sideburns, temples and nape area first.

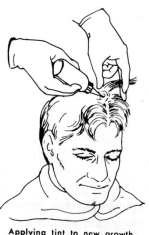

Applying tint to new growth.

2. **Rest of head.** Apply tint to new growth in ¼ inch strands. **Do not overlap.** Check frequently for color development.

3. When color has **almost** developed, dilute the remaining tint by adding a mild shampoo or warm water. Apply and gently work mixture through the hair with fingertips. Then comb-blend from scalp to hair ends for even distribution.

4. Retain for required time. Rinse with warm water to remove excess color.

5. Give a mild (non-strip) shampoo and rinse thoroughly.

6. Dry and comb, or style hair as desired.

7. Remove color stains, if necessary.

8. Fill out record card.

9. Clean up in the usual manner.

THE BARBER-STYLIST MUST BE PROFICIENT

Actually, the efficiency and skill of the colorist is usually demonstrated during a retouch color application. This type of operation requires careful and skillful application because, if it is not done correctly and with speed, light and dark streaks will appear over the head. It is therefore of paramount importance that the practitioner acquire professional skill as to techniques and methods of application.

Hair coloring is a very lucrative service for the barber-styling shop. If skillfully done much added revenue may be derived by both the owner and the artisan. The failure to develop this skill will naturally result in loss of a great deal of additional income.

HAIR LIGHTENING

Lightening the hair is usually a **preparatory** process for the application of a **single action,** penetrating tint or toner.

A lightening product is used to lighten the hair to some desired shade. The hair pigment goes through different changing stages of color as it lightens. The amount of change depends on pigmentation of the hair and the length of time the lightening agent is left on. For example: A natural head of black hair will go from black to brown, to red, to red gold, to yellow, and sometimes to the almost white stage.

Do not promise a client that his or her dark hair can be lightened to a very pale blonde shade if red pigment predominates and he or she desires to have silver or extremely pale toners applied.

Whatever the reason for lightening, it is important to select the right lightener and the **best mixture** for the degree of color change desired. To make an **intelligent choice,** follow the manufacturer's **literature** and **color charts.**

Lighteners are classified as oil lighteners, cream lighteners, and powder or paste lighteners.

1. **Oil lighteners** are usually mixtures of hydrogen peroxide with a sulfonated oil.
   a) **Colored oil lighteners** add temporary color and highlight the hair as they lighten. The colors contained are **certified** and may be used without a **patch** test. They **remove** pigment and **add** color tones at the same time. Basically, they are **classified** according to their **action** on the hair, namely:
      1. **Gold**—lightens and adds red highlights.
      2. **Silver**—lightens and adds silvery highlights to grey or white hair and minimizes red and gold tones on other shades.
      3. **Red**—lightens and adds red highlights.
      4. **Drab**—lightens and adds ash highlights. Tones **down** or reduces red and gold tones.
   b) **Neutral oil lightener** removes pigment without adding color tone. It may be used to pre-soften hair for tint application.
2. **Cream lighteners** are the most popular types of lighteners. They are easy to apply and will not run, drip or dry out. They are easy to control and contain conditioning agents, bluing and thickener, which provide the following benefits:
   a) The **conditioning agents** give some protection to the hair.
   b) The **bluing agent** helps to drab undesirable red and gold tones .
   c) The **thickener** gives control when applying.
3. **Powder or paste lighteners, also called quick lighteners,** contain an oxygen-releasing booster and inert substances for quicker and stronger action.
   a) **Paste lighteners** will hold and not run, but will dry out quickly.
   b) **Cream lighteners** can be controlled to prevent overlapping.
   c) **Powder lighteners** do not contain conditioning agents and may dry the hair and irritate the scalp.

If the scalp shows any sensitivity or abrasions, lighteners are not recommended.

ACTION OF HAIR LIGHTENERS

Hair lighteners, depending on the manufacturer's directions, can be used as follows:

1. To lighten the entire head of hair.
2. To lighten the hair to a particular shade.
3. To brighten and lighten the existing shade.
4. To tip, streak, or frost certain parts of the hair.
5. To lighten hair that has already been tinted.
6. To remove undesirable casts and off-shades.
7. To correct dark streaks or spots in hair that has already been lightened or tinted.

CAUTION. Patch test is required **only** if followed with a toner or tint application.

Together with manufacturer's directions, be guided by the following general rules:

1. Choose a cream lightener (blue base) when pre-lightening for pastel toners, such as blonde, silver, platinum or beige.
2. Choose a neutral oil lightener for the purpose of lightening the hair without adding color.
3. Choose an oil lightener (drab series) to avoid red and gold highlights in the natural color of the hair.

HYDROGEN PEROXIDE

The lightening agent for removing pigment from the hair shaft is **hydrogen peroxide.** The **active** ingredient of hydrogen peroxide is oxygen gas, and to speed the liberation of the oxygen gas, a small quantity of **28% ammonia water** is added. Commercial lightening products now contain substances which modify or prevent straw-like appearance or reddish or brassy tones in the hair.

Hydrogen peroxide, when properly used, can lighten, soften and oxidize the hair. For the purpose of hair lightening, it is used as a 6% solution, capable of producing 20 volumes of oxygen gas. A weaker strength of peroxide is not suitable for lightening and tinting. The use of a higher strength peroxide, even though it may speed up the lightening action, may be harmful to the hair.

Hydrogen peroxide is available in the form of a liquid, cream, powder or tablet. The liquid peroxide should be purchased in pint sizes, kept closed when not in use and stored in a cool, dark, dry place. Do not permit peroxide to come in contact with **metal.** When liquid peroxide is kept too long, exposed to air or stored in a warm place, it will weaken in strength. When using the tablets, powder or cream, follow the manufacturer's directions.

Uses of Hydrogen Peroxide

As a **lightening agent,** hydrogen peroxide solution softens the cuticle of the hair shaft, and lightens the shade of the coloring matter in the hair.

Lightening makes the hair porous and lighter in color. The final shade ranges from light to golden brown to gold and pale gold, depending upon the basic color of the hair or the formula of the lightener. Continued use of lighteners will make some hair over-dry and brittle.

As a **softening agent,** hydrogen peroxide solution softens the cuticle of the hair and makes it more receptive to the penetrating action of an aniline derivative tint. Care must be taken to control the softening process so that the hair is not lightened. It is also used to pre-soften grey hair before applying a toner.

As an **oxidizing agent,** hydrogen peroxide solution is used in all aniline derivative (penetrating) hair tints. It acts as a developer to liberate oxygen gas which changes para-phenylene-diamine into a dark-colored compound capable of tinting the hair.

PRELIMINARY LIGHTENING STRAND TEST

A **preliminary strand test** is necessary to judge the length of time to leave any lightening mixture on the hair, and to find out in what condition the hair is for lightening.

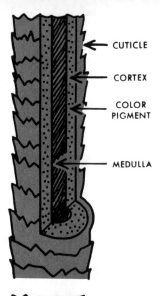

CUTICLE

CORTEX

COLOR PIGMENT

MEDULLA

SEVEN STAGES IN LIGHTENING FROM DARK HAIR TO ALMOST WHITE (Pale Yellow)

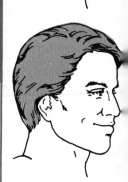

A virgin head of dark hair passes through seven stages before it arrives at the almost white stage.

The change in the color depends upon the type of lightener chosen and the length of time that it remains on the hair.

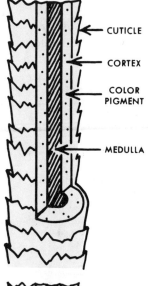

CUTICLE

CORTEX

COLOR PIGMENT

MEDULLA

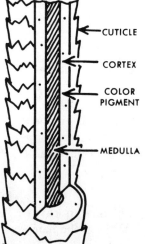

CUTICLE

CORTEX

COLOR PIGMENT

MEDULLA

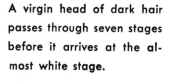

A **patch test** must be made 24 hours previous to the application of a **toner**. To save the patron's time, the strand test for lightening should be made the day he has the patch test.

LIGHTENING VIRGIN HAIR

IMPLEMENTS AND SUPPLIES FOR HAIR LIGHTENING

To produce the best results in hair lightening, the barber-stylist should have available the following:

Towels
Plastic cape
Shampoo and rinse
Cotton
Comb
Record card
Talcum powder
Peroxide (20 volume)

Lightening agent
Applicator bottle
   (plastic, with measurements listed)
Protective gloves
Glass or plastic bowls
Measuring glass or cup
Timer

If a paste type lightener is to be used, a brush applicator or swab will be needed.

PROCEDURE FOR SHORT HAIR

The following general instructions in applying lightening products may be changed by your instructor to conform with the manufacturer's directions.

1. **Prepare client.** Adjust tint cape and towel to cover and protect client's clothing.
2. **Examine scalp and hair.** Do not give a lightening treatment to a client with eruptions or abrasions. Do not brush or shampoo hair.
3. **Section hair** into four quarters.
4. **Put on protective gloves.**
5. **Prepare lightener** and use immediately to prevent deterioration. Follow manufacturer's directions.

The order of applying the lightener around the head is important. If the hair seems resistant or especially dark around the crown, then it is advisable to start at the back of the head to allow for extra time of contact in this region.

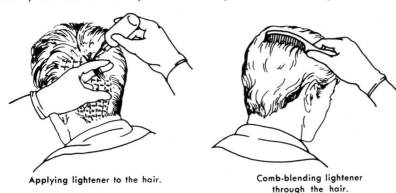

Applying lightener to the hair.

Comb-blending lightener
through the hair.

6. **Apply lightener in ⅛-inch partings** from scalp to hair ends on both top and underside of the hair strand. Continue to do this until the entire head is completed. For even distribution gently comb-blend the lightener through the hair. Be sure to keep the hair moist with the lightener during the bleaching process.

7. **Test for color.** Make first strand test about 15 minutes before the completion of the time required, as indicated by the preliminary test. Remove mixture from strand with wet towel or cotton. Dry the strand. If the shade is not light enough, reapply mixture and continue testing frequently, until desired shade has almost been developed.

8. **Remove lightener.** When desired shade has been reached, rinse with cool water and shampoo hair lightly with a mild shampoo.

9. Dry hair either with towel or under a cool dryer.

10. Examine scalp for abrasions and hair for breakage. If scalp is normal the hair is ready for toner application. (Consult section on **Toners** in this chapter.)

11. Fill out a complete record card.

12. Clean shampoo bowl, sanitize implements, discard used supplies and put work bench in order.

PROCEDURE FOR LONGER HAIR

The procedure for applying a lightener to longer hair is the same as for short hair, with the following variations.

Steps 1 to 5—Same as for short hair.

6. **Apply lightener in ⅛-inch partings.** Start about one-half inch from the scalp and extend lightener to a point where the hair shaft shows signs of damage. Apply lightener to both top and underside of hair strand. Continue until the entire head is completed. Work mixture into hair with fingers. Because the lightener makes the hair fragile, **do not comb it through the hair.** Keep hair moist with lightener during the bleaching process.

7. **Test for color.** Make first strand test about 15 minutes before the completion of the time required, as indicated by the preliminary test. Remove mixture from strand with wet towel or cotton. Dry the strand. If the shade is not light enough, reapply mixture and continue testing frequently, until desired shade has almost been developed.

Scalp area and hair ends. Towel blot excess lightener; if necessary, prepare a fresh mixture of lightener. Use ⅛-inch partings, and:

a) Apply lightener over the entire scalp area and on previously lightened hair, and through the hair ends.

b) Work the lightener through the hair ends with fingertips. **Do not massage the scalp.**

c) Retain lightener for required length of time.

Steps 8 to 12—Same as for short hair.

LIGHTENER RETOUCH

A lightener retouch is the term commonly used when a lightener is applied only to the new growth of hair from the scalp to match the rest of the lightened hair.

As a general rule, black or dark brown hair would require retouch applications more frequently than the lighter shades.

In retouching, the lightener is applied to the **new growth only,** with the following exceptions:

1. If another color is desired.
2. If a lighter shade is desired.
3. If color has become heavy or dull from several applications.

For each of these conditions, wait until the new growth is almost light enough or has developed fully. Then bring the **remainder** of lightener through the hair shaft. One to five minutes is ample time to correct any one of these conditions.

RETOUCH PROCEDURE

The client's record card should be consulted to guide the colorist as to the previous lightener used and time required for the shade to develop.

Cream lightener is generally used for a lightener retouch because its adhesive quality prevents the overlapping of the previously lightened hair.

The **procedure for a lightener retouch** is the same as that for lightening a virgin head, except that the mixture is applied only to the new growth of hair.

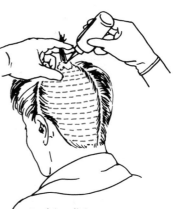

Applying lightener to new growth. Spread with thumb.

DO NOT OVERLAP LIGHTENER

CAUTION. Care should be taken not to **overlap** the lightener on to the previously lightened or tinted hair; to do so may cause breakage and/or streaks. The professional skill of the colorist is truly demonstrated in retouching whether it be in hair coloring or in hair lightening. Poor technical ability in retouching may result in unsatisfactory results and loss of clients.

DOUBLE APPLICATION TINTS
(Cream or Liquid)

Double application tints (two-process tints) can be used to good advantage to achieve a complete color change.

These tints require the use of two basic products, each one having a distinct action on the hair. In the first application, a product is used to lighten the hair, followed by a second application of a suitable aniline derivative tint, which colors the hair to the desired shade. A **patch test** is required.

The importance of selecting tint for virgin hair. Careful judgment must be used in selecting the first shade because the results of this application, if color is properly selected and applied, will improve the patron's appearance. He will, therefore, return for retouch treatments.

Pre-Lighten or Pre-Soften

When using a **double application tint** there is no lightening action. When a color is added to color, the result is a darker shade. Use the following suggestions as a guide to pre-soften or pre-lighten the hair:

1. If the client desires a complete color change to a lighter color, **pre-lighten** the hair before applying the tint.
2. Pre-soften **resistant grey hair** before **color** application.
3. Pre-soften **grey hair** before a **toner** application.
4. **Pre-lighten** the hair **to gold or pale yellow** before a **toner** application.

Color Selection for Double Application Tints

1. If the client's hair is completely grey, select the **exact color** desired.
2. If the hair is about 50% grey, select color that is **one shade lighter.**
3. If the hair is about 25% grey, select color that is **2 to 3 shades lighter.**

DOUBLE APPLICATION TINT FOR VIRGIN HAIR
PRELIMINARY

1. Give 24-hour patch test before tinting.
2. If the patch test is negative and the scalp is normal, without irritation or abrasions, proceed with the color treatment.

PREPARATION

1. Arrange all necessary supplies.
2. Prepare client.
3. If pre-softened, dry under a cool dryer. If pre-lightened, shampoo lightly, rinse thoroughly and dry.
4. Select the desired shade of color.
5. Make color strand test.
6. Put on protective gloves.
7. Prepare formula.

> **COLOR FILLER**
>
> For damaged hair or hair ends, first apply the filler to these areas to equalize hair porosity. Be guided by your instructor.

PROCEDURE

1. **Section hair according to its length.** If hair is long enough, section hair into four quarters.
2. Apply tint to areas where grey hair is most prevalent, usually in the sideburn and temple areas.

308

Use plastic bottle with nozzle or brush to apply tint. Hold ¼-inch strand spread between index and middle fingers in an upward direction away from the scalp. Apply tint evenly to both sides of strand, going from the scalp to hair ends, if the hair is short, and from scalp to within ½ to one inch of the hair ends, if the hair is longer.

When all sections have been treated, check for complete coverage and apply tint where needed.

Considering the manufacturer's directions and porosity of the hair, allow the tint to remain on the hair for the required length of time. This time can be judged by making frequent strand tests.

3. **Strand testing.** Wet a small piece of cotton with soap and water or shampoo. Wring out some of the moisture. Select a section of hair where tint was first applied or where grey hair was most evident. Remove the tint with wet cotton. If the desired shade has not been reached, re-moisten this strand of hair with the tint, and leave it on for another five to ten minutes. Make another test for color.

REMINDER. It is impossible to give definite instructions as to the length of time required for color development, as no two heads of hair are alike.

4. **Apply tint to hair ends.** After developing time has almost elapsed, using a large-tooth comb or fingers, distribute tint through the hair ends.

   Damaged hair ends. Apply color filler before tint application or mix filler with remaining tint and apply to hair ends. Be guided by your instructor.

5. **Rinse hair.** Spray the hair thoroughly with a strong force of water. This serves to set the color and remove excess tint from the hair.

6. **Remove stains.** Remove all tint stains from the skin of hairline, ears and neck. This is accomplished with either left-over tint, commercial tint remover or cream.

7. **Shampoo hair.** The hair is given a mild shampoo and rinsed thoroughly.

8. **Give a neutral rinse.**

9. **Set, dry and style hair.**

10. **Fill out record card.**

11. **Clean up** in the usual manner.

DOUBLE APPLICATION TINT RETOUCH

A "retouch" is the term commonly used when the tint is applied to the new growth of hair at the scalp. To match the color, consult the client's hair tint record card to determine the exact shade of tint, the procedure to use, and how long to keep tint on the hair.

Preparation (up to procedure) is the same as for tinting virgin hair.

PROCEDURE

1. Section hair into four quarters.

2. Outline partings with tint and then apply tint to section where the softener or lightener was last applied.

3. Subdivide one section at a time into ¼-inch strands. Hold the hair upward and away from the scalp and apply color along the part.

4. Distribute the color evenly along the part, out to the previously tinted hair, exercising care not to overlap the previously tinted hair.
5. Take frequent strand tests as indicated on the record card.
6. When desired color has developed, be guided by your instructor as to diluting (with warm water) the remainder of tint that is to be applied to the hair shaft.
7. After color has been distributed through the hair ends, time until the new growth and hair shaft are the same color.
8. Rinse thoroughly, to remove free color.
9. Remove stains from around the hairline, ears and neck.
10. Shampoo hair with mild shampoo and rinse thoroughly.
11. Complete service in the usual manner.
12. Fill out record card.
13. Clean up in the usual manner.

TONERS
(Double Application Method)

Toners are aniline derivative tints, a permanent, penetrating type of hair coloring. Nearly all toners require a patch test. Be guided by the manufacturer's directions

Toners consist primarily of pale, delicate colors and when properly used will achieve certain desired effects.

Toners are applied in the same manner as double application tints.

PRE-LIGHTENING FOR TONERS

Pre-lightening is required for toner color effect. Hair should be pre-lightened to gold or pale yellow, depending on the toner color to be used. Toners penetrate and deposit color in the same manner as other tints. They are dependent upon the preliminary lightening, which must leave the hair both light in color and porous. Some toners (the extreme pale shades) require more pre-lightening than others. The lightener must be kept on long enough to achieve desired porosity. Coarse, resistant or dark hair requires longer lightening time than naturally blonde hair.

Although naturally blonde hair may reach the pale yellow stage very quickly, it may **not be porous** enough to retain a toner. If the required porosity has not been developed, allow for additional lightening time.

White or grey hair requires a certain amount of pre-lightening to make the hair porous enough to receive a toner. Since white or grey hair is almost decolorized, it needs pre-lightening before the application of a blonde, silver or pastel shade toner. Pre-lightening is very important when grey hair is a mixture of light and dark strands. Lengthy lightening will not be necessary, but a certain amount of lightening is required to make the hair porous enough to accept the toner.

CHOOSING TONER SHADES

The pastel colors, such as silver, ash, platinum and beige, are usually in good taste for business or esthetic reasons.

For the client who wants extremely light colored hair, the blonde colors are the perfect color tones.

For the client with grey hair and skin tone changes which accompany the advancing years, the lighter silver tones are becoming.

For the client desiring **extremely** pale toner shades in the **very light** silver, platinum or beige series, the hair must be pre-bleached to the **pale yellow** or almost **white stage.**

In choosing a toner, color selection must frequently be left to the colorist's judgment. Other important factors to be considered are client's age and complexion.

TONING OF MEN'S HAIR

Prelightening of the hair is necessary before applying the toner. After the client has been properly prepared, proceed as follows:

1. Apply suitable toner shade.
2. When the toner has completely covered the hair, distribute it with the fingertips. Do not comb through the hair.
3. Leave toner on the hair the length of time as indicated by the strand test.
4. Apply cool water rinse to remove toner from the hair.
5. Cleanse hair lightly with a non-strip shampoo.
6. Apply cool water rinse again to the hair.
7. Style the client's hair, as desired.

TONER RETOUCH

A toner retouch must be given the same careful consideration as you would give a two-color tint retouch application. The new growth must be pre-lightened to the same degree of lightness as was given in the first toner application.

The lightener is applied to the new growth only. To overlap the lightener on to the already lightened hair will no doubt damage it.

After the lightening process has been completed, the toner is applied to the entire length of the hair in the usual manner.

SUGGESTIONS AND REMINDERS

Toners are completely dependent upon the proper preliminary lightening treatment, and must leave the hair light and porous enough to receive the pale toner shades. A strand test should first be made, and a complete explanation as to the possible outcome given the patron.

The possibility always remains that the hair cannot be decolorized to the stage of receiving his color choice without committing serious damage.

If the red and gold pigment has not been eliminated during the lightening process, the client's choice of toner color might result in a shade with a greenish cast, or the color might not take at all. When this happens, the toner must be deeper and not as pale or silvery as the client might have requested.

During the application and development period, toners have quite a different color than the final shade, depending on their basic color. However, when the color has fully developed the anticipated color will have been achieved. (Example: Ash blonde will have a brownish shade; silver blonde a bluish cast, and platinum a violet cast.)

FROSTING, TIPPING AND STREAKING

Marbleized streaking.

For **partial lightening,** such as frosting, tipping and streaking, quick lighteners are often advisable.

1. **Frosting.** Strands of hair are lightened over various parts of the head. The strands of hair are pulled through the holes of a perforated cap in order to protect the scalp. The effect achieved will depend on where and how many strands of hair are treated.

2. **Tipping is similar to frosting.** Wisps of hair are lightened in various areas, usually across the front of the head. This produces a contrast with the darker shade of hair. The strands of hair are drawn through the holes in a perforated cap.

3. **Streaking.** This is a lightened strand, usually at the front hairline. The width and placement of the lightened strand depends on the "feather" effect to be achieved.

CAP TECHNIQUE FOR FROSTING OR TIPPING

1. Shampoo and dry hair.
2. Comb hair gently.
3. Adjust perforated cap over the head.
4. Draw strands of hair through holes with crochet hook. (Fig. 1)
5. Apply lightener. (Fig. 2)

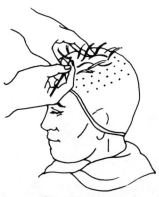

312

Fig. 1. Drawing strands with crochet hook.

Fig. 2. Applying lightener.

Fig. 3. Covering head with aluminum foil or plastic cap to hasten the process.

6. To hasten process, cover head with aluminum foil or plastic cap. (Fig. 3)
7. When hair is sufficiently lightened, remove aluminum foil or plastic cap.
8. With perforated cap still on, shampoo or rinse off lightener. Towel dry.
9. Apply toner in the usual manner.
10. Style hair as desired.

SPECIAL PROBLEMS IN HAIR TINTING AND LIGHTENING
FILLERS

Fillers are preparations which are available in liquid or cream form. They are employed to **revitalize, recondition** and **correct** abused, lightened, tinted or damaged hair.

There are two general classifications of fillers: **conditioner** fillers, which are colorless; and **color** fillers, which range in shades from pale blue to deep brown.

COLOR FILLERS

When To Use A Color Filler

If the hair is in a damaged condition, and if there is any doubt that the finished color will not be an even shade, a color filler is recommended.

A filler is applied after hair has been pre-lightened and before the application of a toner or tint. A filler is also used for the client who has been tinting or lightening his hair and desires to return to his natural color.

Advantages of Color Fillers

1. Deposit color to faded hair shafts and ends.
2. Help hair to hold color.
3. Help to insure a uniform color from the scalp to hair ends.
4. Prevent color streaking.
5. Prevent off-color results.
6. Prevent a dull color appearance.
7. Give more uniform color in a tint back to natural shade.

How To Use Color Fillers

Color fillers may be used **directly** from the containers to **damaged hair** prior to tinting or they may be **added** to the **remainder** of the tint and applied to **damaged hair ends.** Be guided by your instructor.

Selection of Correct Color Filler

To obtain satisfactory results, select the color filler to match the same basic shade as the toner or tint to be used.

Note—Since manufacturers' directions regarding fillers vary as to the color selection and their use and application, be guided by their directions or by your instructor.

RECONDITIONING DAMAGED HAIR

The frequent use of compound henna and metallic dyes coats and damages the hair. Hair in this state must be **reconditioned** before it can **successfully** be tinted or lightened.

Careless application by the barber-stylist of tinting or lightening agents to the hair may result in breakage or a dry, brittle condition.

The use of **highly alkaline shampoos** or **soapless oil shampoos,** or the improper use of water temperature and hair dryer, or extreme exposure to the elements may cause hair to become damaged.

Hair may need reconditioning treatments for reasons other than damage resulting from the use of harmful products. Sometimes hair is naturally brittle, thin and lifeless. Both **neglect** and the **client's physical condition** may be contributing factors to these conditions.

Hair is considered damaged when it:

1. Is over-porous.
2. Is brittle and dry.
3. Breaks easily.
4. Has lost its elasticity.
5. Is rough and harsh to the touch.
6. Is spongy and mats easily when wetted.
7. Rejects color or absorbs too much color during a tinting process.

Any of these hair conditions may create trouble during a tinting or lightening treatment. Therefore, damaged hair should receive reconditioning treatments **prior to and after the application of these chemical agents.**

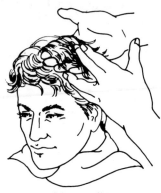

Applying conditioner to the hair.

RECONDITIONING TREATMENT

To restore damaged hair to a more normal condition, commercial products containing lanolin or protein substances should be used.

The reconditioning agent is applied to the hair. If heat is applied, use either a heating cap, a steamer or a heating lamp according to the manufacturer's directions. As to the frequency and length of time for each treatment, be guided by your instructor.

REMOVAL OF ANILINE DERIVATIVE TINTS
(With Prepared Commercial Products)

Sometimes it is necessary to remove or partially remove the tint from the hair in order to correct a previous tinting treatment or to apply some desired new shade.

Commercial products are used to remove penetrating tints and are known as tint or color removers.

They may contain hydrogen peroxide, acids, sodium hydrosulfite, a mixture of mineral and vegetable oils, or sulfonated oils.

The removal of tints can never be done mechanically. Each color removing treatment must be handled as an **individual problem** in which nothing can ever be taken for granted.

Chemicals that are sold for the purpose of removing tints should always be used with caution. Follow the **manufacturer's directions carefully.**

TINT BACK TO NATURAL COLOR

Each tint back to natural color must be handled as an individual problem. Check the natural shade of the hair next to the scalp.

The determining factors in the selection of the tint shade are: (1) the present condition and color of the hair, and (2) the final result desired, which is the original color.

Select an appropriate shade of filler to correspond with the tint to be used. Without the use of an appropriate filler, it will be difficult to obtain a uniform color from the scalp to hair ends since the hair porosity will vary in degree and area.

Such hair coloring problems require two or more strand tests and guidance by the teacher as to color selection and procedure.

LIGHTENING STREAKED HAIR

Streaks of discoloration may often appear on the hair and are caused in part by unsuccessful and unskilled lightener applications.

To correct streaked hair:
1. Prepare lightening formula as for virgin hair.
2. Apply mixture only to the darker streaks.
3. Work one strand at a time.
4. Allow to remain until all streaks are removed.
5. Shampoo hair.

COLORING MUSTACHES AND BEARDS

MUSTACHES

An aniline derivative tint should **never be used** for coloring mustaches; to do so may cause serious irritation or damage to the delicate membrane in the nostrils and the lips. Harmless commercial products are available to color mustaches.

IMPORTANT REMINDER

The procedure given here is one way to apply hair coloring to mustaches and beards. However, your instructor may have developed his own particular technique which is equally correct.

HARMLESS COMMERCIAL PRODUCTS

1. **Crayons** are sticks that come in several colors: blonde, medium and dark brown, black and auburn. The end of the stick, used like a pencil, is applied by rubbing directly on the mustache until the desired shade is reached.

Caution: To avoid staining the skin, a fine-tooth comb may be inserted in the mustache, close to the skin, then the end of the stick is rubbed on the mustache.

2. **Pomade in tubes,** consisting of harmless ingredients, have been com-pounded especially for coloring mustaches. They come in the following shades: black, brown, blonde, chatain (chestnut) and white (neutral). The pomade is applied to the mustache with a small brush and is stroked from the nostrils downward until full coverage is achieved.

Waxing. The pomade also contains a wax ingredient and when used in rolling or twisting the outer ends of the mustache they will remain in that position until the pomade is removed.

3. **Two-bottle set solutions** is another product available for coloring the mustache. The choice of colors is limited to brown and black.

Caution: Never shave around the mustache immediately before or after the color application. To do so may cause the product to irritate shaved areas.

Implements and Supplies

Petroleum jelly (Vaseline)
Coloring solutions (#1 and #2)
Stain remover
Towels
Cotton
Applicator sticks

PROCEDURE

1. Place client in a comfortable position. (Be guided by your instructor.)
2. Place clean towel across his chest.
3. Wash mustache with warm, soapy water.
4. Apply Vaseline around the mustache and on the edge of the upper lip.
5. **Apply solution #1.** Remove cap and moisten cotton-tipped applicator in solution. Touch tip of applicator to towel to remove excess moisture. Apply solution to the mustache until completely moistened. **Replace cap on bottle #1. Discard applicator immediately.**

Moisten fresh cotton-tipped applicator with stain remover and place on edge of towel for future use. Replace cap on stain remover bottle.

6. **Apply solution #2** to mustache in the same manner as solution #1. If stain gets on skin, use stain remover immediately. Replace cap on bottle #2.
7. Wash mustache with soap and cool water.
8. Remove stains with stain remover. Replace bottle cap.
9. Style mustache as desired.
10. Clean up in the usual manner.

BEARDS

The same products that are used for coloring mustaches may be used to color beards.

1. **Crayons.** For even distribution and to avoid staining the skin, crayon should be applied to the beard while holding the hair with a fine-tooth comb.

2. **Tube containing a pomade.** The pomade is applied with a small brush to particular areas of the beard held with a fine-tooth comb. Combing the hair with the comb will give an even distribution to the beard and avoid the staining of the skin.

3. **Two-bottle set in liquid form.** The liquid form may also be used to color beards. The procedure is the same as for coloring mustaches.

DEFINITIONS RELATED TO HAIR COLORING

Virgin hair is hair which has neither been tinted nor lightened. Hair that has been damaged in any way, such as by cold waving, sun, etc., cannot be considered to be **virgin hair.**

A **touch-up or retouch** is the application of coloring to the new growth of hair, using the same procedure and shade as that employed in the previous tinting or lightening treatment.

Blending is the process of making the color uniform throughout the hair during hair coloring applications.

Coating is the accumulation of residue on the outside of the hair shaft.

Certified color is a temporary coloring which coats the hair.

Pre-softening or softening is the application of a lightener to soften resistant hair and make it more receptive to the tint.

Powder lightener is a strong, fast-acting product used for special lightening effect.

Tint back is the coloring of the hair back to its natural shade.

Toner is an aniline derivative tint, delicate in shade, which is applied to highly lightened hair to produce blonde, silver and pastel shades.

Tint removal is the use of a dye solvent, lightener, or softening treatment to remove tint from the hair.

Color testing is a method of determining the action of a selected tint on a small strand of hair by washing and drying in order to observe its progress.

Strand test is a preliminary test given on a small strand of hair before a coloring treatment. It is used to predetermine the mixture and development times required for the treatment.

Developing time is the time needed to develop the color or the lightener. It begins at completion of application.

Semi-permanent hair coloring is hair coloring that lasts through several shampoos. Penetrates hair shaft slightly. Contains no peroxide and needs no peroxide to develop color.

Oxidation is a chemical reaction which takes place when peroxide and tinting solution are mixed and applied to the hair.

A developer is an oxidizing agent, such as 20-volume hydrogen peroxide solution; when mixed with a tint it supplies the necessary oygen gas.

Sensitivity is a condition in which the skin is highly reactive to the presence of a specific chemical. Skin reddens or becomes irritated shortly after application of the chemical. On removal of the chemical the reaction subsides.

Allergy is a hypersensitivity to cosmetics, tints, foods or other substances.

Decolorization is the removal of natural or artificial color pigments from the hair.

Susceptible means capable of being allergic.

Idiosyncrasy is an individual peculiarity which makes one susceptible to chemical substances in cosmetics, drugs and foods.

A skin or patch test is a procedure for determining whether or not a person is allergic to an aniline derivative tint.

Color filler is used to equalize porosity and to deposit a basic color on over-porous hair so that it can take and hold color evenly.

Highlighting refers to the brightening effect on the hair accomplished by the application of suitable color tones or the application of a lightening preparation.

Overlapping is a condition caused in a retouch by having a tint or a lightener overlap any part of the previously tinted or lightened hair.

Line of demarcation is a streak caused by overlapping on previously tinted hair.

Peroxometer or **hydrometer** is an instrument used primarily by chemists to measure the strength of hydrogen peroxide.

Porosity is the extent to which hair is able to absorb moisture or liquid preparations.

Soap cap is the application of a tint diluted with a shampoo. It is worked through the hair like a shampoo.

Plastic cap is used to retain heat on the head in order to hasten the treatment.

Stripping is a term used to indicate the removal of natural hair pigment, coating or penetrating tint, from the hair.

Resistant hair is hair with poor porosity.

Record card is a written record of the client's hair structure, condition, lightening and tinting color used, plus other pertinent information concerning the hair.

Conditioner is a cosmetic applied to hair to restore oils, sheen, and elasticity.

Spot lightening is applying a lightener only to dark areas to even out color.

Spot tinting is applying tint to areas insufficiently colored, in order to produce even results throughout.

Frosting is lightening small sections of hair throughout the head.

SAFETY MEASURES IN HAIR COLORING

HAIR TINTING

1. Make a 24-hour patch test before the application of a tint or toner.
2. Examine the scalp before applying a tint.
3. Do not apply tint if abrasions are present on the scalp.
4. Use only sanitized swabs, brushes, applicator bottles, combs and linens.
5. Always wash your hands before and after serving a client.
6. Do not brush the hair prior to a tint.
7. Do not apply a tint without reading the manufacturer's directions.
8. Make a strand test for color, breakage and/or hair discoloration.
9. Choose a shade of tint which harmonizes with the general complexion.
10. Use an applicator bottle or bowl (plastic or glass) for mixing the tint.
11. Do not mix tint before ready for use; discard left-over tint.
12. If required, use the correct shade of color filler.
13. Make frequent strand tests until the desired shade is reached.
14. Suggest reconditioning treatment for tinted hair.
15. Do not apply tint if metallic or compound dye is present.
16. Do not apply tint if a patch test is positive.
17. Give a strand test for correct color shade before applying tint.
18. Do not use an alkaline or harsh shampoo for tint removal.
19. Do not use water that is too hot for removing tint.
20. Protect the client's clothing by proper draping.
21. Do not permit tint to come in contact with the client's eyes.
22. Do not overlap during a tint retouch.
23. Do not neglect to fill out a tint record card.
24. Do not apply hydrogen peroxide or any material containing hydrogen peroxide directly over dyes known or believed to contain a metallic salt. Breakage or complete disintegration of the hair may result.
25. Wear protective gloves.

HAIR LIGHTENING

1. Analyze the condition of the hair and suggest reconditioning treatments, if required.
2. When working with a cream or paste lightener, it must be the thickness of whipped cream to avoid dripping or running, causing overlapping.
3. Apply lightener to resistant areas first. Pick up ⅛-inch sections when applying lightener. This will insure complete coverage.
4. Make frequent strand tests until the desired shade is reached.
5. After completing the lightener application, check the skin and remove any lightener from these areas.
6. Check the towel around the client's neck. Lightener on the towel allowed to come in contact with the skin will cause irritation.

7. Lightened hair is fragile and requires special care. Use only a very mild shampoo, and cool water for rinsing.
8. If a preliminary shampoo is necessary, comb hair carefully. Avoid irritating the scalp during the shampoo or when combing the hair.
9. Work as rapidly as possible when applying the lightener to produce a uniform shade without streaking.
10. Never allow lightener to stand; use it immediately.
11. Cap all bottles to avoid loss of strength.
12. Keep a completed record card of all lightening treatments.

QUESTIONS ON HAIR COLORING

1. Define hair tinting.
2. Give three reasons why a client may wish to have his or her hair tinted.
3. What three points of knowledge should a barber-stylist know in order to be successful in the technique of hair coloring?
4. Define a virgin head of hair.
5. What are the three main groups of hair coloring?
6. List three temporary hair colorings.
7. For how long are semi-permanent hair tints designed?
8. List four types of permanent hair colorings.
9. What are aniline derivative tints?
10. State two reasons why aniline derivative tints require a 24-hour patch test.
11. Briefly describe the action of aniline derivative tints.
12. How is a skin test given for permanent tints?
13. In giving a patch test for a semi-permanent tint, how does the procedure differ from that given for the permanent tints?
14. How is a positive skin reaction recognized?
15. What are two very important factors to consider when selecting a color shade?
16. Why should a preliminary strand test be given before the application of a tint?
17. List four conditions which would prohibit the application of an aniline derivative tint.
18. Why should an accurate record of each hair coloring treatment be kept?
19. What can be used to lighten and deposit color in the hair in one tint application?
20. List three advantages of single application tints.
21. List three important points to remember when using a double application penetrating tint.
22. What are two purposes of highlighting shampoo tints?
23. When is pre-lightening required?
24. When is pre-softening required?
25. Why is the hair not massaged vigorously prior to a tinting treatment?
26. What type of dyes are never used professionally?
27. List four characteristics of semi-permanent tints.
28. List two reasons for using a temporary color rinse.
29. How are tint stains removed from the skin and scalp?
30. In a retouch, to which part of the hair is a permanent tint applied?

HAIR LIGHTENING

1. Define hair lightening.
2. List three types of commercial lighteners.
3. What agent is used for lightening pigment in the hair shaft?
4. What strength hydrogen peroxide is commonly used?
5. Why do lightening products contain small quantities of 28% ammonia water?
6. When used as a softening agent, what reaction does hydrogen peroxide have on the hair?
7. List the two important purposes for making a preliminary strand test prior to lightening the hair.

8. Why is a patch test required prior to a toner application?
9. What are three causes responsible for over-lightening of the hair?
10. To which part of the hair is a lightener retouch applied?
11. Why should cool water be used during the shampoo following hair lightening?
12. What effects do lightening products have on the hair?
13. Define the word "toners."
14. How are toners applied?
15. Why does white or gray hair require some pre-lightening prior to application of a toner?
16. On what parts of the hair shaft are frosting, tipping and streaking usually applied?

MISCELLANEOUS

1. Why should lightened hair receive corrective treatment?
2. What purposes are served by conditioner fillers?
3. Name two types of fillers.
4. List two reasons for using a color filler.
5. What kind of hair treatment may be used to prevent porous areas of the hair shaft from absorbing too much tint?
6. List two methods by which tint may be removed from the hair.
7. Each color removing treatment must be handled as an .... problem.
8. Why must the tint remover be rinsed thoroughly from the hair?
9. List three precautionary measures to follow when tinting hair back to its natural shade.
10. Briefly define the following terms: a) color filler; b) coating; c) dye removal; d) oxidation.

COLORING MUSTACHES AND BEARDS

1. What kind of tint should never be used to color mustaches? Give reason.
2. List three harmless products that may be used to color mustaches and beards.

Chapter 22
MEN'S HAIRPIECES

INTRODUCTION

The care and fitting of men's hairpieces (toupees) is a rapidly growing service in the barber-styling field. It opens the door to much new and repeat business for the shop. Clients requiring this service are indeed appreciative of the craftsman who can provide it.

WHY MEN WEAR HAIRPIECES

1. **Necessity.** To cover up baldness or bald patches.
2. **Look younger.** A desire to retain a youthful appearance.
3. **Business.** For salesmen, entertainers, and those who must look younger to retain their position in business.
4. **Socially.** For older men who want to look younger socially.

QUALITY IN HAIRPIECES

The quality of a hairpiece varies with the kind of hair it contains, the way it is constructed and how it is fitted to the client's measurements.

Modern hairpieces are so expertly made that they closely resemble the client's own natural hair. They are made of human hair, synthetic hair or a combination of both.

A simple **match** test will tell the difference between human hair and synthetic hair. Cut a small strand of hair from the hairpiece. With a lighted match, burn this hair and observe these differences:

1. **Human hair** burns **slowly** and gives off a strong odor resembling burnt chicken feathers.
2. **Synthetic hair** burns **quickly** and gives off little or no odor. Besides, tiny hard beads are found in the burnt ash.

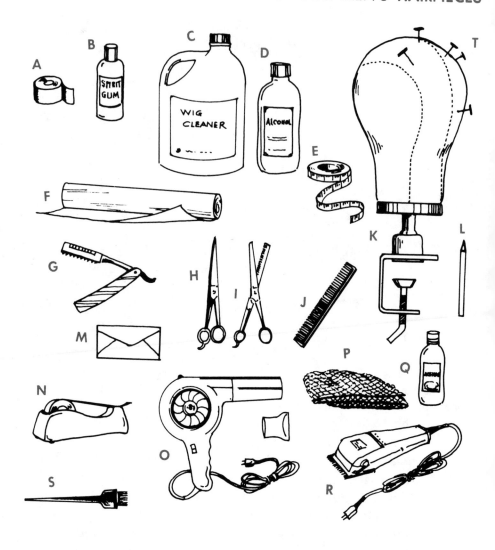

Most of the implements and supplies required for men's hairpiece services are available in the barber-styling shop and the remainder can easily be obtained from a dealer or any stationery store.

A. Two-sided adhesive tape.
B. Spirit gum.
C. Wig cleaner.
D. Alcohol.
E. Measuring tape.
F. Plastic wrap or cellophane.
G. Razor or shaper.
H. Scissors.
I. Thinning scissors.
J. Comb.

K. Styling block.
L. Grease pencil.
M. Envelope.
N. Transparent tape.
O. Hair dryer.
P. Hair net.
Q. Acetone or remover.
R. Clipper.
S. Small brush.
T. T-pins.

Hairpieces constructed of synthetic hair or a blend of human and synthetic or animal hair have the following **disadvantages:**

1. Difficult to handle, tending to mat and tangle easily.
2. Are stiff and show a glassy surface shine.
3. Human hair shades cannot readily be duplicated.

PRELIMINARY HAIRCUT

To achieve a natural look the client's hair should be allowed to grow longer, thus making it much easier to blend the hairpiece into his own hair. When cutting client's hair, trim it very lightly. Leave a low neckline and keep the hair close to the ears at the sides (Figs. 1 and 2).

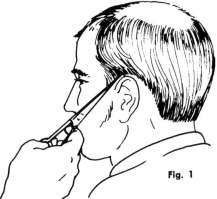

Fig. 1

Fig. 2

When finished with the haircut, gather the longer hair and put it in an envelope for possible use as a color guide.

MEASUREMENTS FOR HAIRPIECES
TAPE MEASUREMENT

For a front hairline to look natural, it should not be too low. You may, of course, lower the hairline a bit to cover a scar or mole. Place three fingers above the eyebrow, directly in line with center of nose (Fig. 1). Make a dot with grease pencil on the forehead to indicate where the hairpiece is to begin.

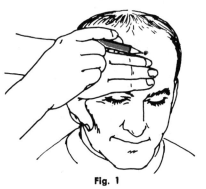

Fig. 1

Place tape measure on the dot. Measure back to where the back hair begins and mark tape measure (Fig. 2). Be sure to measure back to where **substantial** growth begins—disregard sparse hair between forehead and crown bald areas.

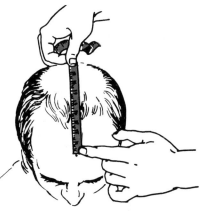

Fig. 2

325

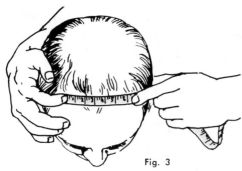

Fig. 3

The next measurement is across the top, directly over the sideburn (normally about 1½ inches back of the forehead dot) (Fig. 3). This is the place where the front hairline of the hairpiece blends in with the client's own hair at the sides of the head. Measure across the crown area if it is noticeably different from the front width.

Manufacturer's Code

Men's hairpieces are commonly referred to by these measurements. For example: a 6 x 4 inch piece would be 6 inches long from front to back and 4 inches wide. The large number refers to the length (unless otherwise indicated) and will be so understood by companies which accept this simple type of measurement. For ordering hairpieces consult page 328.

PATTERN MEASUREMENTS

For the experienced artisan, tape measurements alone can be used in most cases. For the beginner and for odd-shaped areas, a pattern is best. To assemble, prepare plastic wrap, 12 strips of ¾-inch transparent tape(preferably the dull type [Scotch Magic Tape] for easy writing) and a grease pencil (Fig. 1).

Take two feet of plastic wrap (Fig. 2) and place on top of client's head. Twist the sides until they conform to the contour of the head. While client holds the plastic wrap, place each pre-cut strip of tape across the bald area to stiffen the pattern and hold its shape (Fig. 3).

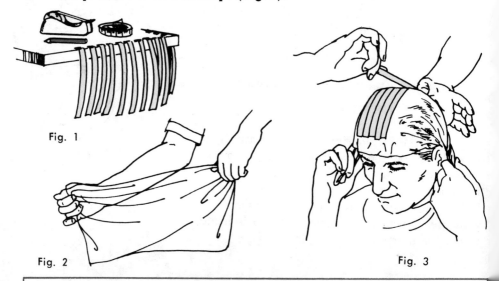

Fig. 1

Fig. 2

Fig. 3

IMPORTANT REMINDER

The instructions contained in this chapter represent the best available information on the fitting and servicing of hairpieces. However, your instructor may have developed his or her own particular techniques which are equally correct.

Next, place three fingers above the eyebrows and make a dot on the pattern to indicate the new hairline (Fig. 4). Place additional dots as follows:

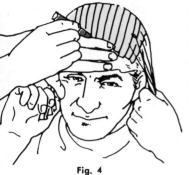

a) Two dots on each side where the front hairline is to meet the client's own hairline.

b) Two dots in back of the head on each side of the balding spot.

c) One dot at the center back edge of the bald spot to determine length of area to be covered.

Connect dots with pencil to outline the balding area. **Ignore minor irregularities and sparse areas** (Fig. 5).

Fig. 4

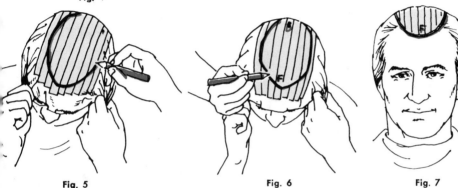

Fig. 5   **Fig. 6**   **Fig. 7**

Mark the front part of the pattern (F) and back (B) as in Fig. 6. Then remove and cut around the edge with scissors. After cutting outline, replace pattern over balding area (Fig. 7). Make sure the bald area is covered exactly. It is better to have a foundation which is slightly smaller than one which is too large. However, accuracy is very important.

HAIR SAMPLES

For a hairpiece to look natural, it is of the utmost importance to take samples of client's hair so that it can be matched by the manufacturer.

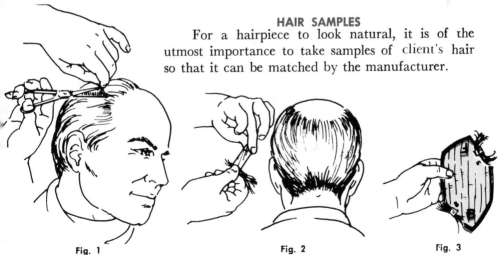

Fig. 1   **Fig. 2**   **Fig. 3**

Take swatch of hair from side with thinning shears, tape it, mark with an "S" and then attach to front side of the pattern (Figs. 1, 2 and 3).

Take swatch at back of head, mark "B", and attach to pattern.

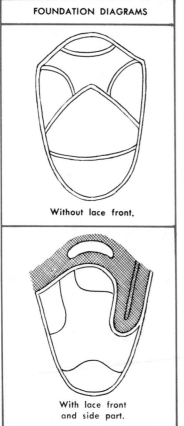

FOUNDATION DIAGRAMS

Without lace front.

With lace front
and side part.

ORDERING HAIRPIECES

Send measurements or pattern to the manufacturer with instructions, covering the following information:

1. Hairpiece **without** lace front .... ☐
   a) Without side part .... ☐
   b) With left side part .... ☐
   c) With right side part .... ☐

2. Hairpieces **with** lace front .... ☐
   a) Without side part .... ☐
   b) With left side part .... ☐
   c) With right side part .... ☐

3. Hair color variations:
   a) Front: Natural ☐ Partly grey ☐ Grey ☐
   Streaked ☐ Front and top lighter ☐
   b) Temples: Natural ☐ Partly grey ☐ Grey ☐
   c) Back: Natural ☐ Partly grey ☐ Grey ☐

4. **Complexion:**
   a) Ruddy complexion ☐ b) Dark complexion ☐
   c) Light complexion ☐

5. **Miscellaneous**—Give details
   a) Partials ☐   Patches ☐   Fill-ins ☐

6. **Photograph.** A Polaroid photo would be quite helpful.

PUTTING ON AND STYLING HAIRPIECE WITHOUT LACE FRONT

APPLYING HAIRPIECE

Before adjusting a hairpiece to the scalp, clean the entire bald area with a piece of cotton wetted with rubbing alcohol or with soap and water.

The foundation of the hairpiece and scalp must be thoroughly dry before adjusting a hairpiece to the scalp.

Place tape (two-sided) in a "V" shape on the front reinforced area of the foundation (Fig. 1). This tape holds the hairpiece close to the scalp and appears to be a part of it.

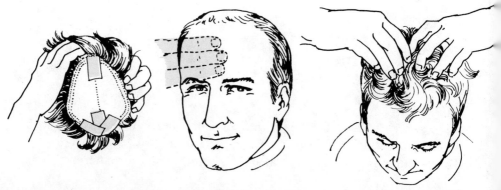

Fig. 1   Fig. 2   Fig. 3

Place additional pieces of tape on the reinforced parts of the foundation at the sides and back part of the hairpiece.

Place three fingers above eyebrow, locating hairline (Fig. 2); position hairpiece at the hairline at center of the nose. When the hairpiece is in proper position, press down firmly on the various tape areas (Fig. 3). The hairpiece is then ready for the next step.

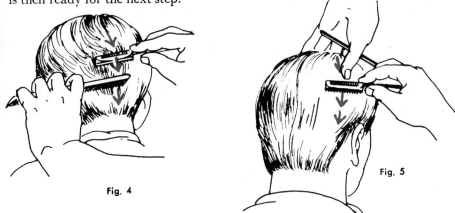

Fig. 4

Fig. 5

CUTTING, TAPERING AND BLENDING

Back and sides. When the hair is combed into desired position, use a razor to taper and blend the hair smoothly at the back of the head (Fig. 4). Then taper and blend the sides (Fig. 5). The tapering should be done smoothly so that the blending with the client's own hair will be undetectable.

Note: A razor should never be used when cutting, tapering or blending synthetic hairpieces. A blending (thinning) shears is a much safer implement to use.

CAUTION. In cutting, tapering and blending the hairpiece, it is better that less hair be removed than too much. If too much hair is removed, it may destroy the hairpiece, since the hair will not grow back.

Top hair. The finger method may be used as in Fig. 6. Comb the hair up, bring it slightly forward and cut. Repeat this operation as needed or utilize the comb method (Fig. 7). Comb up and cut with scissors or thinning shears.

Blend with front side hair. To blend the hairpiece with side hair, cut a small amount of front hair short (Fig. 8) to soften the joining of the hairpiece to the client's hair.

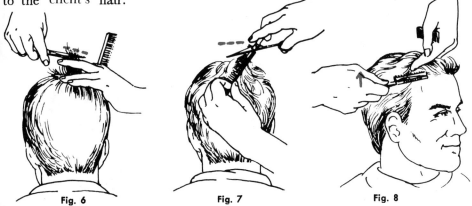

Fig. 6

Fig. 7

Fig. 8

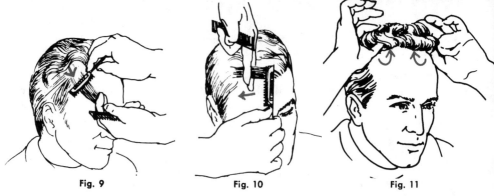

Fig. 9   Fig. 10   Fig. 11

Thick front hairline. If front hairline appears to be heavy, use razor for thinning. In performing this operation be sure that you make very narrow partings in order to form a natural-looking front hairline (Fig. 9). To thin underneath hair, comb hair forward and thin hair with razor (Fig. 10). When combed back, the hair will lie flat.

CAUTION. Use this technique only on a hairpiece **without** a lace front —never on front area of a lace front hairpiece.

REMOVING A HAIRPIECE

Reach up under hairpiece with fingertips and detach the tape from the scalp (Fig. 11). Make sure the tape stays on the foundation. This tape is left on the foundation and it is reactivated with spirit gum each time the hairpiece is worn. An alternate substance for reactivating the tape is nail polish remover.

PUTTING ON AND STYLING HAIRPIECE WITH LACE FRONT

A hairpiece with a lace front is recommended when the hair is worn in an off-the-face style. It is scarcely visible from the front view. The use of a lace front hairpiece gives the required lightness for a natural-looking hairstyle. This natural effect is impossible to achieve with hairpieces not having the front lace.

PUTTING ON A HAIRPIECE

Clean the bald area with rubbing alcohol or with soap and water.

Remove hair on scalp where tape or lace is to be attached (Fig. 1).

Attach strips of tape (two-sided) to reinforced parts of the foundation, usually near front, on sides and on back part of hairpiece (Fig. 2). Reinforced areas vary with design of foundation and manufacturer's preference.

CAUTION. Never use tape directly on the lace.

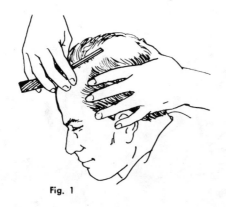

     Fig. 1   Fig. 2

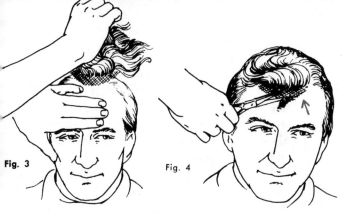

Fig. 3

Fig. 4

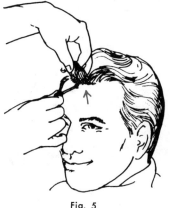

Fig. 5

Fig. 6

Adjust the hairpiece to the desired position, using the three-finger method previously described. Press it down into place (Fig. 3).

Cut, taper and blend the front lace hairpiece to match smoothly with the client's own hair.

Front lace. Trim lace to within ¼ inch of hairline (Fig. 4). Many men prefer to have the lace completely trimmed right down to the contour of the hairline. Others like the greater security afforded by the lace margin. The decision to trim or not to trim should be left until the hairpiece has been worn for awhile. For the time being, leave the small ¼ inch margin of lace.

Lift lace and brush spirit gum sparingly on scalp under it (Fig. 5). When tacky, press down front lace with a moist lint-free cloth.

Raise front hair. To keep front hairline from lying too flat, reach in with comb and then twist comb forward slightly (Fig. 6). This will give the proper lift and make the hair look as if it is really growing out of the scalp.

REMOVING A LACE FRONT HAIRPIECE

Before removing a lace front hairpiece, dampen the lace with acetone or solvent in order to loosen it from the scalp (Fig. 7). Do not pull or stretch lace. To apply solvent, use a piece of cotton or a brush.

Fig. 7

After lace becomes loosened, use fingertips to remove tape from scalp (Fig. 8). Do not pull off hairpiece by tugging on the hair.

The pieces of tape are not removed from the reinforced areas of the hairpiece, but they are reactivated with spirit gum or nail polish remover each time the hairpiece is worn.

Note. It is good business to instruct the patron on how to put on and remove his hairpiece, thereby avoiding possible damage to it.

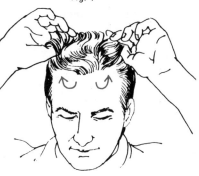

Fig. 8

PARTIAL HAIRPIECES

PARTIAL LACE FRONT FILL-IN

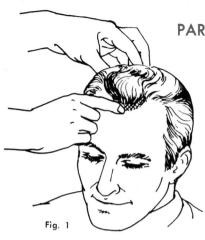

For a small hair loss, a partial lace fill-in may be all that is required. Clean area with soap and water or with rubbing alcohol and allow to dry. Brush on spirit gum and wait until it gets tacky.

Place in proper place (Fig. 1), press down. Comb into rest of hair. If required, taper and shorten to blend with the client's own hair.

Frontal lace partials are made of very fine lace and they are excellent for receding hair-part lines.

Fig. 1

PARTIAL CROWN HAIRPIECE

For clients who are bald at the crown, a small hairpiece may be used. Measure diameter of bald area and send hair sample when ordering.

To attach a partial crown, clean area in the usual manner, dry and apply spirit gum to the outer edges of bald spot. (Fig. 1).

Attach a piece of two-sided tape to the center of the hairpiece. Carefully position the hairpiece over the bald spot, press center firmly to the scalp and then press outer edges into position.

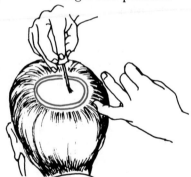 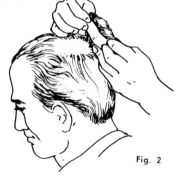

Fig. 2

Once in position, it may be held in place with adhesive tape (two-sided) and/or spirit gum (Fig. 2).

Cut, taper and blend the crown hairpiece with a razor. Comb hair carefully to blend with client's own hair.

PARTIAL TOP HAIRPIECE

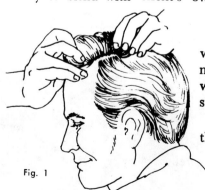

Shave a wide side part, so that the tape will adhere to the scalp. Place partial hairpiece next to the part (Fig. 1). Cut hair to blend with client's own hair. Comb hair into desired style preferably to conceal the front hairline.

Every time the hairpiece is worn, reactivate the tape with spirit gum or nail polish remover.

Fig. 1

READY-MADE FULL WIGS

A number of barber-stylists have developed a very profitable business in the sale and care of full, ready-to-wear wigs. These wigs or hairpieces, usually made of modacrylic fibers, such as kanekalon, dynel, venicelon and others, are ideal to meet the personal needs of clients.

REASONS FOR WEARING FULL WIGS

1. Desire for a complete change of style and image.
2. Desire to temporarily cover longer hair.
3. Desire to hide a balding head.
4. Desire to change one's appearance while job-hunting.
5. Desire to hide a short, military haircut.

CONSTRUCTION AND FIT

Full, ready-made wigs are constructed on a stretch cap made of lightweight elastic. The wig has permanent elastic bands at the sides designed to hold it in place. The wig should fit comfortably, but tight enough to maintain its position without slipping, shifting or lifting. Wigs come in a large variety of colors and in many different styles, designed to suit the taste of all clients.

CLEANING WIGS

An area for steady additional income, for work performed during slow periods, is the cleaning and care of wigs. Cleaning of ready-made wigs is a fairly quick and easy process. However, manufacturer's cleaning instructions should be carefully followed.

GENERAL CLEANING PROCEDURES

1. Brush wig thoroughly to remove all surface dirt and residue.
2. Mix solution of warm water and mild shampoo in bowl.
3. Dip entire wig into solution; swish around in solution.
4. Rinse wig in clean cold water.
5. Blot dry with towel.
6. Turn wig inside out and dry with towel.
7. Pin wig to correct size head mold.
8. Carefully brush hair into shape.
9. Permit wig to dry naturally—pinned to form.
10. If necessary to dry quickly, use cool air.
11. When dry, brush into proper style.
Note: If tape is not clean, carefully use liquid solvent to clean it.

FACIAL HAIRPIECES

Facial hairpieces are attached with spirit gum.

Mustache. Apply spirit gum to the upper lip (Fig. 1), wait until tacky, position mustache and gently press down with lint-free cloth. Trim mustache to desired style (Fig. 2).

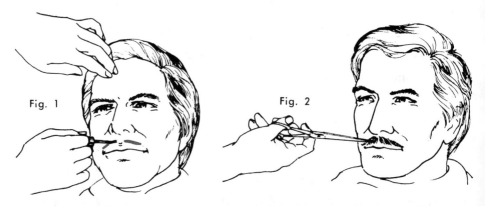

Beard. Apply spirit gum around the circumference of the area to be covered (Fig. 1). Wait until tacky. Position beard and press the edges down with lint-free cloth. Trim beard to desired style (Fig. 2).

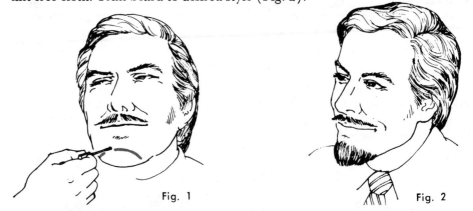

Sideburns may be applied in the same manner as the mustache.

CLEANING AND STYLING HAIRPIECES

CLEANING HAIRPIECES

When a hairpiece becomes soiled it should be cleaned. Great care should be exercised during the cleaning process, otherwise the hairpiece could be damaged.

Carefully remove all old tape (Fig. 1). Clean reinforced areas by rubbing lightly with solvent or wig cleaner.

Put enough cleaner in an open bowl so that the hairpiece can be submerged (Fig. 2). Swish the hairpiece back and forth (or dip it up and down) in the cleaner until all residue is removed from the hair and foundation. Gently press out cleaner or let cleaner drip in bowl (Fig. 3). Fasten hairpiece on covered head mold to dry naturally.

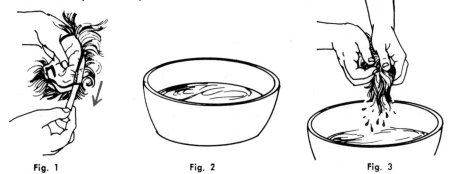

Fig. 1   Fig. 2   Fig. 3

CAUTION. Some cleaning agents are hazardous if not used according to instructions. Be sure to read the label carefully before using any cleaning agent.

STYLING HAIRPIECES ON HEAD MOLD

After the hairpiece has been cleaned, place it on covered head mold and fasten securely with T-pins or straight pins (Fig. 4). Set hair into desired style **while still wet** (Fig. 5).

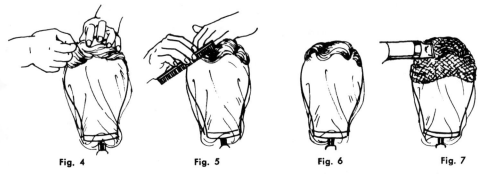

Fig. 4   Fig. 5   Fig. 6   Fig. 7

Drying may be natural (left to dry) (Fig. 6) or a hand blower may be used, only after covering the hairpiece with a hair-net. (Fig. 7).

CAUTION: Avoid heat on grey hair, as the heat tends to make the hair yellow.

STYLING HAIRPIECES ON PATRON'S HEAD

The hairpiece may also be styled after being placed on client's head. The scalp must be clean and dry and the foundation of the hairpiece thoroughly dried on head mold before attaching the hairpiece to the client's scalp.

Moisten the hairpiece with a damp comb and style as desired. Care must be taken not to dampen the foundation. A styling hair net (trainer) is adjusted over the client's head (Fig. 8) and the hair thoroughly dried with a hand dryer.

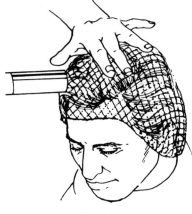

Fig. 8

335

CLEANING SYNTHETIC HAIRPIECES

Synthetic hairpieces should never be washed in solvent.

The hairpiece should be attached to a styrofoam head mold with T-pins. Immerse the hairpiece in lukewarm water with a mild shampoo. (Do not use hot water or the hairpiece will shrink.) Swish the hairpiece around in the shampoo solution. Rinse with clean lukewarm water. Permit the hairpiece to dry naturally, pinned on the mold overnight. If time does not permit, place under dryer with **cool air.** Some hairpiece may be dry cleaned. Follow manufacturer's instructions.

SPECIAL NOTE ABOUT HAIRPIECES

Hairpieces made of human hair must always be dry cleaned. **Never use a shampoo.**

Synthetic hairpieces are usually the mass produced variety, and synthetic fibers are rarely used for lace-type or custom made hairpieces.

When setting hairpieces, use plain water. The use of a small amount of pomade or similar product while setting, will add luster to the hair.

COLORING AND RECONDITIONING HAIRPIECES

PERMANENT HAIR COLORING

It must be pointed out that permanent type hair coloring products (aniline derivatives) can be used only on hairpieces made of 100% human hair.

Procedure

First, the hairpiece is cleaned with a solvent or cleaner.

Cover the head mold with plastic material to prevent damage to the head mold by the coloring product (Fig. 1.)

Secure hairpiece firmly with T-pins or straight pins on the front, back and sides (Fig. 2).

Fig. 1   Fig. 2   Fig. 3

Strand test. Give a strand test on a small section of hair to determine the color desired. If using a tint with peroxide, apply it on a dry hair strand.

The following is a suggested procedure for hair coloring:

1. Mix hair coloring to desired shade.
2. Apply with hair coloring brush (Fig. 3).

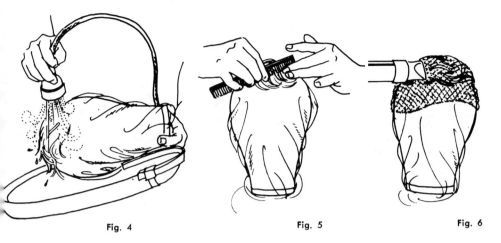

| Fig. 4 | Fig. 5 | Fig. 6 |

3. Comb through lightly, being careful not to saturate the foundation.
4. Test every five minutes until desired shade is obtained.
5. Rinse with warm water (Fig. 4). Do not use soap.
6. Set into desired style (Fig. 5).
7. Dry with hand blower (Fig. 6).
    (Air should not be too hot. Excess heat causes frizziness.)

RECONDITIONING HAIRPIECES

Reconditioning treatments should be given as often as necessary to prevent dryness or brittleness of the hair. Reconditioning treatments may also be used to liven up the appearance of hairpieces which have become dull and lifeless.

The application of a small amount of a reconditioning product may be used as directed by the manufacturer or instructor.

If a slight color adjustment is necessary due to fading, yellowing or sun bleach, a suitable color rinse is recommended. Be guided by your instructor.

Great care must be exercised in the selection of the rinse, or the resultant color may not match the client's hair shade.

> **VERY IMPORTANT.** Any coloring done to a hairpiece is damaging to the foundation. It may not be immediately evident, but it may result in hair loss later on. Therefore, great care must be taken if hair coloring is attempted, because there is no way to predict the outcome.
>
> **Do Not Use Strong Bleaches.** Peroxide tends to damage the foundation of a hairpiece
>
> **Synthetic** hairpieces should not be colored.

STYLES FOR HAIRPIECE WITHOUT LACE FRONT

Hairpiece *without* lace front combed in a pompadour style. To soften the front hairline, a few wispy strands are cut short and combed or brushed forward.

Versatile hairpiece *without* lace front and with side part. Front hair is cut and tapered short, and combed and draped across the hairline in a free, natural arrangement.

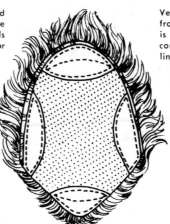

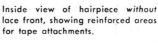

Inside view of hairpiece *without* lace front, showing reinforced areas for tape attachments.

Hairpiece *without* lace front which features wide sideburns and a low shaped napeline. Hair is styled from top left side in a semi-circular manner over top of head and forehead, blended with the client's own hair on sides and back.

Hairpiece *without* lace front, styled from crown towards the front. The hair over the forehead is separated and set into pointed strands, held in place with a hair net (trainer) and dried with hand dryer. The hairpiece is blended with client's own hair on sides and back of head.

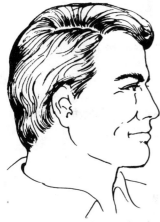

Hairpiece *with* lace front and right side part, styled in a forward wave "dip," and blended in with client's own hair on sides and back.

Inside view of hairpiece *with* front lace, showing reinforced foundation.

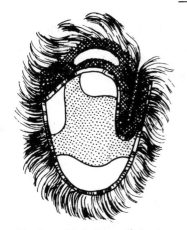

Inside view of hairpiece *with* front lace and side part, showing reinforced attachment tapes.

Silver grey hairpiece *with* lace front and side part is combed in three-quarter pompadour style with front wave.

Front fill-in hairpiece *with* lace front can be styled and combed either forward or toward the back, as desired. This style is combed towards the right side with draped front.

Hairpiece *with* front lace, styled from right side part towards left side with a front draping (shaping). This hairpiece may be combed towards the back, if desired.

339

HAIRPIECES

1. Great care must be taken when combing hairpieces to avoid matting, loss of hair or damage to the foundation.
2. When combing a hairpiece, use a wide-tooth comb to avoid abuse to the foundation.
3. When dry cleaning a hairpiece, never rub or wring the cleaning fluid from it. Let it dry naturally.
4. When cutting, tapering and blending a hairpiece, use great care; once the hair has been cut, it cannot grow back.
5. To assure a comfortable and secure fit of a hairpiece, correct measurements or a suitable pattern of the client's head must be made.
6. Recondition hairpieces as often as necessary to prevent dryness or brittleness of the hair and to liven up the appearance, which may have become dull and lifeless.
7. If required, dry clean hairpieces before styling.
8. Brush and comb hairpieces with a downward movement.
9. To avoid damage to the foundation, never lighten (bleach) a hairpiece.
10. To avoid damage to the foundation, never give a cold wave to a hairpiece.
11. If hair coloring is necessary, it must be done with great care.
12. To reactivate faded hair, a color rinse may be applied.
13. Do not work the tint into the foundation of the hairpiece. This will cause the foundation to deteriorate.
14. Hairpieces made of human hair must be dry cleaned, whereas those made of synthetics may be shampooed or dry cleaned, whichever the manufacturer recommends.

SELLING HAIRPIECES

In order to sell men's hairpieces, it is important to know the answers to the question, "Why do men **buy** hairpieces?"

It has been found that the answer will most likely indicate a desire to retain a youthful appearance. Large corporations have a tendency to place younger men in positions that offer the greatest potential for advancement. With this in mind, it is easy to imagine why an ambitious businessman or executive would be happy to buy something that can immediately make him look ten years younger.

BEFORE AND AFTER

A vivid demonstration of the lace front hairpiece which produces the most lifelike appearance possible when properly fitted and styled. It really defies detection.

340

BEFORE

AFTER

It is quite natural that men should desire to continue to look as attractive as possible to women. This factor, along with the desire to look young for business reasons, contributes a great deal to the salability of hairpieces.

SELLING THE OLDER MEN

Do not attempt to mislead older men into believing that they can recapture the look of their twenties. It simply cannot be done. The skin coloring of a man in his fifties is very different from that which he had in his younger days. Therefore, stay away from a solid black color. It is better to recommend a shade in the pepper and salt or medium brown range. This way the customer will look more believable and truly younger.

DEMONSTRATION TECHNIQUE

One or two correctly styled demonstration hairpieces (Preferably a lace piece in pepper and salt and a regular hairpiece in dark brown) will do wonders in aiding a sale. Whenever a client sees a product, it should look good, so make certain that your sample is clean and has a nice style.

The sample should be large enough to cover the average balding area of a man and give a good impression. Most of your clients will be men with an average amount of hair loss.

WORD-OF-MOUTH ADVERTISING AND WINDOW DISPLAYS

You can do a great deal of hairpiece business simply by word-of-mouth and window displays. It is a wise move to place BEFORE AND AFTER illustrations in the shop or shop window to encourage those clients whom you feel CANNOT be approached directly. You are already selling just as soon as your BEFORE AND AFTER illustrations are seen. On the other hand, many clients can be approached directly. When you meet a client who needs a hairpiece, simply suggest that you have an answer to his problem. A quick demonstration that dramatically convinces him of his greatly-improved appearance will often close the sale.

PRINTED ADS

It is also quite important that you advertise your hairpiece service. In most areas an extra line in the telephone book, mentioning hairpieces, will pay for itself. It will also attract considerable attention to your shop. Your phone book may contain a special listing for hair goods and this is also a good spot for your ad.

In some communities newspaper advertising is often inexpensive and profitable. If you do use printed advertising, be sure to secure the model's release for any illustrations that you might use in your ad. **Even if the model is your best friend, do not assume that a release is unnecessary.**

PERSONAL EXPERIENCE

If you happen to wear a hairpiece yourself, you can develop an excellent promotional approach. Often, nothing sells better than when you take off your own hairpiece and the client can witness for himself the striking change in appearance that takes place. The effect is even greater when the person is unaware that you ever wore a hairpiece. The fact that you have been wearing yours with calm assurance and complete ease can make a very strong impression.

HAIR REPLACEMENT TECHNIQUES

There are two techniques available to the individual who wishes to cover bald areas without the constant "putting on-taking off" and adjusting of wigs or hairpieces. These techniques, which are considered to be either permanent or semi-permanent, are hair transplants and hair weaving.

HAIR TRANSPLANTS

The transplanting of hair is strictly a medical procedure which should be performed by a trained dermatologist.

It is a process which consists of removing hair from normal areas of the scalp, such as the back and sides, and transplanting it into the bald areas. The small, about ⅛ inch, sections of hair (called plugs) including the hair follicle, papilla and hair bulb, are surgically removed and re-set in the bald area according to a pre-planned procedure. The use of a local anesthetic makes the entire operation practically painless.

The transplanted hair grows normally in its new environment. The area from which the hair was removed heals and shrinks in size to a very tiny scar.

The dermatologist must be especially careful when selecting the hair to be transplanted to consider color, texture and type. Very careful consideration must also be given to the placing of the hair in the proper direction of natural growth to permit proper care and grooming.

Transplanted hair can last a lifetime if the dermatologist has performed the service efficiently. If the doctor was properly skilled and the individual cares for the hair as directed, hair transplanting can be a very successful and permanent method of eliminating baldness.

HAIR WEAVING

INTRODUCTION

Hair weaving is a technique which has been practiced in barber-styling shops for many years. It is another method employed, as are transplants, wigs and hairpieces, to cover bald areas of the head.

While there are numerous claims as to new techniques and exclusive methods in hair weaving, basically they more or less all follow the same procedure. The art of hair weaving consists of sewing or weaving a foundation into the remaining hair or on the scalp of an individual's head and then weaving wefts of human hair to this foundation. The two principal techniques followed are the Suture Method and the Hair Weaving Method.

THE SUTURE METHOD

Under this method, a perimeter of "anchor-bases," made of strong, non-reactive, teflon-coated, stainless steel wire, is partially imbedded or sutured into the scalp by a medical doctor. To this imbedded wire, a network of foundation of siliconized Dacron is attached. This foundation must fit very tight and snug to the scalp. Wefts of matching human hair are then sewn or woven to the foundation in a previously determined pattern and style. Since the foundation wires are imbedded into the scalp, this suture method of hair weaving is not affected by hair growth.

While the suture method seems to offer a hair replacement technique involving some semblance of permanency, without constant adjustments, it also presents a number of severe problems. These include, among others, the danger of scalp infection from the teflon wire, the possibility of pain when combing or shampooing the hair and the danger of injury to the scalp caused by the pulling of the wire in combing. Clients should be advised to carefully consider all problems presented before accepting this form of hair replacement.

BEFORE

AFTER

THE HAIR WEAVING METHOD

This method consists of firmly sewing or weaving a foundation into the remaining hair on the individual's head with nylon (or some similar) thread and then sewing or weaving wefts of matching human hair to this foundation in a pre-planned pattern.

Since the foundation is attached to the remaining hair on the head, as the hair grows (about ½ inch per month) the foundation also moves out from the scalp. It is clear, therefore, that continual adjustments are required in order to maintain a desired natural appearance.

The hair woven on the head requires continuous care and servicing. In the hair weaving process, the foundation must be tightened and brought close to the scalp every six to eight weeks.

In cleansing the hair, it must be shampooed carefully, in sections, to avoid pulling and causing damage to the foundation or pain to the client. The hair should also receive periodic conditioning treatments to add luster and to avoid dryness and damage.

CONCLUSION

Whatever method of hair replacement is accepted by the client, he must recognize that each technique or method has its own advantages and disadvantages. The procedure could be a very costly one and involve a number of personal inconveniences. Every method requires constant care and careful grooming if it is to cover bald areas in a natural and satisfactory manner.

QUESTIONS ON MEN'S HAIRPIECES

1. List four reasons why men would want to wear hairpieces.
2. What two kinds of materials are used to make men's hairpieces?
3. How can one distinguish between synthetic and human hair?
4. In what two ways can head measurements be taken for hairpieces?
5. Why should hair samples be taken for every man's hairpiece?
6. In what two ways are hairpieces usually manufactured?
7. Which type of hairpiece is best for an off-the-face hairstyle?
8. What is used to attach a hairpiece to the scalp?
9. What is used to reactivate the pieces of tape attached to the reinforced areas of the hairpiece?
10. How are hairpieces cleaned?
11. To be fully qualified, what points of basic information should the barber-stylist know about men's hairpieces?
12. Why is bleaching (lightening) of a hairpiece not recommended?
13. Why are reconditioning treatments recommended for hairpieces?
14. What should be used in combing a hairpiece to avoid abuse to its foundation?
15. Name five promotional aids for the selling of men's hairpieces.

Chapter 23
THE SKIN AND SCALP

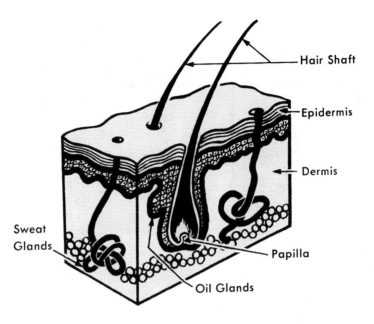

Hair Shaft

Epidermis

Dermis

Sweat Glands

Papilla

Oil Glands

Everyone is concerned with the **health** and **appearance** of the skin. The scientific study of the skin and scalp is of particular importance to the barber-stylist. It forms the basis for an effective program of skin and scalp treatments. The skin is the largest organ of the body and performs many vital functions required for good health. The barber-stylist who has a thorough understanding of the skin, its structure and functions, will be in a better position to give patrons professional advice on scalp and facial care.

A **healthy skin** is slightly moist, soft, flexible, possesses a slightly acid reaction and is free from any blemishes or disorders. Its texture, as revealed by feel and appearance, should be smooth and soft. A good complexion shows itself in a healthy color of the skin.

The skin **varies in thickness**, being thinnest on the eyelids and thickest on the palms and soles. Continued pressure over any part of the skin will cause it to thicken, as in a callous.

The **skin of the scalp** is constructed similar to the skin elsewhere on the human body. However, larger and deeper hair follicles are present on the scalp to accommodate the longer hair of the head.

HISTOLOGY OF THE SKIN

The skin contains two clearly defined divisions: the epidermis and the dermis.

1. The **epidermis** (ep-i-der′mis) is the outermost layer of the skin. This layer is commonly called **cuticle** or **scarf skin.**
2. The **dermis** (der′mis) is the underlying or inner layer of the skin. It is also called **derma, corium, cutis** or **true skin.**

345

DIAGRAM OF A SECTION OF THE SCALP

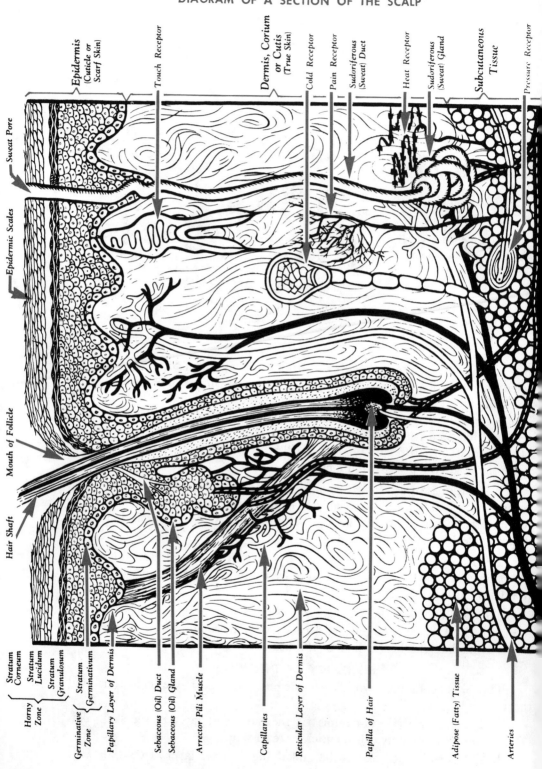

Epidermis (Cuticle or Scarf Skin)

Touch Receptor

Dermis, Corium or Cutis (True Skin)

Cold Receptor

Pain Receptor

Sudoriferous (Sweat) Duct

Heat Receptor

Sudoriferous (Sweat) Gland

Subcutaneous Tissue

Pressure Receptor

Sweat Pore

Epidermic Scales

Mouth of Follicle

Hair Shaft

Stratum Corneum
Stratum Lucidum
Stratum Granulosum
Horny Zone

Stratum Germinativum
Germinative Zone

Papillary Layer of Dermis

Sebaceous (Oil) Duct
Sebaceous (Oil) Gland

Arrector Pili Muscle

Capillaries

Reticular Layer of Dermis

Papilla of Hair

Adipose (Fatty) Tissue

Arteries

The **epidermis** forms the outer protective covering of the skin of the body. It contains no blood vessels but has many small nerve endings. The epidermis contains the following layers:

1. The horny layer (**stratum corneum** — strā'tum kōr'nē-um) consists of tightly packed, scale-like cells which are continually being shed and replaced. As these cells develop from underneath layers, they form **keratin** (ker'ah-tin), a chemical substance which acts as a waterproof covering for the skin.

2. The clear layer (**stratum lucidum** — lū'si-dum) consists of small transparent cells through which light can pass.

3. The grandular layer (**stratum granulosum** — gran-ū-lō'sum) consists of cells which look like distinct granules. These cells are almost dead and undergo a change into a horny substance.

4. The reproductive layer (**stratum germinativum** — jer'mi-nā-ti-vum) is composed of several layers of differently shaped cells. The deepest layer is responsible for the growth of the epidermis. It also contains a dark pigment called **melanin** (mel'ah-nin), which protects the sensitive cells below from the destructive effects of excessive ultra-violet rays of the sun or ultra-violet rays from a lamp.

The **dermis** is the true skin. It is a highly sensitive and vascular layer of connective tissue. Within its structure are found numerous blood vessels, lymph vessels, nerves, sweat glands, oil glands, hair follicles, arrector pili muscles and papillae. The dermis consists of two layers: the papillary or superficial layer, and the reticular or deeper layer.

1. The **papillary** (pap'i-lā-rē) layer lies directly beneath the epidermis. It contains small cone-shaped projections of elastic tissue that point upward into the epidermis. These projections are called **papillae** (pah-pil'ē). Some of these papillae contain looped capillaries, others contain many nerve fiber endings. This layer also contains some of the **melanin skin pigment.**

2. The **reticular** (rē-tik'ū-lar) **layer,** within its network, contains the following structures:

   a) Fat cells
   b) Blood vessels
   c) Lymph vessels
   d) Oil glands
   e) Sweat glands
   f) Hair follicles
   g) Arrector pili muscles

Subcutaneous (sub-kū-tā'nē-us) **tissue** is a layer of fatty tissue found below the dermis. This fatty tissue varies in thickness according to the age, sex and general health of the individual. It gives smoothness and contour to the body, contains fats for use as energy and also acts as a protective cushion for the outer skin. Circulation is maintained by a network of arteries, and lymphatics.

HOW THE SKIN IS NOURISHED

Blood and lymph supply nourishment to the skin. From 1/2 to 2/3 of the total blood supply of the body is distributed to the skin. The blood and

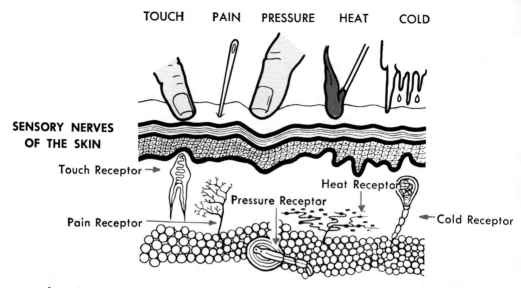

TOUCH   PAIN   PRESSURE   HEAT   COLD

**SENSORY NERVES
OF THE SKIN**

Touch Receptor →

Pain Receptor →

Pressure Receptor

Heat Receptor

← Cold Receptor

lymph, as they circulate through the skin, contribute essential materials for growth, nourishment and repair of the skin, hair and nails. In the subcutaneous tissue are found networks of arteries and lymphatics which send their smaller branches to hair papillae, hair follicles and skin glands. The capillaries are quite numerous in the skin.

NERVES OF THE SKIN

The skin contains the surface endings of many nerve fibers classified as:

1. Motor nerve fibers which are distributed to the arrector pili muscles of the hair follicles.
2. Sensory nerve fibers which react to heat, cold, touch, pressure and pain.
3. Secretory nerve fibers which are distributed to the sweat and oil glands of the skin.

Sense of touch. The papillary layer of the dermis provides the body with the sense of touch. Nerves supplying the skin register basic types of sensations, namely: touch, pain, heat, cold, pressure or deep touch. Nerve endings are most abundant in the fingertips. **Complex sensations,** such as sense of vibration, seem to depend on a combination of these nerve endings.

SKIN ELASTICITY

Pliability of the skin depends upon the elasticity of the fibers of the dermis. For example, when healthy skin expands, it regains its former shape almost immediately.

Aging skin. The aging process of the skin is a subject of vital importance to everyone. Perhaps the most outstanding characteristic of the aged skin is its loss of elasticity.

SKIN COLOR

The color of the skin, whether fair or dark, depends partly upon the blood supply in the skin, but primarily upon the **melanin** or coloring matter which is deposited in the reproductive layer and the papillary layer of the dermis. The pigment varies in different people. In various races and nationalities, the distinctive color of the skin is a hereditary trait.

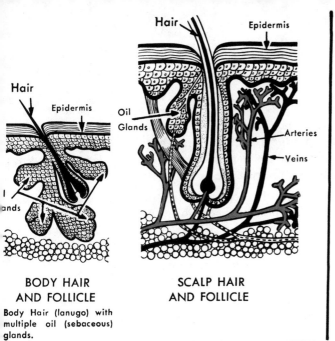

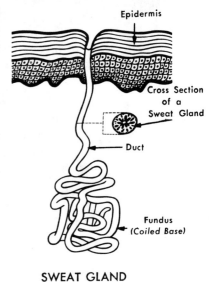

BODY HAIR AND FOLLICLE

Body Hair (lanugo) with multiple oil (sebaceous) glands.

SCALP HAIR AND FOLLICLE

SWEAT GLAND

THE GLANDS OF THE SKIN

The skin contains two types of duct glands which extract materials from the blood to form new substances.

1. The sweat glands (**sudoriferous**—sū-dor-if′er-us) excrete sweat.
2. The oil glands (**sebaceous**—sē-bā′shus) secrete sebum.

The **sweat glands** (tubular type) consist of a coiled base and a tube-like **duct** which terminates at the skin surface to form the **sweat pore.** Practically all parts of the body are supplied with sweat glands. They are more numerous on the palms, soles, forehead and in the armpits. The sweat glands regulate body temperature and help to eliminate waste products from the body. Their activity is greatly increased by heat, exercise, emotions and certain drugs. The excretion of sweat is under the control of the nervous system. Normally, one to two pints of liquids, containing salts, are eliminated daily through the sweat pores in the skin.

The **oil glands** consist of little sacs whose ducts open into the hair follicle. They secrete **sebum** (sē′bum), which lubricates the skin and preserves the softness of the hair. With the exception of the palms and soles, these glands are found in all parts of the body, particularly the face.

Sebum is a semi-fluid oily substance produced by the oil glands. Ordinarily it flows through the oil **ducts** leading to the **mouths** of the hair follicles. However, when the sebum becomes hardened and the duct becomes blocked, a **blackhead** is formed. Cleanliness is of prime importance in keeping the skin free of blemishes.

FUNCTIONS OF THE SKIN

The principal functions of the skin are: protection, sensation, heat regulation, excretion, secretion and absorption.

1. **Protection.** The skin protects the body from injury and bacterial invasion. The outermost layer of the epidermis is covered with a thin layer of sebum, thus rendering it waterproof. It is resistant to ranges of

temperature, minor injuries, chemically active substances, and many microbes. If they do invade, the skin becomes inflamed and gets rid of them.

2. **Sensation.** Through its sensory nerve endings, the skin responds to heat, cold, touch, pressure, pain and location. **Extreme stimulation** of a sensory nerve ending, produces pain. A **minor burn** is very painful, but a **deep burn** that destroys the nerves may be painless. Sensory endings responsive to touch and pressure lie in close relation to hair follicles.

3. **Heat regulation.** The healthy body maintains a constant internal temperature of about 98.6 degrees Fahrenheit. As changes occur in the outside temperature, the blood and sweat glands of the skin make necessary adjustments in their functions. Heat regulation is a function of the skin, the organ that protects the body from the environment. **Heat is lost by the evaporation of sweat.**

4. **Excretion.** Perspiration from the sweat glands is excreted from the skin. Water lost by perspiration carries salt and other chemicals with it.

5. **Secretion.** Sebum is secreted by the sebaceous glands. Excessive flow of oil from the oil glands may produce **seborrhea** (seb-ō-rē′ah). Emotional stress may increase the flow of sebum.

6. **Absorption** is limited, but it does occur. Fatty materials, such as lanolin creams, are absorbed largely through the hair follicles and sebaceous gland openings.

The skin has an immunity responsiveness to many things that touch it or gain entry into it.

The **appendages of the skin** are: hair, nails, sweat glands and oil glands.

QUESTIONS ON THE SKIN AND SCALP

1. Briefly describe a healthy skin.
2. What is the appearance of a good complexion?
3. Name the two main divisions of the skin.
4. Locate the epidermis and give its main function.
5. Name the four layers of the epidermis.
6. Which epidermal layer is continually being shed and replaced?
7. Where is the coloring matter of the skin found?
8. Describe the structure of the dermis.
9. Name the two layers of the dermis.
10. What renders the skin flexible?
11. Name the four appendages of the skin.
12. How is the skin nourished?
13. Name three types of nerve fibers found in the skin.

14. Which part of the body is abundantly supplied with nerve endings?
15. To what structures in the skin are the motor nerve fibers distributed?
16. To what five things will the sensory nerves of the skin react?
17. What are the functions of the nerve fibers distributed to sweat and oil glands?
18. What regulates the temperature of the body?
19. Give an example of a complex sensation.
20. What do complex sensations depend upon?
21. What is meant by pliability of the skin?
22. What is the characteristic of aged skin?
23. What determines the color of the skin?
24. Name one cosmetic which the skin can absorb in small amounts.
25. What are the six important functions of the skin?

SWEAT AND OIL GLANDS

1. What is a gland? Name two types of glands found in the skin.
2. Describe the structure of the sweat glands.
3. Where are sweat glands found?
4. What is the function of the sweat glands?
5. What four things will increase the activity of the sweat glands?
6. Describe the structure of the oil glands.
7. Which substance is secreted by the oil glands?
8. What is the chief function of sebum?
9. On what parts of the body are oil glands found?

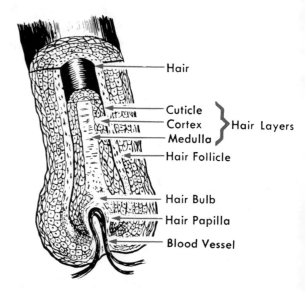

Hair
Cuticle
Cortex
Medulla
Hair Follicle
Hair Bulb
Hair Papilla
Blood Vessel

Hair Layers

Chapter 24

THE HAIR

Hair is an **appendage** (ah-pen'dāj) of the skin. It is a slender, thread-like outgrowth of the skin and scalp of the human body. There is no sense of feeling in the hair, due to the complete absence of nerves in its structure.

The study of the hair, technically called **trichology** (tri-kol'ō-jē) is of paramount importance to the barber-stylist. The chief purposes of the hair are **adornment** and **protection** of the scalp from heat and injury.

To keep the hair healthy and neat, proper attention must be given to its care and treatment. **Knowledge** and **analysis** (a-nal'i-sis) of the client's hair, tactful suggestions for its improvement and sincere interest in maintaining its health and appearance should be the concern of every practitioner.

Abusing the hair by harmful cosmetic applications or faulty hair treatments can cause the hair structure to become weakened or damaged.

COMPOSITION OF HAIR

Hair is chiefly composed of a **protein** (prō'tē-in) called **keratin** (ker'ah-tin), which is present in all horny growths, such as nails, claws and hoofs.

The chemical composition of hair is: carbon, 50.65%; hydrogen, 6.36%; nitrogen, 17.14%; sulphur, 5.0%, and oxygen, 20.85%.

The chemical composition varies with the color of the hair. Light hair contains less carbon and hydrogen and more oxygen and sulphur. Dark hair has more carbon and less oxygen and sulphur.

DIVISION OF HAIR

Full grown hair, as found on the human body, is divided into two principal parts: the hair root and hair shaft.

1. The **hair root** is that portion of the hair structure found beneath the skin surface. This is the portion of the hair enclosed within the follicle.

2. The **hair shaft** is that portion of the hair structure extending above the skin surface.

STRUCTURES ASSOCIATED WITH HAIR ROOT

Structures closely associated with the hair root are the hair follicle, hair bulb and hair papilla.

The **hair follicle** (fol'i-kl) is a tube-like depression or pocket in the skin or scalp encasing the **hair root**. For every hair there is a follicle which varies in depth, depending upon the thickness and location of the skin or scalp.

The bottom of this pocket contains a finger-like projection called the **papilla** (pah-pil'ah), from which the new hair develops.

One or more oil glands are attached to each hair follicle.

The funnel-shaped mouths of hair follicles are favorite **breeding** places for germs and for the **accumulation** of sebum and dirt.

The follicle does not run straight down into the skin or scalp, but is set at an angle so that the hair above the surface has a "natural flow" to one side. This natural flow is sometimes called the "hair stream." Since the angles run according to areas set by nature, hair emerges from the scalp slanting in a given direction

The **hair bulb** is a thickened, club-shaped structure forming the lower part of the hair root. The lower part of the hair bulb is hollowed out to fit over and cover the hair papilla.

The **hair papilla** is a small cone-shaped elevation found at the bottom of the hair follicle that fits into the hair bulb. Within the hair papilla is a **rich blood and nerve supply,** which contributes to the growth and regeneration of the hair. It is through the papilla that nourishment reaches the hair bulb. The papilla has the ability to produce hair cells. It is known as the **"mother"** or **productive organ of the hair.** As long as the papilla functions, the hair will grow. New hair cells cannot be formed nor can the hair grow without the papilla. If the papilla is healthy and well nourished, it will produce a new hair.

STRUCTURES CONNECTED TO HAIR FOLLICLES

The **arrector pili** (ah-rek'tor pī'lī) is a small involuntary muscle attached to the underside of a hair follicle. Fear or cold contracts it, causing the hair **to stand up straight,** giving the skin the appearance of "goose flesh." Eyelash and eyebrow hairs lack arrector pili muscles.

Sebaceous (sē-bā'shus) or **oil glands** consist of little sacular structures situated in the dermis. Their ducts) are connected to hair follicles. Secretion of an oily substance, **sebum** (sē'bum), serves to give lustre and pliability to the hair and keeps the skin surface soft and supple. However, the sebaceous glands frequently become troublemakers. By over-producing, they bring on a common form of oily dandruff and can be an important contributing cause of hair loss or baldness.

SEBUM

The production of sebum is influenced by five factors, some of which are subject to personal control, namely:

1. Diet
2. Blood circulation
3. Emotional disturbance
4. Stimulation of endocrine glands
5. Drugs

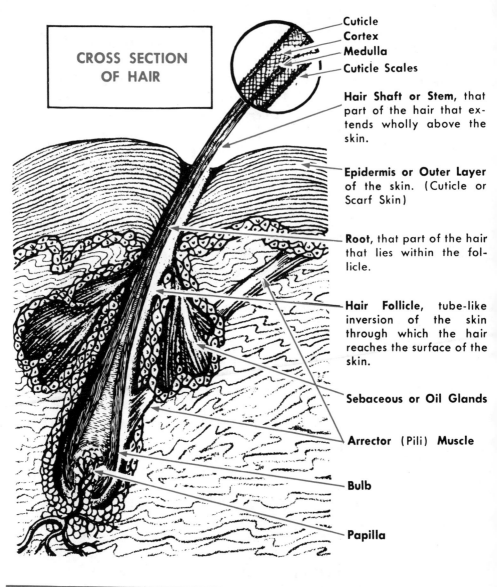

CROSS SECTION
OF HAIR

Cuticle
Cortex
Medulla
Cuticle Scales

Hair Shaft or Stem, that part of the hair that extends wholly above the skin.

Epidermis or Outer Layer of the skin. (Cuticle or Scarf Skin)

Root, that part of the hair that lies within the follicle.

Hair Follicle, tube-like inversion of the skin through which the hair reaches the surface of the skin.

Sebaceous or Oil Glands

Arrector (Pili) Muscle

Bulb

Papilla

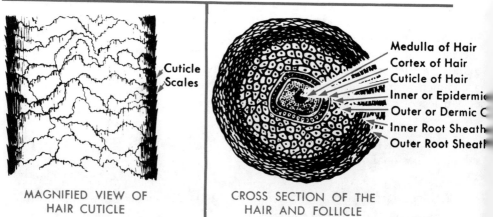

Cuticle Scales

Medulla of Hair
Cortex of Hair
Cuticle of Hair
Inner or Epidermi
Outer or Dermic C
Inner Root Sheath
Outer Root Sheath

MAGNIFIED VIEW OF
HAIR CUTICLE

CROSS SECTION OF THE
HAIR AND FOLLICLE

Diet exerts an influence upon the general health of the hair. It is most easily corrected. The over-eating of sweet, starchy and fatty foods may cause the sebaceous glands to become over-active and secrete too much sebum (oil).

Blood circulation. The hair derives its nourishment from the blood supply which in turn depends upon the foods eaten for certain elements. In the absence of necessary food elements, the health of the hair may decline.

Emotional disturbances or mental tensions are linked with hair health through the nervous system. The well-being of hair is affected by emotional stress. Healthy hair is an indication of a healthy body.

Endocrine (en'dō-krin) **glands** are ductless glands which have their secretions thrown directly into the bloodstream, which in turn influences the welfare of the entire body. The condition of the endocrine glands influences their secretion. During adolescence, they become very active. Their activity usually decreases after middle age. Endocrine gland disturbances, however, influence the health of the hair.

Certain drugs, such as the hormones, if taken without a doctor's advice, may adversely affect the hair.

HAIR STRUCTURE

Shapes of hair. As a rule, hair has one of three general shapes. The hair as it grows out assumes the shape, size and direction of the follicle. **A cross-sectional view** of the hair under the microscope reveals that usually:

> There is no strict rule regarding cross-sectional shapes of hair. Oval, straight or curly hair have been found in all shapes.

1. Straight hair is round.
2. Wavy hair is oval.
3. Curly or kinky hair is almost flat.

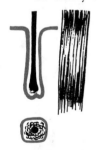  

| 1. Straight hair is usually round. | 2. Wavy hair is usually oval. | 3. Curly or kinky hair is almost flat. |

The structure of the hair is composed of cells arranged in three layers:

1. **Cuticle** (kū'ti-kl), the **outside horny layer**, is composed of transparent, overlapping, protective scale-like cells pointing away from the scalp and towards the hair ends. Chemical solutions raise these scales so that solutions can enter into the hair shaft.

2. **Cortex** (kor'teks), the **middle or inner layer**, provides strength and elasticity, and is made up of a fibrous substance formed by elongated cells. This layer contains the pigment which gives the hair its color.

3. **Medulla** (mē-dul'ah), the **innermost layer**, is referred to as the pith or marrow of the hair shaft, and is composed of round cells. The medulla may be absent in fine and very fine hair.

HAIR DISTRIBUTION

Hair is found all over the body, except on the palms, soles, lips, and eyelids. Hair forms a cushion for the head.

There are three types of hair on the body:

1. **Long hair** grows from the scalp, protects the scalp against the sun's rays and injury, gives adornment to the head, and forms a pleasing frame for the face. **Soft long** hair also grows in the armpits of both sexes and on the faces of men.

2. **Short or bristly hair,** such as the eyebrows and eyelashes, enhance the appearance of the face. **Eyebrows** divert sweat from the eyes. The eyelashes help protect the eyes from dust particles and light glare.

3. **Lanugo** (la-nū'gō) **hair** is the fine, soft, downy (doun'ē) hair of the cheeks, forehead and nearly all areas of the body. It helps in the efficient evaporation of perspiration.

HAIR GROWTH

Hair cycle. If the hair is normal and healthy, each individual hair goes through a steady cycle of events: **growth, fall** and **replacement.**

The formation and growth of hair cells depend upon proper nourishment and oxygen which only the **bloodstream** can supply. Therefore, the function of blood is indispensable to the health and life of hair.

When the body is healthy, hair flourishes. If the body is ill, hair papilla weakens. When the bloodstream provides the hair with food elements, it grows long and strong. If inadequately nourished, it becomes weak, and eventually hair loss occurs.

Normal hair growth. The average growth of healthy hair on the scalp is about one-half inch per month. The rate of growth of human hair will differ on specific parts of the body, between sexes, among races and with age. Scalp hair will also differ among individuals in **strength, elasticity** and **waviness.**

Racial factors have a bearing on hair growth. For example, the American Indians and the Chinese both have long, thick, straight black hair. The Negro's hair is usually short and over-curly.

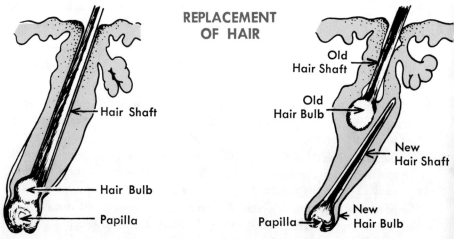

REPLACEMENT OF HAIR

At an early stage of shedding, the hair bulb shows its separation from the papilla.

At a later stage of the hair shedding, you will note a new hair growing from the same papilla.

The growth of scalp hair occurs more rapidly between the ages of 15 and 30, but declines sharply between 50 and 60. Scalp hair grows faster in women than in men.

Hair growth is also influenced by:

1. Seasons of the year
2. Nutrition and hormones

Climatic conditions will affect the hair in the following ways:

1. Moisture in the air will deepen the natural wave.
2. Cold air will cause the hair to contract.
3. Heat will cause the hair to swell or expand and absorb moisture.

Hair growth is not increased by any of the following:

1. Close clipping, shaving, trimming, cutting or singeing have no effect upon the rate of hair growth.
2. The application of ointments or oils will not increase hair growth. They act as lubricants to the hair shaft but do not feed the hair.
3. Hair does not grow after death. The flesh and skin contract, thus giving the appearance of some growth.
4. Singeing the hair will not seal in the natural oil.

Normal hair shedding. A certain amount of hair is shed daily. This is nature's method of making way for new hair. The average daily shedding is estimated at 50 to 80 hairs. Hair loss beyond this estimated average indicates some scalp or hair trouble.

Eyebrow hairs and eyelashes are replaced every four to five months.

REPLACEMENT OF HAIR

Material for the growth of the hair comes from the papilla. As long as the papilla is not destroyed, the hair will grow. If the hair is pulled out from the roots, it will nevertheless grow again. Should the papilla be destroyed, it will **never** grow again.

In human beings, new hair **replaces** old hair in the following ways:

1. The bulb loosens and separates from the papilla.
2. The bulb moves upward in the follicle.
3. The hair moves slowly to the surface, where it is shed.
4. The new hair is formed by cell division from a growing point at the root around the papilla.

LIFE AND DENSITY OF HAIR

The exact life span of hair has not been agreed upon. The average life of hair will range from **two to four years.** Other factors, such as sex, age, type of hair, heredity and health have a bearing on the duration of hair life.

(While the life span of hair may differ with each individual, the figures two to four years indicate a fair estimated period, considering age, health, climate and other personal factors. Some authorities estimate the life span of hair to range up to 7 years.)

The average area of a head is about 120 square inches. There are an average of 1,000 hairs to a square inch.

The number of hairs on the head varies with the color of the hair:

Blonde	140,000	Black	108,000
Brown	110,000	Red	90,000

COLOR OF HAIR

The natural color of hair, its strength and texture depend mainly on hereditary qualities of a physical nature. The color of hair, being an inherited characteristic, is one which is easy to observe and classify. To be successful in giving hair coloring treatments, the barber-stylist should understand the color and distribution of hair pigmentation. The practitioner should also understand hair texture, porosity and elasticity.

The cortex contains coloring matter, minute grains of **melanin** (mel'ah-nin), or pigment. The source of pigment has not been definitely settled. It is probably derived from the color-forming substances in the blood, as is all pigment of the human body. The color of the hair, light or dark, depends upon the color and amount of the grains of pigment it contains.

GREYING OF HAIR

Grey hair is due mainly to the absence of hair pigment in the cortical layer of the hair. Grey hair is really mottled hair—spots of white or whitish yellow scattered about in the hair shafts. Normally grey hair grows out in this condition from the hair bulb. Greying does not take place after the hair has grown.

In most cases, the greying hair is a result of the natural aging process in humans, but it is not related to the hair's texture or growth. Greying can also happen as a result of some serious illness or nervous shock. An early diminishing of the pigment brought on by emotional tensions may also cause the hair to turn grey.

Premature greyness of hair in a young person is usually the result of a defect in pigment formation occurring at birth. Often it will be found that several members of a family are affected with premature greyness.

HAIR DEFINITIONS AND TECHNICAL TERMS

Hirsuties (her-sū'shi-ēz), or **hypertrichosis** (hī-per-tri-kō'sis), means hairy or superfluous hair. It is recognized by the growth of hair in unusual amounts or locations, as on the faces of women.

Albino (al-bī'nō) is a person born with white hair, the result of an absence of coloring matter in the hair shaft, accompanied by no marked pigment coloring in the skin or iris of the eyes.

Definitions of Directional Hair Growth

Hair stream—Hair in an area sloping in the same direction is known as a hair stream. This is due to the follicles arranged in a uniform manner in the area. When two such streams slope in opposite directions, they form a **natural parting** of the hair.

Whorl—Hair which forms in a swirl effect, as in the crown, is called a whorl.

Cowlick—A tuft of hair standing up is known as a cowlick. Areas in which cowlicks are noticeable are usually at the front hairline. However, they may be located in other parts of the scalp. In hairstyling, cowlicks must be considered and the hair styled to minimize their effects.

Cowlick

HAIR ANALYSIS

Because the barber-styling services include the coloring and styling of hair, it is essential for the practitioner to be able to recognize the client's hair texture, hair porosity and hair elasticity. It is of utmost importance that the barber-stylist be able to recognize and distinguish the various types of human hair and conditions.

THE USE OF THE FOUR SENSES

Hair knowledge and skill can be acquired by constant observation and practice in the use of the senses of sight, touch, hearing and smell.

1. **Sight.** Observing the hair will immediately impart some knowledge. Sight alone will not enable accurate judgment of hair qualities. Percentage-wise, sight contributes approximately 15 percent to hair analysis, but the **sense of touch** is the final determining factor.

2. **Touch.** Unless the barber-stylist develops the sense of touch, with relation to hair, to its fullest capacity, he cannot give truly professional hair treatments to patrons.

3. **Hearing.** Some clients like to talk about their hair and health problems and their hair's reaction to applied lotions and its behavior after certain medications have been taken. Since both their health and the application of certain lotions to their hair will affect hair treatments, it is advisable to listen carefully to what they tell you.

4. **Smell.** Uncleanliness and certain scalp disorders will create an odor. If the client has generally good health, and a clean scalp from frequent shampoos, the hair will be free from odor.

The important qualities by which human hair is judged are: porosity, texture, elasticity and condition.

HAIR TEXTURE

Hair texture (teks'tūr) refers to the degree of coarseness or fineness of the hair which varies on different parts of the head. Variations in hair texture are due to:

1. **Diameter of the hair,** viz., coarse, medium, fine and very fine. Coarse hair has the greatest diameter and very fine hair has the smallest.

2. **Feel of the hair,** as harsh, soft or wiry.

Coarse hair contains three layers, namely the medulla, cortex and cuticle. Usually the scales of the outside layer are closely overlapped and raised away from the hair shaft, which is responsible for the ability of coarse hair to readily absorb water.

Medium texture of hair is the normal type most commonly met in the barber-styling shop. The medulla, cortex and cuticle layers are present to a lesser degree than in coarse hair. This type of hair does not present any special problem.

Fine or very fine hair requires special care. A microscopic study of its structure reveals that only two layers, the cortex and cuticle, are present.

Wiry hair, whether coarse, medium or fine, has a hard glassy finish due to the cuticle scales lying flat against the hair shaft. It takes longer to give this type of hair a coloring treatment.

HAIR POROSITY

Hair porosity (pō-ros'i-tē) is the ability of the hair to absorb moisture regardless of whether the hair is coarse, medium or fine.

Good porosity—hair with the cuticle layer raised from the hair shaft. Hair of this type can absorb a fair or normal amount of moisture or chemicals.

Moderate porosity (normal hair)—the average type of hair met in the barber-styling shop. It is less porous than hair with good prosity.

Usually hair with good or moderate porosity presents no problem in giving various hair treatments.

Poor porosity (resistant hair)—hair with the cuticle layer lying close to the hair shaft. This type of hair usually absorbs the least amount of moisture.

Hair with poor porosity requires thorough analysis and strand tests before the application of any cosmetic.

CONDITION OF HAIR

Poor condition—extreme porosity (tinted, lightened or damaged hair)— hair that has been made extremely porous by continuous or faulty treatments. This hair absorbs liquids very easily and quickly, and requires special care.

HAIR ELASTICITY

Hair elasticity (ē-las-tis'i-tē) is the ability of the hair to stretch and return to its original form without breaking. Hair with normal elasticity is springy and gives a live and lustrous appearance. Normal hair is capable of being stretched about one-fifth its length and will spring back when released. However, wet hair can be stretched 40 to 50% of its length. Porous hair will stretch more than hair with poor porosity.

Hair may be classified as having good elasticity, normal elasticity, or poor elasticity.

QUESTIONS ON THE HAIR

1. Why is the study of hair important to the barber-stylist?
2. What is the technical term for the study of hair?
3. Define hair.
4. What is melanin?
5. Give the name of the protein found in the hair.
6. How is each layer of hair held together?
7. What kind of treatment may cause the hair structure to become weakened?
8. How do strongly alkaline solutions harm the hair shaft?
9. Name the two parts into which the length of the hair is divided.
10. What is the hair shaft?
11. What is the hair root?
12. What is the hair follicle?
13. What muscle and gland are attached to the hair follicle?
14. What is the hair bulb?
15. What is the hair papilla?
16. How does the hair receive its nourishment?
17. What is the function of the papilla?
18. What is meant by hair-stream?
19. What is a: a) cowlick; b) whorl?
20. The mouths of hair follicles are favorite breeding places for .... and dirt.
21. What causes "goose pimples"?
22. What function is performed by the oil glands on the scalp?
23. List five factors which influence the production of sebum.
24. What determines the size and shape of the hair?
25. Name three general shapes of hair.
26. Name three layers found in hair.
27. Which layer is sometimes missing in hair?
28. Which hair layer contains coloring matter?
29. Which hair layer serves to protect its inner structure?
30. Which parts of the body do not contain any hair?
31. Briefly describe the appearance of lanugo hair. Where is it usually found?
32. What is the function of lanugo hair?
33. Briefly explain the hair replacement process.
34. What is meant by "hair cycle?"
35. What is the average rate of growth of hair on the head?
36. About how many square inches does an average scalp area contain?

37. List three ways in which climatic conditions will affect the hair.

38. What is the average number of hairs shed daily?

39. What is the average life span of scalp hair?

40. What causes the hair to turn grey?

41. What is an albino?

42. Name the four senses used when analyzing the hair.

43. Name the four important qualities by which hair is judged?

44. Which two senses are used to judge these qualities?

45. Define hair texture.

46. About how many hairs are there on a head of: a) blonde hair; b) black hair; c) brown hair?

47. Define hair porosity.

48. Define hair elasticity.

49. To what extent can normal dry hair be stretched; wet hair be stretched?

50. Which layer of the hair gives strength and elasticity?

Chapter 25
THE NAILS

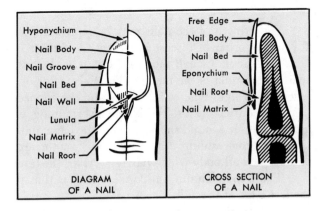

Hyponychium — Nail Body — Nail Groove — Nail Bed — Nail Wall — Lunula — Nail Matrix — Nail Root

DIAGRAM
OF A NAIL

Free Edge — Nail Body — Nail Bed — Eponychium — Nail Root — Nail Matrix

CROSS SECTION
OF A NAIL

INTRODUCTION

Although the nails are not an area of direct interest to the barber-stylist, he should be acquainted with their composition and structure. The all service barber-styling shop offers manicuring as one of its services. It is therefore advisable that the barber-stylist have some knowledge in this area.

The condition of the nail, like that of the skin, reflects the general health of the body. The normal, healthy nail is firm and flexible and exhibits a slightly pinkish color. Its surface should be smooth, curved and unspotted, without any hollows or wavy ridges.

The **nail,** an appendage of skin, is a horny translucent plate which serves to protect the tips of fingers and toes. **Onyx** is the technical term for nail.

NAIL COMPOSITION

The nail is composed mainly of **keratin** (ker´ah-tin), a protein substance which forms the base of all horny tissue. The nail is whitish in appearance. The pinkish color of the nail bed can be seen through the nail. The horny nail plate contains no nerves or blood vessels.

NAIL STRUCTURE

The nails consist of 3 parts: the nail body, the nail root, and the free edge.

The **nail body,** or plate, is the visible portion of the nail which rests upon, and is attached to, the **nail bed.** The nail body extends from the root to the free edge.

Although the nail plate seems to be made of one piece, it is actually constructed in layers. The readiness with which nails split, in both their length and thickness, clearly demonstrates this form of structure.

The **nail root** is at the base of the nail and is imbedded underneath the skin. The nail root originates from an actively growing tissue known as the **matrix** (ma´triks).

The **free edge** is the end portion of the nail plate which reaches over the fingertips.

The **nail bed** is the portion of the skin upon which the **nail body** rests. It is supplied with many blood vessels which provide nourishment for continued growth of the nail. The nail bed is also abundantly supplied with nerves.

The **matrix** is that part of the nail bed that extends beneath the nail root and contains nerves, lymph and blood vessels. The matrix produces the nail as its cells undergo a reproducing and hardening process. The matrix will continue to grow as long as it receives nutrition and remains healthy.

The growth of the nails may be retarded if an individual is in poor health, if a nail disorder or disease is present, or if there is an injury to the nail matrix.

The **lunula** or **half-moon** is located at the base of the nail. The area underneath the lunula is the matrix. The light color of the lunula may be due to the reflection of light where the matrix and the connective tissue of the nail bed join.

The **cuticle** (kū'ti-kl) is the overlapping epidermis around the nail. A normal cuticle around the nail should be loose and pliable.

The **eponychium** (ep-ō-nik'ē-um) is the extension of the cuticle at the base of the nail body which partly overlaps the lunula.

The **hyponychium** (hī-pō-nik'ē-um) is that portion of the epidermis under the free edge of the nail.

The **perionychium** (per-i-ō-nik'ē-um) is that portion of the cuticle surrounding the entire nail border.

The **nail walls** are the folds of skin overlapping the sides of the nail.

The **nail grooves** are slits, or tracks, on the sides of the nail upon which the nail moves as it grows.

The **mantle** (man'tl) is the deep fold of skin in which the nail root is imbedded.

NAIL GROWTH

The growth of the nail is influenced by nutrition, health and disease. The nail grows forward, starting at the **matrix** and extending over the fingertip.

The average rate of growth in the normal adult is about one-eighth of an inch per month, being faster in summer than in winter. The nails of children grow more rapidly, whereas those of elderly persons grow more slowly. The nail grows fastest on the middle finger and slowest on the thumb. Although toenails grow more slowly than fingernails, they are thicker and harder.

NAIL MALFORMATION

If the nail is separated from the nail bed through injury, it becomes distorted or discolored. Should the nail bed be injured after the loss of a nail, a badly formed new nail will result.

The nails are neither shed automatically nor periodically, as hairs are. If the nail is torn off accidentally, or lost through an infection or disease, it will be replaced only as long as the matrix remains in good condition. Nails lost under such conditions are, on regrowth, frequently badly shaped, due to interference at the base of the nail. Replacement of the nail takes about four months.

QUESTIONS ON THE NAILS

1. What are nails?
2. Describe the appearance of a healthy nail.
3. Of what main substance is the nail composed?
4. Locate the following: a) nail root; b) nail body; c) free edge; d) nail bed.
5. What two factors promote the growth of the nails?
6. What three factors retard the growth of the nail?
7. What part of the nail contains the nerve and blood supply?
8. Where does the formation of the nail occur?
9. How does the nail receive its nourishment?
10. What is the average growth of the nail?

Chapter 26

DISORDERS OF THE SKIN, SCALP AND HAIR

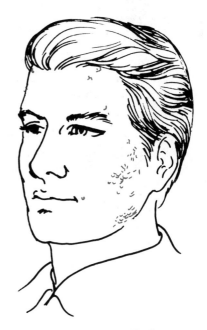

The following chapter has been compiled to help the barber-stylist become more familiar with certain common skin, scalp, and hair disorders which the stylist may come in contact with during the regular course of his or her work.

The barber-stylist must be prepared to recognize certain skin conditions and should know how to act properly with relation to them. Some skin and scalp disorders may be treated in cooperation with and under the supervision of a physician. Medicinal preparations issued under a prescription for scalp, skin or hair disorders may only be applied as prescribed and with the permission of a physician.

Any condition which the practitioner does not positively know to be one of the simple disorders which are rightfully handled in the barber-styling shop should be **referred** tactfully but firmly to a physician.

The most important thing to know is that a client who has an **infection** or **contagious skin disorder** should not be served in the barber-styling shop. The barber-stylist should be able to **recognize** these conditions and **suggest** that proper measures be taken to prevent more serious consequences.

Thus, the barber-stylist **safeguards** his own **health** as well as the health of the **public.**

DEFINITIONS OF IMPORTANT TERMS

Listed below are a number of important terms which should be familiar to the practitioners in order that they properly understand the subject of skin, scalp and hair disorders.

Dermatology (der-ma-tol′ō-jē) is the study of the skin, its nature, structure, functions, diseases and treatment.

Dermatologist (der-ma-tol′o-jist) is a skin specialist.

Trichology (tri-kol′ō-jē) is the study of the hair and its diseases.

Diagnosis (dī-ag-nō′sis) is the recognition of a disease from its symptoms.

Prognosis (prog-nō′sis) is the foretelling of the probable course of a disease. **365**

LESIONS OF THE SKIN

A lesion is a structural change in the tissues caused by injury or disease. There are three types: primary, secondary and tertiary. The barber-stylist is concerned with primary and secondary lesions only.

Knowing the principal skin lesions helps him to distinguish between conditions which may or may not be treated in a barber-styling shop.

Symptom (simp'tum) is a sign of disease. The symptoms in diseases of the skin are divided into two groups.

1. **Subjective** (sub-jek'tiv)—symptoms that can be felt by the patient, as in itching, burning or hurting.
2. **Objective** (ob-jek'tiv)—symptoms that can be seen, as in pimples or boils.

PRIMARY LESIONS

1. **Macule** (mak'ūl)—a small discolored spot or patch on the surface of the skin, neither raised nor sunken, as in freckles.
2. **Papule** (pap'ūl)—a small elevated pimple of the skin containing no fluid, but which may develop pus.
3. **Wheal** (whēl)—an itchy, swollen lesion that lasts only a few hours. (Examples: hives or the bite of an insect, such as a mosquito.)
4. **Tubercle** (tū'ber-k'l)—a solid lump larger than a papule. It projects above the surface or lies within or under the skin. It varies in size from a pea to a hickory nut. (Example: a thick scar.)
5. **Tumor** (tū'mor)—an external swelling, varying in size, shape and color.
6. **Vesicle** (ves'i-k'l)—a blister with clear fluid in it. Vesicles lie within or just beneath the epidermis. (Example: poison ivy produces small vesicles.)
7. **Bulla** (bul'ah)—a blister containing a watery fluid, similar to a vesicle, but larger.
8. **Pustule** (pus'tūl)—an elevation of the skin having an inflamed base and containing pus. (Example: common pimple.)

SECONDARY LESIONS

The secondary lesions are those which develop in the later stages of disease. These are:

1. **Scale** (skāl)—an accumulation of epidermal flakes, dry or greasy. (Example: abnormal or excessive dandruff.)
2. **Crust, scab**—an accumulation of sebum and pus, mixed perhaps with epidermal material. (Example: the scab on a sore.)
3. **Abrasion** (a-brā'shun)—a skin sore produced by scratching or scraping. (Example: a raw surface due to the loss of the superficial skin after an injury.)
4. **Fissure** (fish'ūr)—a crack in the skin penetrating into the derma, as in the case of chapped hands or lips.

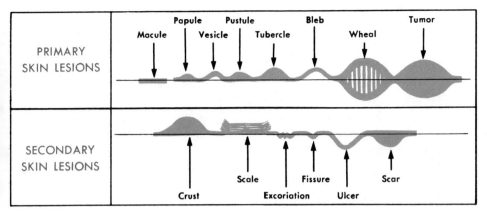

| PRIMARY SKIN LESIONS | Macule Papule Vesicle Pustule Tubercle Bleb Wheal Tumor |
| SECONDARY SKIN LESIONS | Crust Scale Excoriation Fissure Ulcer Scar |

5. **Ulcer** (ul'ser)—an open lesion on the skin or mucous membrane of the body, accompanied by pus and loss of skin depth.

6. **Scar**—Tissue that is likely to form after the healing of an injury or skin condition that has penetrated the dermal layer.

7. **Stain** (stān)—an abnormal discoloration remaining after the disappearance of moles, freckles or liver spots, sometimes apparent after certain diseases.

DEFINITIONS OF COMMON TERMS APPLIED TO DISEASE

Before describing the diseases of the skin and scalp so they will be recognized by the barber-stylist, it is well to understand what is meant by disease.

A **disease** is any departure from a normal state of health.

A **skin disease** is a disorder characterized by objective skin lesions (can be seen) and may consist of scales, pimples or pustules.

An **acute disease** is one indicated by symptoms of a more or less violent character and of short duration.

A **chronic** (kron'ik) **disease** is one of long duration, usually mild but recurring.

An **infectious** (in-fek'shus) **disease** is one due to a pathogenic microorganism or virus taken into the body as a result of contact with a lesion or contaminated object.

A **contagious** (kon-tā'jus) **disease** is one that is readily spread to other persons by contact.

Note—**The terms infectious disease, communicable** (kom-u'ni-ka-b'l) **disease, and contagious disease are often used interchangeably.**

A **congenital** (kon-jen'i-tal) **disease** is one that is present in the infant at birth.

A **seasonal** (se'zon-al) **disease** is one that is influenced by the weather, as prickly heat in the summer and certain forms of eczema which are more prevalent in cold weather.

An **occupational** (ok-ū-pā'shun-al) **disease** is one that is due to certain kinds of employment, such as dermatitis caused by coming into contact with cosmetics, chemicals or tints.

A **parasitic** (par-a-sit'ik) **disease** is one that is caused by vegetable or animal parasites responsible for lice, scabies or ringworm.

A **pathogenic** (path-o-jen'ik) **disease** is one produced by a disease-producing bacteria, such as pus-forming bacteria.

A **systemic** (sis-tem'ik) **disease** is due to under- or over-functioning of the internal glands. It may be caused by faulty diet.

A **venereal** (ve-nē're-al) **disease,** such as syphilis or gonorrhea, is a contagious disease commonly acquired by contact with an infected person during sexual intercourse.

An **epidemic** (ep-i-dem'ik) is the manifestation of a disease that simultaneously attacks a large number of persons living in a particular locality, such as infantile paralysis, influenza, virus or small-pox.

Allergy (al'er-jē) is a sensitivity which certain persons develop to normally harmless substances. Skin allergies are quite common. Contact with certain types of cosmetics, medicines and tints or eating certain foods may bring about an itching eruption, accompanied by redness, swelling, blisters, oozing and scaling.

Inflammation (in-fla-mā'shun) is characterized by redness, pain, swelling and heat.

REMINDER

To avoid the transmission of disease in the barber-styling shop,
be sure to practice sanitation and sanitization at all times.

DISORDERS OF THE SEBACEOUS (OIL) GLANDS

There are several common diseases of the sebaceous (se-bā'shē-us) (oil) glands which the barber-stylist should be able to identify and understand.

Comedones (kom-e'dōnz), or **blackheads,** are a worm-like mass of hardened sebum appearing most frequently on the face, forehead and nose.

Blackheads accompanied by pimples often occur in youths between the ages of 13 and 20. During the adolescent period, the activity of the sebaceous glands is stimulated, thereby contributing to the formation of blackheads and pimples. When the hair follicle is filled with an excess of oil from the sebaceous gland, a blackhead forms and creates a blockage at the mouth of the follicle. This causes irritation and may result in an inflamed pimple filled with pus. Such a lesion is known as **acne.**

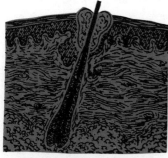

The treatment for blackheads is to reduce the skin's oiliness by local applications of cleaners and the removal of blackheads under sterile conditions. Thorough skin cleansing each night is a very important factor. Cleansing creams and lotions often achieve better results than common soap and water. Should this condition become severe, medical attention is necessary.

Blackhead (plug of sebaceous
matter and dirt) forming around
mouth of hair follicle

Milia (whiteheads)

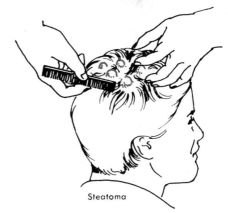

Steatoma

Milia (mil'ē-ah), or **whiteheads**—A disorder of the sebaceous (oil) glands caused by the accumulation of sebaceous matter beneath the skin. This may occur on any part of the face, neck and occasionally on the chest and shoulders. Whiteheads are often associated with dry types of skin.

Steatoma (stē-a-to'mah), or **sebaceous cyst,** is a subcutaneous tumor of the sebaceous glands, the contents consisting of sebum (sē'bum), from pea to orange in size, usually occurring on the scalp, neck and back. A steatoma is sometimes called a **wen.**

Asteatosis (as'tē-a-tō'sis) is a condition of dry, scaly skin, characterized by absolute or partial deficiency of sebum, due to senile (sē'nĭl) (old age) changes or some bodily disorders. In local conditions, it may be caused by alkalies, such as are found in soaps and washing powders.

Seborrhea (seb-ō-rē'ah) is a skin condition due to over-activity and excessive secretion of the sebaceous or oil glands. An itching or burning sensation may accompany it. An oily or shiny condition of the nose, forehead or scalp indicates the presence of seborrhea. On the scalp, it is readily detected by the unusual amount of oil on the hair.

Acne (ak'nē) is a chronic inflammatory disease of the sebaceous glands, occurring most frequently on the face, back and chest. The cause of acne is generally held to be microbic (mī-krōb'ik), but predisposing factors are adolescence and disturbance of the digestive tract.

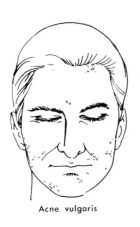

Acne vulgaris

Acne or common pimples is also known as acne simplex or acne vulgaris.

Acne scars

Acne appears in a variety of different types ranging from the simple (non-contagious) pimple to serious deep-seated skin conditions. It is always advisable to have the condition examined and diagnosed by a competent physician before any facial service is given in the barber-styling shop.

Acne rosacea (rō-zā′shē-ah) is a chronic, inflammatory congestion of the cheeks and nose. It is characterized by redness, dilation of the blood vessels, and the formation of papules and pustules. It is usually caused by poor digestion and over-indulgence in alcoholic liquors. It may also be caused by over-exposure to extreme climate, constipation, faulty elimination and hyper-acidity. It is usually aggravated by eating and drinking hot, highly spiced, or highly seasoned foods or drinks. It generally has three stages.

The **first stage** starts with a slight pinkness all over the face, varying with the temperature and the temperament of the individual.

The **second stage** affects the capillaries (kap′i-lā-rēz). Often they become so dilated that they are apparent to the naked eye. At this stage the sebaceous glands are affected. Large pores, oiliness and comedones invariably result.

The **third stage** is very disfiguring. The entire face becomes congested, and the condition may remain chronic, although dormant for years.

DISORDERS OF THE SUDORIFEROUS (SWEAT) GLANDS

Bromidrosis (brō-mi-drō′sıs), or **osmidrosis** (oz-mi-drō′sis), refers to foul-smelling perspiration, usually noticeable in the armpits or on the feet.

Anidrosis (an-i-drō′sis) or lack of perspiration, is often a result of fever or certain skin diseases. Requires medical attention.

Hyperidrosis (hī per-i-drō′sis), or excessive perspiration, is caused by excessive heat or general body weakness. The most commonly affected parts are the armpits, joints and feet. Requires medical treatment.

Miliaria rubra (mil-ē-a′rē-ah roob′rah) (prickly heat)—An acute inflammatory disorder of sweat glands characterized by an eruption of small red vesicles, accompanied by burning and itching of the skin. Caused by exposure to excessive heat and overweight.

DANDRUFF

Dandruff (dan′druf) is the presence of small, white scales usually appearing on the scalp and hair. Dandruff is also known by the medical term of **pityriasis** (pit-i-rī a-sis).

Just as the skin is continually being shed and replaced, in a similar manner the uppermost layer of the scalp is being cast off all the time. Ordinarily, these horny scales are loose and fall off freely. The natural shedding of these horny scales should not be mistaken for dandruff.

Long-neglected dandruff frequently leads to baldness.

The causes of dandruff are:

1. A direct cause of dandruff is the excessive shedding of the epithelial (ep-i-thēl'ē-al) scales. Instead of growing to the surface and falling off, the horny scales accumulate on the scalp.

2. Indirect or associated causes of dandruff are a sluggish condition of the scalp occasioned by poor circulation, infection, injury, lack of nerve stimulation, improper diet and uncleanliness. Contributing causes are the use of strong shampoos and insufficient rinsing of the hair after a shampoo.

The two principal types of dandruff are:

1. **Dry dandruff** (pityriasis capitis — kap'i-tis)
2. **Greasy (waxy) dandruff** (pityriasis steatoides — stē-a-toy'dēz)

Simple dandruff

Excessive dandruff

Dry dandruff (pityriasis capitis simplex) is characterized by an itchy scalp and small, white scales usually attached in masses to the scalp or scattered loosely in the hair. Occasionally, they are so profuse that they fall to the shoulders. Dry dandruff is often the result of a sluggish scalp caused by poor circulation, lack of nerve stimulation, improper diet, emotional and glandular disturbances or uncleanliness.

Treatment. Frequent scalp treatments and mild shampoos, regular scalp massage, daily use of antiseptic scalp lotions, applications of scalp ointment and electrical treatments will correct this condition.

Greasy (waxy) dandruff (pityriasis steatoides) is scaliness of the epidermis mixed with sebum which causes it to stick to the scalp in patches. The associated itchiness causes the person to scratch the scalp. If the greasy scales are torn off, bleeding or oozing of sebum may follow. Medical treatment is advisable.

PRECAUTION

The nature of dandruff is not clearly defined by medical authorities. It is generally believed to be of infectious origin. Some authorities hold that it is due to a specific microbe. However, from the barber-stylist's point of view, both forms of dandruff are to be considered contagious and may be spread by the use of common brushes, combs and other articles. Therefore, the barber-stylist must take the necessary precautions to sanitize everything that comes into contact with the client.

INFLAMMATIONS

Dermatitis (dur-ma-tī tis) is a term used to denote an inflammatory condition of the skin. The lesions come in various forms, such as vesicles or papules.

Eczema (ek′ze-mah) is an inflammation of the skin of acute or chronic nature, presenting many forms of dry or moist lesions. It is frequently accompanied by itching, burning and various other unpleasant sensations. All cases of eczema should be referred to a physician for treatment. Its cause is unknown.

Psoriasis (sō-rī′a-sis) is a common, chronic, inflammatory skin disease, the cause of which is unknown. It is usually found on the scalp, elbows, knees, chest and lower back, rarely on the face. The lesions are round dry patches covered with coarse, silvery scales. If irritated, bleeding points occur. While not contagious, it can be spread by irritation.

Fever blisters (**herpes simplex**—hur′pēz sim′pleks) is a virus infection of unknown origin. It is characterized by the eruption of a single or group of vesicles on a red, swollen base. The blisters usually appear on the lips, nostrils or any part of the face and rarely last more than a week. Indigestion may be one of the causes.

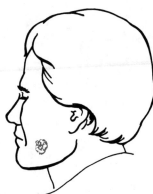

Herpes simplex   Anthrax

Anthrax (an′thraks)—A harmful inflammatory skin disorder which may be caused by the use of an infected shaving brush. It is characterized by the presence of a small, red papule, followed by the formation of a pustule, vesicle and hard swelling. It is accompanied by itching and burning feelings at the point of infection.

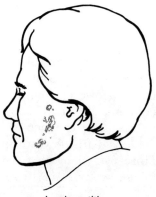

Ivy dermatitis — A skin inflammation caused by exposure to the poison ivy, poison oak or poison sumac leaves. Blisters and itching develop soon after contact occurs. The condition can be spread to other parts of the body by contact with contaminated hands, clothing, objects and anything that was exposed to the plant itself. Serious cases should be referred to physician for treatment.

Ivy dermatitis

Occupational disorders in barber-styling refer to abnormal conditions resulting from contact with chemicals or tints in the course of performing services in the barber-styling shop. Certain ingredients in cosmetics, antiseptics and aniline derivative tints may cause eruptive skin infections known as **dermatitis venenata** (ven-e-na'tah). It is important that practitioners employ protective measures, such as the use of rubber gloves or protective creams, whenever possible.

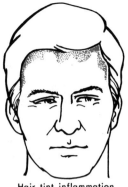

Hair tint inflammation

ALOPECIA

Alopecia (al-ō-pē'shē-ah) is the technical term for any abnormal form of loss of hair.

The natural falling out of the hair should not be confused with alopecia. When hair has grown to its full length, it comes out by itself and is replaced by a new hair. The natural shedding of the hair occurs most frequently in spring and fall. On the other hand, the hair lost in alopecia does not come back, unless special treatments are given to encourage hair growth.

Alopecia senilis (sē-nil'is) is the form of baldness occurring in old age. The loss of hair is permanent.

Alopecia prematura (prē-ma-tū'rah) is the form of baldness beginning any time before middle age by a slow thinning process, and is due to the fact that the first hairs that fall out are replaced by weaker ones.

Alopecia areata (ar-ē-a'tah) is the falling out of hair in round patches, or baldness in spots, sometimes caused by anemia, scarlet fever, typhoid fever or syphilis. Affected areas are slightly depressed, smooth and very pale, due to the decreased blood supply. Patches may be round or irregular, and vary in size from ½ inch to 2 or 3 inches in diameter. In most conditions of alopecia areata, the nervous system has been subjected to an injury. Since the flow of blood is influenced by the nervous system, the affected area is usually poorly nourished as well.

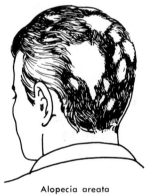

Alopecia areata

Alopecia may appear in a variety of different forms resulting from many abnormal conditions. Sometimes an alopecia condition may be improved by proper scalp treatments.

CONTAGIOUS DISORDERS

Common contagious disorders likely to be met in the barber-styling shop include:

1. **Ringworm,** due to **fungi** (plant or vegetable parasites)
2. **Scabies** and **head lice,** due to animal parasites
3. **Boil, carbuncle** and **inflammations,** traceable to bacterial infections

373

Vegetable Parasitic Infections

Tinea (tin'ē-ah) is the medical term for **ringworm**. Ringworm is caused by **vegetable parasites**. All forms are contagious. **Tinea** is transmissible from one person to another. The disease is commonly passed by scales of hairs containing fungi. Shower baths, swimming pools and unsanitized articles are also sources of transmission. Any ringworm condition should be referred to a physician.

Ringworm starts with a small reddened patch of little blisters. They spread outward and heal in the middle with scaling. Several such patches may be present.

Tinea capitis (ringworm of the scalp) is a contagious vegetable parasitic disease of the hairy scalp, characterized by red papules or spots at the opening of the hair follicles. The patches spread, the hair becomes brittle and lifeless and breaks off, leaving a stump, or falls from the enlarged open follicles.

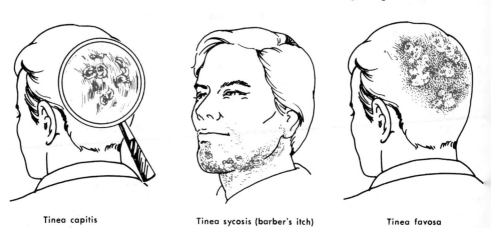

Tinea capitis   Tinea sycosis (barber's itch)   Tinea favosa

Tinea sycosis (sī-kō'sis) (barber's itch) is a fungus infection occurring chiefly over the bearded area of the face. Beginning as small, rounded, slightly scaly, inflamed patches, the areas enlarge, clearing up somewhat centrally with elevation of the borders. As the parasites invade the hairs and follicles, hard lumpy swellings develop. In severe cases, pustules form around the hair follicles and rupture, forming crusts. In the later stage, the hairs become dry, break off, and fall out or are readily extracted. Being highly contagious, medical treatment is required.

Tinea favosa (tin'e-ah fa-vo'sah) (favus [fa'vus] or **honeycomb ringworm**) is an infectious growth due to a vegetable parasite. It is characterized by dry, sulphur-yellow, cup-like crusts on the scalp, having a peculiar mousy odor. Scars from favus are bald patches, pink or white, and shiny. It is very contagious and should be referred to a physician.

Tinea unguium

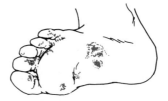

Ringworm of the foot

Tinea unguium (ung'gwē-um) (ringworm of the nails)—a local infectious disease. As the disease spreads, the nails become thickened, brittle and lose their natural shape. It is very contagious.

Ringworm (tinea) of the foot. (Athlete's foot.)—a local infectious disease. The inflamed areas on the sole of the foot and between the toes show signs of redness, blisters and cracking of the skin. Itching and excessive sweating are also present. It is very contagious.

Ringworm of the feet may spread and infect other parts of the body. Every barber-stylist infected must take special precaution to prevent the spread of this disease by sanitizing his hands, feet and socks until cured.

Animal Parasitic Infections

Scabies (skā'bēz) (the itch) is a highly contagious, animal parasitic skin disease caused by the itch mite. Vesicles and pustules may form from the irritation of the parasites or from scratching the affected areas.

Pediculosis (pe-dik-ū-lō'sis) **capitis** is a contagious condition caused by the head louse (animal parasite) infesting the hair of the scalp. As the parasites feed on the scalp, itching symptoms are felt and scratching may cause an infection. The head louse is transmitted from one person to another by intimate contact with infested hats, combs, brushes or other personal articles. To **kill head lice,** advise patron to apply larkspur tincture or other similar medication to the entire head before retiring. The next morning, shampoo with germicidal soap. Repeat treatment as necessary. Never treat in the barber-stylist shop.

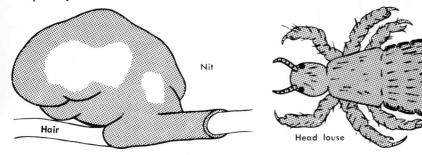

Nit

Hair

Head louse

Bacterial Infections

Sycosis vulgaris (vul-ga'ris) is a chronic bacterial infection involving the hair follicles of the beard and mustache areas. It is caused by the use of unsanitized towels or implements, and made worse by irritation, such as shaving or a continual nasal discharge. The main lesions are papules and pustules pierced by hairs. The surrounding skin is tender, reddened, swollen at times, and tends to itch. Medical care is required. (This infection must not be confused with tinea sycosis, which is due to ringworm fungus.)

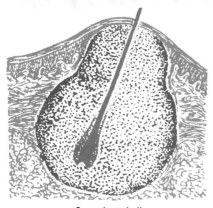
Furuncle or boil

Furuncle (fer-un'k'l), or **boil**, is an acute bacterial infection of a hair follicle, producing constant pain. A furuncle is the result of an active inflammatory process limited to a definite area and subsequently producing a pustule perforated by a hair.

Carbuncle (kar'bun-k'l) is the result of an acute deep-seated bacterial infection and is larger than a furuncle, or boil. It should be referred to a physician.

VENEREAL DISEASES

Syphilis (sif'i-lis) is a dangerous infectious disease. The disease germs enter the body through the skin or mucous membranes of the body by way of sexual intercourse with a person having the disease, kissing an infected person or by the use of infected materials.

The barber-stylist can do his part in preventing the spread of this harmful disease. Through his friendly help, he can direct a client to seek competent advice if there is the slightest suspicion of syphilis. Delay reduces the chances of cure. Only a physician is qualified to diagnose and prescribe treatment for this condition. The infected person must never try to cure himself with patent medicines, but should consult with a competent doctor. If in doubt as to who is qualified to treat syphilis, consult your Health Department.

The symptoms or signs of syphilis appear in three stages.

First stage. Several weeks after the disease germs get into the body, a sore usually appears at the spot where they entered. Little discomfort is experienced in early syphilis. After a few weeks, the sore heals and leaves a scar. In the meantime, the disease germs spread to all parts of the body, where they begin to do their damage.

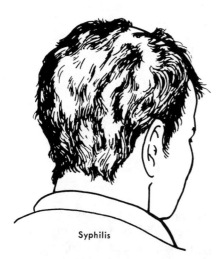
Syphilis

Second stage. This stage of syphilis develops about three to six weeks after the sore has appeared. As the disease progresses, the following symptoms may occur in a mild or severe form:

1. Skin rash
2. Sores in mouth and throat
3. Swollen glands
4. Loss of hair
5. Fever and headache

Third stage. If syphilis has not been treated and cured at this stage, it may damage the vital organs, such as the heart and brain.

Syphilis is most infectious in the primary and secondary stages, especially when the lesions (sores and mucous patches) are located on an exposed part of the body or in the mouth. The open sores contain the germs of the disease

Syphilis can be readily spread from the infected to the healthy person by direct or immediate body-to-body contact, and by indirect means through contact with infected objects. The barber-stylist should refuse to serve any person known to have or suspected of having syphilis in its early stages. If in doubt as to whether a person has syphilis, take every precaution to sanitize all objects coming into contact with the patron.

Gonorrhea (gon-ō-rē'ah) is a contagious disease which generally attacks the mucous membranes covering the mouth, eyes, sex organs and other internal structures of the body. Gonorrhea, like syphilis, is usually spread by sexual relations with an infected person or contact with infected objects.

The first symptoms of gonorrhea usually appear in from two to five days after exposure. At first, itching and burning feelings are experienced in the affected parts. Shortly afterward, a discharge of pus begins to come from the inflamed organ. The pus contains an abundance of disease germs. At this stage, gonorrhea is highly contagious. Take every precaution to prevent its spread.

As with syphilis, the barber-stylist should refuse to serve any person known to have or suspected of having gonorrhea. The best assistance the practitioner can give is to recommend medical treatment as soon as possible.

Failure to treat gonorrhea in its early stages may cause the disease to spread. Occasionally, in the later stages, gonorrhea attacks the lining of the heart, the joints and the lining around the liver.

> A barber-stylist infected with gonorrhea or syphilis must not work during this period because of the possibility of spreading it to other persons.

The Control of Venereal Disease

Penicillin and sulfa drugs are being used for the treatment of venereal (ve-nē'rē-al) diseases. Patients may now be treated in hospitals and rendered non-infectious within a short period of time. Health Departments give free treatments to those who cannot afford a private doctor.

Syphilis and gonorrhea can be treated by a skilled physician as soon as the first sign of infection is detected. If treatment is either neglected or delayed, the treatment may take a long time. Permanent damage may be the final result. Only a reliable physician can safely decide which treatment is best.

The barber-stylist can make his contribution to public health by:

1. Eliminating the sources of infection in the barber-styling shop.
2. Encouraging early medical treatment as needed.
3. Urging the infected person to follow the doctor's instructions.
4. Cooperating with health officials to try to control venereal diseases.

NON-CONTAGIOUS HAIR DISORDERS

Six non-contagious infections of the hair are:

Greyness of hair—technical name—**canities** (ka-nish'ī-ēz)

Split hair ends—technical name—**trichoptilosis** (trī-kop-ti-lō'sis)

Superfluous hair—technical name—**hypertrichosis** (hī-per-tri-kō'sis)

Split
hair ends

Knotted hair—technical name—**trichorrhexis nodosa** (trik-ō-rek′sis nō-dō′sah)

Brittle hair—technical name—**fragilitas crinium** (fra-jil′i-tas krin′e-um)

Beaded hair—technical name—**monilethrix** (mon-il′e-thriks)

Greyness of the hair is caused by the loss of natural pigment in the hair. It may be either of two types.

1. **Congenital**—exists at or before birth. It occurs in albinos and occasionally in persons with perfectly normal hair. The patchy type of congenital canities may develop slowly or rapidly, according to the cause of the condition.

2. **Acquired**—may be due to old age, or premature, as in early adult life. Several causes of acquired greyness of hair are worry, anxiety, nervous strain, prolonged illness, various wasting diseases and hereditary tendency.

Ringed hair. Alternate bands of grey and dark hair.

Superfluous hair (hypertrichosis), also called hirsuties, is an abnormal development of hair on areas of the body normally bearing only downy hair. Treatments:

1. Dark hairs—tweeze or remove by depilatories
2. Severe cases—remove by electrolysis, shaving or epilation

CAUTION. Small pigmented areas—**do not treat.**

Beaded
hair

Split hair ends (trichoptilosis). Treatment: The hair should be well oiled to soften and lubricate the excessively dry hair. The split hair may also be removed by cutting.

Knotted hair (trichorrhexis nodosa) is a dry, brittle condition with the formation of nodular swellings along the hair shaft. The hair breaks easily and shows a queer brush-like spreading out of the fibers of the broken-off hair. Softening the hair with ointments may prove beneficial.

Beaded hair (monilethrix). The hair breaks between the beads or nodes. Scalp and hair treatments may be beneficial.

Brittle hair (fragilitas crinium). The hairs may split at any part of their length. Scalp and hair treatments may be given.

PIGMENTATIONS OF THE SKIN

In abnormal conditions, **pigment** (pig′ment) may come from inside or outside the body.

Abnormal colors are seen in every skin disease and many systemic disorders. Pigmentation due to foreign substances is observed when certain drugs are being taken internally.

Tan is caused by excessive exposure to the sun.

Knotted
hair

Freckles (lentigines—len-ti-jī′nez), (singular, **lentigo**) are small yellowish to brown colored spots appearing on those parts of the body exposed to sunlight and atmosphere, principally the face, hands and arms.

Stains are abnormal brown skin patches having a circular and irregular shape. Their permanent color is due to the presence of blood pigment. They occur during ageing, after certain diseases and after the disappearance of moles, freckles and liver spots. The cause is unknown.

Liver spots (**chloasma**—klō-az'mah) is characterized by increased deposits of pigment in the skin. Found mainly on the forehead, nose and cheeks.

Birthmark (**naevus**—nē'vus) is a small or large malformation of the skin due to pigmentation or dilated capillaries.

Leucoderma (lū-kō-der'mah) refers to abnormal whiteness in patches of the skin due to congenital defective pigmentations. It is a colorless condition of the skin classified as follows:

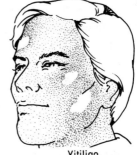
Vitiligo

1. **Vitiligo** (vit-i-lī'go—an acquired condition of leucoderma affecting the skin or the hair. There is no treatment for this condition except the application of a matching cosmetic color, making it less conspicuous.

2. **Albinism** (al'bin-izm)—a congenital absence of melanin pigments in the body, including the skin, hair and eyes. This condition may be partial or entire. The silky hair is white or pale yellow. The skin is pinkish white and will not tan.

HYPERTROPHIES (NEW GROWTHS)

Callous (**keratoma**—ker-a-tō'mah)—an acquired, superficial, round, thickened patch of epidermis, occurring for the most part in regions of **pressure** and **friction** on the hands and feet.

A **mole** (mōl) is a small brownish spot or blemish on the skin. Moles are believed to be inherited. They range in color from pale tan to brown or bluish black. Some moles are small and flat, resembling freckles, while others are more deeply seated and darker in color. Large, dark hairs often occur in moles. If a mole grows in size, gets darker, develops soreness or becomes scaly, medical attention is needed.

CAUTION

Do not treat or remove hair from moles.

Wart (**verruca**—ve-roo'kah). It is carried by a virus and is infectious. It can spread from one location to another, particularly along a scratch in the skin.

Verruca

REMINDERS

Be sure to practice sanitation and sanitization at all times. Obey all rules and regulations set forth by the Board of Health and State Board of Barbering.

QUESTIONS ON DISORDERS OF THE SKIN, SCALP AND HAIR

1. Why should the barber-stylist be able to recognize the common skin, scalp and hair disorders?
2. Why should the barber-stylist refuse to treat a patron with an infectious or contagious disease?
3. What is the purpose of studying infectious diseases of the skin, scalp, and hair?
4. Define disease.
5. What is a lesion?
6. Name eight primary lesions of the skin.
7. What is the difference between objective and subjective lesions? Give one example of each.
8. Name seven secondary lesions of the skin.
9. a) What are scales? b) In which scalp disorder are scales present?
10. Which of the following terms apply to diseases of the sebaceous (oil) glands? Milia, acne, hypertrophies, leucoderma, comedones, seborrhea and hyperidrosis.
11. Define acne.
12. What are the common terms for a) comedones; b) milia?
13. Briefly describe bromidrosis, anidrosis and hyperidrosis.
14. What causes the formation of comedones?
15. Name and briefly describe the two principal types of dandruff.
16. List six conditions which may be the cause of dandruff.
17. Define dermatitis.
18. What is the characteristic appearance of psoriasis?
19. On which five parts of the body is psoriasis usually found?
20. Define alopecia.
21. What is the common term for tinea?
22. What is the cause of tinea?
23. Briefly describe ringworm.
24. What is meant by canities?
25. Briefly describe two types of canities.
26. Briefly describe trichoptilosis.
27. By what two terms is superfluous hair known?
28. By what other two terms is acne, the common pimple, known?
29. What is the medical term for a boil?
30. Name the types of bacteria that cause a boil.
31. What is the common term for pediculosis capitis?
32. Describe vitiligo.
33. Define albinism.
34. What is the common name for naevus?
35. What is the technical term for a wart?
36. What is a mole?

Chapter 27
ANATOMY
AND PHYSIOLOGY

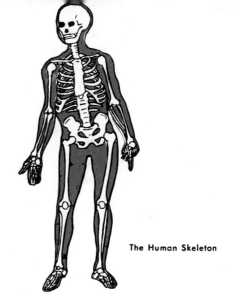

The Human Skeleton

INTRODUCTION

To develop the proper knowledge of how to care for the scalp, skin and hair, the barber-stylist must have a complete understanding of the health and growth of these areas, as well as of their functions. It is, therefore, essential that barber-stylists study and understand the major parts of the body upon which they render services and apply treatments.

The body is composed of cells, tissues, organs and systems. It is made up of one-fourth solid matter and three-fourths liquid.

Anatomy (ah-nat'ō-mē) is the study of the gross structure of the body which can be seen with the naked eye, such as muscles, bones, arteries, veins and nerves. The barber-stylist is concerned only with those parts being treated, such as the head, face and neck.

Histology (his-tol'ō-jē) is the study of the minute structure of the various parts of the body. The barber-stylist is particularly concerned with the histology of the skin and its appendages (hair, sweat and oil glands).

Physiology (fiz-ē-ol'ō-jē) is the study of the functions or activities performed by the various parts of the body.

CELLS

In order to understand anatomy and physiology, it is necessary to study the structure and activities of cells. The human body is composed of millions of specialized cells performing the various functions required for living.

Cells are the basic units of all living things, which include humans, animals, plants and bacteria. Every part of the body is composed of cells, which differ from each other in size, shape, structure and function.

A knowledge of cellular (sel'ū-lar) activities will contribute to an understanding of the skin, scalp and hair, and how they function.

In giving cosmetic treatments, the barber-stylist should keep in mind the ultimate effect of the treatment on the cells of the body.

A cell is a minute (mī-nūt') portion of living substance containing **protoplasm** (prō'tō-plazm), which is a colorless jelly-like substance in which food elements and water are present.

The protoplasm of the cell contains the following important structures:

Nucleus (nū′klē-us) (dense protoplasm) found in the center, which plays an important part in the reproduction of the cell.

Cytoplasm (sī′tō-plazm) (less dense protoplasm) is found outside of the nucleus and contains food materials necessary for the growth, reproduction and self-repair of the cell.

Centrosome (sen′trō-sōm), a small, round body in the cytoplasm, which also affects the reproduction of the cell.

Cell membrane encloses the protoplasm. It permits soluble substances to enter and leave the cell.

STRUCTURE OF THE CELL

Diagrams Illustrating Indirect Division of the Human Cell

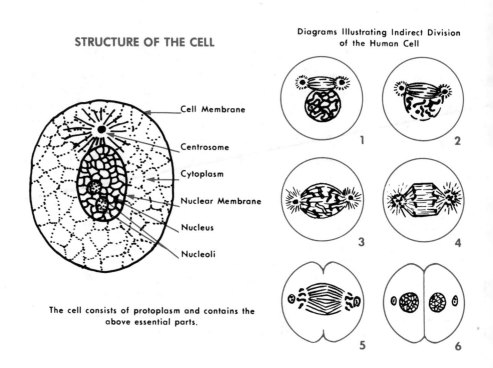

Cell Membrane

Centrosome

Cytoplasm

Nuclear Membrane

Nucleus

Nucleoli

The cell consists of protoplasm and contains the above essential parts.

1 2 3 4 5 6

CELL GROWTH AND PRODUCTION

As long as the cell receives an adequate supply of food, oxygen and water, eliminates waste products, and is favored with proper temperature, it will continue to grow and thrive. However, if these requirements are not fulfilled, and the presence of toxins (poisons) or pressure is evident, then the growth and the health of the cells are impaired. Most body cells are capable of growth and self-repair during their life cycle.

In the human body, when a cell reaches maturity, reproduction takes place by indirect division. This is a process in which a series of changes occur in the nucleus before the entire cell divides in half. Remember that the nucleus is surrounded by a thinner form of protoplasm, called cytoplasm, which supplies the food materials necessary for growth and reproduction.

METABOLISM

Metabolism (me-tab'o-lizm) is a complex chemical process whereby the body cells are nourished and supplied with the energy needed to carry on their many activities.

There are two phases to metabolism:

1. **Anabolism** (an-ab'o-lizm)—the building up of cellular tissues. During anabolism, the cells of the body absorb water, food and oxygen for the purpose of growth and repair.

2. **Catabolism** (kah-tab'ō-lizm)—the breaking down of cellular tissues. During catabolism, the cells consume what they have absorbed in order to perform specialized functions, such as muscular effort, secretions or digestion.

Cells have various duties. They create and renew all parts of the body; they assist in blood circulation by carrying food to the blood and waste matter from the blood, and they control all body functions.

TISSUES

Tissues are composed of groups of cells of the same kind. Each tissue has a specific function and can be recognized by its characteristic appearance. Body tissues are classified as follows:

1. **Connective tissue** serves to support, protect and bind together other tissues of the body. Bone, cartilage, ligament, tendon, and fat tissue are examples of connective tissue.

2. **Muscular tissue** contracts and moves various parts of the body.

3. **Nerve tissue** carries messages to and from the brain, and controls and coordinates all body functions.

4. **Epithelial** (ep-i-thē'lē-al) **tissue** is a protective covering on body surfaces, such as the skin, mucous membranes, linings of the heart, digestive and respiratory organs and glands.

5. **Liquid tissue** carries food, waste products and hormones by means of the blood and lymph.

ORGANS

Organs are structures containing two or more different tissues which are combined to accomplish a specific function.

The most important organs of the body are: the brain, which controls the body; the heart, which circulates the blood; the lungs, which supply oxygen to the blood; the liver, which removes toxic products of digestion; the kidneys, which excrete water and other waste products; and the stomach and intestines, which digest the food.

SYSTEMS

Systems are groups of organs that cooperate for a common purpose, namely the welfare of the entire body. The human body is composed of the following important systems:

Skeletal (skel'e-tal) System—Bones
Muscular (mus'kū-lar) System—Muscles
Nervous (ner'vus) System—Nerves
Circulatory (ser'kū-lah-tō-rē) System—Blood supply
Endocrine (en'dō-krin) System—Ductless glands
Excretory (eks'krē-tō-rē) System—Organs of elimination
Respiratory (re-spīr'ah-tō-rē) System—Lungs
Digestive (dī-jes'tiv) System—Stomach and intestines
Reproductive (rē-prō-duk'tiv) System—Reproducing

All these systems are closely interrelated and dependent upon each other. While each forms a unit specially designed to perform a specific function, that function cannot be performed without the complete cooperation of some other system or systems.

QUESTIONS ON ANATOMY AND PHYSIOLOGY

1. Why should barber-stylists study those parts of anatomy on which they give services?
2. On what parts of the body are barber-styling services applied?
3. Define anatomy and give examples.
4. Define physiology.
5. Define histology and give four examples.

CELLS

1. Why study the structure and activities of the cells?
2. What is a cell?
3. Why is knowledge of cellular activities important to the barber-stylist?
4. Of what substance are cells composed?
5. Name four important structures found in the protoplasm.
6. Give the function of the four structures found in protoplasm.
7. How does reproduction of cells take place?
8. Where does indirect cell division occur?
9. What is metabolism?
10. Name two phases of metabolism.
11. Which activities occur during anabolism or construction process of the cells?
12. What activities occur during catabolism or destructive process of the cells?
13. What is tissue?
14. List five classifications of body tissues.
15. What is the function of liquid tissue? Give two examples.
16. What is an organ?
17. List seven important organs of the body.
18. What are systems?
19. Name nine body systems.

THE SKELETAL SYSTEM

Personal appearance in height and body shape is determined by general body structure, which depends upon the skeleton.

Definition. The scientific study of bones, their structure and functions is called **osteology** (os-tē-ol'ō-jē). **Os** is the technical term for bone.

The **skeletal** (skel'e-tal) **system** is the physical foundation or framework of the body. It is composed of differently shaped bones, cartilages and ligaments united by movable and immovable joints. The **function** of the skeletal system is to serve as a means of protection, of support and of locomotion.

Bone is the hardest structure of the body. It is composed of fibrous tissues firmly bound together, consisting of about one-third animal matter and two-thirds mineral matter.

The following are the functions of bone:
1. To give shape and strength to the body
2. To protect organs from injury
3. To serve as attachments for muscles
4. To act as levers for all bodily movements

BONES OF THE SKULL

The **skull** is the skeleton of the head. It is an oval, bony case that shapes the head and protects the brain. The skull is divided into two parts: the cranium, consisting of eight bones, and the skeleton of the face, consisting of fourteen bones.

EIGHT BONES OF THE CRANIUM

The following bones are involved indirectly in connection with scalp and facial manipulations. *(The bones are numbered to correspond with the bones shown on the illustrations.)*

1. **Occipital** (ok-sip'i-tal) **bone** forms the lower back part of the cranium.
2. **Two parietal** (pah-rī'e-tal) **bones** form the sides and top (crown) of the cranium.

For purposes of scientific accuracy and uniformity, the official B. N. A. (Basle Anatomical Nomenclature) system is the preferred one for classifying anatomical terms and is therefore followed throughout this text.

3. **Frontal** (frun'tal) **bone** forms the forehead.
4. **Two temporal** (tem'pō-ral) **bones** form the sides of the head in the ear region (below the parietal bones).
5. **Ethmoid** (eth'moid) **bones** are light and spongy bones between the eye-sockets and form part of the nasal cavities.
6. **Sphenoid** (sfē'noid) **bone** joins together all the bones of the cranium.

BONES OF CRANIUM, FACE AND NECK

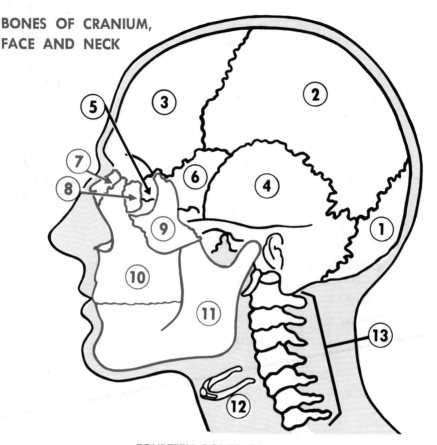

FOURTEEN BONES OF THE FACE

7. **Two nasal** (nā′sal) **bones** form the bridge of the nose.

8. **Two lacrimal** (lak′ri-mal) **bones** are small, fragile bones located at the front part of the inner wall of the eyesockets.

9. **Two zygomatic** (zī-gō-mat′ik), or **malar bones,** form the prominence of the cheeks.

These unnumbered bones do not appear on illustration: Two turbinal (tur′bi-nal) bones are thin layers of spongy bone situated on either of the outer walls of the nasal depression. Vomer (vō′mer) is a single bone that forms part of the dividing wall of the nose. Two palatine (pal′ah-tin) bones form the floor and outer wall of the nose, roof of the mouth and floor of the orbits.

10. **Two maxillae** (mak-sil′ē) are the upper jawbones which join to form the whole upper jaw.

11. **Mandible** (man′di-bl) is the lower jawbone and is the largest and strongest bone of the face. It forms the lower jaw.

BONES OF THE NECK

12. **Hyoid** (hī′oid) **bone,** a "U" shaped bone, is located in the front part of the throat, and is referred to as the "Adam's apple."

13. **Cervical vertebrae** (ser′vi-kal ver′te-brē) form the top part of the spinal column located in the neck region.

QUESTIONS ON THE SKELETAL SYSTEM

1. What is the hardest structure of the body?
2. List four functions of the bones.
3. Define "skull."
4. Into how many parts is the skull divided? Name them.
5. The cranium consists of how many bones?
6. List the skull bones affected by scalp massage.
7. Locate the occipital bone.
8. Locate the parietal bones.
9. Which bone forms the forehead?
10. What bones are located in the ear region?
11. Which bone joins together all the cranial bones?
12. How many bones are found in the face?
13. List the facial bones affected by facial massage.
14. What is formed by the maxillae?
15. Which bony structure is formed by the mandible?
16. Which bones form the prominence of the cheek?
17. Where is the hyoid bone located?
18. Locate the cervical vertebrae.

THE MUSCULAR SYSTEM

No outward sign of human life is more distinctive than that of **muscular** movement.

The **muscular system** covers, shapes and supports the skeleton. Its function is to produce all movements of the body.

The muscular system consists of over 500 muscles, large and small, comprising 40% to 50% of the weight of the human body.

Muscles are contractile fibrous tissue upon which the various movements of the body depend for their variety and action. The muscular system relies upon the skeletal and nervous systems for its activities.

The following are the three kinds of **muscular tissue:** **striated,** striped or voluntary, which are controlled by the will, such as those of the face, arms and legs; **non-striated,** smooth or involuntary, which function without the action of the **will,** such as those of the stomach and intestines; and the **cardiac,** or heart muscle, which is the heart itself and is not duplicated anywhere else in the body.

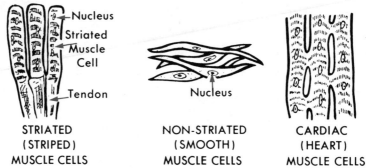

| STRIATED (STRIPED) MUSCLE CELLS | NON-STRIATED (SMOOTH) MUSCLE CELLS | CARDIAC (HEART) MUSCLE CELLS |

ORIGIN AND INSERTION OF MUSCLES

When a muscle contracts and shortens, one of its attachments usually remains **fixed** and the other one **moves.**

Origin of a muscle is the term applied to the more **fixed** attachment, such as muscles attached to bones or to some other muscle. Muscles attached to bones are usually referred to as **skeletal** muscles.

Insertion of a muscle is the term applied to the more **movable** attachment, such as muscles attached to a movable muscle, to a movable bone, or to the skin.

STIMULATION OF MUSCLES

Muscular tissue may be stimulated by any of the following:

1. **Chemicals**—certain acids and salts
2. **Massage**—hand massage and vibrator
3. **Electric current**—high-frequency
4. **Light rays**—infra-red rays
5. **Heat rays**—heating lamps, and heating caps
6. **Moist heat**—steamers, or moderately warm steam towels
7. **Nerve impulses**—through the nervous system

MUSCLES AFFECTED BY MASSAGE

The barber-stylist is concerned with the **voluntary muscles** of the head, face and neck. It is essential to know where these muscles are located, and what they control. The direction of pressure in massage is usually performed **from the insertion to the origin.**

The muscles are numbered to correspond with the muscles shown on the illustration.

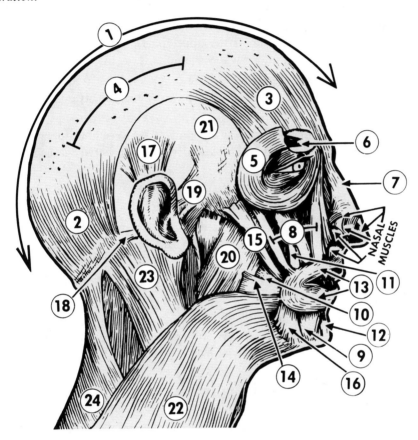

MUSCLES OF THE SCALP

1. **Epicranius** (ep-i-krā′nē-us), or **occipito-frontalis** (ok-sip′i-tō fron-tā′lis), is a broad muscle that covers the top of the skull. It consists of two parts: 2. the **occipitalis** (ok-sip-i-tā′lis), or back part; and 3. the **frontalis** (fron-tā′lis), or front part. Both are connected by a tendon, 4. **aponeurosis** (ap-ō-nū-rō′sis). The frontalis raises the eyebrows, draws the scalp forward and causes wrinkles across the forehead.

MUSCLES OF THE EYEBROWS

5. **Orbicularis oculi** (or-bik-ū-lā′ris ok′ū-lī) completely surrounds the margin of the eyesocket and closes the eye.
6. **Corrugator** (kor′ū-gā-tor) muscle is beneath the **frontalis** and **orbicularis occuli** and draws the eyebrows down and in. It produces vertical lines and causes frowning.

MUSCLES OF THE NOSE

7. The **procerus** (prō-sē'rus) covers the top of the nose, depresses the eyebrow, and causes wrinkles across the bridge of the nose.

The other nasal muscles are small muscles around the nasal openings which contract and expand the opening of the nostrils.

MUSCLES OF THE MOUTH

8. **Quadratus labii superioris** (kwod-rā'tus lā'bē-i sū-pē-rē-or'is) consists of three parts. It surrounds the upper part of the lip, raises and draws back the upper lip, and elevates the nostrils, as in expressing **distaste**.

9. **Quadratus labii inferioris** (in-fē-rē-or'is) surrounds the lower part of the lip. It depresses the lower lip and draws it a little to one side, as in the expression of **sarcasm**.

10. **Buccinator** (buk'sē-na-tor) is the muscle between the upper and lower jaws. It compresses the cheeks and expels air between the lips, as in **blowing**.

11. **Caninus** (kā-nī'nus) lies under the quadratus labii superioris. It raises the angle of the mouth, as in **snarling**.

12. **Mentalis** (men-tā'lis) is situated at the tip of the chin. It raises and pushes up the lower lip, causing wrinkling of the chin, as in **doubt** or **displeasure**.

13. **Orbicularis oris** (or-bik-ū-la'ris o'ris) forms a flat band around the upper and lower lips. It compresses, contracts, puckers and wrinkles the lips, as in **kissing** or **whistling**.

14. **Risorius** (ri-sō'rē-us) extends from the masseter muscle to the angle of the mouth. It draws the corner of the mouth out and back, as in **grinning**.

15. **Zygomaticus** (zī-gō-mȧt'i-kus) extends from the zygomatic bone to the angle of the mouth. It elevates the lip, as in **laughing**.

16. **Triangularis** (trī-ang-gū-la'ris) extends along the side of the chin. It draws down the corner of the mouth.

MUSCLES OF THE EAR

Three muscles of the ear are practically functionless:

17. **Auricularis** (au-rik-ū-la'ris) **superior** is above the ear.

18. **Auricularis posterior** is behind the ear.

19. **Auricularis anterior** is in front of the ear.

MUSCLES OF MASTICATION

20. **Masseter** (mas-ē'ter) and 21. **temporalis** (tem-pō-rā'lis) are muscles that coordinate in opening and closing the mouth, and are referred to as **chewing** muscles.

MUSCLES OF THE NECK

22. **Platysma** (plah-tiz'mah) is a broad muscle that extends from the chest and shoulder muscles to the side of the chin. It depresses the lower jaw and lip, as in the expression of **sadness.**

23. **Sterno-cleido-mastoid** (ster-nō-klī'dō-mas'toid) extends from the collar and chest bones to the temporal bone in back of the ear. It rotates the head and also bends the head, as in **nodding.**

24. **Trapezius** (tra-pē'zē-us) covers the back of the neck and upper part of the back.

QUESTIONS ON THE MUSCULAR SYSTEM

1. Define muscle.

2. What are the important functions of the muscles of the body?

3. Name three kinds of muscular tissue.

4. Distinguish between voluntary and involuntary muscles.

5. On which two systems of the body is the muscular system dependent for its activities?

6. Briefly define: a) origin of muscle; b) insertion of muscle.

7. Name seven sources capable of stimulating muscular tissue.

8. Locate the scalp muscle and name its two parts.

9. What is the function of the frontalis?

10. Which muscle surrounds the eye-socket?

11. Name the muscle of the eyebrow.

12. Which muscle forms a flat band around the upper and lower lips?

13. Which muscle covers the bridge of the nose?

14. Which muscle covers the back of the neck?

15. Which muscle depresses the lower jaw and lip?

16. Which muscle bends the head as in nodding?

THE NERVOUS SYSTEM

The **nervous** (ner'vus) system is one of the most important systems of the body. It controls and coordinates the functions of all the other systems and makes them work harmoniously and efficiently. Every square inch of the human body is supplied with fine fibers which we know as **nerves.**

The **main purposes** in studying the nervous system are to understand:

1. How the barber-stylist administers scalp and facial services for the patron's benefit.

2. What effects these treatments have on the nerves in the skin and scalp, and on the body as a whole.

DIVISIONS OF THE NERVOUS SYSTEM

The principal parts that compose the nervous system are the brain, spinal cord and their nerves. Generally, the nervous system is composed of three main divisions:

1. The **cerebro-spinal** (ser-e'bro-spi'nal) or **central** nervous system

2. The **peripheral** (pe-rif'er-al) nervous system

3. The **sympathetic** (sym-pa-thet'ik) nervous system

The **cerebro-spinal nervous system** consists of the brain and spinal cord. The following are its functions:

1. Controls consciousness and all mental activities

2. Controls voluntary functions of the five senses, such as seeing, smelling, tasting, feeling and hearing

3. Controls voluntary muscle actions, such as all body movements and facial expressions

The **peripheral system.** The sensory and motor nerve fibers extend from the brain and spinal cord and are distributed to all parts of the body: they are referred to as the **peripheral** system. Their function is to carry messages to and from the central nervous system.

The **sympathetic nervous system** is related structurally to the cerebro-spinal (central) nervous system, but its functions are **independent** of the will. (Sympathetic nervous system is also referred to as the autonomic nervous system, meaning self-control, by some anatomists.)

The sympathetic nervous system is **very important** in the operation of the internal body functions, such as breathing, circulation, digestion and glandular activities. Its main purpose is to regulate these internal operations, keeping them in balance and working properly.

392

A **neuron** (nū'ron), or **nerve cell,** is the structural unit of the nervous system. It is composed of a **cell body** and long and short fibers called **cell processes** (pros'e-sez). The short processes, called "dendrites," carry impulses to the cell body. The longer processes, called "axons," carry impulses away from the cell body to the muscles and organs. The cell body stores energy and food for the cell processes, which convey the nerve impulses throughout the body. Practically all the nerve cells are contained in the brain and spinal cord.

Nerves are long, white cords made up of fibers (cell processes) that carry messages to and from various parts of the body. Nerves have their origin in the brain and spinal cord, and distribute branches to all parts of the body, which furnish both sensation and motion.

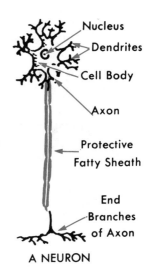

A NEURON

TYPES OF NERVES

Sensory nerves, called **afferent** (af'er-ent) **nerves,** carry impulses or messages from sense organs **to the brain,** where sensations of touch, cold, heat, sight, hearing, taste, smell and pain are experienced.

Motor nerves, called **efferent** (ef'er-ent) **nerves,** carry impulses **from the brain** to the muscles. The transmitted impulses produce movement.

Sensory nerves are situated **near the surface** of the skin. **Motor nerves** are **in the muscles.** As impulses pass from the sensory nerves to the brain and back over the motor nerves to the muscles, a complete circuit is established and movement of the muscle results.

Nerve reflex (re'fleks) is the path traveled by a nerve impulse through the spinal cord and brain, in response to a stimulus. (Example: the quick removal of the hand from a hot object.) A reflex act does not have to be learned.

The **brain** is the largest mass of nerve tissue in the body and is contained in the cranium. The weight of the average brain is 44 to 48 ounces. It is considered to be the central power station of the body, sending and receiving telegraphic messages. Twelve pairs of cranial nerves originate in the brain and reach various parts of the head, face and neck.

The **spinal cord** is composed of masses of nerve cells with fibers running upward and downward. It originates in the brain and extends down to the lower extremity of the trunk, and is enclosed and protected by the spinal column.

Thirty-one pairs of spinal nerves, extending from the spinal cord, are distributed to the muscles and skin of the trunk and limbs.

Some of the spinal nerves supply the internal organs controlled by the sympathetic nervous system.

Nerve fatigue can be caused by excessive mental or muscular work, resulting in an accumulation of waste products. Weariness, irritability, poor complexion and dull eyes may be signs of nerve exhaustion.

The supply of **nerve energy** is dependent upon proper food, exercise and oxygen. Rest and relaxation are absolutely necessary to renew nerve energy.

Appropriate **massage manipulations** help to relieve nerve fatigue.

Nutrition. Nerves are nourished through blood vessels, lymph spaces and lymphatics found in the connective tissue surrounding **them.**

CRANIAL NERVES

There are twelve pairs of cranial nerves, all connected to some part of the brain surface. They issue through openings on the sides and base of the cranium. They are classified as motor, sensory, and mixed nerves containing both motor and sensory fibers.

The cranial nerves are named numerically according to the order in which they arise from the brain and also by names which describe their nature or function.

CLASSIFICATION OF CRANIAL NERVES

Number—Name	Type	Function
1st—Olfactory (ōl-fak′to-rē)	Sensory	Controls the sense of smell
2nd—Optic (op′tik)	Sensory	Controls the sense of sight
3rd—Oculomotor (ok-ū-lō-mō′tor)	Motor	Controls the motion of the eye
4th—Trochlear (trok′lē-ar)	Motor	Controls upward and downward motion of the eye
5th—Trifacial (trī-fā′shal)	Sensory-Motor	Controls the sensations of the face tongue and teeth
6th—Abducent (ab-dū′sent)	Motor	Controls the motion of the eye
7th—Facial (fā′shal)	Sensory-Motor	Controls the motion of the face, scalp neck, ear, palate and tongue
8th—Auditory (aw′di-tō-rē)	Sensory	Controls the sense of hearing
9th—Glossopharyngeal (glos-ō-fah-rin′jēal)	Sensory-Motor	Controls the sense of taste
10th—Vagus (vā′gus)	Sensory-Motor	Sensory nerve of stomach, motor nerve of voice and heart
11th—Accessory (ak-ses′ō-rē)	Motor	Controls the motion of the neck muscles
12th—Hypoglossal (hī-pō-glos′al)	Motor	Controls the motion of the tongue

The cranial nerves which are of interest to the barber-stylist in giving facial and scalp treatments are as follows:

Fifth cranial (trifacial)

Seventh cranial (facial)

Eleventh cranial (accessory)

Also of interest is the spinal (cervical) nerve, which originates in the spinal cord and is involved in scalp and neck massage.

NERVES OF THE HEAD, FACE AND NECK

FIFTH CRANIAL NERVES

Fifth cranial or trifacial nerve is the largest of the cranial nerves. It is the chief sensory nerve of the face, and the motor nerve of the muscles of mastication.

The following are the important branches of the fifth cranial nerve that are affected by massage:

1. **Supra-orbital** (sū'prah-or'bi-tal) **nerve** affects the skin of the forehead, scalp, eyebrows, and upper eyelids.

2. **Supra-trochlear** (sū'prah-trok'lē-ar) **nerve** affects the skin between the eyes and upper side of the nose.

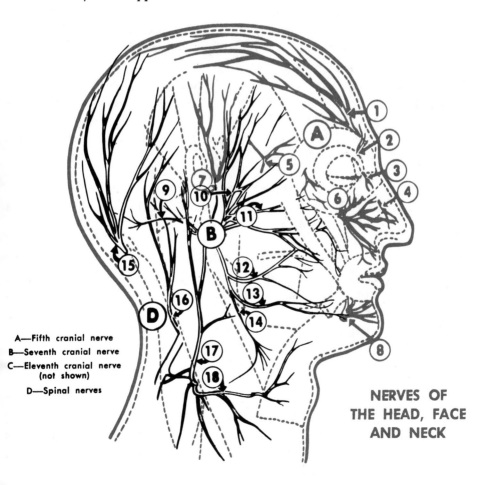

A—Fifth cranial nerve
B—Seventh cranial nerve
C—Eleventh cranial nerve
  (not shown)
D—Spinal nerves

NERVES OF THE HEAD, FACE AND NECK

3. **Infra-trochlear** (in'fra-trok'le̅-ar) **nerve** affects the membrane and skin of the nose.

4. **Nasal** (na̅'zal) **nerve** affects the point and lower side of the nose.

5. **Zygomatic** (zi̅-go̅-mat'ik) **nerve** affects the skin of the temple, side of the forehead and upper part of the cheek.

6. **Infra-orbital** (in'frah-or'bi-tal) **nerve** affects the skin of the lower eyelid, side of the nose, upper lip and mouth.

7. **Auriculo-temporal** (aw-rik'u̅-lo̅ tem'po̅-ral) **nerve** affects the external ear and skin above the temple, up to the top of skull.

8. **Mental** (men'tal) **nerve** affects the skin of the lower lip and chin.

SEVENTH CRANIAL NERVES

The **seventh cranial (facial) nerve** is the chief motor nerve of the face. It emerges near the lower part of the ear; its divisions and their branches supply and control all the muscles of facial expression, and extend to the muscles of the neck. Of all the branches of the facial nerve, the following are the most important:

9. **Posterior auricular** (po̅s-te̅r'ior aw-rik'u̅-lar) **nerve** affects the muscles behind the ear at the base of the skull.

10. **Temporal** (tem'po̅-ral) **nerve** affects the muscles of the temples, side of forehead, eyebrow, eyelid, and upper part of the cheek.

11. **Zygomatic** (zi̅-go̅-mat'ik) **nerve** (**upper and lower**) affects the muscles of the upper part of the cheek.

12. **Buccal** (buk'al) **nerve** affects the muscles of the mouth.

13. **Mandibular** (man-dib'u̅lar) **nerve** affects the muscles of the chin and lower lip.

14. **Cervical** (ser'vi-cal) **nerve** (branch of the facial nerve) affects the side of the neck.

ELEVENTH CRANIAL NERVE

Eleventh (accessory) **cranial nerve** (spinal branch) affects the muscles of the neck and back (not shown on illustration).

CERVICAL NERVES

Spinal or cervical (ser'vi-cal) **nerves** originate at the spinal cord and their branches supply the muscles and scalp at the back of the head and neck, as follows:

15. **Greater occipital** (ok-sip'i-tal) **nerve,** located in the back of the head, affects the scalp as far up as the top of the head.

16. **Smaller (lesser) occipital nerve,** located at base of the skull, affects the scalp and muscles of this region.

17. **Greater auricular** (aw-rik'u̅-lar) **nerve,** located at the side of the neck, affects the external ear, and area in front and back of the ear.

18. **Cutaneous** (ku̅-ta̅'ne̅-us) **colli nerve,** located at side of the neck, affects the front and side of the neck as far down as the breastbone.

NERVE STIMULATION

Stimulation to the nerves causes muscles to **contract** and **expand**.

Heat on the skin causes **relaxation; cold** causes **contraction**.

Nerve stimulation may be accomplished by any of the following:

1. Chemicals (certain acids or salts)
2. Massage (hand massage or electric vibrator)
3. Electrical current (high-frequency)
4. Light rays (infra-red)
5. Heat rays (heating lamps, and heating caps)
6. Moist heat (steamers or moderately warm steam towels)

QUESTIONS ON THE NERVOUS SYSTEM

1. Give two reasons why the barber-stylist should study the nervous system.
2. What are the three principal parts that make up the nervous system?
3. Name the three main divisions of the nervous system.
4. Name the three main functions of the cerebro-spinal nervous system.
5. Explain the peripheral system and what its function is.
6. Name the main function of the sympathetic (autonomic) nervous system.
7. What is a neuron?
8. What is a neuron, or nerve cell, composed of?
9. Define nerves.
10. Name two kinds of nerves which are found in the body.
11. What is the function of sensory nerves?
12. What is another name for: a) sensory nerves; b) motor nerves?
13. What is the function of motor nerves?
14. Give an example of nerve reflex.
15. What are two causes of nerve fatigue?
16. List six agents by which nerve stimulation may be accomplished.
17. How many pairs of cranial nerves are there? Spinal nerves?
18. Which three cranial nerves are the most important in the massaging of the head, face and neck?
19. Which is the largest cranial nerve?
20. What is the function of the fifth or trifacial nerve?
21. Which cranial nerve controls the muscles of facial expression?
22. Which cranial nerve controls the sense of: a) sight; b) smell; c) hearing?
23. Which region of the head is supplied by the greater occipital nerve?
24. Which cranial nerve supplies the neck muscles?
25. Which branches of the trifacial nerve supply the following regions?
    a) forehead
    b) lower side of nose
    c) skin of upper lip
    d) skin of lower lip
    e) skin above temple
    f) skin of upper part of cheek
26. Which branches of the facial nerve supply the following regions or muscles?
    a) muscles of side of forehead
    b) muscles of chin and lower lip
    c) platysma muscle
    d) muscle behind ear
    e) mouth muscle
    f) muscles of upper part of cheek

THE CIRCULATORY SYSTEM

The **circulatory** (ser'kū-lah-tō-rē), or **vascular** (vas'kū-lar), **system** is vitally related to the maintenance of good health. Proper circulation is essential to the entire body, as well as to the skin and hair.

The blood vascular system controls the circulation of the blood through the body in a steady stream by means of the **heart** and the blood vessels (the arteries, veins, and capillaries.)

THE HEART

The heart is an efficient pump. It keeps the blood moving within the circulatory system.

The heart is a muscular, conical-shaped organ, about the size of a closed fist. It is located in the chest cavity and enclosed in a membrane, the **pericardium** (per-i-kar'dē-um). The **10th cranial nerve** (vagus) and nerves from the **sympathetic nervous system** regulate the heartbeat. In a normal adult, the heart beats about 72 to 80 times a minute.

The interior of the heart contains four chambers and four valves. The upper thin-walled chambers are the **right atrium** (ā'trē-um) and **left atrium.** The lower thick-walled chambers are the **right ventricle** (ven'tri-kl) and **left ventricle. Valves** allow the blood to flow in only one direction. With each contraction and relaxation of the heart, the blood flows in, travels from the **atria** (ā'trē-ah) to the ventricles, and is then driven out, to be distributed all over the body. Atrium is also called **auricle** (aw'ri-kl).

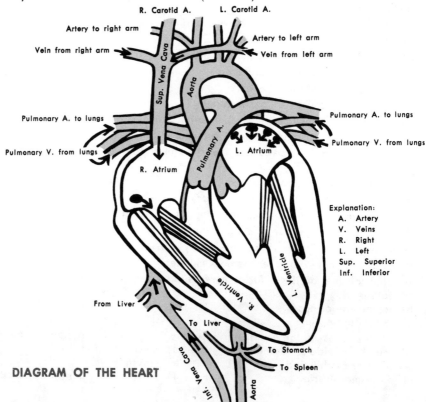

DIAGRAM OF THE HEART

BLOOD VESSELS

The arteries, capillaries and veins are tube-like in construction. They transport blood to and from the heart and to various tissues of the body.

Arteries (ar'ter-ēz) are thick-walled muscular and elastic tubes that carry **pure** blood from the heart to the capillaries.

Capillaries (kap'i-lā-rez) are minute, thin-walled blood vessels that connect the smaller arteries with the veins. Through their walls, the tissues receive nourishment and eliminate waste products.

CROSS SECTION OF A VEIN

Valve Closed

Valve Open

Veins are thin-walled vessels that are less elastic than arteries. They contain cup-like valves to prevent the back-flow, and carry impure blood from the various capillaries back to the heart. Veins are located closer to the outer surface of the body than the arteries.

CIRCULATION OF THE BLOOD

The blood is in constant circulation, from the moment it leaves until it returns to the heart. There are two systems that take care of this circulation:

1. **Pulmonary** (pul'mō-nā-rē) **circulation** is the blood circulation that goes from the heart to the lungs to be purified, and then returns to the heart.
2. **General circulation** is the blood circulation from the heart throughout the body and back again to the heart.

THE BLOOD

BLOOD CELLS

Blood is the nutritive fluid circulating through the circulatory system. It is a sticky, salty fluid, with a normal temperature of 98.6° Fahrenheit, and it makes up about one twentieth of the weight of the body. From eight to ten pints of blood fill the blood vessels of an adult.

Red Corpuscles

Color of blood. The blood itself is bright red in color in the arteries (except in the pulmonary artery) and dark red in the veins (except in the pulmonary vein). This change in color is due to the gain or loss of oxygen as the blood passes through the lungs.

Composition of blood. The blood is composed of one-third cells (red and white corpuscles and blood platelets) and two-thirds plasma. The function of **red corpuscles** (red blood cells) is to carry oxygen to the cells. **White corpuscles** (white blood cells), or **leucocytes,** perform the function of destroying disease causing germs.

Blood platelets are much smaller than the red blood cells. They play an important part in the **clotting of the blood** over a wound.

White Corpuscles

Plasma is the fluid part of the blood in which the red and white blood cells and blood platelets flow. It is straw-like in color. About nine-tenths of the plasma is water, and it carries food and secretions to the cells, and carbon dioxide from the cells.

Platelets

399

The following are the primary functions of the blood:

1. Carries water, oxygen, food and secretions to all cells of the body.
2. Carries away carbon dioxide and waste products to be eliminated through the lungs, skin, kidneys and large intestine.
3. Helps to equalize the body temperature, thus protecting the body from extreme heat and cold.
4. Aids in protecting the body from harmful bacteria and infections, through the action of the white blood cells.
5. Clots the blood, thereby closing injured minute blood vessels and preventing the loss of blood.

LYMPH-VASCULAR SYSTEM

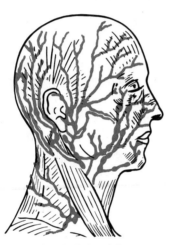

Lymph Nodes of the
Head, Face and Neck

The **lymph-vascular** (limf-vas'kū-lar) system, also called lymphatic system, acts as an aid to the venous system, and consists of lymph spaces, lymph vessels, lymph glands and lacteals.

Lymph is a colorless, watery fluid that circulates through the lymphatic system and is derived from the plasma of the blood, mainly by filtration.

The lymph acts as a middleman between the blood and the tissues. It carries nourishment from the blood to the cells and removes waste material from the cells.

ARTERIES OF THE HEAD, FACE AND NECK

The **common carotid** (kah-rot'id) **arteries** are the main sources of blood supply to the head, face and neck. They are located on either side of the neck and divide into internal and external carotid arteries. The **internal division** of the common carotid artery supplies the brain, eyesockets, eyelids and forehead; while the **external division** supplies the superficial parts of the head, face and neck.

The **external carotid artery** subdivides into a number of branches which supply blood to various regions of the head, face and neck. Of particular interest to the barber-stylist are the following:

A. **Facial artery (external maxillary)** (mak'si-ler-ē) supplies the lower region of the face, mouth and nose. Some of its branches are:

1. **Submental** (sub-men'tal) **artery,** which supplies the chin and lower lip
2. **Inferior labial** (lā'bē-al) **artery,** which supplies the lower lip.
3. **Angular** (ang'gū-lar) **artery,** which supplies side of nose.
4. **Superior labial artery,** which supplies the upper lip, septum of nose and wing of nose.

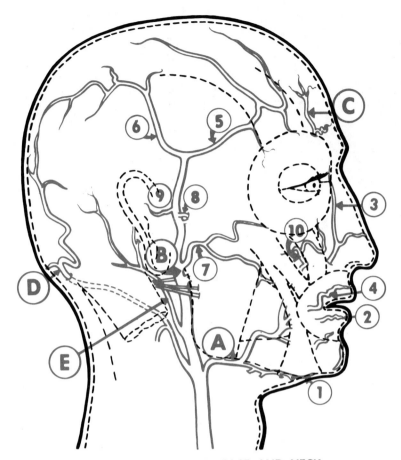

ARTERIES OF THE HEAD, FACE AND NECK

B. **Superficial temporal** (tem'pō-ral) **artery** is a continuation of the external carotid artery, which supplies muscles, skin and scalp to front, side and top of head. Some of its important branches are:

5. **Frontal** (frun'tal) **artery** supplies the forehead.

6. **Parietal** (pah-rīē'tal) **artery** supplies the crown and side of head.

7. **Transverse** (trans-vers') **facial artery** supplies the chewing muscles.

8. **Middle temporal** (tem'pō-ral) **artery** supplies the temples.

9. **Anterior auricular** (aw-rik'ū-lar) **artery** supplies the anterior part of the ear. (Partially shown in illustration.)

C. The **supra-orbital** (sū'prah-or'bi-tal) artery, branch of the internal carotid artery, supplies part of the forehead, the eyesocket, eyelid and upper muscles of the eye.

10. **Infra-orbital artery** originates from the internal maxillary artery, and it supplies the mucles of the eye.

D. **Occipital** (ok-sip'i-tal) **artery** supplies the back of the head, up to the crown.

E. **Posterior auricular** (aw-rik'ū-lar) **artery** supplies the scalp, back and above the ear and skin behind the ear.

401

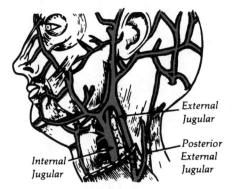

External
Jugular

Posterior
External
Jugular

Internal
Jugular

VEINS OF THE HEAD, FACE AND NECK

The blood returning to the heart from the head, face and neck flows on each side of the neck in two principal veins: the **internal jugular** and **external jugular**. The most important veins are parallel to the arteries and take the same names as the arteries.

QUESTIONS ON THE CIRCULATORY SYSTEM

1. Why is it necessary for the barber-stylist to understand the functions of the circulatory system?
2. What are the five important functions of the blood-vascular system?
3. What is the function of the heart?
4. Name three kinds of vessels found in the blood-vascular system.
5. Which blood vessels carry pure blood from the heart to the body?
6. Which blood vessels are nearest to the skin's surface?
7. What is the function of the veins?
8. Which two systems take care of blood circulation throughout the body?
9. What is the composition of the blood?
10. What is the normal temperature of the blood?
11. What is the composition of blood plasma?
12. What is the most important function of the red blood cells?
13. What is a function of the white blood cells?
14. What is lymph?
15. List the important functions of lymph.
16. From what source is the lymph derived?

QUESTIONS ON THE BLOOD VESSELS OF THE HEAD, FACE AND NECK

1. Which main arteries supply blood to the entire head, face and neck?
2. Name two main divisions of the common carotid arteries.
3. Which branches of the common carotid arteries supply the cranial cavity?
4. Which branches of the common carotid arteries supply blood to various regions of head, face and neck?
5. Give the common name for the external maxillary artery.
6. Name the artery that supplies the chin.
7. Which artery supplies the forehead?
8. What part of the head does the occipital artery supply?
9. Name the arteries that supply the: a) upper lip; b) lower lip.
10. What part of the head does the parietal artery supply? Frontal artery?
11. Which arteries supply the forehead, crown and side of head?
12. What artery supplies that part of the scalp that is in back of and above the ear?
13. Name the artery that supplies the eye muscles.
14. Name the principal veins by which the blood from the head, face and neck is returned to the heart.

THE ENDOCRINE SYSTEM

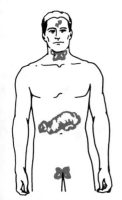

Glands are specialized organs that vary in size and function. The blood and nerves are intimately connected with the glands. The nervous system controls the functional activities of the glands. The glands have the ability to remove certain constituents from the blood and to convert them into new compounds.

There are two main sets of glands:

1. One group is called the **duct glands,** possessing canals that lead from the gland to a particular part of the body. Sweat and oil glands of the skin and intestinal glands belong to this group. (Information on sweat and oil glands can be found in the chapter on **Disorders of the Skin, Scalp and Hair.**)

2. The other group, known as **ductless glands,** has its secretions thrown directly into the bloodstream, which in turn influences the welfare of the entire body.

THE EXCRETORY SYSTEM

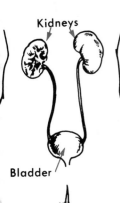

Kidneys

Bladder

The **excretory** (eks′kre-to-re) **system,** including the kidneys, liver, skin, intestines and lungs, purifies the body by elimination of waste matter.

Each plays the following part:

1. The **kidneys** excrete urine.
2. The **liver** discharges bile pigments.
3. The **skin** eliminates perspiration.
4. The **large intestine** evacuates decomposed and undigested food.
5. The **lungs** exhale carbon dioxide.

Metabolism of the cells of the body forms various toxic substances which, if retained, would have a tendency to poison the body.

THE RESPIRATORY SYSTEM

The **respiratory** (re-spir′ah-to-re) **system** is situated within the chest cavity, which is protected on both sides by the ribs. The **diaphragm** (di′ah-fram), a muscular partition that controls breathing, separates the chest from the **abdominal** (ab-dom′i-nal) region.

The **lungs** are spongy tissues composed of microscopic cells into which the inhaled air penetrates.

These tiny air cells are enclosed in a skin-like tissue. Behind this, the fine capillaries of the vascular system are found.

With each **respiratory** cycle, an exchange of gases takes place. During **inhalation** (in-ha-la′shun), oxygen is absorbed into the blood, while carbon dioxide is expelled during **exhalation** (eks-ha-la′shun). Oxygen is required to change food into energy.

Oxygen is more essential than either food or water. Although a man may live more than sixty days without food and a few days without water, if his air is cut off for a few minutes, he dies.

Nose breathing is healthier than mouth breathing because the air is warmed by the surface capillaries, and the bacteria in the air are caught by the hairs that line the **mucous** (mu'cus) membranes of the nasal passages.

The rate of breathing depends on the activity of the individual. Muscular activities and energy expenditures increase the body's demands for oxygen. As a result, the rate of breathing is increased. A person requires about three times as much oxygen when walking than when standing.

Abdominal breathing is of value in building health. **Costal breathing** involves light, or shallow, breathing of the lungs, without action of the diaphragm. Abdominal breathing means deep breathing, which brings the diaphragm into action. The greatest exchange of gases is accomplished with abdominal breathing.

THE DIGESTIVE SYSTEM

The **digestive** (di-ges'tiv) **system** changes food into a **soluble** (sol'yu-bl) form, suitable for use by the cells of the body. Digestion is started in the mouth and completed in the small intestine. From the mouth, the food passes down the **pharynx** (far'inks) and the **esophagus** (e-sof'ah-gus), or food pipe, and into the stomach. The food is completely digested in the small intestine. The large intestine (colon) stores the refuse for elimination through the rectum. The complete digestive process of food takes about nine hours.

Digestive enzymes (en'zyms) present in the digestive secretions are chemicals that change certain kinds of food into a form capable of being used by the body.

Intense emotions, excitement, and fatigue seriously disturb digestion. On the other hand, happiness and relaxation promote good digestion.

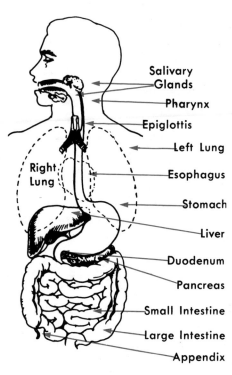

Salivary Glands
Pharynx
Epiglottis
Left Lung
Right Lung
Esophagus
Stomach
Liver
Duodenum
Pancreas
Small Intestine
Large Intestine
Appendix

Diagram illustrating the Human Alimentary Canal with its Principal Digestive Glands.

QUESTIONS ON GLANDS AND OTHER SYSTEMS

1. What two main types of glands are there in the human body?
2. Name the five important organs of the excretory system.
3. Describe a respiratory cycle.
4. Name the important organs of the digestive system.

Chapter 28
ELECTRICITY AND LIGHT THERAPY

ELECTRICITY

The beneficial effects of electrical energy have long been recognized to be of value in the practice of barber-styling. Electricity can be a valuable tool, provided it is used intelligently and carefully. It can be used for the benefit of both the barber-stylist and the client by supplying light, heat and the power to operate electrical appliances. As a result of the careful use of electric power, a considerable amount of time and energy can be saved and the effectiveness of treatments considerably improved.

Although the exact nature of electricity is not yet completely understood, its generating sources and effects are known. It is generally believed that electricity is a form of energy which produces **magnetic, chemical** or **heating** effects.

A current of electricity is a stream of **electrons** (ē-lek′tronz) (negatively charged particles) moving along a conductor.

An electric wire is composed of twisted fine metal threads (conductor) covered with rubber or silk (insulator or non-conductor).

A conductor (kon-duk′tor) is a substance which readily transmits an electrical current. Most metals, carbon, the human body and watery solutions of acids and salts are good conductors of electricity.

Electrodes (ē-lek′trōdz) composed of good conductors serve as points of contact when applying electricity to the body.

A non-conductor or **insulator** (in′sū-lā-tor) is a substance that resists the passage of an electrical current, such as rubber, silk, dry wood, glass, cement or asbestos.

Two forms of electricity are employed, namely:

1. **Direct current (D.C.)** which is a constant and even-flowing current, traveling in one direction.
2. **Alternating current (A.C.)** which is a rapid, interrupted current, flowing first in one direction and then in the opposite direction.

If necessary, one type of current can be changed to the other type by means of a converter or rectifier.

A **converter** (kon-vur'ter) is an apparatus used to change a direct current into an alternating current. A **rectifier** (rek'ti-fi-er) is used to change an alternating current into a direct current when such a current is required.

A **complete circuit of electricity** is the entire path traveled by the current from its generating source through various conductors (wire, electrode or body) and back to its original source.

A **fuse** (fūz) is a safety device which prevents the overheating of electric wires. It will blow out because of overloading (by adding too many connections to one line) or due to a short circuit. To re-establish the circuit, disconnect all apparatus before inserting a new fuse.

Precaution—When replacing a blown fuse make sure **to:**

1. Use a new fuse with the proper rating.
2. Stand on a dry surface.
3. Keep your hands dry.

Circuit Breaker. Modern building construction requires the use of circuit breakers to replace the old fuse box. The circuit breakers supply the same safety control against overloaded lines and faulty electrical apparatus as had been furnished by fuses. When wires become too hot because of overloading or a faulty piece of apparatus, the breaker will "click-off" or disengage, thus breaking the circuit. (Find the cause of the breaker tripping off, either by correcting the overload or disconnecting the faulty piece of apparatus. Then flip the breaker switch back to the "on" position.)

If an electric appliance goes out of order while in operation, disconnect the appliance from the wall plug without delay.

ELECTRICAL MEASUREMENTS

Electrical measurements are expressed in terms of the following units:

The **volt** (vōlt) is a unit of electrical **pressure.**

The **ampere** (am-pair') is a unit of electrical **strength.**

The **ohm** (ōm) is a unit of electrical **resistance.**

An electrical current flows through a conductor when the pressure is sufficiently great to overcome the resistance offered by the wire to the passage of the current. According to **Ohm's law,** the strength of a current (amperage) equals the pressure (voltage) divided by the resistance (ohm).

Instead of the ampere, which is too strong, the **milliampere,** 1/1000th part of an ampere, is used for facial and scalp treatments. The **milliamperemeter is** an instrument for measuring the rate of flow of an electric current.

HIGH-FREQUENCY CURRENT

The **high-frequency** (hi-frē'kwen-sē) **current** is characterized by a high rate of vibration.

Of chief interest to the barber-stylist is the **Tesla** (Tes'lah) **current,** commonly called the violet ray, used for both scalp and facial treatments.

The primary action of this current is thermal, or heat-producing. Because of its rapid vibrations, there are no muscular contractions. The physiological effects are either stimulating or soothing, depending on the method of application.

The electrodes for high-frequency are made of glass or metal. Their shapes vary, the facial electrode being flat and the scalp electrode being rake-shaped. As the current passes through the glass electrode, tiny violet sparks are emitted. All treatments given with high-frequency should be started with a mild current and gradually increased to the required strength. The length of the treatment depends upon the condition to be treated. For a general facial or scalp treatment, only about five minutes should be allowed.

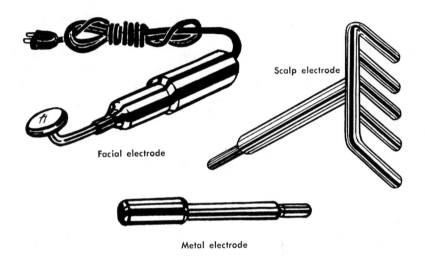

Scalp electrode

Facial electrode

Metal electrode

For proper use, follow the instructions provided by manufacturer.

There are three methods of using the Tesla current:

1. **Direct surface application.** The barber-stylist holds the electrode and applies it over the client's skin. In facial treatments, the electrode is applied directly over the facial cream.

2. **Indirect application.** The client holds the metal or glass electrode while the practitioner uses his fingers to massage the surface being treated. At no time is the electrode held by the barber-stylist. To prevent shock, the current is turned on after the client has the electrode firmly in his hand; current is turned off before removing the electrode from the client's hand.

   CAUTION. Avoid contact by the client with any metal, such as chair arms, stools, etc. A burn may occur at the point of contact.

3. **General electrification.** By holding a metal electrode in his hand, the client's body is charged with electricity without being touched by the barber-stylist.

To obtain relaxing, calming or soothing effects with high-frequency current, the general electrification treatment is used or the electrode is kept in close contact with the parts treated by the use of direct surface application.

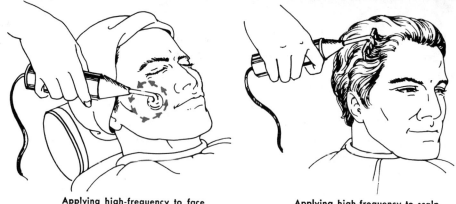

Applying high-frequency to face
using facial electrode.

Applying high-frequency to scalp
using rake electrode.

To obtain a stimulating effect, the electrode is lifted slightly from the parts to be treated by using it through the clothing or a towel.

When using high-frequency with skin and scalp lotions, **never use a lotion with an alcoholic content.** If it is desirable to use this type of lotion, use the electricity **first,** and apply the lotion after the treatment with electricity has been completed.

BENEFITS OF TESLA HIGH-FREQUENCY

1. Stimulates circulation of the blood.
2. Increases glandular activity.
3. Aids in elimination and absorption.
4. Increases metabolism.
5. Germicidal action occurs during use.

The Tesla current may be used to treat falling hair, itchy scalp, tight scalp, excessively oily or dry skin and scalp.

ELECTRICAL EQUIPMENT

The **protection** and **safety** of the client are the primary concern of the barber-stylist. All electrical equipment should be regularly inspected to determine whether it is in good working condition. Carelessness in making electrical connections or in applying various types of currents may result in shocks or burns. The barber-stylist who observes safety precautions will help to eliminate accidents and assure greater satisfaction to all clients.

THE VIBRATOR

The **vibrator** (vī'brā-tor) is an electric appliance, used in massage, to produce a mechanical succession of stimulations. It has an invigorating effect on the muscular tissues, increases the blood supply to the parts treated, is soothing to the nerves, increases glandular activities and stimulates the functions of the skin and scalp.

CAUTION. The vibrator should never be used when there is a known weakness of the heart or in cases of fever, abscesses or inflammation.

The vibrator may be used by attaching it to the back of the hand. The vibrations are thus transmitted through the hand or fingers to the parts being treated.

The vibrator is used over heavy muscular tissue, such as the scalp, shoulder and upper back. It is advisable never to use the vibrator on the face or near the eyes.

STEAMER OR VAPORIZER

Steamers or **vaporizers** (vā′por-ī-zerz) are electrical devices applied over the head or face to produce a moist, uniform heat.

The **steamer** may be used instead of hot towels to cleanse and steam the face. The steam warms the skin, inducing the flow of both oil and sweat. It thus helps to cleanse the skin, clean out the pores and soften any horny scaliness on the surface of the skin.

The steamer may also be used for scalp and hair reconditioning treatments. When fitted over the scalp, it produces controlled moist heat. Its action is to soften the scalp, increase the perspiration and promote the effectiveness of applied scalp cosmetics.

HEATING CAP

Heating caps are electrical devices, applied over the head, to provide a uniform source of heat. Their main use is as part of corrective treatments for the hair and scalp. When used for this purpose, they recondition dry, brittle and damaged hair and also serve to activate a sluggish scalp.

ELECTRIC HAIR DRYER

The electric hair dryer delivers hot, medium or cold air for the proper drying of the hair.

CURLING IRONS AND STYLING COMBS

Electrically heated **curling irons** and **styling combs** come in various types and sizes. They have built-in heating elements and operate from electrical outlets. One type has perforations. Oil is injected into the barrel of the curling iron, where it is vaporized. The vapor leaves the iron through small perforations to condition the hair as it curls.

SAFETY PRECAUTIONS

1. Disconnect appliances when finished using them.
2. Study instructions before using any electrical equipment.
3. Keep all wires, plugs, and equipment in a safe condition.
4. Inspect all electrical equipment frequently.
5. Avoid wetting electric cords.
6. Sanitize all electrodes properly.
7. Protect the client at all times.
8. Do not touch any metal while using any electrical apparatus.
9. Do not handle electrical equipment with wet hands.
10. Do not allow clients to touch any metal surfaces when electric treatments are being given.
11. Do not leave room when client is attached to any electrical device.
12. Do not attempt to clean around an electric outlet when equipment is plugged in.
13. Do not touch two metallic objects at the same time while connected to an electric current.
14. Do not use any electrical equipment without first obtaining full instruction for its care and use.

SAFETY PRACTICES IN ELECTRICITY

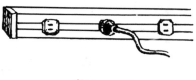

Use only one plug to each outlet. Overloading may cause fuse to blow out.

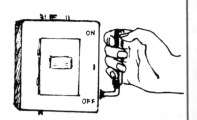

In an emergency, turn off main switch, as illustrated, to shut off electricity for entire salon or building.

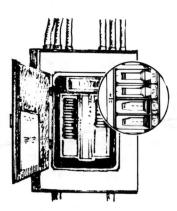

CIRCUIT-BREAKER

The circuit-breaker automatically disconnects any current with a defective appliance. It has the great advantage of restoring the current by a flick of the breaker switch to its "ON" position.

This is very important in the beauty salon by minimizing the possibility of long interruptions in the supply of electricity.

Examine cords regularly. Repair or replace worn cords to prevent short circuit, shock or fire.

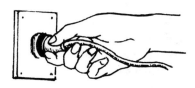

To disconnect current, remove plug without pulling cord. Never pull on cord, as the wires may become loosened and cause a short circuit.

WARNING

Keep a flashlight at top of steps, so you won't stumble down a dark stairway. Using your flashlight, open fuse box and examine each fuse to locate "dead" one. When you replace a burned-out fuse, touch only its rim. Never put a coin in the fuse box instead of a fuse.

Be sure to have some good fuses on hand. To test a fuse, use a flashlight battery, and bulb (or the bulb assembly), and a piece of wire — as shown at right. If fuse is good, bulb will light.

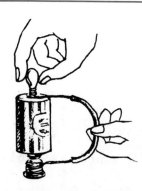

When replacing a blown-out fuse, make sure to:

1. Use new fuse with proper rating.
2. Stand on a dry surface.
3. Keep hands dry.

QUESTIONS ON ELECTRICITY

1. What is the nature of electricity?
2. What is a conductor? What metal serves as a conductor in an electric wire?
3. What is a non-conductor or insulator? Give two examples.
4. What are electrodes?
5. What is a direct current (D.C.)?
6. What is an alternating current (A.C.)?
7. Which apparatus changes a direct current into an alternating current?
8. Which apparatus changes an alternating current to a direct current?
9. What is a volt?
10. What is an ampere?
11. What is an ohm?
12. What is meant by Ohm's law?

HIGH-FREQUENCY OR VIOLET RAY

1. What is a high-frequency current?
2. Which type of high-frequency current is commonly used in the barber-stylist shop?
3. What effects does the Tesla current produce on the body?
4. Name three kinds of electrodes used with high-frequency.
5. Name three methods of applying the Tesla current.
6. Briefly describe how to use direct surface application.
7. Briefly describe how to use indirect application.
8. Briefly describe how to use general electrification.
9. Which method of application produces soothing results?
10. How are stimulating effects produced?
11. How long should a general facial or scalp treatment take to administer?
12. What safety precaution should be observed when using hair tonics having a high alcoholic content?
13. List four benefits obtained by using the Tesla current.
14. List five scalp conditions which may be treated with the Tesla current.

ELECTRICAL EQUIPMENT
VIBRATOR

1. What is a vibrator?
2. Name five benefits produced by vibratory massage.
3. Under what conditions should a vibrator not be used?
4. Over which parts of the body is the vibrator used?

STEAMER

1. How is a steamer or vaporizer used?
2. What are the effects produced by the steamer when used over the face?
3. What are the effects produced by the steamer when used over the scalp?

HEATING CAP

1. What are heating caps?
2. What is their main use?
3. How do heating caps aid in corrective scalp and hair treatments?

LIGHT THERAPY

Light therapy (the′ra-pē) refers to treatment by means of light rays. Light or electrical waves travel at a tremendous speed--186,000 miles per second.

There are many kinds of light rays, but in barber-styling we are concerned with only three—those producing heat, known as infra-red rays; those producing chemical and germicidal reaction, known as ultra-violet rays; and visible lights, all of which are contained within the spectrum of the sun.

If a ray of sunshine is passed through a glass prism (priz′m) it will appear in seven different colors, known as the **rainbow**, arrayed in the following manner: red, orange, yellow, green, blue, indigo and violet. These colors, which are visible to the eye, constitute the **visible rays**, comprising about 12% sunshine.

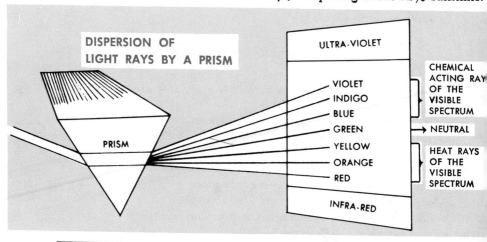

Ultra-Violet Rays			Solar Spectrum	Infra-Red Rays
1847 AU to 3900 AU			3900 AU to 7700 AU	7700 AU to 14,000 AU
Far 1847-2200	Middle 2200-2900	Near 2900-3900	Violet Indigo Blue Green Yellow Orange Red	Penetrating
Germicidal	Therapeutic	Tonic		Analgesic
Cold Invisible Rays			Visible Rays	Invisible Heat Rays

NATURAL SUNSHINE IS COMPOSED OF:
8% ultra-violet rays; 12% visible light rays; 80% infra-red rays.

PROPERTIES OF INFRA-RED RAYS:
1. Long wave length
2. Low frequency
3. Deep penetrating power

PROPERTIES OF ULTRA-VIOLET RAYS:
1. Short wave length
2. High frequency
3. Weak penetrating power

Scientists have discovered that at either end of the visible spectrum are rays of the sun which are **invisible** to us. The rays beyond the violet are the **ultra-violet rays,** also known as **actinic** (ak-tin′ik) rays. These rays are the shortest and least penetrating rays of the spectrum, comprising about 8% of sunshine. The action of these rays is both chemical and germicidal (jur-mi-sĭ′dal).

Beyond the red rays of the spectrum are the **infra-red rays.** These are pure heat rays, comprising about 80% of sunshine.

A **therapeutic** (the-ra-pū′tik) **lamp** is an electrical apparatus capable of producing certain light rays. There are separate lamps for infra-red and for ultra-violet rays.

Ultra-violet (ul′trah-vī′o-let) **lamps.** There are three general types: the glass bulb, the hot quartz (kwōrts) and the cold quartz.

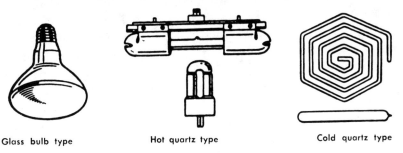

| Glass bulb type | Hot quartz type | Cold quartz type |

The **glass bulb lamp** is used mainly for cosmetic or tanning purposes.

The **hot quartz lamp** is a general all-purpose lamp suitable for tanning, tonic, cosmetic or germicidal purposes.

The **cold quartz lamp** produces mostly short ultra-violet rays. It is used primarily in hospitals.

Infra-red (in′frah-red) **rays** give no light whatsoever, only a rosy glow when active. Special glass bulbs are also used to produce infra-red rays.

The **visible rays,** or dermal lights, are reproduced by carbon or tungsten filaments in clear glass bulbs, which give the white light, or in colored bulbs, which give red or blue colors.

Protecting the eyes. The client's eyes should always be protected by cotton pads saturated with a boric acid or witch hazel solution and placed on the eyelids during final treatments. The barber-stylist and client should always wear safety eye goggles when using ultra-violet rays.

ULTRA-VIOLET RAYS

Ultra-violet rays are invisible rays. Their action is both chemical and germicidal. Plant and animal life need ultra-violet rays for healthy growth. In the human body, these rays produce changes in the chemistry of the blood and also stimulate the activity of body cells.

Effects of ultra-violet rays. Ultra-violet rays increase resistance to disease by increasing the iron and vitamin D content and the number of red and white cells in the blood. They also increase elimination of waste products, restore nutrition where needed, stimulate the circulation and improve the flow of blood and lymph (limf).

The slightest obstruction of any nature whatsoever will hinder ultra-violet rays from reaching the skin. Consequently, the skin must be entirely cleansed before being subjected to ultra-violet rays.

Applying ultra-violet rays

How applied. Ultra-violet rays are the shortest light rays of the spectrum. The farther they are from the visible light region, the shorter they become. The long ultra-violet rays tend to increase the fixation of calcium in the blood. If the lamp is placed from 30 to 36 inches away, practically none of the shorter rays will reach the skin, so that the action is then limited to the effect of the longer rays.

The benefits of the shorter rays are obtained when the lamp is within twelve inches from the skin.

CAUTION. Ultra-violet rays are not only destructive to bacteria, but to tissue as well, if they are allowed to remain exposed for too long a period of time.

Average exposure may produce redness of the skin, and overdoses may cause blistering. It is well to start with a short exposure of two or three minutes, and gradually increase the time to seven or eight minutes. **The barber-stylist and client must wear safety eye goggles to protect their eyes.**

Skin tanning is the result of one or more exposures to ultra-violet rays which stimulate the production of pigment or coloring matter in the skin.

Sunburn may be produced by ultra-violet rays in various degrees; however, for cosmetic purposes, first degree only is given. This is manifested by a slight reddening, appearing several hours after application, without any signs of itching, burning or peeling. Overexposure produces third and fourth degree burns which are destructive to the tissues.

Skin and scalp disorders. Ultra-violet rays are used for acne, tinea, seborrhea and to combat dandruff. They also help to promote healing, as well as stimulate the growth of hair.

INFRA-RED RAYS

Generally speaking, **infra-red rays** produce a soothing and beneficial type of heat which extends for some distance into the tissues of the body.

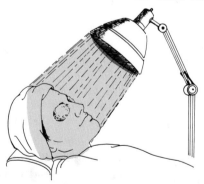

Applying infra-red rays

Effects of infra-red rays on exposed area:

1. Heat and relax the skin without increasing the temperature of the body as a whole.
2. Dilate blood vessels in the skin, thereby increasing blood flow.
3. Increase metabolism and chemical changes within skin tissues.
4. Increase the production of perspiration and oil on the skin.
5. Relieve pain.

How applied. The lamp is operated at an average distance of thirty inches. It is placed closer at the start, and, in order to avoid burning the skin, is then moved back gradually as the surface heat becomes more pronounced. **Always protect the eyes of the client during exposure.** Place cotton pads saturated with boric acid or witch hazel solution over client's eyelids.

CAUTION. Do not permit the light rays to remain on the body tissue more than a few seconds at a time. Move the hand back and forth across the ray's path to break constant exposure. Length of exposure should be about five minutes.

VISIBLE LIGHTS

The lamp used to reproduce visible lights is usually a dome-shaped reflector mounted on a pedestal with a flexible neck. The dome is finished with highly polished metal lining capable of reflecting heat rays. The bulbs used with this lamp come in various colors for different purposes. As with all other lamps, the **client's eyes must be protected from the glare and heat of the light.** For proper eye protection, the client's eyes are covered with cotton pads saturated with boric acid or witch hazel solution.

Effect of the white light:

1. Relieves pain, especially in congested areas, and more particularly around the nerve centers, such as the back of the neck and across the shoulders.

Use and effect of the blue light:

1. Has a tonic effect on the bare skin.
2. Is deficient in heat rays.
3. Has a soothing effect on the nerves.
4. To obtain the desired result, it is always used over the **bare skin.** Cream, oil, or powder must not be present on the skin.

Use and effect of the red light:

1. Has strong heat rays.
2. Has a stimulating effect when used over the skin.
3. Penetrates more deeply than the blue light.
4. Heat rays aid the penetration of lanolin creams into the skin.
5. Is recommended for dry, scaly and shriveled skin.
6. Is used over creams and ointments to soften and relax body tissue.

QUESTIONS ON LIGHT THERAPY

1. What is light therapy?
2. Which rays of the sun are invisible?
3. What is a therapeutic lamp?
4. Name three types of therapeutic lamps which produce ultra-violet rays.
5. Which ultra-violet lamps are desirable for the barber-stylist shop?
6. Which four blood constituents are increased by exposure to ultra-violet rays?
7. What effects do ultra-violet rays have on the body functions?
8. Which skin and scalp disorders are helped by ultra-violet rays?
9. What benefit does the hair receive from ultra-violet rays?
10. What is the shortest distance the ultra-violet lamp should be kept from the skin?
11. Why should the eyes of both barber-stylist and client be covered with safety goggles during exposure to ultra-violet rays?
12. How long should the skin be exposed for the first time?
13. To how many minutes can exposure be gradually increased?
14. Why should prolonged exposure be avoided?
15. What are the signs of a first degree sunburn?
16. What causes the skin to tan?
17. Why should the skin be cleaned before exposure to ultra-violet rays?
18. Which types of therapeutic lamps produce infra-red rays?
19. How should the client's eyes be protected during exposure to infra-red rays?
20. How far should the infra-red lamp be kept from the skin?
21. Why should infra-red light rays be broken with a hand movement?
22. What are the five effects of infra-red rays on the body?
23. Which types of therapeutic lamps produce visible lights?
24. Why should the client's eyes be protected during exposure to therapeutic lamps?
25. What is the benefit of using a white light?
26. Which visible light lacks heat rays?
27. What are the benefits of using a blue light?
28. What are the three benefits of using a red light?

Chapter 29
CHEMISTRY

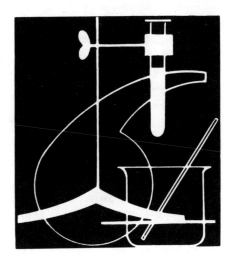

INTRODUCTION

The professional barber-stylist must be more than a practicing technician. At various times, the stylist must serve not only as a hairstylist, but also as a psychologist, a business executive, a chemist, an advisor and an expert in every phase of good grooming.

In order to qualify for this unique position, it is now necessary that the stylist possess a far greater knowledge and understanding of the many facets of the profession than ever before.

A basic knowledge of modern chemistry is an essential requirement for an intelligent understanding of the various products and cosmetics being used in the barber-hairstyling shop. Through the advances in the science of chemistry, new and better products are constantly being developed for the benefit of both the barber-stylist and the client. It is, therefore, important that the professional technician understand these products and learn how to use them for the maximum benefits.

SCIENCE OF CHEMISTRY

Chemistry (kem´is-trē) is the science which deals with the composition, structure and properties of matter and how it (matter) changes under different chemical conditions. The broad subject of chemistry is divided into two areas: 1) organic chemistry, and 2) inorganic chemistry.

ORGANIC CHEMISTRY

Organic (or-gan´ik) **chemistry** is that branch of chemistry which deals with all substances in which carbon is present. Carbon can be found in all plants, animals, petroleum, soft coal, natural gas and in many artificially prepared substances.

Most organic substances are not soluble in water, but they are soluble in organic solvents, such as alcohol and benzene.

Organic substances are slow in their chemical reactions. Examples of organic substances are grass, trees, gasoline, oil, soaps, detergents, plastics, antibiotics.

417

INORGANIC CHEMISTRY

Inorganic chemistry is that branch of chemistry which deals with all substances that do not contain carbon. Inorganic substances will not burn and are usually soluble in water.

Inorganic substances are usually quick in their chemical reactions. Examples are water, air, iron, lead, iodine and bones.

MATTER

Chemistry is the science which deals primarily with the composition, structure and properties of **matter.** It is essential, therefore, that we develop an understanding of what matter really is. Matter may be defined as anything that occupies space. It exists in three physical forms: solids, liquids and gases.

Look around the classroom and note what you see: hair, students, teachers, desks, chairs, walls. These are all matter in a **solid** state.

In the clinic area of the school you see water, shampoos, lotions, hair tonics. These are matter in a **liquid** state.

Take a deep breath. The air you have just brought into your lungs is also matter. It is in a **gaseous** state.

It is not the purpose of this text to train scientists, but to help barber-styling students to learn enough about matter to help them in their professional work. It is, therefore, advisable that we briefly examine the nature and the structure of matter.

ATOMS

An atom is the smallest part of an element that possesses the characteristics of the **element.** Therefore, an atom of hydrogen has the properties of hydrogen. Should this atom be smashed, it would no longer possess the properties of hydrogen, nor would it resemble a hydrogen atom.

MOLECULES

A molecule is the smallest particle of an element or compound that possesses all the properties of the element or compound. If the molecule is of an element, the atoms are the same. If it is of a compound, the atoms are different. For example, a molecule of hydrogen contains two or more atoms of hydrogen, whereas a molecule of the compound of water is composed of two atoms of hydrogen and one atom of oxygen (H_2O).

CHEMICAL ACTIVITIES

In general, when we talk about the chemical activity of an element, we refer to the tendency of its atoms to combine with other elements. For example, hydrogen is a very active element and readily combines with other elements, while neon is completely inactive and does not combine with other elements.

TYPES OF MATTER

Matter exists in an almost infinite variety. This variety is made possible due to the atomic structure of matter, which permits the joining of a number of elements in countless combinations.

Matter exists in the form of elements, compounds and mixtures.

ELEMENTS

An element is the basic unit of all matter. It is a substance that **cannot** be made by the combination of simpler substances and the element itself cannot be reduced to simpler substances. There are now 103 elements that are known, of which some of the more common are iron, sulphur, oxygen, zinc and silver.

Each element is given a letter symbol. Iron is Fe; sulphur, S; oxygen, O; zinc, Zn; and silver, Ag. All symbols can be obtained by referring to a chart of elements.

COMPOUNDS

When two or more elements unite chemically, they form a compound. Each element loses its characteristic properties and the new compound develops its own individual properties. For example, iron oxide (rust) has different properties than the two elements of which it is comprised—iron and oxygen. The new substance, which is a compound, cannot be altered by mechanical means, but only by chemical methods.

ELEMENTS AND COMPOUNDS

	TYPES AND DEFINITION	SMALLEST PARTICLE	ELEMENTS FOUND IN HAIR
MATTER	ELEMENTS SIMPLEST FORM OF MATTER	ATOM *(Cannot be broken down by simple chemical reactions)* *About 100 different kinds*	CARBON NITROGEN OXYGEN SULFUR HYDROGEN PHOSPHORUS
FORMS GASES LIQUIDS SOLIDS	COMPOUNDS FORMED BY COMBINATION OF ELEMENTS	MOLECULE *(Consists of 2 or more atoms chemically combined)* *Unlimited kinds possible*	COMPOUNDS USED ON HAIR WATER HYDROGEN PEROXIDE AMMONIUM THIOGLYCOLATE ANILINE DERIVATIVE TINTS AMMONIA ALCOHOL ACIDS ALKALIS

Compounds can be divided into four classes:

1. **Oxides** are compounds of any element combined with oxygen. For example, one part carbon and two parts oxygen equal **carbon dioxide,** which might be recognized as dry ice. Or, one part carbon and one part oxygen equal **monoxide,** better known as the poisonous exhaust of an automobile

2. **Acids** are compounds of hydrogen, a non-metal, such as nitrogen and, sometimes, oxygen. For example, hydrogen + sulphur + oxygen = **sulphuric acid** (H_2SO_4). Acids turn **blue** litmus paper **red,** providing a quick way to test a compound.

3. **Bases,** also known as alkalies, are compounds of hydrogen, a metal and oxygen. For example, sodium + oxygen + hydrogen = **sodium hydroxide** (NaOH), which is used in the manufacture of soap. Bases will turn **red** litmus paper **blue.**

4. **Salts** are compounds that are formed by the reaction of acids and bases, with water also produced by the reaction. Two common salts and their formulas are sodium chloride (table salt) (NaCl), which contains sodium and chloride; and magnesium sulphate (Epsom salts) ($MgSo_4.7H_2O$), which contains magnesium, sulphur, hydrogen and oxygen.

MIXTURES

A mixture is a substance that is made up of two or more elements, combined **physically** rather than chemically.

The ingredients in a mixture do not change their properties, as they do in a compound, but retain their individual characteristics. For example, concrete is composed of sand, gravel and cement. While concrete is a mixture having its own functions, its ingredients never lose their characteristics. Sand remains sand, gravel is still gravel, and cement, cement.

Differences between mixtures and compounds. In a **compound,** the resulting properties from the chemical union, such as density, color, solubility, etc., are generally completely different from those of the substances combined. Every particle looks and acts like every other particle in the compound. A compound may never be separated by purely mechanical means. In making a compound, there are always energy and matter changes.

In a **mixture,** the resulting properties are the same as they were originally. The particles of one substance differ from another. Mixtures may be separated by mechanical means. In making a mixture, there are no changes in energy.

CHANGES IN MATTER

Matter may be changed in two ways, either through physical or chemical means.

Physical change refers to an alteration of the properties without the formation of any new substance. For example, ice, a solid, melts at a certain temperature and becomes a liquid (water), and water, a liquid, freezes at a certain temperature and becomes a solid. There is no change in the inherent nature of the water, but merely a change in its form.

A **chemical change** is one in which a new substance or substances are formed, having properties different from the original substances. For example, soap is formed from the chemical reaction between an alkaline substance (potassium hydroxide) and an oil or fat. The soap resembles neither the alkaline substance nor the oil from which it is formed. Chemical reaction between the two forms a new substance, having its own characteristic properties.

PROPERTIES OF MATTER

When we talk about the properties of matter, we are talking about how we distinguish one form of matter from another.

PHYSICAL PROPERTIES

These refer to properties, such as **density, specific gravity, odor, color, taste.**

1. **Density** of a substance refers to its weight divided by its volume. For example, the volume of one cubic foot of water weighs 62.4 lbs. Therefore, its density is (weight) 62.4 lbs. ÷ (volume) 1 cubic foot, or water has a density of 62.4 lbs. per cubic foot.

2. **Specific gravity** of a substance is also referred to as its relative density. This means that substances are referred to as either more or less dense than water. For example, copper is 8.9 times as dense as water; therefore, the specific gravity (or relative density) of copper is 8.9.

3. **Odor** of a substance helps us identify it in many instances. For example, the characteristic odor of ammonium thioglycolate, known as the "thio" odor, helps us identify this product.

4. **Color** helps us identify many substances. For example, we recognize the color of gold, silver, copper, brass, coal.

5. **Taste** has helped us identify many substances. For example, oil of wintergreen can be identified by its peppermint-type taste.

CHEMICAL PROPERTIES

The chemical properties of a substance refer to the ability of the substance to react, and the conditions under which it reacts. Two of the more widely known chemical properties a substance possesses are **combustibility** and the ability to **support combustion.** For example:

1. **Phosphorus** is a highly combustible substance. For that reason, it is used on the tips of matches. The heat produced by rubbing the match tip against a surface is enough to cause it to burst into flames.

2. One of the chemical properties of wood is its ability to support combustion. It is, therefore, used in the manufacture of matches. The phosphorous tip starts the fire and the wood supports the fire.

PROPERTIES OF COMMON ELEMENTS, COMPOUNDS AND MIXTURES

Knowledge about the properties of the most common elements, compounds and mixtures can be of great benefit to the student studying the reasons why certain chemical reactions take place.

Oxygen (O) (ok′si-jen) is the most abundant element, being found both free and in compounds, and composes about half of the earth's crust, half of the rock, one-fifth of the air, and 90% of the water. It is a colorless, odorless, tasteless, gaseous substance, combining with most other elements to form an infinite variety of compounds called **oxides.** One of the chief characteristics of this element is that substances burn more readily in oxygen than in air.

Hydrogen (H) (hī′drō-jen) is a colorless, odorless and tasteless gas. It is the lightest element known, being used as a unit of weight. It is inflammable and explosive when mixed with air. It is found in chemical combination with oxygen in water and with other elements in acids, bases and organic substances, such as wood, meat, fish, sugar and butter.

Air is the gaseous mixture which makes up the earth's atmosphere. It is odorless, colorless and consists of about 1 part by volume of oxygen and 4 parts of nitrogen. These proportions vary somewhat according to conditions. It also contains a small amount of carbon dioxide, ammonia, nitrates and organic matter, which are essential to plant and animal life.

Hydrogen peroxide (H_2O_2) (per-ok'sīd) is a compound of hydrogen and oxygen. It is a colorless liquid with a characteristic odor and a slightly acid taste. Organic matter, such as silk, hair, feathers and nails, are bleached by hydrogen peroxide because of its oxidizing power. The 20 to 40 volume hydrogen peroxide solution is used as a bleaching (lightening) agent for the hair. A 3 to 5% solution of hydrogen peroxide possesses antiseptic qualities.

Oxidizing agents (ok-si-dīz'ing). A substance which readily gives up its oxygen is known as an oxidizing agent. Hydrogen peroxide releases oxygen which oxidizes the hair pigment to a colorless compound. The bleaching (lightening) agent is reduced and the pigment is oxidized. When oxygen is taken away from any substance, it is known as a reduction. The substance which attracts the oxygen is the **reducing agent**. Oxidation is always accompanied by reduction.

Nitrogen (N) (nī'trō-jen) is a colorless, gaseous element found free in the air. It constitutes part of the atmosphere, forming about four-fifths of the air. It is necessary to life because it dilutes the oxygen. It is found in nature chiefly in the form of ammonia and nitrates.

ACIDITY AND ALKALINITY

The **pH** (potential hydrogen) of a liquid refers to its degree of acidity or alkalinity. Meters and indicators have been developed for the measurement of pH. Values are illustrated below.

The **pH** scale goes from 0 to 14. The neutral point is 7.

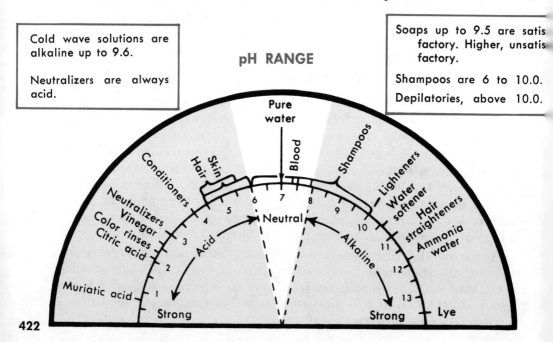

Cold wave solutions are alkaline up to 9.6.

Neutralizers are always acid.

pH RANGE

Soaps up to 9.5 are satis factory. Higher, unsatis factory.

Shampoos are 6 to 10.0.

Depilatories, above 10.0.

Acidity. Anything below 7 is acid. The lower the pH, the greater is the degree of acidity.

Alkalinity. Anything from 7 to 14 is alkaline. The higher the **pH**, the greater is the degree of alkalinity.

Since cosmetics vary in their pH values, be guided by your instructor.

Note—The cleansing action of soaps and shampoos depends upon their alkalinity and contact time with the skin, scalp or hair. Due to the short contact time, highly alkaline products will achieve the desired results without damage.

CHEMISTRY OF WATER

Water (H_2o) is the most abundant of all substances, composing about 75% of the earth's surface and about 65% of the human body. It is the universal solvent. De-mineralized or distilled water is used as a **non-conductor** of electricity. Water containing certain mineral substances is an excellent conductor of electricity.

Water serves many useful purposes in the barber-styling shop. Only water of known purity is fit for drinking purposes. Suspended or dissolved impurities render water unsatisfactory for cleaning objects and for use in shops.

Impurities can be removed from water by:
1. **Filtration** (fil-trā'shun): passing through a porous substance, such as filter paper or charcoal.
2. **Distillation** (dis-til-ā'shun): heating in a closed vessel arranged so that the resulting vapor passes off through a tube and is cooled and condensed to a liquid. This process purifies water used in the manufacture of cosmetics.

Boiling water at a temperature of 212° Fahrenheit (100° Celsius) will destroy most microbic life.

It is very important that **soft water** be used for shampooing, bleaching (lightening) or tinting the hair. **Rain water** is the softest water. **Hard water** contains mineral substances, such as the salts of calcium and magnesium, that curdle or precipitate soap instead of permitting a permanent lather to form. Hard water may be softened by **distillation** or by use of **sodium carbonate** (washing soda) or **sodium phosphate.** To effectively soften hard water in barber-styling shops, zeolite tanks are used.

A good **test for soft water** employs a soap solution made by dissolving three-quarters of an ounce of pure powdered castile soap in a pint of distilled water. A pint bottle is half filled with fresh water and 0.5 ml. (about 7 drops) of the soap solution is added. The bottle is then shaken vigorously. If a lather forms at once and persists, the water is very soft. If a lather does not appear at once, another 0.5 ml. of soap solution is added and the shaking repeated. If an additional 0.5 ml. of the soap solution is needed to produce a good lather, the water is hard and must be softened.

SHAMPOOING

All professional barber-stylists understand the importance of the shampoo and how the cleanliness of the hair affects other hair services. However, it is also important that they know how the shampoo cleanses the hair.

No discussion of the action of shampoos and how they function can be meaningful unless a study is made of the shampoo molecule.

SHAMPOO MOLECULES

Shampoo molecules are large molecules which have been specially treated. They are composed of a **head** and **tail**, each with its own special function.

The **tail** of the shampoo molecule has an attraction for dirt, grease, debris and oil, but has no attraction for or liking of water.

The **head** of the shampoo molecule has a strong attraction for water, but does not like dirt.

Working as a team, both parts of the molecule do an effective job of cleansing the hair.

Shampoo
Molecule

ACTION OF SHAMPOOS

A WATER — SHAMPOO — OIL AND GREASE

Sticky greasy surface attracts and holds dust and other particles of foreign matter to hair cuticle. Water alone is unable to clean hair because water molecules are unable to pull particles free from cuticle.

The tail of the shampoo molecule has a strong attraction for hair, grease and dirt, etc.

B DIRT — OIL AND GREASE

Proper massage of shampoo insures that shampoo molecules are brought in direct contact with these substances.

Each tail of a molecule is attracted to grease and dirt.

Action of shampoo causes grease and oils to roll up into small globules, reducing contact with hair cuticle.

EXCESS shampoo molecules are attracted to imbrications. Alkaline shampoos open imbrications, causing tangling and matting during massage movements as fibers rub together.

C WARM WATER RINSE

Currents of warm rinsing water remove dirt and grease because heads of shampoo molecules are attracted to passing water molecules. Tails of shampoo molecules, attached dirt and foreign matter are bound to heads of shampoo following the rinsing currents of water. Thus foreign matter is removed ONLY during rinsing stages of shampooing.

D CONTINUED RINSING

Excess shampoo molecules are less easily removed from hair shaft. Continued rinsing is essential to cleanse hair of shampoo. Time of rinsing is reduced by restricting amounts of shampoo. Excess swelling of imbrications is prevented by acid, soapless shampoos.

The shampoo is applied and thoroughly worked into the hair. The dirt, grease, debris and oil in the hair are attracted to the tails of the shampoo molecules and become firmly attached to them.

Rinsing. During the rinsing step, as the stream of water is directed through the hair, the "water-loving" molecule heads attach themselves to the water molecules and are carried from the hair, taking with them the tails with the attached dirt.

CHEMISTRY OF SHAMPOOS

By combining an **alkali** with an oil or fat, shampoo soaps are formed. The oil used may be of vegetable origin, such as almond, peanut, coconut, olive, castor and palm-nut.

The fat used may be animal fat, lanolin, tallow and synthetic compounds.

Most shampoos contain varying amounts of the same fatty acids. Therefore, the shampoo soap formed varies with the substances used.

Shampoos with a high pH factor, which are highly alkaline, are especially damaging to all types of hair.

TYPES OF SHAMPOOS

The main purpose of a shampoo is to cleanse the scalp and hair. This may be accomplished by a wet or dry shampoo. Wet shampoos are watery solutions of soap and various cleansing agents. Dry shampoos do not use water, but contain either powdery substances or cosmetic products in liquid form.

Wet shampoos, depending on their composition, are of three basic types:
1. Soap shampoos
2. Soapless shampoos (foaming or foamless)
3. Cream shampoos

Soap shampoos are available in the form of cake, powder, jelly or liquid. The active cleansing agent is a soap made from olive oil, coconut oil or other oils. Liquid soap shampoos contain more than 50% water. When used on the hair, a soap shampoo will produce an alkaline reaction. With soft water, soap shampoos lather readily. When used with hard water, soap shampoos will not lather and tend to produce an insoluble soap residue on the hair.

Soapless shampoos come in the form of a powder, jelly, cream or liquid. They are effective cleansing agents. Their main ingredient is a sulfonated oil. Both the lathering and non-lathering types of soapless shampoos are available.

Soapless shampoos are just as effective in soft, hard, cold or hot water. They should be used with discretion, since frequent applications not only dry the scalp and hair, but render the hair more absorptive than usual.

Cream or **paste shampoos** have a cleansing action due to soap, a synthetic detergent, or a combination of both. They may also contain a reconditioning agent for the hair. Cream shampoos, or pastes, without soap, are usually acid in reaction.

UNITED STATES PHARMACOPEIA (U.S.P.)

The barber-stylist should become familiar with the United States Pharmacopeia (U.S.P.), a book defining and standardizing drugs. The following are some of the terms of interest to barber-stylists:

Alcohol, also known as grain or ethyl alcohol, is a colorless liquid obtained by the fermentation of certain sugars. It is a powerful antiseptic and disinfectant; a 70% solution is usable for sanitizing instruments, and a 60% solution can be applied to the skin. It is widely used in perfumes, lotions and tonics.

Alum is an aluminum potassium or ammonium sulphate, supplied in the form of crystals or powder, which has a strong astringent taste and action. It is used in skin tonics and lotions. It is also used in powder form as a styptic, which is applied to small cuts.

Ammonia water, as commercially used, is a colorless liquid with a pungent, penetrating odor. It is a by-product of the manufacture of coal gas. As it readily dissolves grease, it is used as a cleansing agent, and is also used with hydrogen peroxide in lightening hair. A 28% solution of ammonia gas dissolved in water is available commercially.

Sodium bicarbonate (baking soda) is a precipitate made by passing carbon dioxide gas through a solution of **sodium carbonate.** It is a white powder adapted for uses such as a neutralizing agent.

Sodium carbonate (washing soda) is prepared by heating **sodium bicarbonate.** It is used for water softening and in bath salts. Sodium carbonate may also be used with boiling water in the sterilization of metallic instruments. A small quantity is added to the water to keep the instruments bright.

Bichloride of mercury is usually sold in tablet form of about 7½ grains each. It is shaped peculiarly for ready identification. It is a very strong poison and should be used very sparingly in barber-styling shops.

Boric acid, also called boracic acid, is a powder obtained from sodium borate, which is mined in the form of borax and crystallized with sulphuric acid. It is a mild healing and antiseptic agent. It is sometimes used as a dusting powder and, in solution, as a cleansing lotion or eyewash.

Formaldehyde is a gas, but in water solution containing from 37% to 40% of the gas by weight, it is known as **formalin.** Formaldehyde has a very disagreeable, pungent odor. It is very irritating to the eyes, nose and mouth. Formalin may be used to sanitize instruments.

Glycerine is a sweet, colorless, odorless, syrupy liquid, formed by the decomposition of oils, fats or molasses. It is an excellent skin softener, and is an ingredient of cuticle oil, facial creams and lotions.

Tincture of iodine is a 2% solution of iodine in alcohol. If the patron is not allergic to iodine, it can be safely used on the skin to treat minor cuts and bruises. Iodine stains are readily removed with alcohol. **Mercurochrome,** or a 3-5% peroxide solution, may also be used for cuts.

Phenol, or **carbolic acid,** is not actually an acid, but is a coal tar derivative, appearing as a crystalline substance having a slightly acid reaction. Glycerine is added to make it more readily soluble in water. A 5% solution of phenol is used to sanitize metallic instruments.

Potassium hydroxide (caustic potash) sticks are dissolved in distilled water to form an alkaline solution. When not in use, the sticks must be kept in sealed containers, as they tend to absorb moisture from the air and deteriorate. They are used in the making of soaps and cosmetic creams.

Zinc oxide is a heavy white powder made by burning zinc carbonate with coal in a special furnace. It is used as a dusting powder and as an ointment for some skin conditions.

Witch hazel is a solution of alcohol and water, containing an astringent agent extracted from witch hazel bark.

Quaternary ammonium compounds (Quats) are a group of effective disinfectants used as sanitizing agents in barber-styling shops.

CHEMISTRY AS APPLIED TO COSMETICS

Cosmetic chemistry is both a science and an art. The **science** of chemistry consists of knowing what to do in the correct manner; **art** involves the proper methods of preparing and applying the cosmetic to the body.

Barber-stylists will be better equipped to serve the public if they have an understanding of the chemical composition, preparation and use of cosmetics which are intended to cleanse and improve the hygiene of the external portions of the body.

Cosmetics may be classified according to their physical and chemical nature and the characteristics by means of which they are recognized. The object in classifying cosmetics is to assist in their study and identification.

PHYSICAL AND CHEMICAL CLASSIFICATION OF COSMETICS

1. Powders
2. Solutions
3. Suspensions
4. Emulsions
5. Ointments
6. Soaps

POWDERS

Powders are a uniform mixture of insoluble substances (inorganic, organic and colloidal) which have been properly blended, perfumed and/or tinted to produce a cosmetic which is free from coarse or gritty particles.

Mixing and sifting are employed in the process of making powders.

SOLUTIONS

A **solution** is a preparation made by dissolving a solid, liquid or gaseous substance in another substance, usually liquid.

A **solute** (sol′ūt) is a substance dissolved in a solution.

A **solvent** (sol′vent) is a liquid used to dissolve a substance.

Solutions are clear and permanent mixtures of solute and solvent which do not separate on standing. Since a good solution is clear and transparent, filtration is often necessary, particularly if the solution is cloudy.

427

Solutions are easily prepared by dissolving a powdered solute in a warm solvent and stirring at the same time. The solute may be separated from the solvent by applying heat and evaporating the solvent.

Water is a universal solvent. It is capable of dissolving more substances than any other solvent. Grain alcohol and glycerine are frequently used as solvents. Water, glycerine and alcohol readily mix with each other; therefore they are miscible (mis'i-b'l) (mixable). On the other hand, water and oil do not mix with each other; hence they are immiscible (unmixable).

The **solute** may be either a solid, liquid or gas. For example: **boric acid solution** is a mixture of a solid in a liquid; **glycerine and rose water** is a mixture of two miscible liquids; **ammonia water** is a mixture of a gas in water.

Solutions containing volatile (vol'a-til) substances, such as ammonia and alcohol, should be stored in a cool place; otherwise the volatile substance will evaporate.

There are various kinds of solutions:

A **dilute** (dī-lūt') **solution** contains a small quantity of the solute in proportion to the quantity of solvent.

A **concentrated** (kon'sen-trā-ted) **solution** contains a large quantity of the solute in proportion to the quantity of solvent.

A **saturated** (sat'ūr-ā-ted) **solution** will not dissolve or take up more of the solute than it already holds at a given temperature.

EMULSIONS

Emulsions (ē-mul'shunz) (creams) are permanent mixtures of two or more immiscible substances (oil and water) which are united with the aid of a binder (gum) or an emulsifier (soap). Emulsions are usually milky white in appearance. If a suitable emulsifier and the proper technique are employed, the resultant emulsion will be stable. A stable emulsion can hold as much as 90% water. Depending on the amount of water and wax present, the cream may be either liquid or semi-solid in character. The amount of emulsifier used depends on its efficiency and the amount of water or oil to be emulsified.

Emulsions are prepared by hand or with the aid of a grinding and cutting machine, called a colloidal mill. In the process of preparing the emulsion, the emulsifier forms a protective film around the microscopic globules of either the oil or water. The smaller the globules, the thicker and more stable will be the emulsion.

Emulsions basically fall into two different classes: oil-in-water (O/W) and water-in-oil (W/O).

Oil-in-water (O/W) emulsions are made of oil droplets suspended in a water base. In addition to the emulsifier, which coats the oil droplets and holds them in suspension, there may be a number of additional ingredients present which are designed to cause certain reactions in the hair. Examples of O/W emulsions are permanent wave solutions, lighteners (bleaches), neutralizers and tints.

Water-in-oil (W/O) emulsions are formed with drops of water suspended in an oil base. These are usually much thicker and oilier than the O/W emulsions. Examples of W/O emulsions are hair grooming creams, cleansing creams cold creams and similar products.

OINTMENTS

Ointments (oynt′ments) are semi-solid mixtures of organic substances (lard, petrolatum, wax) and a medicinal agent. No water is present. For the ointment to soften, its melting point should be below that of the body temperature (98.6° Fahrenheit).

Ointments are prepared by melting the organic substances and mixing the medicinal agent into the mixture.

ASTRINGENTS

An **astringent** is an agent which causes contraction of the tissues. A number of face lotions are astringents, and are employed to close the pores of the face after shaving. Examples of astringents are tannic acid, zinc sulphate, and powdered or liquid alum.

FACE LOTIONS

Face lotions usually have antiseptic and astringent properties. They are usually employed in the finishing phase of a shave or a facial treatment. Common ingredients found in face lotions are tannic acid, zinc sulphate, menthol, and glycerine. Examples of face lotions are witch hazel and bay rum.

BRILLIANTINE

Brilliantine is an oil compound designed to add brilliance or sheen to the hair. There are three types of brilliantine:

1. Plain — a mixture of oils
2. Combination — a mixture of oils and alcohol
3. Paste — a mixture of petrolatum jellies and other oils or **waxes**

HAIR TONICS

A **hair tonic** is a cosmetic liquid used on the hair and scalp. The hair tonic is designed to groom the hair and stimulate the scalp. While some hair tonics contain ingredients which stimulate the scalp tissues, such stimulation is primarily achieved by the massage movements employed when the tonic is applied. Some of the types of tonics are:

1. Hydro-alcohol
2. Non-alcoholic
3. Oil mixtures
4. Cream oils

FACE CREAMS

Several kinds of face creams are used in the barber-styling shop. A **face cream** is principally an emulsion of **oils**, **waxes** and **water**. An emulsion is the conversion of an oil, wax and water into a permanent mixture. Some of these creams are:

1. Cold cream
2. Cleansing cream
3. Tissue cream
4. Astringent cream
5. Vanishing cream
6. Rolling cream
7. Medicated cream
8. Emollient cream

1. **Cold cream:**
   (1) It consists of oil, borax, wax, perfume and **water**.
   (2) It has been called an "all purpose" cream. It is used as a base for massaging, to cleanse and protect, and to lubricate the skin.

2. **Cleansing cream:**
   (1) It consists of a cold cream base, but has a high content of mineral oil.
   (2) It is intended mainly for cleansing the skin. Some cleansing creams are liquid. A good cleansing cream should leave the face smooth, not sticky or greasy, perfectly clean and relaxed.
3. **Tissue cream:** Theoretically, tissue cream is skin food cream, but this claim should be accepted with definite reservation.
   (1) It contains such ingredients as oil, water, wax, lanolin, perfume and cocoa butter.
   (2) It is softening and helps replace natural oil.
   (3) It is ideal as a base for face massaging.
4. **Astringent cream:** A cold cream becomes an astringent cream when an astringent, such as alum or tannic acid, is added. It is recommended for an oily skin with large pores.
5. **Vanishing cream:** It is also called a finishing cream or a foundation cream.
   (1) It is an oil-in-water greaseless emulsion. The basic formula is modified by cocoa butter, lanolin, glycerine, mineral oil, stearic acid, borax and alcohol.
6. **Rolling cream:**
   (1) This is a casein base cream with a solid filler. It is usually pink.
   (2) It cleanses the skin by a crumbling frictionite action.
7. **Medicated cream:** This term also should be accepted with reservation. It contains some ingredient to give it an astringent effect or some drug that is medicinal.
8. **Emollient cream:** Emollient cream contains lubricating ingredients that smooth and soften the skin. Such ingredients as honey, olive oil, cocoa butter, lanolin, sweet almond oil and glycerine are found in good emollients.

CREAMS

Of all cosmetics used for the skin or face, creams comprise the largest and most varied group. Basically, creams are either stable emulsions or oily and watery substances, or an ointment base without water. Creams do not actually feed the tissues, but they do lubricate the skin.

HAIR RINSES

A hair rinse consists of water alone or a mixture of water with a mild acid, coloring agent or special ingredients. Hair rinses are given for the following purposes:

1. To add temporary color to the hair
2. To dissolve soap curds from the hair
3. To give a soft, lustrous appearance
4. To neutralize the yellow tinge of white or grey hair
5. To seal in tint or toner after a color treatment

VINEGAR (ACID) RINSE

A vinegar (acetic) rinse is used to separate the hair; dissolve soap curds; give hair brightness; make hair soft and pliable.

A vinegar rinse may also be used to counteract the alkalinity of hair after a bleach (lightening), tint or cold wave.

Formula: Two tablespoons of white vinegar to one pint of tepid water.

Use as a last rinse after a shampoo. After using the vinegar rinse, run water quickly over the hair to remove the odor.

LEMON (ACID) RINSE

A lemon rinse has a slight lightening quality, is effective on bleached (lightened) and blonde hair, and separates the hair strands.

Formula: Use the strained juice of one or two lemons or a few drops of concentrated lemon extract in one quart of warm water.

Rinse the hair with the lemon mixture several times. Finally, rinse the hair with clear warm water to remove all the lemon juice.

CITRIC ACID RINSE

A citric acid rinse is often used in place of a lemon rinse.

Formula: Place one tablespoonful of citric acid crystals into a pint container, and pour four ounces of boiling water over them. Fill the rest of the container with warm water, stirring while you add the water. Apply as for lemon rinse.

BLUING RINSE

A prepared rinse, containing a blue base color, is used to give yellowish hair a silvery grey or white color tone. The porosity of the hair must be taken into consideration to avoid a two-toned effect on the porous ends. Follow manufacturer's directions when mixing to achieve the desired silver or slate color tone.

COLOR RINSES

Color rinses are prepared rinses used to highlight or add temporary color to the hair. These rinses remain on the hair until the next shampoo.

MEDICATED RINSES

These are formulated with some medicinal properties to control minor conditions of dandruff. Follow manufacturer's instructions.

CREAM RINSE

A cream rinse is a commercial product having a creamy appearance and is used as a last rinse. It tends to soften the hair, adds lustre and makes tangled hair easier to comb.

Cream rinses depend for their effectiveness on one or more chemicals having one property in common—that of being "substantive" to hair. Some substances will adhere to the hair shaft and refuse to be washed off by ordinary rinsing. This is specifically so in the materials used in a cream rinse. The result is that the hair has a nice soft feel and is much easier to comb and handle.

A cream rinse does not have the same function as an acid rinse. While cream rinses are slightly acid in reaction, this is due to the nature of the ingredients used. Moreover, the acidity is so low that, in the dilutions used, it would have no effect as a soap film remover.

SOAPS

Soaps are compounds formed in a chemical reaction between alkaline substances (potassium or sodium hydroxide) and the fatty acids in the oil or fat. Besides soap, glycerine is also formed. Potassium hydroxide produces a **soft soap**, whereas sodium hydroxide forms a **hard soap**. A mixture of the two alkalies will yield a soap of intermediate consistency.

A good soap does not contain an excess of free alkali and is made from pure oils and fats.

KINDS OF SOAPS

Good toilet soaps should be made from purified fats which will not become rancid in the soap, and should not contain excessive free alkali. Soaps having a pH value above 9.5 tend to dry and roughen the skin. A pH value of about 8 is considered normal for the skin.

Kinds of Soaps		
Soaps	**Common Ingredients**	**Uses**
Castile soap (pure)	Olive oil and soda.	Best for the skin — produc little lather.
Castile soap (other kinds)	Synthetic detergents, olive or other oils.	Used for normal skin.
Green soap	Made from potash and olive or linseed oil and glycerine.	A medicinal liquid soap used f oily skin.
Tincture of green soap	Mixture of green soap in about 35% alcohol and a small amount of perfume.	Used for correcting oily skin a scalp. Very drying, if used normal or dry skin over a peri of time.
Medicated soap	Contains a small percent of cresol, phenol or other antiseptics.	Used for acne conditions.
Shaving soap	Contains alkalies, coconut oil, vegetable and animal fats and a small amount of gum.	Used for shaving. The alkalin softens the hair. The thi lather keeps the hair erect.
Shaving soap in pressure can	Shaving soap and gas under pressure.	Used the same as shaving so
Carbolic soap	A disinfectant soap containing 10% phenol.	Used for oily skin and ac infection.
Transparent soap	Contains glycerine, alcohol and sugar, which render it transparent.	Used for normal skin.
Super-fatted soap	Contains a fatty substance, such as lanolin or cocoa butter.	Recommended for dry or sen tive skin. Keeps the skin s after washing. Not suitable f hard water.
Naphtha soap	Contains naphtha, obtained from petroleum.	Do not use on face or scalp. L mainly for laundry purposes.
Hard water soap	Contains coconut oil, varying amounts of washing soda or borax, sodium silicate and a phosphate.	Used only on oily skin. T alkaline substances will dry skin.

SHAVING SOAPS

Shaving soaps can be purchased in various forms and shapes. Hard shaving soaps include those sold in cake, stick or powdered form, and are similar in composition to toilet soaps. Available as soft soap is shaving cream in a tube, jar, or press-button container. Liquid soap can also be used by the barber-sylist.

Whatever form of shaving soap is used, it usually contains animal and vegetable oils, alkaline substances and water. The presence of **coconut oil improves the lathering qualities** of the shaving soap.

Cosmetics for the Skin, Scalp and Hair		
Name	**Composition**	**Use**
oap (Hard or soft)	Contains oils and fats combined chemically with hydroxides as potassium hydroxide.	Cleanses the skin.
having soap	Contains soap combined with water and glycerine.	Softens the hair and lubricates the skin prior to shaving.
old cream	Contains oil, borax, wax, water and perfume.	All-purpose cream used to cleanse, protect and lubricate the skin.
leansing cream	Contains a cold cream base with a high content of mineral oil.	Melts quickly and cleanses the skin.
mollient or ssue cream	Contains oil, water, lanolin, wax and perfume.	Softens the skin and replaces any natural deficiency of oil.
assage cream	Contains a cold cream base with starch or casein.	Cleanses the skin and aids in facial massage.
uscle oil	Contains vegetable or mineral oil, lecithin or cholesterol.	Softens and lubricates the skin and aids in facial massage.
stringent(after-ave) lotion	Contains alcohol, astringent and perfumed water.	Closes the pores, and corrects an oily skin.
itch hazel	Contains alcohol, water and extract of witch hazel bark.	Cools and refreshes the skin after shaving.
ay rum	Contains alcohol, oil of bay or other fragrant oils.	Cools and refreshes the skin after shaving.
alcum powder	Contains insoluble magnesium compounds and perfume.	Soothes and dries the skin after shaving. Used on back of the neck before and after haircutting.
hampoo	Contains soap in liquid form.	Cleanses the scalp and hair.
air rinse	Contains water and a mild acid or coloring agent.	Removes insoluble soap residue from the hair, or temporarily colors the hair a definite shade.
air tonic or alp lotion	Contains, alcohol water, oil, perfume and medicinal agent (either antiseptic or irritant).	Stimulates circulation, reduces dandruff, keeps scalp clean and healthy, and dresses the hair.
alp ointment or ndruff ointment	Contains lanolin, petrolatum and medicinal agents.	Used to correct dandruff and stimulate circulation of blood to the scalp.
rilliantine or made	Available in liquid and solid form and contains vegetable or mineral oil, wax and perfume.	Used as a hair dressing to keep the hair in place.

The **brushless or latherless shaving cream** differs from any other shaving preparation. Its principal ingredients are uncombined fatty acids (stearic and palmitic acids) together with large amounts of water. Other chemicals present in this type of shaving cream may be soda, potash and special agents. This type of shaving cream is not used to any extent by the professional barber-stylist.

SCALP LOTIONS AND OINTMENTS

Scalp lotions and ointments usually contain medicinal agents for the purpose of correcting a scalp condition and reconditioning the hair. The active ingredients of such preparations are irritants which stimulate the circulation of the scalp and hasten the shedding and renewal of epithelial tissue.

Scalp lotions contain such ingredients as lecithin, quinine, sulphur, salicylic acids, oils, resorcin, camphor and capsicum. Resorcin and quinine, used over a period of time, may discolor blonde hair.

Lotions for an **oily scalp** should contain a high percentage of alcohol and ingredients which possess astringent properties. On the other hand, lotions for a **dry scalp** should contain little or no alcohol or astringents. Instead, emulsified vegetable or animal oils should be the predominant ingredient.

Hair lotions or **tonics** are divided into groups according to the purpose for which they are used, some being used to regulate the activity of the oil glands of the scalp; others, to remove dandruff. They are found in liquid, oil or cream form.

For dry scalp, use olive oil, delicately perfumed.

For oily scalp, use sweet oil and alcohol.

Sulphur ointment contains precipitated sulphur in benzonated lard and is used in skin and scalp disorders.

HAIR DRESSINGS

Hair dressings are used to impart a gloss or fragrance to the hair and to keep unruly or curly hair in a fixed position.

Hair creams in both liquid and semi-solid form are used after a shampoo to give the hair gloss. They may be applied to either wet or dry hair. Such creams consist of lanolin, oil emulsions, fatty acids, waxes, mild alkalies and water. Hair creams are generally used on dry types of hair.

Other hair dressings which are used for oily types of hair and applied before the hair is set may contain resins, gums, starch or other thickeners in water and alcohol. They hold the hair in place, leave a light film when dry, but give less gloss to the hair.

HAIR SPRAYS

Styling trends led to a demand for a quick-drying preparation which would impart sufficient rigidity to the hair to keep it in place, control loose ends and not detract from its natural sheen.

A new type of hair spray was developed with the production of plastics, such as polyvinylpyrrolidone (PVP). This hair spray gives a film with enough strength to control the hair, but with sufficient elasticity to allow combing without distorting the style. A product of this type can be used on wet hair as a setting lotion after the shampoo, thereby extending the duration of the style. The effect of this spray is better on weak, lightened or over-processed hair.

LOTIONS

Lotions are popular products used to a considerable extent in various kinds of hair and facial treatments. They are available as a clear solution or as a suspension, having an insoluble sediment at the bottom of the container.

Lotions		
Kind	**Common Ingredients**	**Uses**
Aromatic water	Essential oil (oil of rose, geranium, lavender, etc.) dissolved in distilled water with the aid of talc.	Imparts a cooling and fragrant effect to skin tonics and lotions.
Cleansing lotions	Alcohol or a sulfonated compound.	For oily skin.
Astringent lotions	Zinc, alum, boric or salicylic acid, in solution of water, glycerine and alcohol.	For oily skin and large pores.
Skin freshener lotions	Witch hazel, camphor, boric acid, mild organic acids, perfume and coloring.	Slightly astringent solution for dry skin.
Acne lotions	Precipitated sulfur, glycerine, spirits of camphor and distilled water.	Used to sponge the skin where simple acne exists.
Witch hazel	A solution of alcohol and water containing the astringent from witch hazel bark.	Used as an astringent and cooling lotion.
Eye lotions	Boric acid, bicarbonate of soda, zinc sulfate and glycerine, witch hazel or other herbs.	Used to soothe, cleanse and brighten the eyes.
Calamine lotion	Suspension of prepared calamine and zinc oxide in glycerine, bentonite and lime water.	Used as a soothing application to irritated surfaces of the skin and as a protective lotion.
Hardy's lotion	Corrosive sublimate, alcohol, zinc sulfate, lead acetate and water.	Recommended by a physician to remove freckles.
Medicated lotions	Antiseptics, sulphur compounds, or other medicinal agents.	Recommended by a physician for acne or other skin eruptions.
Sunburn preventive lotion	Dilute solution of methyl salicylate in alcohol, glycerine and water.	Filters out most of the ultraviolet rays of the sun and produces a uniform tan.
Sunburn remedial lotion	Dilute solution of astringent or cooling agent (camphor) in alcohol, glycerine and water.	Helps to heal a first degree burn.

Next to creams, powders are widely used and constitute a profitable source of income. Since each kind of powder serves a particular purpose, the barber-stylist should be acquainted with the advantages of the powder used.

Face powder consists of a powder base, mixed with a coloring agent (pigment). A good face powder for a normal skin should possess the following characteristics:

1. **Slip**—having a smooth feel to the skin. This quality is imparted by the talc or zinc stearate. The French or Italian talc, 200 mesh, is the best for face powders.

2. **Covering power**—having easy and even spread in order to cover skin shine, skin defects and enlarged pores. Zinc oxide, kaolin or titanium dioxide may be used.

3. **Adherency**—the ability to remain on the skin. Zinc or magnesium stearate is used.

Toilet powder is used after bathing and shaving to relieve irritated surfaces. Talcum is the most satisfactory base for a toilet powder, as it is not absorbent and is not affected by moisture.

DEODORANTS AND ANTI-PERSPIRANTS

Few preparations can be classified separately as deodorant or anti-perspirant products, since most combine the features of both. **A deodorant** is an agent which neutralizes or destroys disagreeable odors without suppressing the amount of perspiration. An **anti-perspirant** checks perspiration by its astringent action. The skin surrounding the pores swells, thereby temporarily closing the pores.

Deodorants and anti-perspirants are available in the form of creams, sticks, solutions and powders.

Deodorants and Anti-Perspirants		
Kind	**Common Ingredients**	**Uses**
Deodorant powders	Mixture of powder base, zinc compounds, boric acid, astringents and antiseptics.	Destroy the odor of sweat without stopping perspiration.
Deodorant creams	Vanishing cream base, antiseptic and astringent.	Destroy the odor of sweat without stopping perspiration.
Deodorant solutions	Solution containing an antiseptic, an astringent, alcohol, glycerine and water.	Used to mask odor. The skin should be dry before wearing clothing. The acidity of the aluminum chloride will destroy clothing.
Deodorant sticks	Waxes and an astringent (zinc sulphocarbolate).	Easy to apply. Destroy odor without stopping perspiration.
Creams or liquids	Strong astringents, such as aluminum compounds.	Contract the sweat gland at the place of application. Prevent excessive sweating under the arms.

BARBER-STYLING SERVICES

Barber-stylists are no longer content to confine their activities to haircutting, with an occasional shave, massage or shampoo. The professional artisan is involved in every phase of hair and skin service. In addition to cutting, styling, shaving, massaging, etc., the scope of activities in the shop includes permanent waving, hair straightening, hair curling and hair coloring. We will briefly discuss the chemistry and science involved in performing these services.

PERMANENT WAVING

COMPOSITION OF HAIR

In order to understand the chemical actions of permanent waving, it is first necessary to understand the composition of the hair and hair bonds.

Hair is made of a hard protein called **keratin.** It has three layers: cuticle, cortex, medulla. Since permanent hair waving takes place in the cortical layer, special attention is given to a study of the cortex.

The **cortex** is composed of numerous parallel fibers of hard keratin, referred to as polypeptide chains. These parallel fibers are twisted around one another in a manner resembling the twisting of the fiber strands in rope.

PEPTIDE BONDS

Each amino-acid is joined to another by peptide bonds (end bonds), forming a chain as long as the hair. They are the strongest bonds in the cortex and most of the strength of hair is due to their properties.

Peptide bonds are chemical bonds and if even a few are broken, the hair is weakened or damaged. If many of these bonds are broken, the hair will break off.

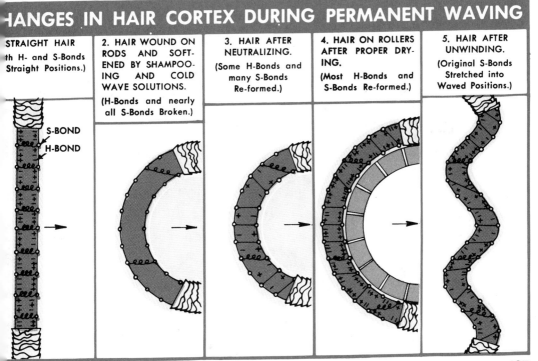

HANGES IN HAIR CORTEX DURING PERMANENT WAVING

| STRAIGHT HAIR th H- and S-Bonds Straight Positions.) | 2. HAIR WOUND ON RODS AND SOFT-ENED BY SHAMPOO-ING AND COLD WAVE SOLUTIONS. (H-Bonds and nearly all S-Bonds Broken.) | 3. HAIR AFTER NEUTRALIZING. (Some H-Bonds and many S-Bonds Re-formed.) | 4. HAIR ON ROLLERS AFTER PROPER DRY-ING. (Most H-Bonds and S-Bonds Re-formed.) | 5. HAIR AFTER UNWINDING. (Original S-Bonds Stretched into Waved Positions.) |

S-BOND
H-BOND

CROSS-BONDS

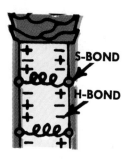

S-BOND

H-BOND

It is the presence of cross-bonds or links, however, that has given hair the ability to be permanently waved. Two types of cross-bonds are of major concern in hair work. Sulphur bonds (chemical), called S-bonds, and hydrogen bonds (physical), called H-bonds.

Hydrogen bonds are much more numerous than sulphur bonds, but they are much weaker and can be broken easily with water or chemicals. Sulphur bonds are very strong and can only be broken by a strong chemical.

THIO SOLUTION

A thio solution (ammonium thioglycolate) with a pH of 9.4 to 9.6 causes the cuticle of the hair to swell and the imbrications to open, allowing the solution to penetrate into the cortex. The solution breaks down all the H-bonds and many of the S-bonds, permitting a "slippage" or alteration in the polypeptide chains. The chains assume contour of rods around which hair is wound.

NEUTRALIZER

When sufficient processing has taken place, the thio is rinsed from the hair and neutralizer is applied. The neutralizer is an acid solution with a pH of 3.0 to 4.0. This solution stops the action of the thio and re-hardens the hair by re-forming many of the S-bonds and some of the H-bonds. The rest of the H-bonds are re-formed during the drying of the hair. The S-bonds and H-bonds hold the polypeptide chains in their newly curled formation.

CAUTION must be exercised in the use of a thio solution. If it is permitted to remain in the hair for too long, it could weaken and break the polypeptide chains by destroying the end-bonds, thus causing hair breakage.

ACID AND NEUTRAL PERMANENT WAVING

In recent years, manufacturers have developed permanent wave solutions that are less damaging to the hair than thio. This type of permanent waving is developed from two solutions, one highly alkaline and the other very low in acidity, which must be mixed together immediately before use. This combined solution has a slightly acid pH factor (4.5-6.5). Winding is the same as for the usual thio permanent. Since this low pH causes no swelling of the hair, a new factor (heat) must be introduced to achieve penetration of the hair shaft.

PROTEIN FILLERS

Protein fillers are used to recondition over-porous or damaged hair before a permanent waving lotion is applied. The filler is a jelly-like, colorless substance made of a mixture of protein and keratin. Some also contain lanolin and cholesterol to protect hair against the harshness of the permanent waving lotion.

The chemical properties of the filler are similar to those of the hair, so the filler is able to even out the hair's porosity along the entire hair shaft. This evening-out process takes place because the porous sections of the hair shaft absorb the filler more rapidly than do the less porous sections.

CHEMICAL HAIR RELAXING (Processing)

The procedure for chemical hair relaxing is very similar to the technique followed in permanent waving. However, since the objective to be attained is exactly the reverse of permanent waving, some of the techniques must also be reversed.

The barber-stylist starts with hair that is excessively curly, and his objective is to remove the curl permanently.

As in permanent waving, the process requires the breaking down of the S-bonds and the H-bonds in the cortex. The relaxing process, however, requires that the hair be held or directed in a straight position.

TWO TYPES OF CHEMICAL RELAXERS

The two types of chemical hair relaxers that are in general use by professional barber-stylists are thio (thioglycolate), pH 9.4 to 9.6, and sodium hydroxide, pH 10 to 14. The over-all objective of both these products is exactly the same. Students must be cautioned, however, that sodium hydroxide is much stronger than thio, and, if not properly used, it can cause great damage to the client's hair. If left on the hair too long, it may change the hair color. If left on longer than 10 minutes, it may dissolve the hair.

Fixative. The neutralizer, or fixative, is employed in an acid solution with a pH of 3.0 to 4.0.

Before either of these products is employed, it is extremely important to read the chapter on Chemical Hair Relaxing for a detailed study of their application and the safety precautions required.

CHEMICAL HAIR STRAIGHTENING - SODIUM HYDROXIDE

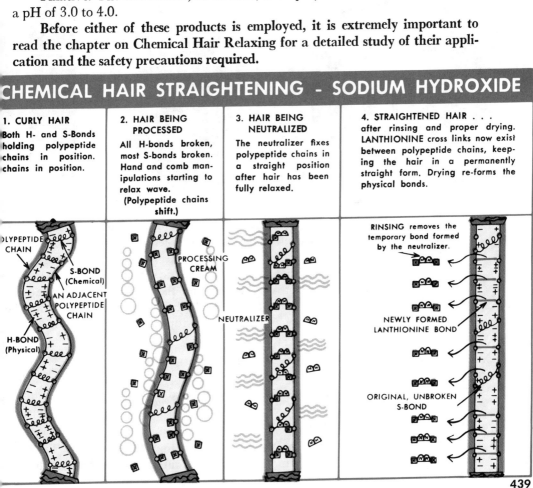

1. CURLY HAIR	2. HAIR BEING PROCESSED	3. HAIR BEING NEUTRALIZED	4. STRAIGHTENED HAIR . . .
Both H- and S-Bonds holding polypeptide chains in position. chains in position.	All H-bonds broken, most S-bonds broken. Hand and comb manipulations starting to relax wave. (Polypeptide chains shift.)	The neutralizer fixes polypeptide chains in a straight position after hair has been fully relaxed.	after rinsing and proper drying. LANTHIONINE cross links now exist between polypeptide chains, keeping the hair in a permanently straight form. Drying re-forms the physical bonds.

POLYPEPTIDE CHAIN

S-BOND (Chemical)

AN ADJACENT POLYPEPTIDE CHAIN

H-BOND (Physical)

PROCESSING CREAM

NEUTRALIZER

RINSING removes the temporary bond formed by the neutralizer.

NEWLY FORMED LANTHIONINE BOND

ORIGINAL, UNBROKEN S-BOND

HAIR COLORING

This presentation is limited to a discussion of the chemical composition, actions and reactions of the various types of hair colorings. See chapter on **Hair Coloring** for information on techniques, application and use of hair colorings.

Temporary colorings for the hair come in various forms, such as color rinses, color sprays and color shampoos. They come in a wide range of colors and are easily applied. Temporary colors are washed out with the first shampoo. For these reasons, they are useful to a patron who is experimenting with new hair colors or for a client seeking a particular hair effect for a special occasion.

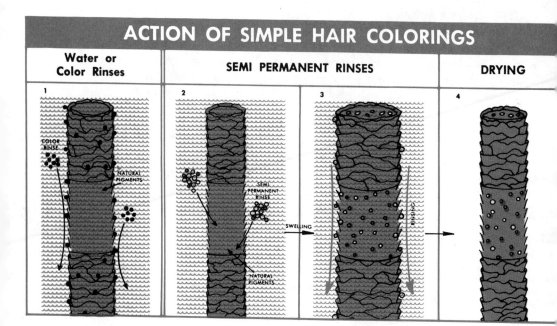

ACTION OF SIMPLE HAIR COLORINGS

Water or Color Rinses	SEMI PERMANENT RINSES		DRYING

Temporary colorings are harmless to the hair because they contain "true stains," which are colors accepted by the government for use in foods, drugs and cosmetics. They are also called "certified colors." Temporary colorings are composed of large molecules that are acid in chemical composition and unable to penetrate into the cortical layer. They shrink the cuticle scales, closing the imbrications and preventing the entrance of the large color molecules into the cortex. The coloring substance can only be trapped behind the imbrications of the cuticle.

Temporary coloring is easily washed from the hair because the shampoo is alkaline and opens the imbrications. The rinsing action of the shampoo then easily washes out the coloring substance. Lightened hair is able to absorb more of the coloring substance because the lightener has already opened the cuticle, thus allowing more of the color to enter.

Semi-permanent colorings (tints) last from four to six weeks. They are aniline derivative tints, the same as permanent tints, but their molecules are larger than those of the permanent tints.

Semi-permanent tints offer clients a number of benefits which are not found in other forms of hair coloring. Besides lasting from four to six shampoos, they have a very good range of colors. Semi-permanent tints are easily applied and do not require the use of hydrogen peroxide. They are effective in covering or blending partially grey hair without affecting the natural color. They also serve to highlight and bring out the natural color of the hair.

Semi-permanent tints are alkaline in chemical composition and cause an alkaline reaction on the hair. The alkali swells the cuticle, opening the imbrications and permitting the color molecules to enter the cortex. However, since semi-permanent tints are only mildly alkaline, the swelling of the cuticle and the opening of the imbrications are limited, permitting only a small number of the large molecules to enter into the cortex.

A neutral or slightly acid rinse is used to close the imbrications and trap the colored molecules inside the cortex. Gradually, the semi-permanent tints are washed out of the hair by alkaline shampoos, which open the cuticle imbrications, permitting the colored molecules to pass out of the cortex.

PERMANENT HAIR TINTS

Most clients prefer their hair coloring to last much longer than a few shampoos. Originally, hair tints were intended solely to hide greying hair. Today, clients of all ages choose to color their hair simply to enhance their appearance. Permanent hair tints may be found in a number of different types: aniline derivative tints, vegetable tints and metallic dyes.

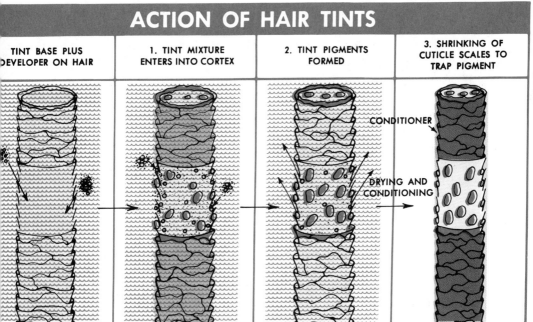

ACTION OF HAIR TINTS

TINT BASE PLUS DEVELOPER ON HAIR	1. TINT MIXTURE ENTERS INTO CORTEX	2. TINT PIGMENTS FORMED	3. SHRINKING OF CUTICLE SCALES TO TRAP PIGMENT

CONDITIONER

DRYING AND CONDITIONING

Aniline derivative tints, or oxidizing tints, are the primary tints used in professional services. They offer a number of distinct advantages over all other forms of coloring. They give a permanent color to the hair, requiring no further coloring treatment, except for new growth. A wide range of aniline derivative colors has been developed to meet every client's desires. Of special interest is the fact that aniline derivative tints permit other services to be given to tinted hair.

These tints are composed of very small, colorless molecules which experience no difficulty in passing through the cuticle imbrications and penetrating into the cortex. A developer, usually hydrogen peroxide, is added to the tint immediately before application. Once inside the cortex, the developer combines the small, colorless molecules into giant, colored molecules. These large molecules cannot be shampooed from the hair because they are too large to pass out through the imbrications. In addition, they form bonds with the keratin chains in the cortex, and thus become firmly affixed. These bonds are acid and, therefore, leave the H-bonds and the S-bonds free for other hair treatments.

HAIR LIGHTENING

Hair lightening is the process which decreases or removes the natural color pigments in the hair.

Hair color pigments are:

Melanin—black to brown shades
Oxymelanin—red to yellow shades

Hair lightening occurs in two ways: through natural conditions or through artificial conditions.

Natural conditions: Color may be removed from the hair by the sun's rays, chlorinated water or other natural action.

Artificial conditions: This usually occurs through chemical means. Chemical hair lightening is a two-stage process. The first stage involves changing the melanin pigments into oxymelanin. The second stage, depending on the degree of lightening desired, involves the continued breaking down of the oxymelanin pigment until the desired effect is achieved.

CHEMICAL AGENTS

The chemical agent used for removing pigments from the hair shaft is a 6% (20-volume) solution of hydrogen peroxide.

The active ingredient of hydrogen peroxide is oxygen gas. To speed the liberation of oxygen gas, a small quantity of 28% ammonia water is added, which increases the pH to 10.0.

There are a number of commercial lighteners available to the barber-stylist. These products are:

1. Oil lighteners—mixtures of hydrogen peroxide and sulfonated oils
2. Cream lighteners, containing conditioning agents, bluing and thickener
3. Powder lighteners, containing an oxygen releasing booster and inert substances

The chemical action of all the commercial lighteners is basically the same as outlined above.

442

TONERS

Toners are permanent aniline derivative hair colorings. They consist primarily of pale, delicate colors requiring very careful application.

Since a toner is an aniline derivative tint, it must be handled exactly as other permanent aniline tints. The chemical actions are identical with those described for aniline derivative tints.

Toners are usually applied to lightened hair to add color and highlights to the hair.

QUESTIONS ON CHEMISTRY

GENERAL CHEMISTRY

1. Why is a basic knowledge of chemistry important to the barber-stylist?
2. What is organic chemistry? Give five examples of organic substances.
3. In what type of liquids are organic substances soluble? Give two examples.
4. What is inorganic chemistry? Give five examples of inorganic substances.
5. What is matter?
6. In what three physical forms does matter exist?
7. What is an element? How many are there?
8. What is the smallest part of an element?
9. What is a molecule?
10. What do we mean by the "chemical activities" of an element?
11. What is a compound?
12. Name and describe the four classes of compounds.
13. What is a mixture?
14. What are the two ways in which matter may be changed? Give an example of each.
15. What is a physical change?
16. What is a chemical change?
17. List the five properties of matter.
18. What is meant by pH?
19. How do acids register on the pH scale?
20. How do alkalines register on the pH scale?
21. What is the most abundant of all substances?
22. What two methods are employed to remove impurities from water?
23. What two types of water are found?
24. Why is hard water unsuitable for shop use?
25. What is the chemical symbol for water?

SHAMPOOING

1. What are the two parts of the shampoo molecule?
2. What purpose is served by (a) the tail of the shampoo molecule, and (b) the head?
3. Describe the action of the two parts of the shampoo molecule in cleansing the hair.
4. What is the chemical composition of shampoo?
5. What are the three types of shampoos?

CHEMISTRY AS APPLIED TO COSMETICS

1. Name the six physical and chemical classifications of cosmetics.
2. What are the two classes of emulsions?
3. What service is performed by astringents?
4. What is the function of face lotions?
5. What purpose is served by hair tonics?
6. What five functions are served by hair rinses?
7. What is soap?
8. Describe the composition of a good soap.
9. For what purpose are scalp lotions and ointments used?
10. What do hair dressings do for hair in addition to giving a gloss or fragrance?
11. For what purpose are hair sprays used by the barber-stylist?
12. List the three characteristics of a good face powder.
13. What is a deodorant?
14. How does an anti-perspirant function?

BARBER-STYLING SERVICES

1. Why must special attention be given to the cortical layer of the hair when studying permanent waving?
2. What are the parallel fibers of hard keratin called?
3. How are the amino-acids in the polypeptide chains joined?
4. Which type of bonds gives hair the ability to be permanent waved?
5. What are the two types of cross-bonds?
6. How is slippage or alteration in the polypeptide chains brought about?
7. How is the action of the "thio" solution halted after sufficient processing has taken place?
8. How does the neutralizer halt the action of the "thio?"
9. What are protein fillers used for?
10. How does chemical hair relaxing differ from permanent waving?
11. What are the two types of chemical relaxers in general use?
12. What are the three types of hair colorings in general use?
13. Why do temporary colors last only a short time?
14. How long do semi-permanent colors last?
15. What is the chemical composition of semi-permanent tints?
16. How long do permanent colors last?
17. Why do permanent tints last indefinitely?
18. How does hair lightening differ from hair tinting?
19. What are the two hair color pigments?
20. What is the chemical agent used to remove color pigment from the hair shaft?

Chapter 30

BARBER-STYLING SHOP MANAGEMENT

Many opportunities exist for a successful career as the owner or manager of a barber-styling shop. However, in order to be successful, a barber-styling shop must be carefully planned and efficiently managed.

Barber-styling shop management concerns the direct control and coordination of all activities that occur while the shop is in operation. It also includes the proper planning, location and physical arrangement of the shop.

It should be understood that it would be impossible to present a detailed study in management in a single chapter. This chapter will introduce those business principles and management techniques necessary to satisfactorily operate a barber-styling shop. A more detailed and broader coverage would require special texts and training in business management.

Going into your own business is a big responsibility. An understanding of business principles, bookkeeping, business laws, insurance, salesmanship and psychology are all very important for a successful operation. In addition to having a thorough knowledge and understanding of the practice of barber-styling, it is important to be able to cooperate with employees and to get along well with clients. Shop management includes all the principles, sensitivities, methods and understanding of the techniques by which a business is conducted.

MANAGEMENT FUNCTIONS

There are eight essential functions performed by every barber-styling shop owner or manager. They are:

1. Arranging for financing or the capital investment
2. Finding the best location for the shop
3. Purchasing of the equipment, furniture and fixtures
4. Arranging for the best and widest publicity for the shop
5. Developing sales techniques for shop services and saleable merchandise
6. Establishing and maintaining systematic records
7. Developing good public relations with clients and encouraging new clients
8. Establishing and enforcing shop policies

445

FINANCING (CAPITAL INVESTMENT)

The type of business organization to be employed in setting up the barber-styling shop depends largely upon the amount of capital available. There are three types of business organizations to be considered, namely: the sole proprietor, the partnership and the corporation.

SOLE PROPRIETOR

If the individual has enough money to finance the cost of setting up and operating the barber-styling shop, the individual form of ownership (sole proprietor) should be considered.

The **individual** form of organization has certain **merits** over the partnership and corporation.

1. The owner is his own boss and manager.
2. The owner can determine his own policies and decisions.
3. The owner receives all the profits.

The individual form of organization has the following **disadvantages:**

1. The owner's expenditures are limited by the amount of capital investment.
2. The owner is personally liable for all debts of the business.

PARTNERSHIP

A lack of sufficient capital could necessitate the formation of a partnership.

The **partnership,** being a combination of two or three people, has certain advantages over the individual form of ownership. There should always be a written agreement defining the duties and responsibilities of each member. The main **advantages of a partnership** are:

1. More capital is made available to equip and operate the shop.
2. Work, responsibilities and losses are shared.
3. The combined ability and experience of each partner assist in the solution of business problems.

The chief **disadvantages** of a partnership are:

1. Each partner is responsible for the business actions of the other.
2. Disputes and misunderstandings may arise between partners.
3. Each partner is personally liable for all debts of the business.

CORPORATION

When three or more individuals intend to operate a barber-styling shop, the corporation is probably the best form of organization.

A **corporation** has the advantage over a partnership in that its stockholders are not legally responsible in case of loss or bankruptcy. The earning capacity is in proportion to the profits and the number of stocks the individual has in the corporation. Although the corporation has a considerable financial backing, it may only do what is specifically authorized in the charter and approved by the board of directors. The corporation is subject to taxation and regulation by the state.

Federal tax laws allow some types of small corporations to be taxed on a partnership basis. Barber-styling shops come into this category. An accountant should be consulted on all matters.

SELECTING A LOCATION

When planning to open a barber-styling shop, careful consideration must be given to the selection of a location. The selection of a desirable site is just as important as the capital investment.

A good location is in an area large enough to support the barber-styling shop. It should be near other active business places which attract people and has a large number of people passing its windows. In a residential neighborhood, the main source of clients will be from the immediate vicinity. In a transient area, clients will come from surrounding and distant places.

Before selecting a location, consult the local bank, real estate agents and other local merchants for assistance. Find out what the earning capacity and the living standards are of the people in the particular neighborhood. This information will help in deciding policies and prices. It is not advisable for a beginner to open a barber-styling shop in a locality where there are many competitors.

In judging the merits of a particular site, consideration must be given to the entrance, the window space, the inside area of the store, a good water supply, lighting and heating facilities, the presence of adequate toilet facilities and a sufficient number of windows for good ventilation or air conditioning.

THE LEASE

After the best site has been selected, by making comparisons of the various locations, it is advisable to check local zoning ordinances. Before signing a lease, it is important to make certain that the area is zoned to permit the operation of a barber-styling shop.

After all facts have been checked and all obstacles are removed, a lease should be negotiated for the premises. A lease serves to protect the barber-stylist owner against unexpected increases in rental; it serves to protect the continued occupancy of the shop, and it clearly sets forth the rights and obligations of both the landlord and the barber-stylist owner.

The lease should contain provisions concerning alterations, decorating, heating and water supply. Before signing the lease, it should be carefully read and clearly understood to avoid future controversies. In fact, the barber-stylist owner should have the lease analyzed by his attorney to be certain that it gives him the proper protection.

CHECKING ACCOUNTS

In **transacting business** for the individual, partnership or corporation, a checking account is a convenient and safe way to make payments and withdrawals. The cancelled checks serve as receipts. If one person is the sole owner, the bank and checking accounts are in his own name. In a partnership, there is usually a joint account, in which one or both partners may sign checks and withdraw money. A corporation bank account is issued in its own name, with a responsible person authorized to withdraw money and issue checks.

LEGAL REGULATIONS

In conducting a business and employing help, it is necessary to comply with local, state and federal regulations and laws.

Local regulations may cover building and renovations (local building code) and zoning laws.

Federal law covers social security, unemployment compensation or insurance, and cosmetics and luxury tax payments.

State laws cover sales taxes, licenses and workmen's compensation.

Income tax laws are covered by both the state and federal governments. Some localities have local income tax laws.

Insurance covers malpractice, premises liability, fire, burglary and theft, and business interruption.

EQUIPPING THE BARBER-STYLING SHOP

When the location of the shop has finally been determined, the premises have been rented and the lease signed, it is then ready to be furnished with fixtures and equipment.

The layout of the barber-styling shop takes a considerable amount of planning in order to achieve maximum efficiency and economy.

The barber-styling shop should be planned to provide:
1. Maximum efficiency of operation.
2. Adequate aisle space.
3. Enough space for each piece of equipment.
4. Furniture, fixtures and equipment chosen on a basis of cost, durability, utility and appearance. The purchase of standard, durable and guaranteed equipment, either new or renovated, is a worthwhile investment. If, in the future, equipment must be replaced, repaired or matched, it is fairly easy to duplicate standard fixtures.
5. Premises which are painted and decorated in colors which are restful and pleasing to the eye.
6. A clean restroom containing toilet and basin.
7. Good plumbing and sufficient lighting for adequate services.
8. Air conditioning and heating.
9. Proper electrical outlets and current to adequately service all equipment.
10. The reception or waiting area is not to be overlooked. An attractive, adequately furnished and comfortable waiting area can be one of the best promotional devices. It should immediately make the client comfortable and relaxed, and it should give the client the impression that the barber-stylist is really interested in his/her comfort.

The most important requisites for an attractive barber-styling shop are cleanliness and comfort. The equipment should be easily accessible, arranged in an orderly manner, and maintained in good working condition. The electric lighting must be neither too dull nor too bright. Sanitation and sanitary rules must be strictly enforced for the public's protection.

ADVERTISING

Advertising includes all those activities which attract favorable attention to the barber-styling shop. They are intended and planned to create a pleasing impression on the public. It is obvious, therefore, that the personalities and ability of the owner or manager and the staff, the quality of the work performed and the attractiveness of the shop are all natural advertising assets.

The right kind of publicity is important because it acquaints the public with the various services offered. The best kind of publicity, of course, is that which reaches the greatest number of people at the cheapest cost.

A pleased client is the best form of advertising.

To be effective, advertising must attract and hold the attention of those individuals to whom it is directed. It must create a desire for the services or merchandise offered.

The choice of advertising medium is based on the judgment as to which would accomplish the desired objective most effectively. For advertising to be effective, it must be repeated to make a lasting impression. Advertising media to be considered are:

1. Newspaper advertising
2. Distribution of circulars
3. Direct mail, which creates a more intimate contact with recipients
4. Classified advertising, which is comparatively inexpensive
5. Yellow Pages of the telephone directory
6. Radio advertising, which is more expensive, but could be quite effective
7. T.V. advertising, which is dramatic, but quite expensive
8. Attractive window display, which acts as a salesman to every passerby

Once a client is attracted to the barber-styling shop, courteous and efficient service will bring him/her back and encourage the recommendation of the shop. People go where they are invited and return to where they are well treated.

A pleasing personality is a priceless asset that creates goodwill and a friendly atmosphere. The barber-stylist must be mindful of his/her hygienic habits. He/she must take pains at all times to be clean and tidy in clothing and extremely careful to avoid body odors or bad breath. Good public relations require that the barber-stylist consider the thoughts and feelings of clients and avoid antagonizing them by word or action.

BUSINESS OPERATION

Business problems are numerous, especially when a new barber-styling business is organized. Contributing causes to shop failures are:

1. Inexperience in dealing with the public and employees
2. Insufficient capital to carry on the business until established
3. Poor location
4. Too high cost of operation
5. Lack of proper basic training
6. Careless bookkeeping methods
7. Business neglect

The owner or manager of the barber-styling shop must have good business sense, knowledge, ability, good judgment and diplomacy.

Smooth management of a barber-styling shop depends on:

1. Sufficient investment capital
2. Efficiency of management
3. Cooperation between management and employees
4. Use of good business judgment
5. Trained and experienced personnel to serve patrons

SALESMANSHIP

The satisfaction of clients depends upon the extent to which their needs were fulfilled in the barber-styling shop. In addition to trying to improve the quality of the basic services, such as haircuts, hairstyles and shaves, the practitioner should try to sell additional services. Services such as hair coloring, shampoos, facial and scalp massage, hair waving, hair tonics, hairpieces and others should be offered to the client. The barber-stylist should be acquainted with all the various services offered. He/she should know the names of the various cosmetic products, their cost and the proper manner of application. The barber-stylist also should be thoroughly knowledgeable of the benefits to be derived from all additional services.

By selling these extra services, the barber-stylist becomes of greater value to the client and in addition helps to increase the profits of the shop.

In addition to selling extra services, it is well to carry a good line of tonics, creams and lotions to sell for home use. These products will not sell themselves, but a word to a client at the proper time often results in a sale. This is an excellent way to increase income.

The barber-stylist has occasion to use the art of salesmanship in convincing clients as to the merits and benefits of various facial and scalp preparations and treatments. A good salesman knows all about the service or product he/she is selling. After a basis for confidence has been established, suggestive language, without any high-pressure tactics, may create a desire in the client to try the new service or product. An attractive feature is to offer combination services at special prices.

RECORD KEEPING

Good business administration demands the keeping of a simple and efficient record system. Records are of value only if they are correct, concise and complete. Bookkeeping means keeping an accurate record of all income and expenses. Income is usually classified as income from services and income from retail sales. Expenses include rent, utilities, salaries, advertising, supplies, equipment and repairs. The assistance of an accountant will prove valuable. Retain check stubs, cancelled checks, receipts and invoices.

Proper business records are necessary to meet the requirements of local, state and federal laws regarding taxes and employees.

All business transactions must be recorded in order to maintain proper records. These are required for the following reasons:
1. For efficient operation of the barber-styling shop
2. For determining income, expenses, profit and loss
3. For proving the value of the barber-styling shop to prospective buyers
4. For arranging a bank loan
5. For such reports as income tax, social security, unemployment and disability insurance, wage and hour law, accident compensation and labor taxes

One of the causes for failure in operating a barber-styling shop is the lack of complete and systematic records. All business transactions must be recorded in order to judge the condition of the business at a particular time.

Keeping daily records enables the owner or manager to know just how the business is progressing. A weekly or monthly summary helps to:

1. Make comparisons with other years
2. Detect any changes in demands for different services
3. Order necessary supplies
4. Check on the use of materials according to the type of service rendered
5. Control expenses and waste

Each expense item affects the total gross income. Accurate records show the cost of operation in relation to income.

Keep daily sales slips, appointment book and petty cash book for at least six months. Payroll book, cancelled checks, monthly and yearly records are usually held for at least seven years. **Service** and **inventory** records are also important to keep. Sales records help to maintain a perpetual inventory. An organized **inventory** system can be used to:

1. Prevent overstocking
2. Prevent running short of supplies needed for services
3. Help in establishing the net worth at the end of the year

If a barber-styling shop is to operate profitably, a simple system of book-keeping must be instituted. An easy plan is to keep a daily account of income and expenses. The cash register indicates the daily income, whereas the receipts and cancelled checks constitute proof of payments. By adding the daily total income and expense, the weekly and monthly totals can be obtained. The difference between the total income and the total expense is the net profit. A profit accrues when the income is greater than the expense. When the expense is greater than the income, a loss occurs. Continued profits spell success and continued losses may finally result in bankruptcy.

A budget must be kept in order that the income of money will be sufficient to cover the expenses. The following list of expenses are commonly met in the barber-styling shop:

Operating and Administrative Expenses

Salaries	Advertising and printing
Rent	Heat, light and water
Taxes	Sundry supplies, such as soaps,
Insurance	tonics, towels, etc.
Repairs	Telephone
Cleaning	Miscellaneous

The payments made on debts, equipment and fixtures are not classified as expenses, but are considered as a reduction in indebtedness which in turn adds to the value of the barber-styling shop, except when considering depreciation on equipment for income tax purposes.

From time to time, an inventory must be taken of all sundry supplies in the barber-styling shop. This record will show what supplies have been consumed and what new supplies are needed. It is a better policy to have a slight excess of materials rather than a deficiency.

THINGS TO CONSIDER WHEN GOING INTO BUSINESS

CAPITAL
- Amount available
- Amount required

ORGANIZATION
- Individual
- Partnership
- Corporation

BANKING
- Opening a bank account
- Deposits
- Drawing checks
- Monthly statements
- Notes and Drafts

SELECTING LOCATION
- Population
- Transportation facilities
- Transients
- Trade possibilities
- Space required
- Zoning ordinances

DECORATING and FLOOR PLAN
- Selection of furniture
- Floor covering
- Installing telephone
- Interior decorating
- Exterior decorating
  - Window displays
  - Electric signs

EQUIPMENT and SUPPLIES
- Selecting equipment
- Comparative values
- Installation
- Labor-saving steps

ADVERTISING
- Planning
- Direct mail
- Local house organs
- Newspaper
- Radio
- Television

LEGAL
- Lease
- Contracts
- Claims and lawsuits

BOOKKEEPING SYSTEM
- Installation
- Record of appointments
- Receipts
- Disbursements
- Petty cash
- Profit and loss
- Inventory

COST OF OPERATION
- Rent, Light
- Salaries
- Supplies
- Depreciation
- Linen service
- Sundries
- Taxes

MANAGEMENT
- Methods of building goodwill
- Analysis of materials and labor in relation to service charges
- Greeting patrons
- Adjusting complaints
- Handling employees
- Selling merchandise

OFFICE ADMINISTRATION
- Stationery and office supplies
- Inventory

INSURANCE
- Public liability and malpractice
- Compensation
- Unemployment
- Social Security
- Fire, theft and burglary

METHODS OF PAYMENT
- In advance
- C.O.D.
- Open account
- Time payments

COMPLIANCE WITH LABOR LAWS
- Minimum wage and hour law
- Hours of employment
- Minors

ETHICS
- Courtesy
- Observation of trade practices

COMPLIANCE WITH STATE LAWS concerning equipment, size and placement of barber-styling chairs and lavatories.

LICENSING of barber-styling shop managers and barber-stylists.

452

TELEPHONE TECHNIQUES FOR THE BARBER-STYLING SHOP

An ever-increasing part of the barber-styling shop business is being handled over the telephone. Good telephone habits and techniques make it possible for the shop owner and barber-stylist to increase business and win friends. With each call the opportunity is provided to build up the shop's reputation by giving service of a high caliber.

The telephone serves many useful purposes in the barber-styling shop, such as:

1. To make or change appointments
2. To go after new business, or strayed or infrequent patrons
3. To remind patrons of needed services
4. To answer questions and render friendly service
5. To adjust complaints and satisfy patrons
6. To receive messages
7. To order equipment and supplies

Your success in using the phone depends to a large extent on the thoughtful effort exerted in observing certain fundamental principles. To the extent that these requirements are fulfilled, the telephone can be a very helpful aid to the success of the shop.

It is important to have the phone placed in a convenient and quiet place. A comfortable seat should be provided. There should be readily accessible an appointment book, a pencil or ball-point pen and a paper pad. To save time, have an up-to-date list of telephone numbers commonly called and a recent telephone directory.

Good business practice requires that the barber-styling shop's telephone number be freely and prominently displayed on stationery, advertising circulars and in newspaper ads. Business cards should be readily available in the waiting area. They save clients the trouble of being required to look up the shop's phone number, thus making it easier for them to call.

Good telephone usage can best be described as the golden rule of dealing with others as you would have them deal with you. The motto should be **"Phone as you would be phoned to."** When put into daily practice, it really means saying or doing the right thing, at the right time, and in the right manner.

Good telephone usage requires the application of a few basic principles which add up to **"common sense and common courtesy."**

Any barber-stylist should be able to learn the following four basic rules and to follow them to improve his/her own telephone conversations:

1. Display an interested, helpful attitude, as revealed by the tone of your voice and what you have to say.
2. Be prompt. Answer all calls as quickly as possible. Nothing irritates the caller more than waiting for you to answer.
3. Practice giving all necessary information to the caller. This means identifying yourself and your shop when making or receiving a call. If the

requested information is not readily available, be courteous enough to say, "Will you please hold the line while I get the information for you?"

4. Be tactful. Avoid saying or doing anything which may offend or irritate the caller. The tactful telephone user is careful:

    a) To inquire who is calling by saying, "Who is calling, please?" Refrain from using such blunt questions as "Who's calling?"

    b) To address people by their last names. Make use of such expressions as "Thank you," "I'm sorry" or "I beg your pardon." The caller appreciates such courtesy and consideration.

    c) To avoid making side remarks during a call.

    d) To let the caller end the conversation. Do not bang down the receiver at the end of a call.

Every time you telephone someone, you make a definite impression—good, bad or indifferent. Your voice, what you say, and how you say it are what reveal you to others.

If you want a **good telephone personality,** then be sure to acquire the habit of:

1. Clear speech
2. Correct speech
3. Pleasing tone of voice

In this way, the other person hearing your voice will readily understand what you are saying.

As a general rule, the most effective speech is that which is correct and, at the same time, natural. A cheerful, alert and enthusiastic voice most often comes from a person who has these desirable qualities as part of his/her personality.

To make a good impression over the phone, assume good posture; relax and draw a deep breath before answering the phone. Open the mouth, pronounce the words distinctly, use a low-pitched natural voice and speak at a moderate pace. Clear voices carry better than loud voices over the phone.

If your listeners sometimes break in with such remarks as "what was that?" or "I'm sorry, I didn't get that," it usually means that your voice is not doing its job well. In that event, you should try to find out what is wrong and correct it. The more common causes of this condition may be:

1. You are speaking too loudly or too softly.
2. Your lips are too close or too far away from the mouthpiece. They should be about the width of two fingers from the mouthpiece.
3. The pitch of your voice is too low or too high.
4. Your pronunciation is not precise.

The telephone, when properly used, is a valuable aid for obtaining more business and for making appointments. Every time the telephone is used, it affords an opportunity to render service and spread goodwill for the barber-styling shop.

TACTFUL PHRASEOLOGY FOR TELEPHONE USE IN THE BARBER-STYLING SHOP

DON'T SAY:	DO SAY:
"Who is this?" "Who's calling?" "Who are you?"	"Who is calling, please?" "May I tell him who is calling, please?" "May I tell him who called, please?" "May I take a message for him, please?" "May I have him call you?"
"What's your name?"	"May I have your name, please?" "I am sorry, but I did not get your name." "I'll be glad to help you. May I ask who's calling?"
"What's the address?" "What's your telephone number?" "What's the telephone number?"	"May I have your street address, Mr. Jones?" "May I have your telephone number, Mr. Smith?" "Do you know the telephone number, Mr. Jones?"
"What do you want to talk to him about?" "What information do you want?"	"Mr. Jones is not in at the moment. May I help you?" "May I help you?"
"You'll have to check that with Mr. Smith." "You'll have to talk to Smith about that."	"Mr. Smith, our stylist, handles that. May I transfer you?" "Mr. Smith handles that. May I transfer you?" "Mr. Smith handles that. If you wish, I will refer it to him and have him call you."
"I don't know anything about that."	"I am sorry, but our stylist is not in today. May he call you tomorrow?" "If you wish, I will refer the matter to the proper person and ask him to call you."
"I don't know what you are talking about."	"I'm not sure that I understand your problem, Mr. Jones." "I want to be sure I get this right. Would you mind repeating that, Mr. Williams?"
"Speak up, please."	"I'm sorry, I cannot hear you. Could you speak a little louder, please?"

DON'T SAY:	DO SAY:
"We can't do that for you until tomorrow."	"We'll do this for you just as soon as possible, Mr. Perkins. Will tomorrow be all right?" "I'm sorry, but we won't be able to do that for you until tomorrow. Will that be satisfactory?" "We'll be able to schedule this for you for tomorrow."
"You didn't talk to me." "I didn't take your call."	"I'm sorry, Mr. Smith, some other clerk must have talked to you on this, but I'll be glad to take care of it for you."
"If you don't send in your duplicate bill number, we don't know where to apply the payment."	"We would appreciate your sending the bill stubs with your checks. Then we will have the bill number, and we can apply the payments properly."
"What's your duplicate bill number?"	"Would you give me the account number shown at the top of your bill, please?"
"The bill is for 9/5 to 10/5."	"The bill is for the period of September 5th to October 5th."
"Your bill is being reviewed now."	"I'm sorry, but our accountant is working on our books today. Can we call you in a few days about it, Mr. Brown?"
"You'll have to pay . . ." "You are charged . . ."	"Your balance is . . ."
"Wait a minute." "Just a minute." "Hold the line." (Nothing said before leaving line.)	"Would you please hold the line a moment while I check this for you?" "It will take a little time to check. Could I call you back, Mr. Brown?" "Will you hold the line please, while I find out about that for you?" "Will you excuse me just a moment, please? I would like to consult our records on this." "I am sorry, but it will take a little time to get that information. If you wish, I will call you as soon as I have it." "Would you like me to call you as soon as I can get that information, or do you prefer to wait?"

DON'T SAY:	DO SAY:
	"It will probably take a few minutes to check that for you. Would you like to wait, or may I call you as soon as I get it for you?"
	"Do you mind waiting while I check that for you?"
"You pay . . ."	"There is a charge for . . ."
"You'll have to bring in your bills."	"It would help clarify this if we could go over your bills and receipts with you, Mr. White. Could you bring them along the next time you call at our shop?"
(After keeping someone waiting on the line:) "That went out this morning."	"I have the information for you now." "Thank you for waiting, Mr. Smith." "I'm sorry to have kept you waiting so long, Mr. Jones."
"The price will be . . ."	
"You have to . . ." "You must . . ." "It's required . . ." "It's necessary . . ."	"We would like to have . . ." "Would it be convenient for you to . . ."
"Tell Mr. Smith to call Mr. Brown."	"Will you ask Mr. Smith to call Bob Brown, please?"
"He's in conference. . ."	"He's in a meeting . . ." "He's talking on another line." "He's talking to someone else right now. May I help you, or may I have him call you?"
"I don't handle that, you'll have to talk to someone else."	"May I refer you to Mr. Williams, who does all our buying?" "May I refer you to Mr. Jones, our stylist?" "May I transfer your call to Mr. Williams, who will check your account?"
"You'll have to call for an appointment."	"May I refer you to Mr. Lawrence, who will be pleased to make the appointment you want?"
"I have nothing to do with hiring people."	"Mr. Williams personally handles all personnel matters. May I transfer you to his phone?"

AVOID THE FOLLOWING EXPRESSIONS:

Bye, bye

Be seeing you.

To be truthful

Okay.

We don't know whether we are coming or going.

Oke doke.

Goodbye now.

All righty.

Lady.

Watcha say?

Ma'm.

Yah.

TO BE SUCCESSFUL

In addition to being well-groomed and proficient in your work, you must learn to do the little things that will make patrons like you. Have you done a good deed today? If not, try tomorrow.

BUSINESS LAW FOR THE BARBER-STYLING SHOP

A barber-styling shop may be owned and operated by an **individual,** a **partnership,** or a **corporation.** Before deciding which type of ownership is most desirable, one should be acquainted with the relative merits of each.

Individual Ownership
1. The proprietor is boss and manager.
2. The proprietor can determine policies and make decisions.
3. The proprietor receives all profits and bears all losses.

Partnership
1. More capital is available for investment.
2. The combined ability and experience of each partner makes it easier to share work and responsibilities and make decisions.
3. Profits are equally shared.
4. Each partner assumes unlimited liability for debts and bankruptcy.

Corporation
1. A charter has to be obtained from the state.
2. A corporation is subject to taxation and regulation by the state.
3. The management resides in a board of directors who determine policies and make decisions in accordance with the constitution of the charter.
4. The dividing of profits is proportionate to the number of shares of stock possessed by each stockholder.
5. The stockholder is not personally responsible for losses or bankruptcy.

Before Buying Or Selling A Barber-Styling Shop
1. A written purchase and sale agreement should be formulated in order to prevent any misunderstandings or errors between the contracting parties.
2. For safe keeping and enforcement, the written agreement should be placed in the hands of an impartial third person who is to deliver the agreement to the grantee (one to whom the property is transferred) upon the fulfillment of the specified contract.
3. The buyer or seller should take and sign a complete statement of inventory (goods, fixtures, etc.) and the value of each article.
4. If there is a transfer of chattel mortgage, notes, lease, and bill of sale, an investigation should be made to determine any default in the payment of debts.
5. Consult your lawyer for additional guidance.

A buyer should check equipment prices against cost of new equipment to avoid overpayments for used equipment. Failure to do this is a common fault of the new barber-stylist desiring to start a business. The result is overpayment on the purchase.

Goodwill in a barber-styling shop is difficult to buy or sell.

An Agreement To Buy An Established Barber-Styling Shop Should Include
1. Correct identity of owner.
2. True representations concerning the value and inducements offered to buy the shop.
3. Use of shop's name and reputation for a definite period of time.

4. A written agreement. An understanding that the seller will not compete with the prospective owner within a reasonable distance from present location.

Protection In Making A Lease
1. Secure exemption of fixtures or appliances which may be attached to the store or loft, so that they can be removed without violating the lease.
2. Insert into lease an agreement relative to necessary renovations, such as painting, plumbing, fixtures and electrical installation.
3. Secure option from landlord to assign lease to another person in the event of the sale of the shop.

Protection Against Fire, Theft And Lawsuits
1. Employ honest and able employees and keep premises securely locked.
2. Follow safety precautions to prevent fire, injury and lawsuits. Liability, fire and burglary insurance should be obtained.
3. Do not violate the medical practice law of your state by attempting to diagnose, treat or cure disease.
4. Become thoroughly familiar with the law and sanitary code of your city and state.
5. Keep accurate records of number of workers, salaries, length of employment and Social Security numbers for various state and federal laws affecting the social welfare of employees.

Remember — Ignorance of the Law is No Excuse for its Violation.

WARNING

DO NOT HAVE BUSINESS TRANSACTIONS WITH A TOTAL STRANGER, AND NEVER PAY A STRANGER CASH. NEVER MAKE OUT A CHECK TO AN INDIVIDUAL WHO IS WORKING FOR A FIRM; MAKE CHECK PAYABLE TO THE FIRM.

FIRST AID

Emergencies arise in every line of business, and a knowledge of first aid measures is invaluable to the shop manager and staff.

A physician (or emergency ambulance) should be called as soon as possible after any accident has occurred, both as a courtesy to the client and as a protection to the shop. There are certain first aid treatments, however, that the layman can give while awaiting medical assistance. Have a well-equipped first aid kit where it is within easy access. When possible the shop owner, manager, and employees should take a course in first aid.

For more information about emergency care, consult the latest edition of the First Aid Manual published by the American Red Cross.

Abrasions. When the skin is cut or broken by accident, an antiseptic, such as tincture of iodine, hydrogen peroxide, or mercurochrome, should be applied.

Burns. Burns may be caused by electricity or flames, while scalds usually are due to exposure to hot liquids or live steam. Burns are classified as first degree, characterized by redness; second degree, having watery blisters; and third degree, involving deeper structures of the flesh with possible charring of tissues. In case of accidental burns, see that the client gets immediate medical attention by a physician.

A quick, safe, and temporarily effective method of treating burns is to immediately apply ice or cold water to the affected area.

Electric shock. The clothing should be loosened and the client removed to a cool place. The head should be raised and the tongue drawn forward to prevent strangulation. Apply artificial respiration. Stimulants should not be given.

Heat exhaustion. Heat exhaustion is a general functional depression due to heat. It is characterized by a cool, moist skin and collapse. Clothing should be loosened and the client removed to a cool, dark, quiet place. The client should be kept lying down for several hours, as rest and quiet will hasten recovery.

Nose bleed. Nose bleed is a hemorrhage from the nose, and is treated by loosening the collar and applying pads saturated with cool water to the face and back of the neck.

Foreign body in the eye. If this is under the lower lid, pull the lid down gently while the client looks up. If the hair or speck of dust can be seen, it should be removed with the corner of a clean, moistened handkerchief or with a twist of clean cotton.

If it is under the upper lid, pull the lid down over the eye and the speck should then be apparent when the client opens his or her eye again. Remove in same way as above.

Fainting. Fainting is caused by a lack of blood flow to the brain, bad air, indigestion, nervous condition, unpleasant odors, etc., and is characterized by pallor and loss of muscular control. There is a temporary suspension of respiration and circulation. If there is a sign of fainting, and before it actually occurs, have the client hold his/her head between the knees, as this action may check the faintness by causing the blood to flow quickly to the head.

Treatment for fainting consists of loosening all tight clothing, being sure there is fresh air in the room, and placing the client in a reclining position with the head slightly lower than the body. If the client is conscious, hold aromatic spirits of ammonia near his/her nose or offer stimulants, such as hot coffee, tea, or milk. If the client is unconscious, apply cold applications to the face, chest and over the heart. Do not dash cold water in the client's face.

Epileptic fit. An epileptic fit is a nerve disorder characterized by unconsciousness, convulsions, contortions of the face, foaming at the mouth, and rolling of the eyes. In such a case, call for immediate medical attention.

Emergency treatment consists of lying client on the side and fixing a wad of cotton between the teeth to prevent biting of the tongue. Mild stimulants may be administered in moderation after recovery. If the client falls into a deep sleep after the attack, he/she should not be disturbed, but allowed to awaken naturally.

In case of emergency. Every shop should have information that may be needed in case of an emergency posted or placed (in clear view) near the telephone. The owner of the shop or manager should have the names, addresses, and telephone numbers of employees on file in case of an emergency. The file that is kept for regular clients also should have information that might be needed in case of an emergency. Addresses and telephone numbers for the following services should be placed near the shop telephone: fire station; police (local and state); emergency ambulance; nearest hospital emergency room; doctors; taxi service; telephone company and telephone numbers of persons and organizations that provide service.

Utility service companies, such as electricity, water, heat, air-conditioning, etc., also should be posted. Additional information to be included are the names and telephone numbers of the owner and/or manager, custodian and others who might need to be called if something goes wrong in the shop.

Each employee should know where exits are located and how to evacuate a building quickly in case of fire or other emergencies. Fire extinguishers should be placed where they can be reached easily, and employees should know how to use them. A well-stocked first aid kit should be kept within easy reach.

ARTIFICIAL RESPIRATION

To deal with occurrences such as severe electric shock, protracted fainting, poisoning, and gas suffocation, the most currently acceptable methods are mouth-to-mouth breathing or mouth-to-nose breathing.

Procedure

1. Place client on a flat surface.
2. Place one hand on back of client's neck, one hand on forehead, and tilt the head backward until the chin is pointed upward.
3. Lift client's lower jaw forward to move the tongue away from the throat.
4. Pinch client's nose closed.

5. Seal your mouth on client's mouth and give four quick breaths.
6. Listen for client's breathing and check pulse. (Pulse can be checked by placing fingers on carotid artery.)
7. If there is no pulse, continue giving at least one breath every five seconds until you see client's chest rising and falling.
8. For mouth-to-nose breathing, follow the same procedure as for mouth-to-mouth breathing, except that you close the client's mouth with your hand and blow into the nose.

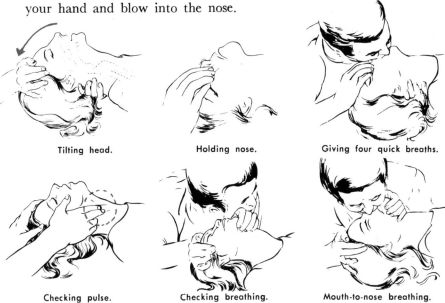

Tilting head.   Holding nose.   Giving four quick breaths.

Checking pulse.   Checking breathing.   Mouth-to-nose breathing.

BREATHING OBSTRUCTION (ABDOMINAL THRUST)

If client's breathing becomes obstructed due to choking, immediate help must be given.

Procedure

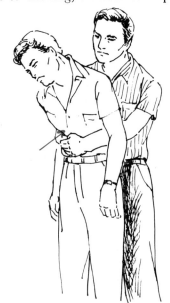

1. Standing behind client, hit client rapidly between the shoulder blades.
2. Wrap your arms around client's waist. Make a fist and place the thumb just below the breastbone.
3. Hold your fist with your other hand and press it into client's abdomen, using four quick upward thrusts.
4. Repeat the procedure if necessary.

Positioning hand.   Positioning hand.   Thrusting upward.

QUESTIONS ON BARBER-STYLING SHOP MANAGEMENT

1. Name eight essential functions performed by a barber-styling shop owner or manager.

2. List three important shop policies which should be explained to new employees.

3. Name three forms of ownership.

4. What is the best location for a barber-styling shop?

5. Of what protection is a lease for a barber-styling shop?

6. What is the best form of advertising?

7. Of what value are records in the barber-styling shop?

8. Name at least seven uses for a telephone in the barber-styling shop.

9. What are four basic rules to follow when using a telephone?

FIRST AID

1. When an accident occurs, when should a physician be called?

2. What should be done when the skin is accidentally cut?

3. What causes heat exhaustion?

4. How is a nose bleed treated?

Chapter 31

SELLING IN THE BARBER-STYLING SHOP

INTRODUCTION

The success of any barber-styling business is based upon the professional skill and selling ability of its personnel.

The revenue of the barber-styling shop is derived from the performance of the various services and the sale of grooming aids. In both of these areas the ability of the professional barber-stylist to sell additional services and/or grooming supplies will greatly influence earnings.

Today, more than ever, successful American men are good-grooming conscious and are interested in improving their appearances for both social and business reasons. To this end, they spend many millions of dollars each year in the barber-styling shop for professional services and the purchase of grooming supplies for home use. The progressive barber-stylist can and should obtain an ever-increasing share of these expenditures by understanding and applying the principles of sales psychology and salesmanship.

The professional barber-stylist, in the capacity of friend and advisor, is in a very favorable position to render a complete grooming service to clients. Having the confidence of his or her clients, the stylist can sell grooming supplies and accessories, as well as professional services. He or she has the important advantage of being in the position of not only **giving** professional services, but also is **trained to advise** as to the selection and application of proper grooming supplies.

Financial success in the barber-styling shop may depend, to a great degree, upon the effort expended by the practitioner to sell grooming supplies, as well as additional services. The keynote of the modern shop is personal service. The professional artisan who gives the best complete service has the greatest opportunity to develop the qualities which make for success.

PSYCHOLOGY OF SELLING

Successful selling in the barber-styling shop is dependent upon a number of elements. A very important one is the understanding of the psychology of selling, or, to put it another way, "why people buy."

The psychology of selling is simply establishing a clear and definite understanding of the patron's needs and desires. To overcome sales resistance and to be able to satisfy his patrons, the barber-stylist should have a fair knowledge of the psychological factors which control the patron's actions and behavior.

It does not matter how good a service or a grooming aid may be; unless the client feels a need for it, there will be no sale. In order to effectuate a sale, it becomes necessary that the barber-stylist create a need or a desire for a particular item or service. He or she must arouse the client's interest to the extent that the client wishes to make the purchase or receive the service.

PLACE YOURSELF IN THE PATRON'S POSITION

The barber-stylist now finds it necessary to place himself or herself in the position of the client and to try to think for the client. This requires a great deal of imagination and perception on the part of the practitioner. He or she must try to visualize the manner of reasoning of the client. The stylist must formulate clean, vivid and logical thoughts as to what would motivate this particular client to buy either the service or supplies.

THE MOTIVATION TO BUY

Before a barber-stylist can properly sell, he or she must have a thorough understanding of what motivates a client to purchase either a product or a service. Some of these motivating factors are:

1. The desire to improve his or her appearance or well-being.
2. The drive to obtain recognition or praise from others.
3. The wish to improve his or her social relationships.
4. The desire to retain a youthful appearance in order to improve business and promotional opportunities.
5. The desire to get the most value for his or her money.
6. The appreciation of beauty and the wish to impress the opposite sex.
7. The desire to improve his or her own feeling of well being.

NEVER USE "HIGH-PRESSURE" TACTICS

Clients usually resent "high-pressure" selling tactics. The barber-stylist must, therefore, be careful in his or her efforts lest he or she antagonize instead of creating confidence. The approach must be subtle and friendly. His or her entire manner must be one of complete honesty and sincerity. Building up the client's confidence in the judgment of the practitioner creates a reservoir for many future sales.

Be neat, clean, attractive, and free from body odors and halitosis (bad breath).

Psychology in selling can be as important in the barber-styling shop as it is in the financial and trading world. A basic knowledge and understanding of the few simple principles set forth above may mean the difference between financial success and failure for the professional barber-stylist.

SELLING YOURSELF

Important as good service and good products may be, neither can be sold unless the barber-stylist first sells himself or herself. The real professional knows that primarily he or she must get the client to like him or her. It is not always an easy task to develop a good rapport with clients. It requires constant cheerfulness, patience and tolerance. It is the barber-stylist's responsibility to develop this feeling; the client does not have to make any effort in this direction.

EXTEND CLIENT EVERY COURTESY

The barber-stylist's selling power will increase progressively as he or she makes the client aware of a personal interest in the client's welfare. Treat each client with smiling friendliness and extend every courtesy to him or her. Attention to little details for the client's added comfort will be greatly appreciated. Barber-styling services may be obtained in many places; however, the personality behind the service is the factor which brings the client back.

DEVELOP A PLEASING PERSONALITY

Every person gives forth an atmosphere which either attracts or repels others. Since a pleasing personality is conducive to making friends and increasing sales, it is to the barber-stylist's interest to develop the qualities which contribute to an outstanding personality.

Maintain Sound Physical Health

The first requirement for a good personality is sound physical health. A healthy body displays vitality and strength capable of withstanding the demands and rigors required of the professional barber-stylist. A healthy body enables the mind to function properly and to think effectively. Physical well-being is mandatory if the barber-stylist is to develop a pleasing personality.

Besides developing a healthy body, the barber-stylist must be especially careful of his or her personal appearance and hygiene. A neat, clean and well-fitting uniform helps to enhance the morale and confidence of the practitioner and attracts clients. An attractive appearance and correct posture serve to impress shop clients.

Avoid Obnoxious Odors

It is most necessary to avoid body odors and bad breath. Daily bathing and the use of a good mouth wash and deodorants are absolutely necessary to maintain proper appearance and hygiene.

Be a Living Example

The barber-stylist's own well-groomed hair, hands and clean-shaven face serve to act as subtle influences and arouse the client's interest in similar services. The stylist should be a living example of what' he or she is trying to sell. The barber-stylist should use the services and grooming aids sold in the shop to serve as living examples of their benefits.

A Smile Opens the Door

A pleasant smile is the key which opens even the most stubborn door. The most difficult situations are often corrected by a smile. It is very difficult to be disagreeable to a person who greets you with a smile. A congenial smile makes the work of selling agreeable both to the practitioner and to the client.

Maintain Your Dignity

In order that the barber-stylist's personality be attractive and pleasing, it is necessary to combine dignity and charm of manner with courtesy and cleanliness. Dignity and poise do not permit loud and boisterous laughter, arguments, loss of temper, profanity or gossip.

Never Offend Anyone

To develop a pleasing personality, the barber-stylist should talk, act and express himself without hurting or offending anyone. To influence clients the stylist must be forgetful of self and have an interested and sympathetic attitude. The more effort exerted by the barber-stylist to please his or her clients, the better chance he or she has of retaining their continued patronage and increasing sales.

The three most important factors in developing a pleasing personality and selling one's self to his clients are a pleasant smile, a courteous manner and a neat, clean appearance.

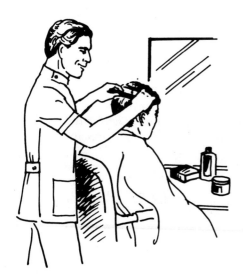

During a haircut you have the opportunity to examine the hair and scalp.

SELLING ADDITIONAL SERVICES

The primary function of the barber-styling shop is to sell service. Shop income, to a large degree, depends upon the quantity and quality of the service being given. The professional barber-stylist can increase his own income, as well as that of the shop, by courteously selling as many services as possible to each client.

ADDITIONAL SERVICES MUST BE AVAILABLE

It is difficult for a barber-styling shop to be financially successful just by selling haircuts. There are numerous additional services which should be offered to clients that will bring in a great deal of additional revenue. If a shop is forced to depend solely upon the income from haircuts, it would be difficult to survive. Additional income from extra services may mean the difference between "just getting along" and doing well financially.

KNOWLEDGE OF ADDITIONAL SERVICES REQUIRED

In order to be able to successfully sell additional services to clients it is necessary that the barber-stylist have a thorough knowledge of the services available. The stylist must not only know of each service, but must also know how to administer it and the benefits to be derived. He or she should also be observant and alert enough to know when a client is in need of some added service and be able to explain why.

USE TACT

Tact is doing and saying the right thing at the right time. The need for tactfulness cannot be stressed too strongly. Many good clients have been lost to a shop by the undiplomatic, blundering tactics of an over-zealous practitioner. In trying to sell an additional service the barber-stylist should above all, be tactful, diplomatic and considerate.

BE DIPLOMATIC

Additional services can be diplomatically suggested with careful consideration and attention. Engaging a client in conversation in which you carefully point out some additional treatment or service, and explaining the benefits to be received, could very well be a successful approach. Clients may feel flattered by the interest that the artisan is showing in their welfare and well-being.

Tact will succeed where abruptness would only annoy and offend the client.

The client considers the barber-stylist to be an expert in good grooming. The client looks to the stylist for suggestions and advice. It is the responsibility of the barber-stylist to be well-informed on all grooming matters so that he or she can give correct advice.

PRACTITIONER MUST BE COMPLETELY SINCERE

It is advisable in selling any service to be quite frank and explain that best results are obtained from consistent treatments. One treatment or service can, of course, be helpful; but for lasting benefits, services should be received regularly and consistently. Patrons are influenced by frankness and honesty and thus far better results will be obtained in selling additional services.

NEVER ARGUE

It is important to remember, when serving a client, that the barber-stylist can never win an argument. A client never returns to a shop where the practitioners are insolent or argumentative. If a barber-stylist is of the argumentative type, his or her career in an industry which is based almost exclusively on service is apt to be short-lived.

To the wide awake, progressive barber-stylist who can combine aggressiveness with courtesy, knowledge and willingness to work, the selling of services offers an almost unlimited field for additional income.

HELPFUL SUGGESTIONS ON HOW TO SELL ADDITIONAL SERVICES

The modern trend in haircutting is to develop new styles and methods more suitable to the individual. Clients are becoming increasingly aware of these new techniques. The barber-stylist can very easily recommend a new hairstyle or haircut to clients. Suggestions to be offered are:

1. **A razor cut,** which would give a more even and finer blend.
2. **Air-waving,** which would create a new and more youthful style.
3. **Finger waving,** which would create a completely new style.
4. **Hair straightening** to make hair more manageable and permit more modern styling.

Shaving

The professional barber-stylist has the opportunity to observe the condition of the client's skin while shaving him. The stylist may tactfully suggest one of the following:

1. Plain facial—beneficial for stimulating action on skin and for toning facial muscles
2. Facial for correcting dry skin condition
3. Facial for correcting oily skin condition
4. Facial for correcting acne condition
5. Facial to remove blackheads
6. Hot oil mask for correcting dry skin condition
7. Clay pack to prevent wrinkling of skin

Mustache and/or Beard

If the client wears a mustache and/or beard, you might ask him if he desires to have them trimmed or styled.

Shampooing

While cutting a client's hair, you may tactfully suggest that a shampoo might be beneficial and refreshing. You can readily observe the condition of his or her hair and appropriately suggest one of the following:
1. Shampoo for dry hair and scalp
2. Shampoo for oily hair and scalp
3. Liquid cream shampoo, to make the hair feel softer
4. Liquid dry shampoo, in the event that water cannot be used due to illness
5. Hair tonic with or without scalp steam application

Scalp Treatments

After observing the condition of the client's hair and scalp, perhaps one of the following treatments would be more desirable. The power of suggestion may guide the client to accept your recommendation, since you cannot just ask, "Do you want a scalp treatment instead of a shampoo?" The use of one or more electrical appliances for hair and scalp treatments is appreciated by the client, especially when these are professionally handled. They include:
1. Normal scalp treatment which is invigorating, prevents dandruff and retards hair loss
2. Treatment for dry scalp and hair
3. Treatment for oily scalp and hair
4. Treatment for dandruff
5. Treatment for alopecia (baldness)
6. Series of corrective treatments (once a week for several weeks)

Rinses

It would be a good time to suggest one of the following rinses in connection with a shampoo:
1. If hard water is used, then an acid rinse should be recommended.
2. If the client has dandruff, recommend that the shampoo be finished with a dandruff rinse which might help the condition.
3. If the client has discolored grey hair, recommend a bluing rinse, to neutralize the yellowish condition of the hair.

Hair Coloring

A client with grey hair is most receptive to suggestions for improving his or her appearance. Suggest a **color rinse** that would match the client's own natural shade, and which can be rinsed out in the event he or she does not like it. Mention that a service charge will be made only if he or she wants to leave the rinse on.

Remember, if the client likes the color rinse, and members of his or her family encourage him or her that the color becomes the client, he or she may later want to try semi-permanent color . . . and then eventually go into permanent color.

Hairpieces

Men are becoming increasingly interested in acquiring hairpieces to cover bald areas. Carefully suggesting to a client that a hairpiece might make him look much younger, and even having him try one on, may result in a sale.

Types of hairpieces available are:
1. Hairpiece without lace front
2. Hairpiece with lace front
3. Partial hairpiece
4. Partial fill-in hairpiece
5. Facial hairpieces
   a) Mustache
   b) Beard
   c) Sideburns

SELLING GROOMING SUPPLIES

The sale of good-grooming aids and supplies properly belongs in the barber-styling shop and should go hand in hand with the sale of services. The purchase of such items as shaving creams, powders, lotions, razor blades, etc., should be done in the barber-styling shop, the center for good grooming.

Many millions of dollars are spent each year for the purchase of grooming supplies in drug stores and super-markets. There is no proper reason why these items should be purchased in the drug store or supermarket, except that these tradesmen have made the products available. Barber-stylists are passing up this very ready and very lucrative source of income through sheer carelessness and neglect.

WIDE ASSORTMENT OF GROOMING AIDS AVAILABLE

Barber-styling shops should maintain a wide assortment of good quality grooming aids to meet the demands and tastes of their clients.

Clean, tasteful display cabinets should be placed in strategic areas in the shop to attract the attention of the clients. It takes very little additional effort for the stylist to call a client's attention to the variety of grooming supplies available. The stylist should talk-up proper products to clients and call their attention to new products and the qualities of each.

BARBER-STYLIST BEST QUALIFIED TO ADVISE ON GROOMING

No one is better able to explain to a client various products and the benefits to be received from their use than the barber-stylist. The stylist however, should acquire a complete knowledge of each product, its contents and its reaction on skin and hair. Thus, he or she may give expert advice to clients as to the proper products for their use. Clients soon learn to look for and appreciate the expert advice they receive from the professional barber-stylist.

SALE OF ONE ITEM LEADS TO OTHER SALES

The sale of one item inevitably leads to the sale of others providing, of course, that they are available. Once the client begins to buy grooming supplies in the barber-styling shop, the buying habit will continue as long as high quality products and services are available.

In order to receive the maximum returns from the sale, the inventory must be properly maintained at all times. Re-order regularly to assure a fresh and complete stock. Display cabinets must be kept attractive looking to create client interest and are often a subtle inducement to purchase.

REMEMBER—Dusty, sloppy displays never promote sales. Therefore, dusting and straightening out the display cabinet at regular intervals **is a must.**

LIST OF GROOMING SUPPLIES

The well equipped barber-styling shop should have available display cabinets featuring the following items to supply the grooming requirements of all clients.

A. **Shaving Supplies**
 1. **Razors**
   (a) Safety razors
   (b) Razor blades
 2. **Creams**
   (a) Brushless shaving cream
   (b) Aerosol shaving cream
   (c) Brush lather cream
   (d) Lather brushes
 3. **Lotions**
   (a) Pre-shave lotion
   (b) After-shave lotion
   (c) Bay rum
 4. **Powders and Styptics**
   (a) After-shave powder
   (b) Styptic powder
   (c) Styptic pencils
   (d) Liquid styptics

B. **Shampoos**
 1. Regular shampoo
 2. Dry hair shampoo
 3. Oily hair shampoo
 4. Dandruff shampoo

C. **Hair Supplies**
 1. Hair combs
 2. Hair conditioners
 3. Hair dressings
   (a) Non-oily
   (b) Hair oils
   (c) Pomades
   (d) Hair creams
 4. Styling lotions
 5. Hair spray
 6. Butch wax sticks and jars

D. **Mustache Supplies**
 1. Mustache wax
 2. Mustache pomade

E. **Hairpiece Accessories**
 1. Spirit gum
 2. Cleaners
   (a) Jars, bottles or cans
   (b) Aerosol containers
 3. Double-sided tape

F. **Miscellaneous Supplies**
 1. Face lotions
 2. Suntan lotions
 3. Deodorants
 4. Nail clippers
 5. Electric razor
    pre-shave lotion

SELLING THE BARBER-STYLING SHOP TO CLIENTS

The location of the barber-styling shop is most important to insure the maximum income. The shop should be situated in a convenient area, properly illuminated and easy to find. A ground floor shop is usually far more accessible to patrons.

KEEP CLIENTS INTERESTED IN SHOP

It is in the interest of all shop personnel to keep clients interested in the shop and in the atmosphere which surrounds it.

It is to the advantage of the owner to have the shop furnished with the most modern equipment available. Even if the service is efficient, but the equipment is antiquated, the client is tempted to go where everything is modern, comfortable and attractive. It is natural for clients to be attracted to the shop where comfort, convenience and speed are the policy.

Every client is a potential source of new business. If a client is pleased with the shop, the services and treatment, he or she will not hesitate to recommend it to others.

SHOP MUST BE KEPT CLEAN AND SANITARY

A barber-styling shop must be kept clean and sanitary at all times. The shop should never be permitted to deteriorate to a dirty condition. Shampoo basins must be kept clean and not encrusted with dirty soap suds. Cut hair caught around the sprays or in the drain must be cleaned regularly.

Floors must be swept regularly during the course of the day. Solutions and supplies must be kept covered, and each client furnished with clean towels. Combs, brushes and all implements must be sanitized after each use. A dirty shop drives patrons away and may actually spread disease.

BE CONSIDERATE OF CLIENT'S EMOTIONS

In addition to making every effort to protect the physical well-being of the shop client, consideration must be given to the client's nerves and emotions. The barber-styling shop should be a place for pleasant relaxation and rest. The shop that retains the interest of clients is one where the atmosphere is restful and quiet. In order to sell the shop and its services, it is important to eliminate all disagreeable and grating noises. Clients will very often tolerate somewhat less efficiency if they can receive, in exchange, tranquility and relaxation while receiving treatments.

MAINTAIN OVERALL FRIENDLY ATMOSPHERE

The overall atmosphere of the shop is a most important factor in determining success or failure. A shop that emanates an unfriendly, cold or disagreeable atmosphere cannot retain its clientele. No client will return to a shop where the personnel are unfriendly or uncooperative in any way. If repeat business is desired, it is important that all barber-stylists in the shop cultivate a friendly atmosphere. They should learn to smile and actually mean it. Barber-stylists who glare or grumble serve to drive clients to other shops and actually endanger the survival of the business.

PHYSICAL EQUIPMENT AND FIXTURES PLANNED FOR CLIENT'S COMFORT

Improper lighting, which may cause irritation to the client's eyes, or improper ventilation contribute to driving clients from the shop.

Poor ventilation may not only annoy clients, but may cause the barber-stylist to become sluggish and listless. Air conditioning has the advantage of permitting changes in the quality and quantity of air brought into the shop.

When planning a barber-styling shop it is indeed very important to consider the physical arrangement in order to attract and keep clients and to permit barber-stylists to work in pleasant and healthful surroundings.

SUMMARY

The financial success of the barber-styling shop is dependent upon many factors.

The barber-stylist must have a definite and complete understanding of the psychology of selling in the shop.

Before a professional barber-stylist is prepared to successfully operate in the shop, the stylist must sell himself or herself to clients—as to personal appearance and proper grooming.

It requires more than competent professional skills to attain financial success as a barber-stylist. The stylist must be capable of tactfully selling needed additional services to clients. The sale of additional services means additional income to the shop.

A great deal of additional income may be received in the shop by the sale of grooming supplies. Sincere effort should be made by employees to promote and sell grooming supplies in the shop. This type of business should bring additional income to the barber-styling shop instead of diverting it to drug stores and supermarkets.

In order to build a successful barber-styling business, it is necessary to build a shop that is accepted by clients. It must be attractive, healthful and pleasant to both clients and employees. It should be an enjoyable experience for a person to receive barber-styling services in a modern and pleasant environment.

QUESTIONS ON SELLING IN THE BARBER-STYLING SHOP

1. What is meant by "Psychology of selling?"
2. List seven (7) factors that motivate a client to purchase either a product or service.
3. Why is it important to first "sell yourself?"
4. Why is it important to sell the barber-stylist shop to clients?
5. What is the foundation of good salesmanship?

Chapter 32
LICENSING LAWS

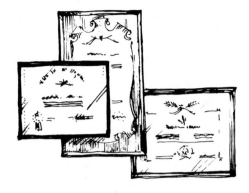

LICENSE LAW REVIEW QUESTIONS

Although the barber-styling license laws and Barber State Board rules differ in the various states, there are a number of basic license law concepts that are the same in all licensing jurisdictions. The following questions with answers are designed to review such general concepts.

1. **What government body is responsible for the efficient and orderly administration of the barber-styling license law?**
    The Barber State Board.

2. **Where does the authority to conduct disciplinary hearings rest?**
    With the Barber State Board.

3. **What additional authority is given to the Barber State Board in order to properly administer the barber-styling license law?**
    The power to issue rules and regulations.

4. **What is the primary objective of the barber-styling license law?**
    To protect the public.

5. **What is the objective of the barber-styling license examination?**
    To evaluate a license applicant's competency.

6. **How may the State Board abuse the intent of the barber-styling license law?**
    By using the law to limit the number of licensees.

7. **What is one of the important personal requirements of an applicant for a barber-styling license?**
    That he/she be of good moral character.

8. **Under what circumstances should a barber-stylist be forbidden to perform services upon patrons?**
    When he/she is suffering from a communicable disease.

9. **How may the State Board discipline a barber-stylist?**
    By revocation or suspension of his/her license.

10. **What protection does the licensee have against unlawful action of the State Board?**
    The barber-stylist is protected by the laws of the State.

11. **What action must be taken by the State Board before it can revoke or suspend a license?**
    It must grant the licensee a hearing.

12. **What can be done to a licensee who violates the provisions of the barber-styling license law?**
    He/she can be cited for disciplinary action.

13. **Of what is a person guilty if he/she acts as a barber-stylist without obtaining a license?**
    Of practicing in an unlawful manner.

14. **What recourse is available to a barber-stylist whose license has been suspended or revoked?**
    The right to appeal to the courts.

15. **Of what crime is a person guilty when he/she is convicted of violating any of the provisions of the license law?**
    He/she is guilty of a misdemeanor.

16. **What purpose is served by the periodic inspection of barber-styling shops?**
    To be certain that they are complying with sanitary requirements.

17. **Of what is a barber-stylist guilty if he/she willfully fails to display his/her license or certificate?**
    Guilty of violation of the barber-styling law.

18. **What does the law require be done with a barber-stylist's license that has been suspended or revoked?**
    It must be surrendered to the Barber State Board.

19. **How may the State Board punish a barber-stylist who is guilty of immoral behavior?**
    It may suspend or revoke his/her license.

20. **How may a barber-stylist guilty of gross malpractice be punished by the State Board?**
    By suspension or revocation of his/her license.

21. **Who is responsible for posting the barber-styling law and/or the State Board rules and regulations in the barber-styling shop?**
    The shop owner.

22. **Who practices barber-styling under the constant and direct supervision of a licensed barber-stylist?**
    A barber apprentice.

Chapter 33
HISTORY OF
BARBERING

The history of hairstyling and barbering is deeply rooted in the progress of mankind. Archeological examinations reveal that some crude forms of facial and hair adornment were practiced even by prehistoric people as far back as the glacial age. Ancient relics reveal that as early as 6000 years ago the Egyptian nobility had become regular patrons for hairstyling and barbering services.

As civilization advanced, the practice of hairstyling and barbering developed from its insignificant beginning to a recognized vocation. To study the history of hairstyling and barbering is to learn to appreciate the accomplishments and the position of high esteem attained by the early practitioners. The rich cultural heritage they developed should be the basis for the great prestige and respect they deserve for their service to the public.

Archeological studies reveal that primitive man had devised a number of crude instruments with which to cut and shape hair. These very simple implements were usually formed from sharpened flints or oyster shells. To this very day the primitive tribes of Polynesia still use similar objects for cutting the hair.

SUPERSTITIONS

The early beginnings of barbering were steeped in strange superstitions.

There was a general belief among many savages that people could be bewitched by hair clippings. Hence, the privilege of haircutting was reserved for the priest or medicine man of the tribe.

The Irish peasantry believed that if hair cuttings were burned or buried no evil spirits would haunt the individual.

Among the American Indians, the belief existed that the hair had a vital connection with the body, and that "anyone possessed of a lock of hair of another might work his will on that individual." Thus, the Indian custom of "scalping" had its origin in this superstition.

It was the widespread ancient belief in the magic influence of long-haired persons which caused Roman judges to order the hair of Christian martyrs cut off before putting them to death.

477

ORIGIN OF THE BARBER

As far back as four hundred years before Christ, shaving was introduced by the Macedonians. Later it spread to Egypt and all Eastern countries, including China. The word "barber" is derived from the Latin word "barba" meaning beard. The word "tonsorial" in Latin means the cutting, clipping and trimming of hair with shears or cutting with a razor. In fact, barbers have often been referred to as "Tonsorial Artists."

BEAUTIFYING THE BODY

The Egyptians were the first to cultivate beauty in an extravagant fashion. Excavations from tombs have brought to light such relics as combs, brushes, mirrors and cosmetics. Eye paint was the most popular of all cosmetics. Slaves enhanced the beauty of the Egyptian ladies by applying perfumed oil to their skins and henna to their hair. Egyptian henna is still used on the hair to some extent even to this day.

SIGNIFICANCE OF THE BEARD

Although the importance of the beard belongs more with the past than with the present, nevertheless, it is interesting to note the various fashions and customs associated with it. A curious custom of the Middle Ages was that of imbedding three hairs from the king's beard in the wax of the seal. During the reign of Queen Elizabeth in England, it was fashionable to dye the beard and cut it into a variety of shapes.

In early times the beard was considered by almost all nations as a sign of wisdom, strength and manhood, and was carefully cherished as being almost sacred. Among the Orthodox Jews, the beard was regarded as a symbol of religious devotion. To cut off the beard was contrary to the Mosaic law. According to the Greek philosopher, Pythagoras, the hair was the source of the brain's inspiration and the cutting of the hair decreased intellectual capacity. In Rome, the first day of shaving (22nd birthday) was looked upon as a sign of manhood and was celebrated with great festivities.

The commands of certain rulers were at times responsible for the removal of beards. For instance, Alexander the Great ordered his soldiers to shave so that their enemies might not seize their beards in battle. After the Gauls were conquered, Julius Caesar compelled them to cut off their beards. Peter the Great made shaving compulsory by imposing a tax on beards.

In the spread of the Christian faith, long hair gradually came to be despised because it was considered sinful. Hence the clergy were directed to shave their beards. Among the Orthodox Jews, shaving of the beard was forbidden, but they used the scissors to remove all excess hair. The Moslems observed great care in trimming the beard after prayer and the hairs that fell out were carefully picked up and preserved for subsequent burial with the owner. The partial beard, commonly known as "goatee," has become popular in modern times.

Barbers first became popular in Rome about the year 296 B.C. In Greece, barbers became popular as early as 500 B.C.

GREEK AND ROMAN INFLUENCE

In Greece and Rome, hairstyling and barbering were highly developed arts. Persons of means were shaved by their valets. The common people frequented the barber shops, which were the resorts of loungers and newsmongers.

The Greeks and Romans gave considerable attention to beautifying the hair. Sparkling gems and hairpins of silver and gold adorned the elegant hairstyles of the Greek women. The Roman women often dyed their hair and some replaced their hair with fashionable wigs.

In ancient Rome, the color of a woman's hair indicated her rank. Women of the nobility tinted their hair red; those of the middle class colored their hair yellow; while women of the poorer classes were compelled to dye their hair black.

ENGLISH INFLUENCE

The ancient Britons were extremely proud of the length and beauty of their hair. Their yellow hair was brightened with washes composed of tallow, lime and the ashes of certain vegetables. The Danes and Anglo-Saxons also admired long, flowing locks. The young Danes were particularly attentive to dressing the hair, which they combed at least once a day in order to capture the affections of English ladies.

THE RISE AND FALL OF BARBER-SURGEONS

During the Middle Ages, the barbers not only practiced shaving, haircutting and hairdressing, but also dressed wounds and performed surgical operations. For this reason they were called barber-surgeons. Much of their experience was acquired from the monks, whom they assisted in the practice of surgery and medicine. The barber-surgeons formed their first organization in 1096, in France.

The barber-surgeons became quite numerous when Pope Alexander III forbade the clergy to shed blood in surgical operations. As a result of this decree, most of the surgery performed was done by barbers. The barbers did bloodletting and pulled teeth. In fact the only practice of dentistry was that performed by barbers.

To protect themselves, the Barbers' Company of London was organized in the thirteenth century. The object of this trade guild was to regulate the profession for the benefit of its members. One of the regulations passed was that no barber was to keep more than four apprentices in his establishment.

The Barbers' Company was ruled by a Master, and consisted of two classes of barbers, viz: those who practiced barbering and those who specialized in surgery. Under Edward III, the barbers made a complaint against unskilled practitioners in surgery. As a result, the court chose two Masters to inspect and rule the guild and give examinations to test the skill of applicants.

The sign of the barber-surgeon consisted of a striped pole from which was suspended a basin: the fillet around the pole indicating the bandage twisted around the arms previous to blood-letting and the basin the vessel for receiving blood. Another interpretation of the colors on the barber's pole was that red represented the blood, blue the veins, and white the bandage. The white represented the bandage before use. After they were used the bandages were washed and hung out to dry. The blood-stained bandages would blow and twist together forming a pattern similar to our modern barber pole. This sign, without the basin, has been generally retained by the modern hairstylist-barber.

Besides the Barbers' Company, there was also a Surgeons' Guild in England. There was reason to believe that competition and antagonism existed between these two organizations. In 1450, both groups were united by law for the purpose of fostering the science of surgery. A law was enacted that no one doing surgery should practice barbering and that no barber should practice any phase of surgery except the pulling of teeth. The long slumbering jealousy between the two guilds soon reached a climax. The surgeons harbored a dislike for a system under which diplomas were signed by Governors, two of whom were always barbers. Finally, in 1745 a bill was passed separating the barbers from the surgeons.

The barber-surgeons also flourished in France and in Germany. In 1371, a corporation was organized by the French barber-surgeons under the rule of the King's barber. With the advent of the French revolution, the corporation was dissolved. Wigs became so elaborate in the nineteenth century that a separate corporation of barbers was founded in France. Not until 1779 was a corporation formed in Prussia. This was disbanded in 1809 when new unions were started.

The Dutch and Swedish settlers in America brought with them barber-surgeons from their native countries to look after the well-being of the colonists. They not only shaved, but performed everyday medical and surgical procedures.

MODERN TRENDS

By the nineteenth and twentieth centuries, barbering was completely separated from religion and medicine, and began to take on an independent position. Rapid strides have been made in hairstyling and barbering since the invention of electricity, the development of better instruments for cutting hair and shaving beards, and advances in hygiene, chemistry and medicine.

With the exception of several counties in Alabama, all states have passed laws regulating the practice of hairstyling and barbering. The state boards are primarily interested in maintaining high standards of education and training, in order to assure competent and intelligent service. The schools, the unions, and the master barbers associations have cooperated in the enforcement of state laws and in the protection of the practitioners' rights and privileges.

Important discoveries which have improved the practice of hairstyling and barbering in recent times are as follows:
1. The use of electricity and electrical appliances in the hairstyling and barbering shop
2. The use of better professional implements
3. The improved practice of sanitation in the shop
4. The study of anatomy dealing with those parts of the body (face, head and neck) which are serviced by the hairstylist-barber
5. The study of cosmetic preparations used in connection with facial, scalp and hair treatments

The Journeymen Barbers' Union was organized in 1887, and the first convention was held on November 5, 1887, in Buffalo, New York.

The first barber school in the United States was started by A. B. Moler in Chicago, in 1893.

The first textbook on the subject of barbering was written by A. B. Moler in 1893. This text was "The Moler Manual of Barbering."

The first state to pass a barber license law was Minnesota in 1897.

The Associated Master Barbers of America was organized in 1924, in Chicago, Illinois. It adopted a Barber Code of Ethics in 1929 at its convention in St. Paul, Minnesota.

The National Association of Barber Schools was organized in 1927, in Cleveland, Ohio.

QUESTIONS ON THE HISTORY OF BARBERING

1. What is the origin of the word "barber"?

2. Why did men wear beards in ancient times?

3. Name two ancient nations which practiced barbering.

4. When did the Macedonians introduce the practice of shaving?

5. In what year did barbers become known in Rome?

6. When did barbers become popular in Greece?

7. Who were the barber-surgeons?

8. When did the barber-surgeons start their practice?

9. What were the duties of the barber-surgeons?

10. Describe the barber's sign used by the barber-surgeons.

11. What was the origin of the modern barber pole?

12. What kind of organization was the Barber's Company of London?

13. When was the Barber's Company organized in London?

14. When was the first corporation for barber-surgeons organized in France?

15. Who brought the barber-surgeons to America?

16. In what year did A. B. Moler open the first barber school in America?

17. In what year did the State of Minnesota pass the first barber license law?

18. What are three important advantages of having barber-styling license laws?

19. Which important discoveries improved the practice of barber-styling in recent years?

HYGIENE AND GOOD GROOMING—Page 10

1. The science that concerns itself with healthful living.
2. The care given by the individual to preserve good health.
3. Sanitary measures taken by the government to promote public health.
4. Cleanliness, oral hygiene, posture, exercise, relaxation, adequate sleep, balanced diet and wholesome thoughts.
5. Pure air, pure food, pure water, adequate disposal of sewage, control of disease and adequate medical facilities.
6. Cheerfulness, courage and hope.
7. Worry and fear.
8. clean.
9. deodorant.
10. mouthwash.
11. contagious

PROFESSIONAL ETHICS—Page 16

1. Ethics deal with proper conduct and business dealings in relation to employer, patrons and co-workers.
2. Courtesy, honesty, obeying the law and keeping your word.
3. Because they offend both clients and co-workers.
4. It will cause loss of confidence.
5. The use of profane language denotes lack of culture.
6. They are acting in line of duty and contribute to the higher standards of professional practice.
7. By complying with the law, the barber-stylist is contributing to the health, welfare and safety of the community.

BACTERIOLOGY—Page 22

1. The science that deals with the study of bacteria.
2. Minute, one-celled, vegetable microorganisms found nearly everywhere.
3. Non-pathogenic bacteria: non-disease producing—beneficial or harmless type. Pathogenic bacteria: disease producing—harmful type.
4. Because they are very minute, 1500 rod-shaped bacteria barely reaching across a pinhead.
5. Coccus—round shape.
   Bacillus—rod shape.
   Spirillum—corkscrew shape.
6. Through the mouth, nose, eyes or ears and through a break in the skin.
7. Each bacterial cell divides crosswise in half, forming two daughter cells which grow to full size and then reproduce again.
8. Staphylococcus and streptococcus.
9. Pathogenic bacteria, being harmful and disease producing, make the practice of sterilization necessary.

10. a) Pathogenic: disease producing—harmful.
    b) Non-pathogenic: non-disease producing—beneficial or harmless.
11. One that spreads from one person to another by contact.
12. Disinfectants, intense heat and ultra-violet rays.
13. Natural immunity is natural resistance to disease. Acquired immunity is secured after the body has overcome certain diseases by itself or by inoculation against those diseases.
14. The body's inability to cope with bacteria and their harmful toxins.
15. A local infection is indicated by a boil or pimple that contains pus. A general infection, such as blood poisoning, results when the bloodstream carries bacteria and their toxins to all parts of the body.
16. Microorganisms, germs and microbes.
17. a) Certain bacteria, when adverse conditions arise, form spherical spores having a tough, resistant covering.
    b) Anthrax and tetanus bacilli.
18. a) Parasites are plants or animals that live off another living organism.
    b) Animal parasite—pediculosis. Plant parasite—ringworm.
19. By practicing personal hygiene and public sanitation at all times.
20. The ability of the body to resist invasion of bacteria and to destroy them once they have entered the body.
21. A person who, although immune to the disease himself, can infect other persons with the germs of the disease. Two examples are diphtheria and typhoid fever.
22. Tuberculosis, virus infections, ringworm and head lice.
23. Unbroken skin; body secretions, such as perspiration; white blood cells and antitoxins.
24. To protect the student, the barber-stylist and the client against disease-producing bacteria.

SANITATION AND STERILIZATION—Page 31

1. The process of making an object germ-free by destroying all kinds of bacteria, whether harmful or beneficial.
2. chemical.
3. Ultra-violet rays and vapors keep objects clean after they have been sanitized.
4. Pathogenic bacteria.
5. Infectious diseases may be spread from one person to another.
6. Asepsis—free from disease germs.
   Sterile—free from all germs.
   Sepsis—poisoning due to germs.
7. hot
8. formalin.
9. A chemical agent that may kill or retard the

growth of bacteria.
10. A chemical agent that destroys bacteria.
11. A vapor used to keep clean objects in a sanitary condition until ready for use.
12. a) Quats — 1 to 5 minutes.
    b) 25% formalin — 10 minutes.
    c) 10% formalin — 20 minutes.
13. A receptacle containing a disinfectant solution. By immersing clean implements into it for required time.
14. Thoroughly wash each object with soap and water and place into a suitable disinfectant solution for required time.
15. Convenient to prepare, quick acting, non-corrosive, non-irritating to skin, odorless and economical.
16. Rinse them in clean water, dry with a clean towel and place in a dry or cabinet sanitizer until ready for use.
17. Wrap them in individual paper envelopes or place them in a cabinet sanitizer or ultraviolet ray cabinet until ready for use.
18. A closed, airtight cabinet containing an active fumigant (formaldehyde gas).
19. Place one tablespoon of borax and one tablespoon of formalin solution on a small tray or blotter on the bottom of cabinet sanitizer.
20. 37% to 40% solution of formaldehyde gas in water.
21. Rub the surface and sharp edges with a cotton pad dampened with 70% alcohol.
22. Gently rub exposed surface with a cotton pad dampened with 70% alcohol.
23. infections.
24. a) 25%
    b) 5%
25. a) Short disinfection time, odorless, non-toxic and stable.
    b) 1:1000 solution
26. a) 8 oz.
    b) 16 oz.
27. Purchase chemicals in small quantities and store in cool, dry place. Measure carefully. Label all containers. Keep under lock and key. Avoid spilling.
28. No. All have the power to destroy both harmful and harmless bacteria.

SANITATION—Page 32
1. The application of measures designed to promote public health and prevent spread of infectious disease.
2. Contact with a person having an infectious disease; unclean hands; use of unsanitized instruments; common use of towels, combs, brushes, drinking cups, shaving mugs or styptic pencils.
3. Wash hands with tincture of green soap and water and apply 60% alcohol or rinse hands in an antiseptic solution.
4. Keep the shop well ventilated and lighted. Keep the walls, curtains and floor coverings in a clean condition. Have a continuous supply of running hot and cold water.

Thoroughly cleanse hands before and after serving a client. Keep all waste materials in closed containers and have them removed regularly.
5. Cover the headrest with a clean towel or paper tissue and change it for each client.
6. To prevent the shaving cloth or chair cloth from touching the client's neck.
7. Keep them in closed, clean containers.
8. With a sanitized spatula.
9. In closed, clean cabinet.
10. In closed containers, separate from the clean towels.
11. Neck strip, headrest covering and towels.
12. To prevent spread of infection.
13. Sanitize it before using on a client.
14. To help prevent disease.
15. Keep them in covered receptacles and remove regularly.
16. It is one of the most common means of transmitting disease.

IMPLEMENTS—Page 52
1. Razors, shears and clippers.
2. Hone, strop, strop dressing, lather receptacles, lather brush, shaving soap, comb, hair brush, tweezer, comedone extractor and electric hair vacuum.
3. High quality, good workmanship, guarantee and reliability of the manufacturer.

STRAIGHT RAZORS—Page 52
1. Their various parts, styles, widths, balance, lengths, tempers, grinds, and finishes.
2. Head, back, shoulder, pivot, blade, point, edge, heel, shank, tang and handle.
3. The back and edge are straight and parallel; the handle is flat or slightly round; the heel is round while the point is square.
4. To prevent scratching the skin during shaving.
5. 4/8, 5/8, 6/8, 7/8 and 9/16 of an inch. 5/8 and 9/16 of an inch are the most commonly used.
6. The blade.
7. Its final polish.
8. A steel surface polished with crocus or rouge powder.
9. For greater ease in handling the razor during shaving.
10. The proper degree of hardness imparted to the steel of the razor.
11. After it is used, strop and dry the razor and then apply a little castor oil over the blade.

SHEARS—Page 52
1. Moving point, moving blade, still point, still blade, two cutting edges, pivot screw, two shanks, finger grip, thumb grip and finger brace.
2. The German type has no finger brace. The French type has a brace for the small finger.
3. Shears are usually measured by half inches. 7 and 7½ inch lengths are mostly used.

4. The plain grind and the corrugated grind. The plain grind is mostly used.
5. Smooth, medium and coarse. The medium finish is preferred.

CLIPPERS—Page 52
1. Hand clipper and electric clipper.
2. Magnetic type and motor driven.
3. Cutting blade, still blade, heel, switch, set screw and conducting cord.
4. Edger or outliner.
5. #0000.

ACCESSORY IMPLEMENTS—Page 52
1. A solid block containing an abrasive for sharpening razors.
2. Natural hone, synthetic hone and combination hone.
3. Water hone and Belgian hone.
4. It is a slow-cutting hone with a grey or brown appearance.
5. It is a slow-cutting hone but it is a little faster than the water hone. Its upper surface is yellow and the bottom portion is dark red.
6. Water hone and Belgian hone.
7. Synthetic hones.
8. A fast-cutting hone gives a quick sharp edge. Carborundum.
9. Those made from canvas, cowhide, horsehide and imitation leather.
10. Bone, hard rubber and plastic.
11. Hard rubber comb.
12. Press button can latherizer; electric latherizer; paper-lined lather mug.

HONING AND STROPPING—Page 58
1. By consistent practice and experience.
2. The razor acquires a perfect cutting edge.
3. Hold the razor at an angle and use smooth, even strokes and pressure on both sides of the blade.
4. Stroke the razor blade to the left diagonally across the hone, from heel to point towards the edge.
5. Turn the razor over on its back and stroke the blade to the right diagonally across the hone, from the heel to the point towards the edge.
6. The abrasive material on the hone makes small cuts in the sides of the razor's edge.
7. To determine if the razor edge is either blunt, keen, coarse or rough.
8. It has five teeth and tends to dig into the nail with a smooth, steady grip.
9. It passes over the nail smoothly, without any cutting power.
10. It tends to dig into the nail with a jerky feeling.
11. It has large teeth which stick to the nail and give a harsh, grating sound.
12. Follow manufacturer's directions. After using, wipe clean and keep covered.
13. To smooth the razor's edge.
14. The stroking of the razor blade in stropping

is just the reverse of honing.
15. The leather strop.
16. Grasp the end of the strop with the left hand and hold it firmly.
17. Hold the razor in the right hand with the fingers wrapped around the handle and shank at the pivot.
18. Start at the top edge of the strop closest to the hydraulic chair.
19. Place the razor flat against the strop with the back towards the barber-stylist. Draw the razor towards the barber-stylist. Turn the razor over on its back with the fingers. Draw the razor away from the barber-stylist. Repeat these movements until razor is properly stropped.
20. The thumb and next two fingers of the right hand.
21. Use normal pressure at the point and heel for both sides of the razor.
22. Touch the razor edge lightly over the cushion part of the thumb.
23. It produces a keen drawing sensation, and the razor does not slide over the thumb.
24. It produces no drawing sensation, sliding freely over the thumb.
25. Apply lather or soap to it, and then wipe it clean to remove accumulated grit.
26. To smooth and shape the edge of the razor into a keen cutting implement.
27. Either suspended, attached to a swivel, or laid flat.
28. A good quality strop dressing.

SHAVING—Page 78
1. Sensitivity of skin, texture of hair and grain of beard.
2. Properly sanitized razor, hands and towels; properly honed and stropped razor; well-lathered beard; properly heated and applied towels; smoothly cut beard; lather completely removed; properly applied astringent or face lotion; thoroughly dried face; evenly applied powder.
3. Arrange chair cloth. Change headrest paper and adjust headrest to proper level. Recline chair to comfortable position. Tuck in towel.
4. Apply lather to face. Apply steam towel over lather. Remove lather with steam towel. Re-lather beard.
5. Use clean hands, sanitized razor, sanitary receptacle for shaving soap, sanitary tissue to wipe lather from razor, and clean linen.
6. Use the cushion tips of fingers in a rotary movement.
7. It softens the hair and lubricates the skin and beard.
8. The heat softens the outer layer of the hair and stimulates the flow of oil from the skin glands. The added lubrication helps the razor to glide over the face.
9. If the face is very sensitive, irritated, chapped or blistered.
10. Free hand, back hand, reverse free hand and reverse back hand.

11. Hold the razor in a free hand position. Use a gliding stroke towards the point of the razor in a forward sawing movement.
12. Hold the razor in a back hand position and stroke it in a forward sawing movement away from you towards the point of the razor.
13. The razor is held similarly to the free hand position. The stroke is performed with a slight rotation of the wrist, forming a small upward arc.
14. With the grain of the hair.
15. To make the left sideburn outline and for shaving the left side behind the ear.
16. 14.
17. The right side is shaved first. The free hand stroke is the first stroke.
18. When performing each of the 14 shaving steps, a few more strokes across the grain may be taken, thereby assuring a complete and even shave with a single lathering.
19. The sides below the ears.
20. Comb the hair neatly. Wipe off excess powder and any loose hair.
21. As the last steam towel is being removed.
22. Just before combing the hair.
23. Offensive body, breath or tobacco odor; dull or rough razors; unclean hands, towels and chair cloth; cold fingers; heavy touch of hand; poorly-heated towels; too cold or too hot lather; sticking fingers in client's mouth; glaring overhead lights; unshaven hair patches; scraping of skin and close shaving.
24. A hair that has grown beneath the skin.
25. It is usually caused by very close shaving and shirt collars that rub against the neck.
26. To remove an ingrown hair, open the affected part with a sanitized needle and then pull out the hair with a sanitized tweezers. Then apply an antiseptic, such as peroxide or tincture of iodine.
27. By shaving the beard against the grain of the hair during the second time over.
28. It may irritate the skin and cause ingrown hairs or infection.

MEN'S HAIRCUTTING—Page 112

1. The process of cutting and arranging hair to client's requirements.
2. Cutting the hair lightly.
3. By competent instruction and patient practice.
4. Sideburn and nape area—edging; contour area (middle section)—siding; top cut area—topping.
5. Flat top, crew cut and butch cut.
6. Finish one vertical strip at a time before proceeding with the next strip to the left. Working from right to left gives a better view of the work.
7. Wash hands and use only sanitized implements, clean towels and clean linens on clients.
8. Seat client comfortably in chair, place neck-strip or towel around neck and then

adjust chair cloth over neck strip or towel.
9. On the left side of the head and carried around to the right side.
10. They find it a more convenient way to work.
11. Gradually tilt the blade so that the clipper rides on the heel of the bottom blade.
12. The comb is held parallel to the shears.
13. It shortens the hair evenly and helps to reduce any ridges that may appear in the haircut.
14. Depending on the desired hairstyle, shave around the top and back of the ears and the sides and back of the neck.
15. a) Use a free hand stroke. b) Use a reverse back hand stroke.
16. Offensive body odor, bad breath or tobacco odor; improper hairstyle; poor workmanship; cutting off too much or too little hair; irregular hairlines; unsanitary practices, such as unsanitized implements, unclean towels or chair cloths; allowing cut hairs to fall on the client's back or neck; pulling of hair with dull shears or clippers; blowing loose hair off client's neck; scratching client's scalp when combing the hair.

BASIC PRINCIPLES OF MEN'S HAIRSTYLING—Page 112

1. Study the client's features in order to suggest the most suitable hairstyle.
2. To be able to give the proper styling advice.
3. Seven—oval, round, square, oblong, pear shape, heart shape and diamond.
4. The oval.
5. To give the appearance of a thinner face.
6. To minimize its length and hide its angularity.
7. Arrange the top front hair over the forehead.
8. By bringing the hair forward at the forehead and back at the sides.
9. Leave hair long or fuller at the neck.
10. Cut hair shorter at the nape and leave the neck exposed.

CUTTING AND STYLING CURLY AND OVER-CURLY HAIR—Page 138

1. The process of cutting and arranging hair to client's requirements.
2. By competent instruction and patient practice.
3. Sideburn and nape area—edging; contour area (middle section)—siding; top cut area—topping.
4. Wash hands and use only sanitized implements, clean towels and clean linens on clients .
5. Seat client comfortably in chair, place neck-strip or towel around neck and then adjust chair cloth over neck-strip or towel.
6. On the left side of the head and carried around to the right side. Some barber-stylists prefer to start clipper work on the right side of head and proceed to the left side. Each procedure is correct.

7. Gradually tilt the blade so that the clipper rides on the heel of the bottom blade.
8. The comb is held parallel to the shears.
9. Finish one vertical strip or area at a time before proceeding with the next strip or area to the left. Working from right to left gives a better view of the work.
10. Depending on the desired hairstyle, shave the sideburns, around the ears and the sides and back of the neck.
11. a) Use a free hand stroke.
    b) Use a reverse back hand stroke.
12. Offensive body, breath or tobacco odor; improper hairstyle; poor workmanship; cutting off too much or too little hair; irregular hairlines; unsanitary practices, such as unsanitized implements, unclean towels or chair cloths; allowing cut hair to fall on the client's back or neck; pulling hair with dull shears or clipper; blowing loose hair off client's neck; scratching client's scalp when combing the hair.
13. Wipe off loose hair from client's neck. Remove towel and chair cloth from client. Make out check for client. Thank client as you hand him the check.
14. Discard used towel and neck-strip. Shake chair cloth at the base of chair, fold and place on arm of chair. Clean and sanitize used implements. Place implements into dry (cabinet) sanitizer. Sweep hair from floor and place into a closed container. Assemble needed supplies for next client. Wash hands.

MUSTACHES AND BEARDS—Page 146
1. For personal adornment.
2. In accordance with the facial features of the wearer.
3. It should correspond with the size of the client's facial features.
4. To cover facial blemishes.
5. The Van Dyke beard.

SHAMPOOING AND RINSING—Page 154
1. To keep hair and scalp in a clean and healthy condition.
2. As often as necessary.
3. Plain liquid soap or a detergent-based product.
4. Proper preparation of client; selection of a good shampoo; proper application of shampoo and water; sufficient scalp massage to stimulate scalp; thorough rinsing to remove dirt and lather; drying and combing the hair.
5. Soft, warm water. Hard water will not produce any lather unless softened.
6. Shampoo, warm and cold water, chair cloth and towels.
7. Arrange necessary supplies and wash hands with soap and warm water.
8. Seat client in a comfortable position. Properly drape client. Adjust towels and chair cloth.

9. To loosen dandruff and stimulate circulation of the blood to the scalp.
10. Apply shampoo to all parts of scalp. Gradually apply enough warm water to make an abundance of lather. Massage scalp for several minutes. Rinse hair with warm water and, if necessary, repeat lathering. Rinse hair with cool water or a reconditioning rinse. Wipe face and ears thoroughly. Dry and comb hair.
11. After lathering, stand behind the client. Place fingertips at the back of the head just below the ears. Apply rotary movements from the ears to the temples up to the forehead, then over the top of the head down to the neck. Repeat these movements for several minutes.

HAIR RINSES—Page 154
1. It cleanses the hair and scalp; brings out hair lustre; conditions the hair and scalp; adds highlights and color to the hair.
2. Water, acid, dandruff and bluing rinses.
3. Acetic acid.
4. Acid rinse.
5. It eliminates yellow tinge in grey hair and brightens black hair.

HAIR CONDITIONERS—Page 165
1. Dry, brittle, damaged or over-porous hair.
2. Give a reconditioning treatment.
3. The hair shaft.
4. Give a reconditioning treatment.
5. It helps restore some of the natural oils that have been removed by the chemical hair processor.
6. Apply a color filler.
7. Proteins and cholesterol.
8. To prevent dryness or brittleness of the hair and to liven up dull and lifeless hairpieces.
9. Reconditioning treatments help keep the hair in the best possible condition.
10. Apply a conditioner to the hair and scalp.
11. They make the hair soft and pliable.
12. By giving a series of hair conditioning treatments.
13. A hair conditioning emulsion.
14. After the hair and scalp are towel dried.
15. Such treatment could create a sensitive scalp.
16. Reconditioning treatments.
17. Fillers.
18. Conditioner and color fillers.
19. By reconditioning treatments.

SCALP TREATMENTS—Page 168
1. To maintain a healthy scalp and hair and to combat such disorders as dandruff and excessive hair loss.
2. The blood flow is increased, while the nerves are rested and soothed.
3. To keep the scalp and hair clean and healthy, to promote hair growth and to try to prevent excessive hair loss.

4. It stimulates the blood supply to the scalp.
5. If there is a deficiency of natural oil in the scalp and hair.
6. Leading an indoor life; frequent washing of hair; continued use of drying lotions, tonics and shampoos.
7. Excessive intake of fatty foods in the diet, resulting in overactivity of the oil glands.
8. The appearance of white scales on the scalp and hair accompanied by itching scalp.
9. Poor circulation of blood to the scalp; improper diet; uncleanliness; infection.
10. Poor blood circulation; lack of proper stimulation; improper nourishment; certain infectious scalp diseases, such as ringworm; constitutional disorders.
11. Stimulating the blood supply to the hair papillae encourages the growth and replacement of hair.
12. Apply regular scalp manipulations. Steam the scalp with either hot towels or a scalp steamer. Apply hair tonic carefully and massage it well into the scalp. Comb hair to desired style.

HAIR TONICS—Page 168
1. Cosmetic solutions used on the hair.
2. To correctly advise clients about their uses for specific purposes.
3. The steaming of the scalp by means of steaming towels or a scalp steamer, usually followed by the application of a hair tonic.
4. Grooms the hair. Helps correct an oily dandruff condition. Helps correct a dry dandruff condition. Stimulates the scalp. Offsets an itching scalp. Maintains a normal healthy scalp.
5. Massage scalp. Apply steam towels or scalp steamer. Apply suitable hair tonic. Massage scalp. Comb hair to desired style.

THEORY OF MASSAGE—Page 172
1. A system of manipulations applied with the hands or with the aid of electrical devices.
2. The head, face and neck.
3. Effleurage, or stroking movements; petrissage, or kneading movements; friction, or deep rubbing movements; percussion (tapotement), or tapping, slapping or hacking movements; vibration, or shaking movements.
4. The skin and all its structures are nourished.
5. It is increased.
6. They are rested and soothed.
7. They are stimulated and strengthened.

FACIAL TREATMENTS—Page 184
1. They cleanse the skin; increase circulation; activate glandular activity; relax tense nerves; maintain muscle tone; strengthen weak muscle tissue; correct certain skin disorders; help prevent the formation of wrinkles and ageing lines; improve skin texture and complexion; help reduce fatty tissues.
2. Loosening of elastic skin fibers because of abnormal tension or relaxation of facial muscles; shrinking of skin tissue because of advancing years; excessive dryness or oiliness of the skin; facial expressions that continually crease and fold the skin; improper hygienic care of the skin.
3. Hot and cold water, towels, vibrator, therapeutic lamp and various preparations, such as facial creams, ointments, lotions, oils, packs, masks and powders.
4. In order to select the proper cream for each type of skin and be able to apply the proper massage manipulations.
5. In order to select and recommend the proper preparation for the particular condition of the skin being treated.

SCIENTIFIC REST FACIAL—Page 184
1. Make client comfortable and give a facial as restful and refreshing as possible.
2. To avoid inhaling each other's breath or smelling each other's body odor.
3. The barber-stylist should never use tobacco while working on a client. If tobacco was used, rinse mouth before starting to work.
4. Arrange all necessary supplies. Wash hands. Adjust linens and towels. Protect client's hair by fastening a towel around his head. Recline the patron.
5. Apply cleansing cream over the face, using stroking and rotary movements. Remove cleansing cream with a smooth, warm, damp towel. Steam face mildly with three towels. Apply tissue cream to the skin with fingertips. Gently massage the face, using continuous and rhythmic movements. Wipe off excess cream with a hot towel. Steam the face with hot towels. Remove hot towels and follow with a cool towel. Pat an astringent or face lotion over the face and dry. Apply powder over the face and remove excess powder. Raise hydraulic chair. Comb hair to desired style.
6. Have client thoroughly relaxed. Provide quiet atmosphere. Maintain clean, orderly arrangement of supplies. Follow systematic procedure. Give facial massage properly.
7. Offensive body, breath or tobacco odor; harming or scratching the skin; excessive or rough massage; getting facial cream into eyes; using towels that are too hot; breathing into the client's face; not being careful or sanitary; not showing interest in the client's skin problems; carelessness in removing cream, by leaving a greasy film behind the ears, under the chin and in other areas; not permitting the client to relax, either by talking or being tense while giving facial manipulations; leaving chair to get materials or supplies; heavy, rough or cold hands.

SPECIAL PROBLEMS—Page 184

1. To stimulate the activity of the oil glands and to replenish a deficiency of natural oil in the skin.
2. Excessive intake of starchy and oily foods, and faulty hygienic habits.
3. Sanitized comedone extractor.
4. It has a mild tonic effect which helps prevent undue wrinkling of the skin.
5. Acne facial.
6. Clay pack, acne facial and hot oil mask.
7. Oily skin facials and acne facials.
8. Extremely dry, parched and scaly skin.

MEN'S RAZOR HAIRCUTTING—Page 206

1. The client's wishes, features, head shape, facial contour and hair texture.
2. To thin and shorten hair; taper and blend hair; make resistant hair more manageable.
3. Coarse hair with good and moderate porosity; medium (average) hair with good and moderate porosity; fine hair; wiry or resistant hair; over-curly hair.
4. Guarded and straight open-blade razors.
5. The guarded razor.
6. Free hand and straight handle positions.
7. Light taper-blending, heavier taper-blending, terminal blending.
8. Light taper-blending.
9. With continuous movements, the hair is cut with the razor and removed with the comb. At the same time, the hair is re-combed for the next stroking.
10. a) Use more strokes and heavier tapering. b) Use fewer strokes and lighter pressure.
11. Short hair or hair that is cut regularly.
12. To remove dirt, dandruff or foreign matter from the hair and make the hair soft for cutting.
13. To detect any unusual condition, such as the presence of any growths, scars, disorders or thinning areas.
14. In a damp condition.
15. Tapering too close to the hair part; thinning hair too close to the scalp; over-tapering the hair.
16. The beginner should use a razor with a guard. Avoid annoyance or distraction while cutting the hair. Keep sharp implements in a closed case.

WOMEN'S HAIRCUTTING—Page 220

1. It serves as the foundation for modern hairstyles.
2. Haircutting shears, razor, thinning shears, combs and clipper.
3. It removes excess bulk without shortening length of hair.
4. If coarse hair is thinned too close to the scalp the short, stubby hair ends will protrude through the top layer, while fine hair, being softer and more pliable, will lay flatter on the head.
5. a) Fine hair—from ½-1". b) Medium hair—from 1-1½". c) Coarse hair—from 1½-2".

6. Hairline at the nape of the neck (ear to ear); at the side of the head (above ears); around facial hairline; and in hair part.
7. The cut ends would be seen in the finished hairstyle.
8. It is impossible to correct a haircut when too much hair has been removed during the thinning process.
9. Cutting the hair close to the nape and gradually longer toward the crown, without showing a definite line.
10. In order to avoid pulling the hair and prevent dulling the razor.
11. The bridge of the nose.
12. Combing the short hair of the strand toward the scalp.
13. Thinning and tapering the hair at the same time by using regular haircutting shears.
14. Shortening the hair in a graduated effect.
15. A hair lifter or wide-tooth comb, to avoid hair breakage.

FINGER WAVING MEN'S HAIR—Page 224

1. The technique of creating hairstyles in wet hair by means of the fingers and a comb.
2. By proper draping with a clean towel and shampoo cape.
3. By placing a styling hair net over the hair.
4. Naturally wavy hair and permanently waved hair.
5. It should harmonize with client's head shape and facial features.
6. Because they do not contain harmful ingredients.
7. To protect the client from excessive heat of the pedestal type of hair dryer.

AIR-WAVING—Page 240

1. The temporary reshaping of the client's hair with the aid of a styling dryer, comb, brush and special cosmetics.
2. Blow-waving, wind-waving and air-jet waving.
3. Styling dryer (air-waver), combs (metal and/or hard rubber) and styling brushes.
4. Styling dryer without attachments and styling dryer with attachments.
5. By adjusting a dial on the side of the dryer.
6. Cutting, shampooing and towel drying of the hair.
7. In a moist or damp condition.
8. Styling lotion.
9. Styling gel.
10. Along the side of the ridge, in a back-and-forth movement.
11. Each ridge and wave should match evenly without a break in the ridge or the wave.
12. Brush the hair towards the back and with a twist of the wrist, turn and push the brush forward, creating a lift. The hair is held in this position until it is dried with hot air from the blower.
13. To keep the finished hairstyle in place.
14. Dry and brittle hair.
15. In a rotating or back-and-forth movement, directed to the hair.

16. A metal comb retains heat and if permitted to touch the scalp it may cause a burn.

CURLING IRON TECHNIQUES—Page 248

1. The technique of styling hair with the aid of curling irons and without styling or setting creams or lotions.
2. The rod and shell.
3. Less heat than for normal hair.
4. On a tissue neck strip.
5. In a position that is comfortable and permits complete control.
6. Metal combs.
7. To create volume or lift in finished hairstyle.

PERMANENT WAVING FOR MEN—Page 268

1. A procedure involving physical and chemical actions on the hair.
2. rods.
3. neutralization.
4. Waving solution and neutralizer or fixative.
5. Softens the hair to the shape of the curling rods.
6. Stops the action of the waving lotion and rehardens the hair into a new position.
7. A correct analysis of the client's scalp and hair condition.
8. Scalp condition, hair porosity, hair texture, hair elasticity, hair density and hair length.
9. The elasticity and texture of the hair.
10. To permit better saturation and action of the waving solution and neutralizer.
11. Follow your teacher's instructions or the manufacturer's directions.
12. The size of the rod, the blocking (subsectioning), hair texture and hair elasticity.
13. To determine in advance how the client's hair will react to the permanent waving process.
14. Immediately after the last rod is secured; following the rewet application of lotion; every 30 seconds thereafter.
15. When the wave forms a firm letter "S".
16. Weak or fine hair.
17. To protect the client.
18. It is very curly when wet, frizzy when dry and is difficult to comb into a wave pattern.
19. If a tint is given first, the waving solution will lighten the hair and may cause an uneven color. If the permanent wave is given first, the tint may distort or weaken the wave pattern.
20. It may disturb the wave pattern.
21. Hair porosity, texture and elasticity.
22. When the waving solution remains on the skin or scalp too long.
23. Absorb the solution with pledgets saturated with cold water or neutralizer.
24. Apply a milder waving solution to those hair sections that are too curly. Retain it on the hair until the curl has relaxed sufficiently. Then, thoroughly neutralize the hair.
25. A mild strength waving solution.
26. To protect dry, brittle and damaged hair.
27. Diameter of rod and density and texture of the hair.
28. The length of the blockings.
29. The texture and porosity of the hair.
30. Without elasticity, the hair will not hold the curl or wave.

CHEMICAL PROCESSING, CHEMICAL BLOW-OUT AND SOFT CURL PERMANENT—Page 284

1. It has a softening and swelling action on the hair.
2. To determine the true condition of the client's hair in order to give a correct hair processing treatment.
3. Porosity, texture, elasticity and any possible hair damage.
4. The stabilizer. Fixative.
5. Hair strand test.
6. After the hair has received a series of reconditioning treatments and it has returned to a healthy condition.
7. To determine the degree of porosity, to determine the elasticity, and to determine the results to be expected.
8. Because the chemical hair processor may cause serious infection if any scalp eruptions or abrasions are present.
9. It serves as a guide for return treatments.
10. To help protect against lawsuits.
11. Hair previously treated with hot irons or severely damaged hair.
12. To protect the scalp and hairline from irritation caused by the chemical hair processor.
13. The chemical in the hair processor may be very harmful to the skin.
14. To help stop the action of the chemical processor by removing most of it from the hair.
15. To avoid irritation to the scalp by the teeth of the comb, which may cause infection.
16. The cream shampoo will readily stick to the hair and help to prevent tangling.
17. The hair is very fragile due to the action of the processor and tangled ends can be broken easily.
18. In order to remove all chemicals from the hair. Any chemical left in the hair will cause continuous processing and breakage.
19. It stops the softening action of the processor on the hair shaft and rehardens the hair into its new shape.
20. The hair is ready for combing when the stabilizer has rehardened the hair.
21. It is given in the same manner as for a regular chemical processing treatment except that the processor is applied to the new growth only.
22. The shampoo is given prior to the application of the processor.

23. By a three-step rinsing process:
    a) Rinse out half of the cream with warm water.
    b) Comb the hair, with the balance of the processor, for five minutes.
    c) Rinse balance of cream from the hair.
24. By combing the hair away from direction of the natural growth.
25. Faster, provides thorough coverage and underneath hairs are covered.
26. Wide-tooth combs.
27. To restore some of the natural oils which have been removed by the chemical processor.
28. A color rinse.
29. The heat applied over processed hair would cause damage to the hair.
30. The reaction of the chemical in the processor would damage the hair.
31. A method of permanently waving over-curly hair.

HAIR COLORING—Page 321

1. The science and art of changing color of hair.
2. To restore his grey hair to its natural color; to change the shade of his hair because he feels present shade is a handicap to his business; to maintain a youthful appearance.
3. The general structure of hair and scalp; proper selection and application of hair tints and lighteners; chemical reactions following their applications.
4. One that has had no previous lightening or tinting treatment.
5. Temporary, semi-permanent and permanent.
6. Color rinses, highlighting color shampoos and crayons.
7. To color the hair for a period of four to six weeks.
8. Aniline derivative tints, pure vegetable tints, metallic or mineral dyes and compound dyes.
9. Hair colorings with a base derived from aniline, a coal tar product.
10. It is required by federal law, and to determine whether or not the client is allergic to the tint.
11. When mixed with peroxide, they penetrate the cuticle layer of the hair shaft and deposit the coloring in the cortical layer of the hair.
12. Wash a spot behind the ear or on the inner fold of the elbow with mild soap and water. Blot the area dry. Mix a capful of 20-volume peroxide and a capful of the tint to be used. Cover the area with the mixture. Do not disturb for 24 hours. After 24 hours, check for irritation.
13. In the preparation of the tint. The semi-permanent tint is applied to the patch test area without mixing with hydrogen peroxide.
14. By the presence of redness, swelling, burning, itching, blisters or eruptions.
15. Client's age and skin tones.
16. To determine the actual color and condition of client's hair.
17. Signs of a positive skin test; scalp sores or eruptions; contagious scalp or hair disease; presence of either a metallic or a compound dye.
18. To use as a guide for future hair coloring treatments.
19. A single application tint.
20. Save time by eliminating pre-shampooing, or pre-lightening. The hair may be colored lighter or darker than client's natural color. Leave no line of demarcation.
21. A patch test is required. Pre-lightening is necessary if hair color is to be made lighter. Pre-softening is necessary when hair is resistant.
22. They cleanse the hair and highlight its natural color in a single operation.
23. When using a double application tint and if the client desires a complete color change to a lighter shade.
24. When grey hair is resistant to color or before toner is applied.
25. To avoid irritation to the scalp.
26. The metallic and compound dyes.
27. Color is self-penetrating. Color is applied the same way each time. Retouching is eliminated. Color does not rub off.
28. To bring out highlights and to temporarily restore faded hair to its natural shade.
29. With soap and water. For difficult stains, apply pledget of cotton dipped in leftover tint in a circular motion or use prepared tint stain remover.
30. Applied only to the new growth of the hair.

HAIR LIGHTENING—Page 321

1. Hair lightening is the partial or total removal of the natural pigment or artificial color from the hair.
2. Oil lighteners, cream lighteners and powder or paste lighteners.
3. Hydrogen peroxide.
4. 20-volume strength.
5. It speeds the liberation of oxygen gas which hastens the lightening (bleaching) action.
6. It softens the cuticle of the hair and makes it more receptive to the penetrating action of an aniline derivative tint.
7. To judge the length of time required to leave mixture on the hair and to find out in what condition the hair is for lightening.
8. Because a toner contains an aniline derivative product.
9. Use of a strong lightening formula, overlapping, or retaining the lightener too long on the hair.
10. Only to the new growth of the hair.

11. To prevent hair breakage and/or scalp irritation.
12. They make the hair porous and lighter in color.
13. Toners are aniline derivative tints of a pale and delicate color.
14. In the same manner as double application tints.
15. To make it porous enough to accept the toner.
16. Frosting – strands of hair are lightened over various parts of the head. Tipping – wisps of hair are lightened in various areas of the head. Streaking – lightened strand, usually at front hairline.

MISCELLANEOUS—Page 322
1. Since lightened hair is over-porous, it requires corrective treatments to help prevent it from breaking.
2. They recondition lightened, tinted, or otherwise damaged hair.
3. Conditioner and color fillers.
4. If hair is in a damaged condition and if there is doubt that finished color will be an even shade.
5. A color filler treatment.
6. Lightening and dye solvent methods.
7. Individual
8. Because heat sets the chemical and may cause dark streaks or uneven areas throughout the hair.
9. To prevent its chemical action from continuing on the hair.
10. Check the natural color of the hair at the scalp area. Make two or more test strands. Select the appropriate color filler shade.
11. a) An agent that deposits a basic color and gives uniform porosity to the hair. b) Accumulation of residue on the outside of the hair shaft. c) A method of removing tint from the hair by means of a dye solvent, commercial product or lightening treatment. d) A chemical reaction that takes place when peroxide and a tinting solution are mixed.

COLORING MUSTACHES AND BEARDS —Page 322
1. An aniline derivative tint. It may cause serious irritation or damage to the delicate membranes in the nostrils or to the lips.
2. Crayons, pomades in tubes and two-bottle set solutions.

MEN'S HAIRPIECES—Page 344
1. To cover up baldness or bald patches; to retain a youthful appearance; to look younger for business reasons; to look younger socially.
2. Human hair and synthetic fibers.

3. Cut a small piece of hair from the hairpiece. Burn this hair. Human hair burns slowly and gives off a strong odor. Synthetic hair burns more quickly and gives off little or no odor, and tiny hard beads can be felt in the burnt ash.
4. By using a tape measure and by making a pattern.
5. So that the manufacturer can match the ordered hairpiece with the client's hair.
6. Without front lace and with front lace.
7. The hairpiece with a front lace.
8. Two-sided tape.
9. Spirit gum.
10. Remove all old tape from the foundation. Swish the hairpiece back and forth in a cleaner in an open bowl. Gently press out cleaner or allow it to drip into the bowl. Fasten hairpiece on covered head mold and allow to dry naturally.
11. How to sell, measure, fit, cut, style, service and recondition them.
12. Because the products in the bleach tend to damage the foundation.
13. To prevent dryness or brittleness of the hair and to liven up the appearance of the hairpiece.
14. A wide-tooth comb.
15. Word-of-mouth advertising; window display; before and after pictures of men wearing hairpieces; barber-stylists wearing hairpieces; listing in the telephone directory.

THE SKIN AND SCALP—Page 350
1. It is slightly moist, soft and flexible; slightly acid in reaction; free from any disorder or disease.
2. Soft, smooth, and with a healthy color.
3. The epidermis and dermis.
4. It is the outermost layer of the skin and is the outer protective covering of the body.
5. Stratum corneum (horny layer); stratum lucidum (clear layer); stratum granulosum (granular layer); stratum germinativum (germinative layer).
6. Stratum corneum.
7. In the deepest layer of the stratum germinativum of the epidermis and the papillary layer of the dermis.
8. It consists of an elastic network of cells containing blood and lymph vessels, nerve endings, sweat glands, oil glands and hair follicles.
9. Papillary and reticular layers.
10. The elastic fibers in the dermis.
11. Hair, nails and sweat and oil glands.
12. By blood and lymph.
13. Motor, sensory and secretory.
14. The fingertips.
15. To muscles attached to hair follicles.
16. Heat, cold, touch, pressure and pain.
17. They regulate the excretion of perspiration from sweat glands and control the flow of sebum to the surface of the skin.

18. Blood circulation through the skin and evaporation of sweat.
19. Sense of vibration.
20. A combination of nerve endings.
21. After expansion, such as swelling, the skin regains its former shape almost immediately.
22. Its loss of elasticity.
23. The coloring matter (melanin) in the skin, and the blood supply.
24. Lanolin cream.
25. Protection, heat regulation, secretion, excretion, sensation and absorption.

SWEAT AND OIL GLANDS—Page 351

1. An organ that removes certain materials from the blood and forms new substances. Sudoriferous, or sweat glands; sebaceous, or oil glands.
2. They consist of a coiled base and a tube-like duct which forms a pore at the surface of the skin.
3. Practically all parts of body, but more numerous on the palms, soles, forehead and in armpits.
4. Help to eliminate waste products from the body in the form of sweat and regulate body temperature.
5. Heat, exercise, emotions and certain drugs.
6. They consist of small sacs whose ducts open into the hair follicles.
7. Sebum, an oily substance.
8. It lubricates the skin and hair, keeping them soft and pliable.
9. On all parts of the body, with the exception of the palms and soles.

THE HAIR—Page 361

1. To understand the proper hair care and treatment beneficial to patrons.
2. Trichology.
3. A slender thread-like outgrowth of the skin and scalp of the human body.
4. The coloring matter in hair.
5. Keratin.
6. Each layer is laced together to form coiled strands.
7. Harmful cosmetic applications or faulty hair treatments.
8. They cause intense swelling of the hair and breakage of the bonds.
9. Hair root and hair shaft.
10. That portion of the hair that extends beyond the skin.
11. That portion of the hair structure found beneath the skin surface.
12. A tube-like depression or pocket in the skin.
13. Arrector pili muscle and sebaceous gland.
14. A club-shaped structure forming the lower part of the hair root. It fits over and covers the papilla.

15. A small cone-shaped elevation at the bottom of the hair follicle that fits into the hair bulb.
16. From rich blood and nerve supply in the papilla.
17. The papilla produces hair cells during hair growth.
18. The direction of the natural flow of hair on the scalp.
19. a) A cowlick is a tuft of hair standing up.
    b) A whorl is an area of the scalp where the hair forms in a swirl effect, such as in the crown area.
20. germs
21. Fear or cold. which causes the arrector pili muscles to contract.
22. Oil glands secrete sebum, an oily substance, which keeps the hair and scalp in a soft and pliable condition.
23. Diet, blood circulation, emotional disturbances, stimulation of endocrine glands and drugs.
24. The shape and size of the hair follicle.
25. Straight hair, which is usually round. Wavy hair, which is usually oval. Curly hair, which is usually flat.
26. Medulla, cortex and cuticle.
27. The medulla.
28. The cortex.
29. The cuticle.
30. Palms, soles, lips and eyelids.
31. Lanuga hair is fine, soft and downy and is usually found on all areas of the body.
32. It helps in the evaporation of perspiration.
33. The new hair is formed by cell division from the growing point at the root of the hair around the papilla.
34. Growth, fall and replacement of hair.
35. About ½" per month.
36. About 120 square inches.
37. Moisture in the air deepens the natural wave. Cold air will cause hair to contract. Heat will cause hair to expand and absorb moisture.
38. Between 50 and 80.
39. From 2 to 4 years.
40. The loss of natural pigment and the presence of air spaces in the hair.
41. A person who is born with white hair and without pigment to color the skin or iris of the eyes.
42. Sight, touch, hearing and smell.
43. Texture, porosity, elasticity and condition of the hair.
44. Touch and sight.
45. Degree of coarseness or fineness of the hair.
46. a) Blonde – 140,000.   b) Black – 108,000.
    c) Brown – 110,000.
47. Ability of hair to absorb moisture.
48. Ability of hair to stretch and return to its original form without breakage.
49. Normal hair can be stretched about one-fifth its length; wet hair can be stretched from 40-50% its length.
50. The cortical layer.

THE NAILS—Page 364

1. Horny protective coverings at the tips of the fingers and toes.
2. It is firm and flexible, and exhibits a slightly pinkish color. Its surface is smooth, curved and unspotted, without any hollows or wavy ridges.
3. Keratin.
4. a) The nail root is at the base of the nail, underneath the skin. b) The nail body is the visible portion of the nail resting upon the nail bed. c) The free edge is that portion of the nail which extends over the fingertip. d) The nail bed is the part of the skin upon which the nail rests.
5. Nutrition and general good health.
6. General poor health, disease of the nails and injury to the matrix.
7. The matrix.
8. In the matrix.
9. From the matrix, which contains nerves, lymph and blood vessels.
10. About 1/8" per month.

DISORDERS OF THE SKIN, SCALP AND HAIR—Page 380

1. To prevent their spread and avoid more serious conditions.
2. To safeguard his own and the public's health.
3. To be able to recognize the various infectious diseases and suggest proper measures to be taken to prevent more serious consequences.
4. Any departure from a normal state of health.
5. A structural change in the tissues caused by injury or disease.
6. Macule, papule, wheal, tubercle, tumor, vesicle, bulla and pustule.
7. An objective lesion can be seen, as pimples. A subjective lesion can be felt, as itching.
8. Scale, crust, abrasion, fissure, ulcer, scar and skin stain.
9. a) Dry or greasy epidermal flakes. b) Dandruff.
10. Milia, acne, comedones and seborrhea.
11. Acne is a chronic inflammatory disease of the sebaceous (oil) glands.
12. a) Blackheads. b) Whiteheads.
13. Bromidrosis refers to foul-smelling perspiration. Anidrosis is lack of perspiration. Hyperidrosis is excessive perspiration.
14. A worm-like mass of hardened sebum obstructing the duct of the oil glands.
15. Pityriasis capitis simplex (dry dandruff) and pityriasis steatoides (greasy or waxy type of dandruff).
16. Poor circulation, lack of nerve stimulation, improper diet, uncleanliness, infection and injury.
17. An inflammatory condition of the skin.
18. The lesions are round, dry patches covered with coarse, silvery scales.
19. On the scalp, elbows, knees, chest and lower back.
20. Alopecia is the technical term for any form of abnormal loss of hair.
21. Ringworm.
22. Vegetable parasites.
23. A small, reddened patch of little blisters, which spread outward and heal in the middle with scaling.
24. It is the technical term for grey hair.
25. Congenital — exists at or before birth and occurs in albinos and occasionally in persons with normal hair. Acquired — may be due to old age or premature, as in early adult life.
26. Split hair ends.
27. Hirsuties and hypertrichosis.
28. Acne simplex and acne vulgaris.
29. Furuncle.
30. Staphylococci.
31. Head louse.
32. Abnormal white patches in the skin or the hair.
33. A congenital absence of pigment in the body including the skin, hair and eyes.
34. Birthmark.
35. Verruca.
36. A small, brownish spot or blemish on the skin.

ANATOMY AND PHYSIOLOGY—Page 384

1. To have constructive knowledge of those parts receiving treatments.
2. The head, face and neck.
3. The study of the gross structures of the body. Examples: muscles, bones, arteries, veins and nerves.
4. The study of the functions or activities performed by the various parts of the body.
5. The study of the minute structures of the body. Examples: histology of skin, hair, sweat glands and oil glands.

CELLS—Page 384

1. To understand anatomy and physiology.
2. The basic unit of all living matter.
3. It will contribute to an understanding of the skin, scalp and hair and how they function.
4. Protoplasm.
5. Nucleus, cytoplasm, centrosome and cell membrane.
6. Nucleus — affects reproduction of the cell. Cytoplasm — contains food materials for growth, reproduction and repair of cell. Centrosome — also affects reproduction of the cell. Cell membrane — permits soluble substances to enter and leave the cell.
7. By direct or indirect division.
8. In the human body.
9. A complex chemical process whereby cells are nourished and supplied with energy to carry on their many activities.

10. Anabolism and catabolism.
11. The cell absorbs whatever food, water and oxygen it needs.
12. The cell uses up whatever it has absorbed.
13. Groups of cells of the same kind performing a specific function.
14. Connective, muscular, nerve, epithelial and liquid tissues.
15. It serves as a carrier of food, waste products and hormones. Examples: blood and lymph.
16. A structure containing two or more different tissues combining to accomplish a definite function.
17. Brain, heart, lungs, kidneys, liver, stomach and intestines.
18. Groups of organs that work together for the welfare of the entire body.
19. Skeletal, muscular, nervous, circulatory, endocrine, excretory, respiratory, digestive and reproductive systems.

SKELETAL SYSTEM—Page 387

1. Bone.
2. Give shape and strength to the body. Protect the organs from injury. Serve as attachments for muscles. Act as levers for all bodily movements.
3. The skeleton of the head.
4. Two parts. The cranium and the skeleton of the face.
5. Eight bones.
6. Occipital, two parietal, frontal, and two temporal.
7. Forms the lower back part of the cranium.
8. The sides and top of head.
9. The frontal bone.
10. Temporal bones.
11. Sphenoid bone.
12. Fourteen bones.
13. Two nasal bones, two zygomatic bones, two maxillae bones and mandible bone.
14. The whole upper jaw.
15. The lower jaw.
16. Zygomatic bones.
17. In the front part of the throat.
18. It forms the top part of the spinal column and is located in the neck region.

MUSCULAR SYSTEM—Page 391

1. It is a contractile, fibrous tissue upon which various movements of the body depend.
2. They cover, shape and support the skeleton and produce all body movements.
3. Voluntary or striated muscle; involuntary or non-striated muscle; cardiac or heart muscle.
4. Voluntary muscles are controlled by the will. Involuntary muscles are not controlled by the will.
5. The skeletal and nervous systems.

6. a) Origin of a muscle refers to its more fixed attachment. b) Insertion of a muscle refers to its more movable attachment.
7. Chemicals, massage, electric current, light rays, heat rays, moist heat, nerve impulses.
8. The epicranius covers the entire top of the skull. The occipitalis is the back portion; the frontalis is the front portion.
9. It raises the eyebrows and draws the scalp forward, causing wrinkles across the forehead.
10. The orbicularis oculi.
11. Corrugator.
12. Orbicularis oris.
13. Procerus.
14. Trapezius.
15. Platysma.
16. Sterno-cleido-mastoid.

NERVOUS SYSTEM—Page 397

1. To understand how to administer scalp and facial treatments for the client's benefit and what effects these treatments have on the nerves in the skin and scalp and on the body as a whole.
2. The brain, spinal cord and their nerves.
3. The cerebro-spinal, the peripheral and the sympathetic nervous systems.
4. It controls consciousness, voluntary functions of the five senses, and voluntary muscle actions.
5. It consists of sensory and motor nerve fibers which carry messages to and from the cerebro-spinal nervous system.
6. Its functions are independent of the will. This system controls internal body functions, such as breathing, circulation, digestion and glandular activities.
7. The structural unit of the nervous sytem.
8. A cell body and long and short fibers called cell processes.
9. Long, white cords made up of fibers, which carry messages to and from various parts of the body.
10. Sensory and motor nerves.
11. To carry messages regarding touch, heat, cold, sight, hearing, smell, taste and pain to the nerve centers in the brain.
12. a) Sensory nerves—afferent nerves.
    b) Motor nerves—efferent nerves.
13. To carry impulses from the brain to the muscles, which produce movements of the body.
14. A quick removal of the hand from a hot object.
15. Excessive mental work or excessive muscular activity.
16. Chemicals, massage, electrical currents, light rays, heat rays, moist heat.
17. There are 12 pairs of cranial nerves and 31 pairs of spinal nerves.
18. The fifth or trifacial nerve; the seventh or facial nerve; the eleventh or accessory nerve.

19. The fifth cranial nerve.
20. It is the chief sensory nerve of the face and the motor nerve of the muscles of mastication.
21. The seventh cranial nerve.
22. a) The optic nerve. b) The olfactory nerve. c) The auditory nerve.
23. The scalp at the back part of the head, as far up as the top of the head.
24. The spinal portion of the eleventh cranial nerve.
25. a) Supra-orbital. b) Nasal. c) Infra-orbital. d) Mental. e) Auriculo-temporal. f) Zygomatic.
26. a) Temporal. b) Mandibular. c) Cervical. d) Posterior auricular. d) Buccal. e) Zygomatic.

CIRCULATORY SYSTEM—Page 402

1. Because the circulatory system supplies nourishment to the entire body as well as to the skin, hair and nails.
2. It carries water, oxygen, food and secretions to all cells of the body; carries away carbon dioxide and waste products for elimination; helps to equalize body temperature; aids in protecting the body from harmful bacteria and infections through action of the white blood cells; clots the blood.
3. It keeps the blood moving within the circulatory system.
4. Arteries, veins, capillaries.
5. The arteries.
6. The veins.
7. They carry impure blood from various capillaries back to the heart.
8. Pulmonary system and general or systemic system.
9. It consists of plasma, red and white corpuscles and blood platelets.
10. 98.6 degrees Fahrenheit.
11. It is composed of about 9/10 water and carries food elements, waste products and other substances to and from cells.
12. To carry oxygen to the cells of the body.
13. To protect the body against disease.
14. Lymph is a colorless, watery fluid, circulating through the lymph-vascular system.
15. It acts as a middleman between blood and tissues; carries nourishment from blood to cells; removes waste materials from cells.
16. From the blood plasma.

BLOOD VESSELS OF THE HEAD, FACE AND NECK—Page 402

1. Common carotid arteries.
2. Internal common carotid artery and external common carotid artery.
3. Internal branches of the common carotid arteries.
4. External branches of the common carotid arteries.
5. Facial artery.
6. Submental artery.
7. Frontal artery.
8. The back of the head up to the crown.
9. a) Superior labial artery. b) Inferior labial artery.
10. Parietal artery—the crown and side of the head. Frontal artery—the forehead.
11. Frontal and parietal arteries.
12. Posterior auricular artery.
13. The infra-orbital artery.
14. Internal jugular and external jugular.

GLANDS AND OTHER SYSTEMS—Page 404

1. Duct glands and ductless glands.
2. The kidneys, liver, skin, large intestine and lungs.
3. With each cycle an exchange of gases takes place. During inhalation, oxygen is absorbed into the blood, while carbon dioxide is expelled during exhalation.
4. Mouth, pharynx, esophagus, stomach and small intestine.

ELECTRICITY—Page 411

1. A form of energy capable of producing magnetic, chemical or heat effects.
2. A substance that readily carries an electric current. Most metals are used as conductors.
3. A substance that resists the passage of an electric current. Examples: rubber and silk.
4. They serve as points of contact when applying electricity to the body.
5. A constant and even-flowing current, traveling in one direction.
6. A rapid interrupted current, flowing first in one direction and then in the opposite direction.
7. A converter.
8. A rectifier.
9. A unit of electrical pressure.
10. A unit of electrical strength.
11. A unit of electrical resistance.
12. Ohm's law states that the strength of a current (amperage) equals the pressure (voltage) divided by the resistance (ohm).

HIGH-FREQUENCY OR VIOLET RAY—Page 411

1. A current having a high rate of vibration.
2. Tesla current.
3. Either stimulating or soothing, depending on the method of application.
4. Facial electrode, scalp electrode and metal electrode.
5. Direct surface application, indirect application and general electrification.

6. The barber-stylist holds the electrode and applies it directly over client's skiln.
7. While the client holds a metal or glass electrode, the barber-stylist massages the surface being treated.
8. The patron holds the metal electrode in his hand, thereby charging the body with electricity.
9. General electrification.
10. By lifting the electrode slightly from the area being treated and applying current through towel or clothing.
11. About five minutes.
12. Use high-frequency current first, followed by application of hair tonic.
13. Stimulates blood circulation. Increases glandular activity. Aids in elimination and absorption. Increases metabolism.
14. Falling hair, itchy scalp, tight scalp, dry and oily scalp and skin conditions.

ELECTRICAL EQUIPMENT
Vibrator—Page 411
1. An electrical appliance used as an aid in massage.
2. Stimulates the functions of the skin and scalp. Stimulates muscular tissues. Increases blood supply to the part being massaged. Increases glandular activities. Soothes the nerves.
3. If the client has a weak heart, fever, inflammation or abscess.
4. Over heavy muscular tissue, such as the scalp, shoulders and upper back.

Steamer—Page 411
1. It is applied over the head or face.
2. The steam warms the skin, inducing the flow of oil and sweat; helps cleanse the skin; helps soften the surface of the skin; cleans out pores.
3. It softens the scalp; increases perspiration; promotes effectiveness of scalp cosmetics.

Heating Cap—Page 411
1. Electrical devices applied over the head to provide a uniform source of heat.
2. As part of corrective treatments for the scalp and hair.
3. They aid in reconditioning dry, brittle and damaged hair and help to activate a sluggish scalp.

LIGHT THERAPY—Page 416
1. Treatment by means of light rays.
2. Ultra-violet rays and infra-red rays.
3. An electrical apparatus used in producing certain light rays.
4. Glass bulb lamp, hot quartz lamp and cold quartz lamp.

5. Glass bulb lamp and hot quartz lamp.
6. Iron, vitamin D, red and white blood cells.
7. Increase the blood and lymph flow; restore nutrition; increase the elimination of waste products.
8. Acne, tinea, seborrhea and dandruff.
9. They stimulate the growth of hair.
10. About twelve inches.
11. To prevent irritation and injury to the eyes.
12. About two or three minutes.
13. To seven or eight minutes.
14. It may cause severe sunburn and blisters.
15. Slight reddening of the skin, appearing several hours after application of ultra-violet rays without any signs of itching, peeling or burning.
16. The ultra-violet rays stimulate the production of pigment or coloring matter in the skin.
17. The slightest covering on the skin prevents these rays from reaching the skin.
18. Special glass bulbs.
19. Cover the eyes with pads dipped into boric acid or witch hazel solution.
20. About 30" from the skin.
21. To prevent constant exposure of the tissues.
22. Heat and relax the skin. Dilate blood vessels in the skin, thereby increasing blood flow. Increase metabolism and chemical changes within skin tissues. Increase the production of perspiration and oil on the skin. Relieve pain.
23. Dermal lights, with a tungsten or carbon filament in clear or colored bulbs.
24. To protect the eyes from the heat and glare of the light.
25. The heat relieves pain in congested areas.
26. Blue light.
27. It has a tonic effect on the bare skin and soothes the nerves.
28. Has a stimulating effect on the skin. Aids penetration of creams and ointments into skin. Softens and relaxes body tissue.

CHEMISTRY
General Chemistry—Page 443
1. For an intelligent understanding of the various products and cosmetics being used in the shop.
2. The branch of chemistry that deals with all substances containing carbon. Examples: plants, animals, petroleum, coal, natural gas.
3. Organic solvents. Examples: gasoline, benzine.
4. The branch of chemistry that deals with all substances that do not contain carbon. Examples: water, air, iron, lead, iodine, bones.
5. Anything that occupies space.
6. Solids, liquids and gases.
7. The basic unit of all matter. 103.
8. An atom.

9. The smallest particle of an element or compound that possesses all the characteristics of that element or compound.
10. The tendency of its atoms to combine with other elements.
11. The chemical joining of two or more elements to form a new substance.
12. Oxides—compounds composed of any element combined with oxygen. Acids—compounds of hydrogen, a non-metal and, sometimes, oxygen. Bases (alkalies)—compounds of hydrogen, a metal and oxygen. Salts—compounds formed by the reaction of acids and bases.
13. A physical combination of two or more elements that retain their individual identities.
14. Physical change—ice to water. Chemical change—soap formed from the chemical reaction of an alkaline substance and an oil.
15. An alteration of the properties without the formation of a new substance.
16. Where a new substance is formed, having properties different from the original substances.
17. Density, specific gravity, odor, color and taste.
18. Potential hydrogen, or degree of acidity or alkalinity of a liquid.
19. Below 7.
20. Above 7.
21. Water.
22. Filtration and distillation.
23. Soft and hard water.
24. It contains mineral substances which curdle soap instead of permitting it to lather.
25. H_2O.

Shampooing—Page 443
1. Head and tail.
2. a) The tail of the molecule attracts dirt, debris, grease, oil, etc. b) The head has an attraction for water.
3. The shampoo is applied and worked into the hair. The dirt is attracted to the tails of the molecules and becomes firmly attached to them. During the rinsing, the heads are attracted to the water and are carried from the hair, taking the tails with attached dirt with them.
4. An alkali mixed with an oil or fat.
5. Soap, soapless and cream.

Chemistry As Applied To Cosmetics—Page 444
1. Powders, solutions, emulsions, ointments, soaps and suspensions.
2. Oil-in-water and water-in-oil.
3. Since astringents cause contraction of the tissues, they are employed to close the pores of the skin.
4. Because of their astringent and antiseptic properties, they are used in the finishing phase of a facial or a shave.
5. To groom the hair and stimulate the scalp.

6. Add temporary color to hair. Dissolve soap curd from hair. Give a soft, lustrous appearance to hair. Neutralize the yellow tinge of white or grey hair. Seal in a tint or toner after a color treatment.
7. A compound formed by a chemical reaction between an alkaline substance and fatty acids in oil or fat.
8. It is made of pure oils and fats and does not contain an excess of alkali.
9. To correct a scalp condition and recondition the hair.
10. They keep unruly or curly hair in a fixed position.
11. To keep hair in place and control loose ends.
12. Slip, covering power and adherency.
13. An agent that destroys or neutralizes disagreeable odors.
14. It checks perspiration by its astringent action.

Barber-Styling Services—Page 444
1. Because the process of permanent waving takes place in the cortex.
2. Polypeptide chains.
3. By peptide bonds.
4. Cross-bonds or links.
5. Sulphur bonds (S-bonds) and hydrogen bonds (H-bonds).
6. The thio solution (pH 9.4 to 9.6) penetrates into the cortex and breaks down the sulphur and hydrogen bonds.
7. The excess thio is rinsed from the hair and a neutralizer is applied.
8. The thio is an alkali and the neutralizer is an acid solution with a pH of 3.0 to 4.0. This solution stops the action of the thio and rehardens the hair.
9. To recondition over-porous or damaged hair.
10. The objective is entirely the reverse. Permanent waving is intended to give or impart a wave to the hair; chemical hair relaxing is intended to remove wave or curl from the hair.
11. Thio and sodium hydroxide.
12. Temporary color, semi-permanent tints and permanent tints.
13. Because they color only the surface, they are easily washed from the hair.
14. Four to six weeks.
15. They are aniline derivatives and chemically they are alkalies.
16. Permanent colors last indefinitely. Only the new growth of hair requires more color.
17. Because they are composed of very small molecules which penetrate into the cortex. In the cortex, the developer (hydrogen peroxide) causes these molecules to join and form giant molecules which no longer can penetrate the imbrications of the cuticle.
18. Hair tinting adds color to hair. Hair lightening removes color from hair.
19. Melanin and oxymelanin.
20. 20-volume solution of hydrogen peroxide.

BARBER-STYLING SHOP
MANAGEMENT—Page 464

1. Arranges for financing or capital investment. Finds best location for shop. Purchases equipment, furniture and fixtures. Arranges best publicity for shop. Uses good sales techniques. Establishes and maintains records. Develops good public relations techniques. Establishes and enforces shop policies.
2. Service requirements, employee duties and shop procedures.
3. Individual ownership, partnership and corporation.
4. A convenient location that has the greatest number of people passing its windows.
5. It protects against any possible increase in rent and defines the rights and responsibilities of the tenant.
6. A pleased client.
7. To determine income, expenses, profit and loss; to prove value of shop to a prospective buyer; to arrange for a bank loan; for government reports.
8. To make or change appointments; go after new business; remind clients of needed services; adjust complaints and satisfy clients; answer questions; receive messages; order equipment and supplies.
9. Display an interested, helpful attitude. Be prompt in answering the phone. Give all necessary information to the caller. Be tactful.

FIRST AID—Page 464

1. As soon as possible after any accident has occurred.
2. An antiseptic, such as tincture of iodine, hydrogen peroxide or mercurochrome, should be applied.
3. A general functional depression due to excessive heat.
4. By loosening the collar and applying pads saturated with cool water to the face and back of neck.

SELLING IN
THE BARBER-STYLING
SHOP—Page 474

1. Establishing a clear, definite understanding of the client's needs and desires.
2. Improved appearance; recognition or praise of others; improved social relationships; improved business and promotional opportunities; getting the most value for his money; impressing the opposite sex; improving his feeling of well-being.
3. You can't sell goods or services unless the client has complete confidence in you.
4. To build a successful barber-styling business, it is necessary to have your shop accepted by clients.
5. Sincerity and honesty.

HISTORY OF BARBERING—Page 481

1. The word barber is derived from the Latin word "barba," meaning beard.
2. As a sign of wisdom, strength and manhood or for religious reasons.
3. Ancient Egypt and China.
4. About 400 years B.C. (before the birth of Christ).
5. About 296 B.C.
6. About 500 B.C.
7. Barbers who assisted the clergy in the practice of surgery and medicine.
8. During the Middle Ages (after the birth of Christ).
9. Besides barbering, they did blood-letting, performed operations, pulled teeth and dressed wounds.
10. A striped pole, from which was suspended a basin. The white band around the pole indicated the ribbon for bandaging the arm, the red band indicated the bleeding and the basin was intended to receive blood.
11. It started in the days when the barber-surgeons bled their patients when treating diseases.
12. A trade guild or society formed for the protection of barber-surgeons.
13. During the thirteenth century.
14. In 1371.
15. The early Dutch and Swedish settlers.
16. In 1893.
17. In 1897.
18. Elevate the standards and practice of barbering. Eliminate incompetent barber-stylists who lack the required training and experience. Protect the public health and assure better service.
19. The use of electricity and electrical appliances in the barber-styling shop. The use of better barber-styling implements. The improved practice of sanitation in the barber-styling shop. The study of anatomy dealing with those parts of the body (face, head and neck) that are serviced by the barber-stylist. The study of cosmetic preparations used in connection with facial, scalp and hair treatments.

499

GLOSSARY

CROSS INDEX

GLOSSARY

Compiled of words used in connection with barbering. Defined in the sense of anatomical, medical, electrical and barber profession relationship only. Key to pronunciation is as follows:

fāte, senȧte, câre, ăm, finâl, ärm, ȧsk, sofá; ēve, ĕvent, ĕnd, recĕnt, evẽr; īce, ĭll; ōld, ȯbey, ŏdd, cônnect, sŏft, fo͞od, fo͝ot; ūse, ûnite, ûrn, ŭp, circûs; those

—————————— A ——————————

abducent nerve (ăb-dū′sênt nûrv): the sixth cranial nerve; a small motor nerve supplying the external rectus muscle of the eye.

abrasion (ă-brā′zhûn): scraping of the skin.

abscess (ăb′sĕs): an enclosed cavity containing pus.

absorption (ăb-sôrp′shûn): assimilation of one body by another; act of absorbing.

accessory nerve (ăk-sĕs′ô-rē nûrv): spinal accessory nerve; eleventh cranial nerve; affects the sterno-cleido-mastoid and trapezius muscles of the neck.

acetic (ă-sĕt′ĭk): pertaining to vinegar; sour.

acetone (ăs′ĕ-tōn): a colorless, inflammable liquid, miscible with water, alcohol, and ether, and having a sweetish, ethereal odor and a burning taste.

acid (ăs′ĭd): a sour substance; any chemical compound having a sour taste.

acid rinse (ăs′ĭd rĭns): a solution of water and lemon juice or vinegar.

acne (ăk′nē): inflammation of the sebaceous glands from retained secretion.

acoustic (ă-kōōs′tĭk): auditory; eighth cranial nerve; controlling the sense of hearing.

activator (ăk′tĭ-vā-têr): a substance employed to hasten the action of hair coloring products.

acute (ă-kūt′): attended with severe symptoms; having a short and relatively short course; not chronic, said of a disease.

additive: a substance which is to be added to another product.

adipose tissue (ăd′ĭ-pōs tĭsh′û): fatty tissue; below the dermis; also called subcutaneous tissue.

adnata, alopecia (ăd-nă′tă, ăl-ô-pē′shē-ă): baldness at birth.

adolescence (ăd-ô-lĕs′ĕns): state or process of growing from childhood to manhood or womanhood.

adrenal (ăd-rē′năl): an endocrine gland situated on the top of the kidneys, secretes hormones into the blood stream; increases energy.

adulterate (ă-dŭl′têr-āt): to falsify; to alter, make impure by combining other substances.

aeration (ā-êr-ā′shûn): airing; saturating a fluid with air, carbon dioxide or other gas; the change of venous into arterial blood in the lungs.

aerobic (ā-êr-ō′bĭk): unable to live without oxygen.

aerosol (â′rô-sōl): colloidal suspension of liquid or solid particles in a gas; aerosol container filled with liquified gas and dissolved or suspended ingredients which can be dispersed as a spray.

afferent nerves (ăf′êr-ênt): convey stimulus from the external organs to the brain; sensory nerves.

affinity (ă-fĭn′ĭ-tē): 1) inherent likeness or relationship; 2) chemical attraction; the force that unites atoms into molecules.

air waving: a procedure used in styling the hair which uses a blower dryer together with a comb and/or brush.

albino (ăl-bī′nō): a person with very little or no pigment in the skin, hair or iris.

alcohol (ăl′kō-hōl): a readily evaporating color-less liquid used to sanitize sharp implements, electrodes and skin.

alimentary (ăl-ĭ-mĕn′tă-rē): relating to food or nutrition; the alimentary canal extends from the mouth to the anus.

alkali (ăl′kă-lī): a base having a pH above 7. Used in the manufacture of soap and other cosmetic products such as permanent wave solution.

alkaline (ăl′kâ-līn): having the qualities of, or pertaining to, an alkali.

allergy (ăl′êr-jē): a skin disorder, such as a rash or inflammation due to extreme sensitivity to certain foods or chemicals.

alopecia (ălô-pē′shē-ă): deficiency of hair; term for loss of hair.

alopecia adnata (ăd-nă′tă): baldness at birth.

alopecia areata (ā-rē-ă′tă): baldness in spots or patches.

alopecia follicularis (fă-lĭk-ū-lăr′ĭs): loss of hair as a result of the inflammation of the hair follicles.

alopecia prematura (prē-mă-tū′ră): baldness beginning before middle age.

alopecia senilis (sĕ-nĭl′ĭs): baldness occurring in old age.

alopecia totalis (tŏ′tăl-ĭs): complete loss of hair from the entire scalp.

alternating current A.C. (ôl′têr-nāt-ĭng kŭr′ênt): a rapid and interrupted electrical current, flowing first in one direction and then in the opposite direction.

alum, alumen (ăl′ŭm, ă-lū′mên): sulphate of potassium and aluminum; an astringent; used as a styptic.

amino acid (ăm′ĭ-nō ăs′ĭd): an important constituent of proteins.

amitosis (ăm-ĭ-tō′sĭs): cell multiplication by direct division of the nucleus in the cell, usually takes place in the reproduction of bacteria.

ammonia (ă-mō′nē-ă): a colorless gas with a pungent odor; very soluble in water.

ammonium thioglycolate (ă-mō′nē-ŭm thī-o-glī′kô-lāt) (thio): a chemical hair relaxer, and permanent wave solution.

ampere (ăm-pâr): the unit of measurement of strength of an electric current.

anabolism (ăn-ăb′ō-lĭz′m): constructive metabolism; the process of assimilation of nutritive matter and its conversion into living substance.

analysis (ă-năl′ĭ-sĭs): a process by which the nature of a substance is recognized and its chemical composition determined.

analysis, hair (hâr): an examination to determine the condition of the hair prior to a hair treatment.

anaphoresis (ăn-ă-fôr-ē′sĭs): the process of forcing liquids into the tissues from the negative toward the positive pole.

anatomy (â-năt′ō-mē): the study of the gross structure of the body which can be seen with the naked eye.

anemia (ă-nē′mē-ă): a deficient blood condition in which the blood is lacking in red blood cells or in hemoglobin or in total volume.

angiology (ăn-jē-ŏl′ô-jē): the science of the blood vessels and lymphatics.

angular artery (ăng′û-lăr är′tĕr-ē): supplies the lacrimal sac and the eye muscle.

anidrosis, anhidrosis (ăn-ĭ-drō′sĭs): a condition which indicates a deficiency in perspiration.

aniline (ăn′ĭ-lĭn, -lēn): a product of coal tar used in the manufacture of artificial dyes.

anode (ăn′ōd): the positive terminal of an electric source.

anterior (ăn-tē′rē-ĕr): situated before or in front of.

antibody (ăn′tĭ-bŏd-ē): a substance in the blood which builds resistance to disease.

antidote (ăn′tĭ-dōt): an agent preventing or counteracting the action of a poison.

anti-perspirant (ăn-tĭ-pĕr-spĭ′rânt): a strong astringent liquid or cream used to stop the flow of perspiration in the region of the armpits, hands or feet.

antiseptic (ăn-tĭ-sĕp′tĭk): a chemical agent that prevents the growth of bacteria.

antitoxin (ăn-tĭ-tŏk′sĭn): a substance in serum which binds and neutralizes toxin (poison).

aorta (ā-ôr′tă): the main arterial trunk leaving the heart, and carrying blood to the various arteries throughout the body.

aponeurosis (ăp-ô-nū-rō′sĭs): a broad, flat tendon; attachment of muscles.

appendage (â-pĕn′dĕj): that which is attached to an organ, such as hair and nails which are appendages of the skin.

aqueous (ā′kwē-ûs): watery; pertaining to water.

aromatic (ăr-ô-măt′ĭk): pertaining to or containing aroma; fragrant.

arrector pili (â-rĕk′tôr pī′lĭ): plural of arrectores pilorum.

arrectores pilorum (â-rĕk-tō′rēz pĭ-lôr′ûm): the minute involuntary muscle fibers in the skin inserted into the bases of the hair follicles.

arteriole (är-tē′rē-ōl): a minute artery; a terminal artery continuous with the capillary network.

artery (är′tĕr-ē): a vessel that carries blood from the heart.

articulation (är-tĭk-û-lā′shûn): joint; a connection between two or more bones.

asepsis (ă-sĕp′sĭs): a condition in which pathogenic bacteria are absent.

aseptic (ă-sĕp′tĭk): free from pathogenic bacteria.

asteatosis (ăs-tē-ă-tō′sĭs): a deficiency or absence of secretions from the sebaceous glands, causing the skin to become dry and scaly.

astringent (ăs-trĭn′jênt): a substance or medicine that causes contraction of the tissues, and checks secretions.

asymmetric (ă-sĭm-mĕt′rĭk): without harmony and correspondence between parts; an imbalance of proportions.

athlete's foot (ăth′lĕts fŏŏt): a fungus foot infection; epidermophytosis.

atom (ăt′ûm): the smallest quantity of an element that can exist and still retain the chemical properties of the element.

atrium (ăt′rē-ûm); pl., **atria** (-ă): the auricle of the heart.

atrophy (ăt′rô-fē): a wasting away of the tissues.

auditory (ô′dĭ-tô-rē): eighth cranial nerve; controlling the sense of hearing.

auricle (ô′rĭ-k'l): the external ear; one of the upper cavities of the heart.

auriculo temporal (ô-rĭk′û-lô tĕm′pôr-âl): sensory nerve affecting the temple and pinna.

auricular (ô-rĭk′û-lâr): pertaining to the ear or cardiac auricle.

autonomic nervous system (ô-tô-nŏm′ĭk nûrv′ûs sĭs′tĕm): the sympathetic nervous system; controls the involuntary muscles.

axons (ăk′sŏns): long nerve fibers extending from the nerve cell.

B

bacillus (bă-sĭl′ûs); pl., **bacilli** (-ī): rod-like shaped bacterium.

back combing (băk kōm′ĭng): combing the short hair toward the scalp while the hair strand is held in a vertical position; also called teasing.

bacteria (băk-tē′rē-ă): microbes, or germs.

bactericide (băk-tē′rĭ-sīd): an agent that destroys bacteria.

bacteriology (băk-tē-rē-ŏl′ô-jē): the science which deals with bacteria.

bacterium (băk-tē′rē-ûm); pl., **bacteria** (-ă): one celled vegetable micro-organism.

baldness (bôld′nĕss): a deficiency of hair; hair loss.

bang (băng): the front hair cut so as to fall over the forehead; often used in the plural, as to wear bangs.

basal layer (bās′âl lā′ĕr): the layer of cells at base of epidermis closest to the dermis.

base (bās): the lower part or bottom; chief substance of a compound; an electropositive element that unites with an acid to form a salt.

base, protective (prō-tĕk′tĭv): see protective base.

benign (bê-nīn′): mild in character.

benzine (bĕn′zēn): an inflammable liquid derived from petroleum and used as a cleansing fluid.

benzoin (bĕn′zô-ĭn, -zoin): a balsamic resin used as a stimulant, and also as a perfume.

bicarbonate of soda (bī-kär′bôn-āt of sō′dă): baking soda; relieves burns, itching, urticarial lesions and insect bites; is often used in bath powders as an aid to cleansing oily skin. Adding baking soda to the water in which instruments are to be boiled will keep them bright.

biceps (bī′sĕps): the two headed muscle on the front of the upper arm; functions to lift the forearm, flexes the elbow and turns the palm downward.

bichloride (bī-klō′rīd): a compound having two parts or equivalents of chlorine to one of the other element.

bile (bīl): a yellowish or greenish viscid fluid secreted by the liver; an aid to digestion.

binding posts (bīn′dĭng pōsts): small metal posts in which are fitted the metal tips of the conducting cords.

biology (bī-ŏl′ô-jē): the science of life and living things.

bipolar (bī-pō′lär): having two poles.

blackhead (blăk′hĕd): see comedone.

bleach (blēch): see hair lightener.

bleaching solution (blēch′ĭng sô-lū′shûn): hydrogen peroxide with addition of ammonia.

bleached hair (blēcht hâr): hair from which the color has been wholly or partially removed by means of a bleaching or lightening agent.

bleb (blĕb): a blister of the skin filled with watery fluid.

blending (blĕnd′ĭng): the physical act of fusing the color of hair during tinting and lightening applications.

blister (blĭs′tĕr): a vesicle; a collection of serous fluid causing a raised elevation of the skin.

block (blŏk): a head-shaped form upon which a wig is placed for a specific purpose.

blonde; blond (blŏnd): a person of fair complexion, with light hair and eyes.

blood (blŭd): the nutritive fluid circulating through the arteries and veins.

blood vascular system (văs′kū-lăr sĭs′tĕm): comprised of structures (the heart, arteries, veins and capillaries) which distribute blood throughout the body.

blood vessel (vĕs′êl): an artery, vein or capillary.

blow dryer (blō drī′ĕr): a hairstyling device which dries the hair by means of a stream of hot or cool air. It has the advantage of permitting the cosmetologist to style the hair (with comb or brush) while it is being dried.

blowout (blō′ôwt): see chemical blowout.

bluing rinse: a solution used to neutralize the unbecoming yellowish tinge on gray or white hair.

blunt cutting: cutting the hair straight off without thinning or slithering.

boil: a furuncle; a subcutaneous abscess. It is caused by bacteria which enter through the hair follicles.

boiling point: 212° F. or 100° C. The temperature at which a liquid begins to boil.

bond: 1) the linkage between different atoms or radicals of a chemical compound, usually effected by the transfer of one or more electrons from one atom to another; 2) it can be found represented by a dot or a line between atoms shown in various formulas.

booster (bōōs′tĕr): oxidizer added to hydrogen peroxide to increase its chemical action; such chemicals as ammonium persulfate or percarbonate are used.

borax (bō′răks): sodium tetraborate; a white powder used as an antiseptic and cleaning agent.

boric acid (bō′rĭk): acidum boricum; used as an antiseptic dusting powder; in liquid form, as an eye wash.

bowl (bōl): see shell.

brain (brān): that part of the central nervous system contained in the cranial cavity, and consisting of the cerebrum, the cerebellum, the pons, and the medulla oblongata.

brilliantine (brĭl-yân-tēn′): an oily composition that imparts luster to the hair.

bristle: the short, stiff hair of a brush; short, stiff hairs of an animal, used in brushes.

bromidrosis (brō-mĭ-drō′sĭs): perspiration with a foul smell.

bronchus (brŏn′kûs); pl., **bronchi** (-kī): the main branch of the windpipe.

buccal nerve (bŭk′âl nûrv): a motor nerve affecting the buccinator and the orbicularis oris muscle.

buccinator (bŭk′sĭ-nā-tĕr): a thin, flat muscle of the cheek, shaped like a trumpet.

bulla (bōōl′ă): a large bleb or blister.

—————————— **C** ——————————

calamine lotion (kăl′ă-mĭn; -mĭn): zinc carbonate in alcohol used for the treatment of dermatitis in its various forms.

calcium (kăl′sē-ŭm): a brilliant silvery-white metal; enters into the composition of bone.

callous, callus (kăl′ûs): skin which has become hardened or thick-skinned, due to friction.

calory, calorie (kăl′ô-rē): a unit of heat energy.

camphor (kăm′fĕr): a mild cutaneous stimulant; medicated ingredient often used in cosmetics.

cancellous (kăn′sê-lûs): having a porous or spongy structure.

caninus (kă-nīn′ûs): the levator anguli oris muscle which lifts the angle of the mouth.

canities (kă-nĭsh′ĭ-ēz): grayness or whiteness of the hair.

canvas head (kăn′văs hĕd): a canvas covered, head shaped form, filled with cork or sawdust. Used in the setting and servicing of wigs.

cap (kăp): the netting and binding of a hairpiece which together form the base to which the hair is attached.

capillaries (kăp′ĭ-lâ-rēz): hair-like, minute blood vessels which connect the arteries and veins.

capitate (kăp′ĭ-tāt): the large bone of the wrist.

caput (kā′pût); poss., **capitis** (kăp′ĭ-tĭs): pertaining to the head.

carbohydrate (kär-bô-hī′drāt): a substance containing carbon, hydrogen, and oxygen, the two latter in the proportion to form water; sugars, starches and cellulose belong to the class of carbohydrates.

carbolic acid (kär-bŏl′ĭk ăs′ĭd): phenol made from coal tar; a caustic and corrosive poison; used in dilute solution as an antiseptic.

carbon (kär′bôn): a chemical element found in hair and in all organic compounds.

carbon-arc lamp (kär′bôn ärk lămp): an instrument which produces ultra-violet rays.

carbon dioxide (dī-ŏk′sīd): carbonic acid gas; a colorless gas formed by the decomposition of organic substances.

carbuncle (kär′bûn-k′l): a large circumscribed inflammation of the subcutaneous tissue that is similar to a furuncle, but much more extensive.

cardiac (kär′dē-ăk): pertaining to the heart.

cartilage (kär′tĭ-lâj): gristle; a non-vascular connective tissue softer than bone.

catabolism (kă-tăb′ô-lĭz′m): chemical changes which involve the breaking down process within the cells.

catalyst (kăt′ă-lĭst): a substance having the power to increase the velocity of a chemical reaction.

cathode (kăth′ōd): the negative pole or electrode of a constant electric current.

caustic (kôs′tĭk): an agent that burns and chars tissue.

cell (sĕl): a minute mass of protoplasm forming the structural unit of every organized body.

cellular (sĕl′ū-lăr): consisting of, or pertaining to cells.

centrosome (sĕn′trŏ-sōm): a cellular body which controls the division of the cell.

cerebellum (sĕr-ĕ-bĕl′ŭm): the posterior and lower part of the brain.

cerebrospinal system (sĕr-ĕ-brŏ-spī′nâl sĭs′tĕm): consists of the brain, spinal cord, spinal nerves and the cranial nerves.

cerebrum (sĕr′ĕ-brŭm): the superior and larger part of the brain.

cetified color (sûr′tĭ-fĭd kŭl′ĕr): a commercial coloring product which temporarily coats the hair shaft; color rinse.

cervical (sûr′vĭ-kâl): a branch of the seventh cranial nerve, affects the side of the head.

cervical bones (bōnz): the top seven vertebrae of the spinal column located in the neck region.

chemical blowout (kĕm′ĭ-kâl blŏ′ŏwt): a chemical hair relaxing technique which is employed to achieve more natural hairstyles; it removes only a small amount of curl but leaves the hair more manageable.

chemical change: alteration in the chemical composition of a substance.

chemical dye remover (kĕm′ĭ-kâl dī rĕ-mōōv′ĕr): a dye remover containing a chemical solvent.

chemical hair relaxer (hâr rĕ-lăks′ĕr): a chemical agent which is employed to straighten over-curly hair.

chemistry (kĕm′ĭs-trē): the science dealing with the composition of substances; the elements and their mutual reactions, and the changes which these substances undergo.

chloasma (klŏ-ăz′mă): large brown irregular patches on the skin, such as liver spots.

chlorine (klō″rĭn, -rēn): greenish yellow gas, with a disagreeable suffocating odor; used in combined form as a disinfectant.

cholesterin; cholesterol (kŏ-lĕs′tĕr-ĭn; -ōl): a waxy alcohol found in animal tissues and their secretions; it is present in lanolin, and used as an emulsifier.

chronic (krŏn′ĭk): long-continued disease; the reverse of acute.

cicatrix (sĭ-kā′trĭks, sĭk′ă-trĭks); pl., **cicatrices** (sĭk-ă-tr-′sēz): the skin or film which forms over a wound, later contracting to form a scar.

cilia (sĭl′ĭ-ă): the eyelashes; microscopic hair-like extensions which assist bacteria in locomotion; also called flagella.

circuit (sûr′kĭt): the path of an electric current.

circuit breaker (brā′kĕr): an automatic switch which disconnects any current with a defective appliance or an overloaded line.

circulation (sûr-kŭ-lā′shŭn): the passage of blood throughout the body.

citric acid (sĭt′rĭk ăs′ĭd): acid found in the juice of the lemon; used for making a lemon rinse.

clavicle (klăv′ĭ-k′l): collar bone, joining the sternum and scapula.

clay (klā): an earthy substance containing kaolin, etc., and used for facial packs.

clipping (klĭp′ĭng): the act of cutting split hair ends with the scissors; the operation of removing the hair by the use of hair clippers.

clockwise: the movement of hair, in shapings or pin curls, in the same direction as the hands of a clock.

clot (klŏt): a mass or lump of coagulated blood.

club cutting (klŭb kŭt′ĭng): cutting the hair straight off without thinning or slithering.

coagulate (kŏ-ăg′ū-lāt): to clot; to convert a fluid into a soft jelly-like solid.

coating (kōt′ĭng): residue left on the hair shaft.

coating tint (tĭnt): a tint which deposits color only on the cuticle layer of the hair shaft; for example as a color rinse.

coccus (kŏk′ŭs); pl., **cocci** (kŏk′sī): round cell bacterium.

coiffure (kwä-fūr′): a French term indicating the arrangement or dressing of the hair.

cold waving (kōld wāv′ĭng): a system of permanent waving involving the use of chemicals rather than heat.

cold waving solution (sŏ-lū′shŭn): a chemical solution which softens the hair in cold waving.

collodion (kŏ-lō′dē-ŏn): a thick liquid used to form an adhesive covering.

colloid (kŏl′oid): particles having a certain degree of fineness and possessing a sticky consistency.

colorfast shampoo (kŭl′ĕr-făst shăm-pōō′): a shampoo specially prepared to minimize the removal of color from lightened or tinted hair.

color filler (fĭl′ĕr): a preparation containing a certified color which is used to equalize porosity in damaged hair so that it will take color evenly.

color remover (rĕ-mōōv′ĕr): a prepared commercial product which removes tint from the hair.

color rinse (rĭns): a rinse which gives a temporary tint to the hair.

color shampoo (shăm-pōō′): a preparation which is designed to cleanse the hair and add color at the same time.

color test (tĕst): a method of determining the action of a selected tint on a small strand of hair; strand test.

comedone (kŏm′ĕ-dōne): blackhead; a wormlike mass in an obstructed sebaceous duct.

comedone extractor (ĕks′trăk′tĕr): an instrument used for the removal of blackheads.

common carotid (kâ-rŏt′ĭd): the main source of blood supply to the head, face and neck.

compact tissue (kŏm′păkt): a dense, hard type of bony tissue.

compound dye (dī′): a combination of vegetable dyes and metallic salts.

compound henna (kŏm′pound hĕn′ă): Egyptian henna to which has been added one or more metallic preparations.

compounds (kŏm′poundz): 1) made of two or more parts or ingredients; 2) in chemistry, a substance which consists of two or more chemical elements in union.

concentrated (kŏn′sĕn-trāt-ĕd): condensed; increasing the strength by diminishing the bulk.

conditioning (kŏn-dĭ′shŭn-ĭng): the application of special chemical agents to the hair to help restore its strength and give it body in order to protect it against possible breakage.

conducting cords (kŏn-dŭckt'ĭng kôrdz): insulated copper wires which convey the current from the wall plate to the customer and practitioner.

conductor (kŏn-dŭk'tĕr): any substance which will allow a current to flow through it easily.

congeal (kŏn-jēl'): to change from a fluid to a solid state.

congenital (kŏn-jĕn'ĭ-tâl): existing at birth; born with.

congestion (kŏn-jĕs'chŭn): overfullness of the capillary and other blood vessels in any locality or organ; local hyperemia.

connecting cords (kŏn-ĕkt'ĭng kôrdz): the insulated strands of copper wires which join together the apparatus and the commercial electric current.

connective (kŏ-nĕk'tĭv): connecting; joining.

constitutional (kŏn-stĭ-tū'shŭn-âl): belonging to or affecting the physical or vital powers of an individual.

contagion (kŏn-tā'jŭn): transmission of specific diseases by direct or indirect contact.

contagious (kŏn-tā'jŭs): the state or condition of being communicable by contact.

contraction (kŏn-trăk'shŭn): having power to become shorter; the act of shrinking, drawing together.

converter (kŏn-vûr'tĕr): an apparatus used to convert the direct current to alternating current.

corium (kō'rē-ûm): the derma or true skin.

cornification (kôr-nĭ-fĭ-kā'shŭn): the process of becoming a horny substance or tissue; a callosity.

corpuscles, red (kôr'pŭs'lz, rĕd): cells in blood whose function is to carry oxygen to the cells.

corpuscles, white (whĭt): cells in the blood whose function is to destroy disease germs.

corrugations (kŏr-ŭ-gā'shŭns): alternate ridges and furrows; wrinkles.

corrugator supercilli (kŏr'ŭ-gā-tĕr sū-pĕr-sĭl'ē-ī): draws eyebrows inward and downward, thus causing vertical wrinkles at the root of the nose.

cortex (kôr'tĕks): the second layer of the hair.

cortical (kôr'tĭ-kâl): pertaining to the cortex.

cosmetic dermatology (kŏz-mĕt'ĭk dûr-mă-tol'ō-jē): a branch of dermatology devoted to improving the health and beauty of the skin and its appendages; i.e., hair and nails.

cosmetology (kŏz-mĕ-tŏl'ō-jē): the science of beautifying and improving the complexion, skin, hair and nails.

counter-clockwise: the movement of hair in shapings or pin curls, in the opposite direction to the hands of a clock.

cowlick: a tuft of hair standing up usually in the crown area.

cranium (krā'nē'ûm): the bones of the head excluding bones of the face; bony case for the brain.

cream: a semi-solid cosmetic.

crepe wool (krăp wōōl): a sheep wool substance used as tissue strips, headbands, fillers or for confining hair ends in winding.

cresol (krē'sŏl): a colorless, oily liquid or solid derived from coal tar and wood tar and used as a disinfectant.

crest: a ridge, as a crest between two waves.

croquignole (krō'kĭ-nōl): winding of the hair under from ends to the scalp.

cross bonds: the bonds holding together the long chains of amino-acids, which compose hair.

crown: the top part of the head.

crust (krŭst): a scab.

curd (kûrd): soap residue found on the hair after an unsatisfactory shampoo.

curl: a circle, or circles, within a circle.

curl, base: the stationary or immovable part of the curl, which is attached to the scalp.

curl, cascade (kăs'kād): a "stand-up" curl which is wound from the hair ends to the scalp.

curl direction: see direction, curl.

curling iron (kûrl'ĭng ī'rûn): see thermal irons.

curl, pin: a strand of hair which is combed smooth and ribbon-like and wound into a circle with the ends on the inside; sometimes called a flat curl—sculpture curl.

curl, ridge: a curl placed behind and close to the ridge of a finger wave.

curl, roller: a curl formed over a specially made roller.

curl, sculpture (skŭlp'tyûr): same as pin curl.

curl, stand-up: see curl, cascade.

curl stem: that part of the pin curl between the base and the first arc of the circle.

curl, thermal (thûr'mâl): a curl formed with thermal irons.

current, alternating; A.C. (kŭr'ĕnt, ŏl'tĕr-nāt-ĭng): a rapid and interrupted current, flowing first in one direction and then in the opposite direction.

current, direct; D.C. (d-'rĕkt): a constant and even flowing current, traveling in one direction.

current, high-frequency (hī-frē'kwĕn-sē): an electric current characterized by a high rate of vibration.

cutaneous (kū-tā'nà-ûs): pertaining to the skin.

cuticle (kū'tĭ-k'l): the outer layer of the skin or hair.

cutis (kū'tĭs): the deeper layer of the skin (dermis).

cycle (sī'k'l): circle; a complete wave of an alternating current.

cyst (sĭst): a closed, abnormally developed sac containing fluid, semi-fluid or morbid matter.

cysteine (sĭs'tĭ-ēn): an amino acid produced by digestion; it is easily oxidized to cystine; also obtained by reduction of cystine.

cystine (sĭs'tĭn): a sulphur containing amino acid found in hair and nails.

cytoplasm (sī'tŏ-plăz'm): the protoplasm of the cell body, exclusive of the nucleus.

D

dandricide (dăn'drĭ-sīd): a chemical substance; counteracts the effects of dandruff.

dandruff (dăn'drŭf): pityriasis; scurf or scales formed in excess upon the scalp.

decolorize: see hair lightening.

deltoid (dĕl'toid): a muscle of the shoulder.

demarcation (dē-mär-kā'shŭn): a line setting bounds or limits; line indicating the dividing point of a color application.

dendrite (dĕn′drīt): a tree-like branching of nerve fibers extending from a nerve cell.

dense (dĕns): close; thick; heavy.

deodorant (dā-ō′dĕr-ânt): a substance that removes or conceals offensive odors.

depilatory (dĕ-pĭl′á-tô-rē): a substance, usually a caustic alkali, used to destroy or to remove unwanted hair.

depressor (dĕ-prĕs′ĕr): that which presses or draws down; a muscle that depresses.

derma (dûr′mă): the true skin; the sensitive layer of the skin below the epidermis; also called dermis, corium or cutis.

dermal (dûr′mâl): pertaining to the skin.

dermatitis (dûr-mă-tī′tĭs): inflammation of the skin.

dermatology (dûr-mă-tŏl′ô-jē): the science which treats of the skin and its diseases.

dermis, derma (dûr′mĭs, dûr′mă): see derma.

detergent (dâ-tûr′jĕnt): an agent that cleanses.

developer: an oxidizing agent, such as 20-volume hydrogen peroxide solution; when mixed with an aniline derivative tint it supplies the necessary oxygen gas.

diagnosis (dī-ăg-nō′sĭs): the recognition of a disease from its symptoms.

dialysis (dī-ăl′ĭ-sĭs): the process of separating different substances in solution by diffusion through a moist membrane; separation.

diaphragm (d-′ă-frăm): a muscular wall which separates the thorax from the abdomen.

diathermy (dī′á-thûr-mē): a method of treating an area of the body by the application of a high-frequency current to the deep tissues.

diffusion (dī-fū′zhûn): a spreading out; dialysis.

digestion (dī-jĕs′chûn): the process of converting food into a form which can be readily absorbed by the body.

digits (dĭj′ĭts): fingers or toes.

dilator naris anterior (dī-lā′tĕr nā′rĭs ăn-tē′rē-ĕr): a muscle which expands and contracts the nostril.

dilute (dĭ-lūt′; dī-): to make thinner by mixing, especially with water.

diplococcus (dī-plô-kŏk′ûs): bacteria exhibiting pairs.

direct current (dī′rĕkt kûr′ênt): see current, direct.

direction, curl (dĭ-rĕk′shûn, kûrl): the movement of hair in order to form a particular pattern or style. Forward: toward the face; backward (reverse): away from the face.

direction, stem: the direction in which the stem of a strand of hair moves from the base to the first arc.

disease: a pathologic condition of any part or organ of the body, or of the mind.

disease carrier: a healthy person capable of transmitting disease germs to another person.

disinfectant (dĭs-ĭn-fĕk′tânt): an agent used for destroying germs.

dispensary (dĭs-pĕn′sà-rē): a place where medicines or other supplies are prepared and dispensed.

dispersion (dĭs-pûr′shôn): 1) the act of scattering or separating; 2) the incorporation of the particles of one substance into the body of another, comprising solutions, suspensions and colloid solutions.

distal (dĭs-tâl): farthest from the center or median line.

distill (dĭs-tĭl′): to extract the essence or active principle of a substance.

disulfide (dī-sŭl′fīd): (sulphur): a chemical compound in which two sulphur atoms are united with a single atom of an element; i.e., carbon.

dormant (dôr′mânt): inactive; asleep.

double application tints: products requiring two separate applications; also called two process tints or two step tints.

double process tints: (dôbl prô′cĕs tĭnts): see double application tints.

dry sanitizer (drī să-nĭ-tīz′ĕr): an airtight cabinet containing a disinfectant, fumigant (usually formalin) used to keep sanitized implements sanitary.

duct (dŭkt): a passage or canal for fluids.

duct glands: (glăndz): glands that produce substances which are secreted to other organs or parts of the body through ducts; i.e., sweat and oil glands in the skin.

ductless glands: glands which do not have ducts but secrete their hormones directly into the bloodstream.

dye remover: see color remover.

─────────── **E** ───────────

eczema (ĕk′zē-mă): an inflammatory itching disorder of the skin.

edging (ĕj′ĭng): the process of cutting the sideburn and nape area; feathering.

efferent (ĕf′ĕr-ênt): conveying outward, as efferent nerves conveying impulses away from the central nervous system; see: motor nerve.

effilate (ĕf′ĭ-lāt): to cut the hair strand by a sliding movement of the scissors; slither.

effleurage (ĕ-flū-razh′): a stroking movement in massage.

egg shampoo (ĕg shăm-poo′): a special shampoo containing egg, used on damaged hair.

Egyptian henna (ĕ-jĭp′shân hĕn′á): a pure vegetable hair dye.

elasticity (ē-lăs′tĭs′ĭ-tē): the property that allows a thing to be stretched and return to its former shape.

electric curling iron (ē-lĕk′trĭk): a form of thermal iron heated by electricity; see thermal iron.

electric current: see current.

electric heater (hēt′ĕr): a portable stove especially designed to heat thermal irons and combs.

electricity (ē-lĕk-trĭs′ĭ-tē): the form of energy provided by an electric current; when in motion it exhibits magnetic, chemical or thermal effects.

electric pressing comb (prĕs′ĭng): a thermal (steel) instrument which is heated and employed to temporarily straighten over-curly hair.

electric sanitizer (săn-ĭ-tīz′ĕr): a form of dry sanitizer which employs an ultra-violet lamp to keep sanitized implements sanitary.

electrification (ē-lĕk′trĭ-fĭ-kā′shûn): the application of electricity to the body by holding an electrode in the hand and charging the body with electricity.

507

electrode (ê-lĕk'trōd): a pole of an electric cell; an applicator for directing the use of electricity on a customer.

electrology (ê-lĕk-trŏl'ŏ-jē): science in relation to electricity.

electrolysis (ê-lĕk-trŏl'ĭ-sĭs): the technique of permanently removing unwanted hair by destroying the hair papilla with an electrified needle.

electron (ê-lĕk'trŏn): an extremely minute corpuscle or charge of negative electricity, the smallest known to exist.

electrotherapy (ê-lĕk-trō-thĕr'â-pē): the practice of any cosmetic or medical treatment employing an electrical current.

element (ĕl'ê-mĕnt): the simplest form or basic unit of all matter; an element is composed of like atoms and cannot be reduced to a simpler substance.

elevation (ĕl-ê-vā'shûn): the height at which a strand of hair, a curl or a ridge is held up from the scalp.

emollient (ê-mŏl'yênt): an agent that softens, lubricates or soothes the surface of the skin.

emulsifier (ê-mŭl'sĭ-fī-ēr): a substance, as gelatin, gum. etc., which is used to produce an emulsion of a fixed oil.

emulsion (ê-mŭl'shûn): a milky fluid obtained by suspending oil in water; a preparation of one liquid distributed in small globules throughout the body of a second liquid.

end bonds (peptide bonds) (pĕp'tĭd): the chemical bonds which join together the amino-acids to form the long chains which are characteristic of all proteins.

endocrine (ĕn'dŏ-krĭn): any internal secretion or hormone.

end papers (ĕnd' pā'pērz): special porous papers especially designed to control the hair ends as they are being wrapped on permanent wave rods.

enzyme (ĕn'zīm): a digestive substance which causes chemical changes in certain foods in the body, without causing any change in itself.

epicranium (ĕp-ĭ-krā'nē-ŭm): the structure covering the cranium.

epicranius (ĕp-ĭ-krā'nē-ûs): the occipito frontalis; the scalp muscle.

epidemic (ĕp-ĭ-dĕm'ĭk): a prevailing disease which attacks many people at the same time.

epidermis (ĕp-ĭ-dûr'mĭs): the outer epithelial portion of the skin; also called cuticle or scarf skin.

epilation (ĕp-ĭ-l'shûn): the removal of hair by the roots.

eponychium (ĕp-ŏ-nĭk'ē-ûm): the extension of cuticle at base of nail-body.

erythrocyte (ê-rĭth'rŏ-sīt): a red blood cell; red corpuscle.

esophagus; oesophagus (ê-sŏf'ă-gûs): the canal leading from the pharynx to the stomach.

ethics: principles of good character and proper conduct.

ethmoid (ĕth'moid): resembling a sieve; a bone forming part of the walls of the nasal cavity.

etiology (ê-tē-ŏl'ŏ-jē): the science of the causes of disease.

evaporation (ê-vă̆p-ōw-rā'shûn): change from liquid to vapor form.

excoriation (ĕks-kō-rē-ā'shûn): act of scraping the skin; an abrasion.

excrete (ĕks-krēt'): to separate (waste matter) from the blood or tissue and eliminate from the body as through the kidneys or sweat glands.

excretion (ĕks-krē'shûn): that which is thrown off or eliminated from the body.

excretory system (ĕks'krē-tŏ-rē sĭs'tĕm): the excretory system purifies the body by the elimination of liquid, gas and solid waste.

exhalation (ĕks-hă-lā'shûn): the act of breathing outward.

extensibility (ĕks-tĕn-sĭ-bĭl'ĭ-tē): capable of being extended or stretched.

extensor (ĕks-tĕn'sôr): a muscle which serves to extend or straighten out a limb or part.

external jugular (ĕks'tēr-nâl jōō'gû-lâr): one of the two principal veins returning blood to the heart from the head, face and neck.

extremity (ĕks-trĕm'ĭ-tē): the distant end or part of any organ; a hand or foot.

exudation (ĕks-û-dā'shûn): act of discharging from the body through pores as sweat, moisture or other liquid.

F

facial (fā'shâl): pertaining to the face; the seventh cranial nerve.

facial nerve (nûrv): the seventh cranial nerve.

Fahrenheit (fä'rĕn-hīt): pertaining to the Fahrenheit thermometer or scale; water freezes at 32° F. and boils at 212° F.

fascia (făsh'ē-ă): a sheet of connective tissue covering, supporting, or binding muscles together.

feathering (fĕ-thŭr'ĭng): shortening the hair into a graduated effect; tapering.

fermentation (fûr-mĕn-tā'shûn): a chemical decomposition of organic compounds into more simple compounds, brought about by the action of an enzyme.

fetid (fĕt'ĭd): having a foul smell.

fever blister: an acute skin disorder characterized by the presence of vesicles over an inflammatory base; herpes simplex.

fibrin (fī'brĭn): the active agent in coagulation of the blood.

fifth cranial nerve (krā'nē-âl): see: trigeminal nerve.

filler (fĭl'ēr): a preparation used to recondition lightened, tinted or damaged hair; see: color filler.

filter (fĭl'tēr): anything porous through which liquid is passed to cleanse or strain it.

finger test: a test given to determine the degree of porosity in the hair.

finger wave (fĭng'ēr wāv): the process of setting the hair in a wave pattern by using the fingers, lotion and a comb.

fission (fĭsh'ŭn): reproduction of bacteria by cellular division; any splitting or cleaving; atomic f.: the splitting of the neutrons of an atom into two main fragments.

fissure (fĭsh'ûr): a narrow crack in the skin which penetrates into the derma; examples: chapped hands or lips.

fixative (fĭk′să-tĭv): a chemical agent capable of stopping the processing of the permanent wave solution or the chemical hair relaxer and hardening the hair in its new form; neutralizer; stabilizer.

flagella (flă-jĕl′ă): slender whip-like processes which permit locomotion in certain bacteria.

flexor (flĕk′sôr): a muscle that bends or flexes a part or a joint (bending of the elbow).

fluorescent (floō′ôr-ĕs′n′t): an ability to emit light after exposure to light, the wave length of the emitted light being longer than that of the light absorbed.

"fly away": an excessive electrostatic condition of hair which causes individual hair strands to repel one another and stand away from the head.

follicle (fŏl′ĭ-k′l): a small secretory cavity or sac; the depression in the skin containing the hair root.

formaldehyde (fôr-măl′dē-hīd): a pungent gas possessing powerful disinfectant properties.

Formalin (fôr′mă-lĭn): a 37% to 40% solution of formaldehyde.

formula (fôr′mŭ-lă): a prescribed method or rule; a recipe or prescription.

foundation (foun-dā′shŭn): the base of any hairpiece to which the hair is attached.

fragilitas crinium (fră-jĭl′ĭ-tăs krĭ′nē-ûm): technical term for brittle hair.

freckle (frĕk″l): a yellow or brown spot on the skin; lentigo.

free edge (frē′ ĕdj): that part of the nail plate which extends over the fingertip.

frequency (frē′kwĕn-sē): the number of complete cycles per second of current produced by an alternating current generator; standard frequencies are 25 and 60 cycles per second.

friction (frĭk′shŭn): the resistance encountered in rubbing one body on another.

frizzy (frĭ′zē): hair having too much curl, such as overprocessed hair.

frontal: relating to the forehead; the bone of the forehead.

frontalis (frŏn-tā′lĭs): anterior portion of the muscle of the scalp.

frosting (frŏst′ĭng): to lighten or darken small selected strands of hair over the entire head to blend with the rest of the hair.

fuller's earth (fōōl′ĕrz ûrth): a soapy clay often used as a foundation for packs and masks.

fulling (fōōl′ĭng): a massage movement in which the limb is rolled back and forth between the hands.

fumigant (fŭ′mĭ-gănt): a gaseous substance employed in a dry sanitizer to destroy bacteria and keep sanitized implements sanitary.

fumigate (fū′mĭ-gāt): disinfect by the action of smoke or fumes.

fungus (fŭn′gŭs): a vegetable parasite; a spongy growth of diseased tissue on the body.

furuncle (fū-rŭn′k′l): a small skin abscess (boil).

fuse: a special device which prevents excessive current from passing through a circuit.

fusion (fū′zhŭn): the act of uniting or joining together.

---------- **G** ----------

ganglion (găn′glē-ôn); pl., **ganglia** (-ă): bundles of nerve cells in organs of special sense; or forming units of the sympathetic nervous system.

gastric juice (găs′trĭk): the digestive fluid secreted by the glands of the stomach.

gauze: a thin, open-meshed cloth used for dressings.

genetic (jĕ-nĕt′ĭk): the genesis or origin of something.

gentian violet jelly: (jĕn′shân): an antiseptic used in the first aid treatment of a scalp burn.

germ: a bacillus; a microbe; an embryo in its early stages.

germicide (jûr′mĭ-sīd): any chemical, especially a solution that will destroy germs.

germinative layer (jûr-mĭ-nā′tĭv): stratum germinativum; the deepest layer of the epidermis resting on the dermis.

gland: a secretory organ of the body.

globule (glŏb′ūl): a small, spherical droplet of fluid or semi-fluid material.

glossopharyngeal (glŏs-ô-fă-rĭn′jē-āl): pertaining to the tongue and pharynx; the ninth cranial nerve.

glycerin; glycerine (glĭs′ĕr-ĭn): sweet, oily fluid, used as an application for roughened and chapped skin; also used as a solvent.

granulosum (grăn-ū-lōs′ûm): granular layer of the epidermis.

great auricular (grāt ô-rĭk′ū-lär): a nerve affecting the face, ear, neck and parotid gland.

greater occipital (ŏk-sĭp′ĭ-tâl): sensory and motor nerve affecting the back part of the scalp.

groom (grōōm): to make neat or tidy.

groove (grūv): see: shell.

ground wire (ground wīr): a wire which connects an electric current to a ground (waterpipe or radiator).

guideline (gīd′lĭn): a hair strand used as a guide, especially in hair shaping (cutting).

---------- **H** ----------

hacking (hăk′ĭng): a chopping stroke made with the edge of the hand in massage.

hair (hâr): pilus; a slender thread-like outgrowth on the scalp, face and the body.

hair bulb: the lower extremity of the hair.

hair clipping: removing the hair by the use of hair clippers; removing split hair ends of the hair with the scissors.

hair coloring: artificially changing the color of the hair.

hair conditioning: see conditioning.

haircutting: shortening and thinning of the hair, and molding the hair into a becoming style; hair shaping.

hair density: the number of hairs per square inch on the scalp.

hair dressing: the art of arranging the hair into various becoming shapes or styles.

hair follicle (fŏl′ĭ-k′l): the depression of the skin containing the root of the hair.

hair lace (lās): the net foundation of a hairpiece, made of stiffened human hair.

hair lightener: a chemical substance used to remove the natural color pigment from the hair.

hair lightening (lī'těn-ĭng): the removal of natural pigment or artificial color from the hair; bleaching; decolorizing.

hairline (hâr'līn): the line of hair outlining the outer part of the face and neck.

hair papilla (hâr pă-pĭl'ă): a small cone-shaped elevation at the bottom of the hair follicle.

hairpiece (hâr'pēs): toupee; a small wig used to cover the top or crown of a man's head.

hair pressing (prĕs'ĭng): a method of straightening curly or kinky hair by means of a heated iron or comb; hair silking; hair straightening.

hair pressing oil (oil): an oily or waxy mixture used in hair pressing.

hair relaxing, chemical (rê-lăk'sĭng, kĕm'ĭ-kăl): a permanent method of straightening overcurly hair.

hair restorer (rê-stōr'ēr): a preparation containing a metallic dye.

hair root (rōot): that part of the hair contained within the follicle.

hair shaft (shăft): the portion of the hair which projects beyond the skin.

hair shaping (shāp'ĭng): the art of haircutting.

hair straightener (strāt'ĕn-ēr): a physical or chemical agent used in straightening kinky or over-curly hair.

hair straightening: see hair pressing.

hair stream: the natural direction in which the hair grows after leaving the follicle.

hair, superfluous (sŭ-pûr'flōō-ŭs): unwanted or excess hair, usually found on the faces of women; see: hirsuties.

hair test: a sampling of how the hair will react to a particular treatment.

hair texture (tĕks'tŭr): the general quality of hair, as to coarse, medium or fine; the feel of the hair.

hair tint (tĭnt): a hair coloring.

hair tinting (tĭnt'ĭng): the physical act of adding color pigment to either virgin or tinted hair.

hair transplant (trănz'plĕnt): a procedure whereby hair is surgically removed from one area of the scalp and transferred to another area.

hair trim (trĭm): trimming; cutting the hair lightly over the already existing formed lines.

halitosis (hăl-ĭ-tō'sĭs): offensive odor from the mouth; foul breath.

hangnail (hăng'nāl): torn cuticle at the side of the nail; agnail.

hard water (härd wô'tēr): water containing certain minerals; does not lather with soap.

H-bond: see hydrogen bond.

heating cap: a thermal cap, applied over the head, to provide a uniform source of heat.

heating coil: an electric coil which heats the air in a hair dryer.

hemoglobin; haemoglobin (hē-mō-glō'bĭn): the coloring matter of the blood.

hemorrhage (hĕm'ô-râj): bleeding; a flow of blood, especially when profuse.

henna (hĕn'ă): the leaves of an Asiatic thorny tree or shrub used as a dye, imparting a reddish tint; it is also used as a cosmetic.

henna, compound (kŏm'pound): Egyptian henna to which has been added one or more metallic preparations.

heredity (hĕ-rĕd'ĭ-tē): the inborn capacity of the organism to develop ancestral characteristics.

herpes (hûr'pēz): an inflammatory disease of the skin having small vesicles in clusters.

herpes simplex (sĭm'plĕks): fever blister; cold sore.

hexachlorophenol (hĕks-ă-klō-rō-fē'nōl): white, free flowing powder, essentially odorless; used as a bactericidal agent in antiseptic soaps, deodorant products and various cosmetics.

high-frequency (hī-frē'kwĕn-sē): violet ray; an electric current of medium voltage and medium amperage, characterized by a high rate of vibration.

highlighting shampoo tint: a preparation used with shampoo when a very slight change in hair shade is desired.

hirsute (hûr'sūt, hĕr'sūt'): hairy; having coarse long hair; shaggy.

hirsuties (hûr-sū'shĭ-ēz): hypertrichosis; growth of an unusual amount of hair in unusual locations, as on the faces of women or the backs of men; hairy; superfluous hair.

histology (hĭs-tŏl'ô-jē): the science of the minute structure of organic tissues; microscopic anatomy.

homogeneous (hō-mōj'ē-nŭs): having the same nature or quality; a uniform character in all parts.

homogenizer (hō-mōj'ê-nīz-ēr): serving to produce a uniform suspension of emulsions from two or more normally immiscible substances.

hormone (hôr'mōn): a chemical substance formed in one organ or part of the body and carried in the blood to another organ or part which it stimulates to functional activity or secretion.

human disease carrier (hū'măn dĭ-zēz' căr'ē-ēr): an individual who may be immune to a disease but carries the germs and infects other people.

humerus (hū'mēr-ŭs): the bone of the upper part of the arm.

humidity: moisture; dampness.

hydro (hī'drō): a prefix denoting water; hydrogen.

hydro carbon: any compound composed only of hydrogen and carbon.

hydrogen: (hī-drō'jĕn): the lightest element; it is an odorless, tasteless, colorless gas found in water and all organic compounds.

hydrogen bond (bōnd) **(physical bond):** the physical cross bonds helping to hold the polypeptide chains in hair together; hydrogen bonds are formed by the joining of two molecules.

hydrogen peroxide: a powerful oxidizing agent; in liquid form it is used as an antiseptic and for the activation of lighteners and hair tints.

hydrophilic (hī-drō-fĭl'ĭk): capable of combining with or attracting water.

hygiene: the science of preserving health.

hygroscopic (hī-grō'skōp'ĭk): readily absorbing and retaining moisture.

hyoid (hī'oid): the "u" shaped bone at the base of the tongue.

hyperemia (hī'pēr-ē'mē-ă): the presence of an excessive quantity of blood in a part of the body; congestion.

hyperhidrosis, hyperidrosis (hĭ′pĕr-ĭ-drō′sĭs): excessive sweating.

hypertrophy (hĭ′pĕr-trō′fē): abnormal increase in the size of a part of an organ; overgrowth.

hypodermic (hĭ′pō-dûr′mĭk): beneath the skin; a liquid injected into the subcutaneous tissues.

hypoglossal (hĭ′pō-glŏ′săl): the twelfth cranial nerve; motor nerve to base of tongue.

hyponychium (hĭ-pō-nĭk′ē-ûm): the portion of the epidermis upon which the nail-body rests under the free edge.

—————— **I** ——————

idiosyncrasy (ĭd-ē-ō-sĭn′kră-sē): an individual characteristic or peculiarity; a susceptibility; individual hypersensitivity as to a drug or to food.

imbrications (ĭm-brĭ-kā′shŭnz): cells arranged in layers overlapping one another; found in cuticle layer of hair.

immersion (ĭ-mûr′chŭn): plunging or dipping into a liquid, especially so as to cover completely.

immune (ĭ-mūn′): free from or resistant to a disease.

immunity (ĭ-mūn′ĭ-tē): freedom from, or resistant to disease.

immunity, acquired (ă-kwĭrd′): freedom from or resistance to a specific disease as a result of having received an inoculation (vaccination) against that disease, or once having it and therefore building up an immunity against it.

immunity, natural (năch′ĕr-âl): being born with an immunity against a disease.

incubation (ĭn-kû-bā′shŭn): the period of a disease between the implanting of the contagion and the development of the symptoms.

index: the forefinger.

infection (ĭn-fĕk′shŭn): the invasion of the body tissues by disease germs.

infection, general (jĕn′ĕr-âl): the result of the disease germs gaining entrance to the blood stream and thereby circulating throughout the entire body.

infection, local (lō′kâl): confined to only certain portions of the body, such as an abscess.

infectious (ĭn-fĕk′shŭs): capable of spreading infection.

inferioris (ĭn-fē′rē-ŏr′ĭs): below; lower.

inflammation (ĭn-flă-mā′shŭn): the reaction of the body to irritation with accompanying redness, pain, heat, and swelling.

infra-orbital (ĭn-fră ôr′bĭ-tâl): below the eye-socket; a nerve affecting the cheek muscles, nose, and upper lip.

infra-red: rays pertaining to that part of the spectrum lying outside of the visible spectrum and below the red rays.

infra-trochlear (trŏk′lē-âr): sensory nerve affecting the skin of the nose and the inner muscle of the eye.

ingredient: any one of the things of which a mixture is made up.

ingrown hair: a wild hair that has grown underneath the skin, which may cause an infection.

ingrown nail: the growth of the nail into the flesh instead of toward the tip of the finger or toe, which may cause an infection.

inhalation (ĭn-hă-lā′shŭn): the inbreathing of air or other vapors.

inoculation (ĭn-ŏk-ū-lā′shŭn): the process by which protective agents are introduced into the body.

inorganic ĭn-ôr-găn′ĭk): composed of matter not relating to living organisms.

insanitary; unsanitary: not sanitary or healthful; injurious to health; unclean.

insoluble (ĭn-sŏl′û-b'l): incapable of being dissolved or very difficult to dissolve.

insulator (ĭn′sû-lā-tĕr): a non-conducting material or substance; materials used to cover electric wires.

intensity (ĭn-tĕn′sĭ-tē): the amount of force or energy of heat, light, sound, electric current, etc. per unit area; the quality of being intense.

intercellular (ĭn-tĕr-sĕl′û-lär): between or among cells.

internal jugular (ĭn-tĕr′nâl): one of the two principal veins which return blood to the heart from the head, face and neck.

intestine (ĭn-tĕs′tĭn): the digestive tube from the stomach to the anus.

involuntary muscles (ĭn-vŏl′ûn-tâ-rē): function without the action of the will.

iodine: a non-metallic element used as an antiseptic for cuts, bruises, etc.

ion: an atom or group of atoms carrying an electric charge.

ionization (ī-ŏn-ĭ-zā′shŭn): the separating of a substance into ions.

iris: the colored, muscular, disk-like diaphragm of the eye which regulates the pupil or opening in the center.

irradiation (ĭ-rā′dē-ā′shŭn): the process of exposing an object to the natural or artificial sunlight.

irreversible (ĭr-ê-vĕr′sĭ-b'l): not capable of being reversed.

irritability (ĭr-ĭ-tà-bĭl′ĭ-tē): readily excited or stimulated.

—————— **J** ——————

joint: a connection between two or more bones.

jowl: the hanging part of a double chin.

jugular (jōō′gû-lär): pertaining to the neck or throat; the large vein in the neck.

—————— **K** ——————

keratin (kĕr′ă-tĭn): a fiber protein that is the principal ingredient of hair and nails.

keratinization (kĕr′ă-tĭn-ĭ-zā′shŭn): the process of being keratinized.

keratoma (kĕr-ă-tō′mă): a callosity; a horny tumor; an acquired thickened patch of the epidermis.

kidney: a glandular organ which excretes urine.

kilowatt (kĭl′ō-wŏt): one thousand watts of electricity

knead (nēd): to work and press with the hands as in massage.

L

labii (lā′bē-ī): of or pertaining to the lip.

labium (lā′bē-ûm); pl., **labia** (-ă): lip.

laceration (lăs′ēr-ā′shŭn): a tear of the skin or tissues.

lachrymal; lacrimal (lăk′rĭ-mâl): pertaining to tears or weeping; bone at the front of the orbits.

lacquer, nail (lăk′ĕr): a thick liquid which forms a glossy film on the nail.

lanolin (lăn′ô-lĭn): purified wool fat.

lanugo (lă-nū′gō): the fine hair which covers most of the body.

larynx (lăr′ĭnks): the upper part of the trachea or wind pipe; the organ of voice production.

lateral (lăt′ĕr-âl): on the side.

lather (lath′ĕr): froth made by mixing soap and water.

lemon rinse (lĕm′ûn rĭns): a product containing lemon juice or citric acid; used to eliminate soap curds. Long period of use will slightly lighten the hair.

lentigo (lĕn-tī′gō); pl., **lentigines** (lĕn-tĭ-jĭ′nēz): a freckle; circumscribed spot or pigmentation in the skin.

lesion (lē′zhûn): a structural tissue change caused by injury or disease.

lesser occipital (lĕs′ĕr ŏk-sĭp′ĭ-tâl): the nerve supplying muscles at the back of the ear.

leucocyte (lū′kô-sīt): a white corpuscle; white blood cell.

leucoderma (lū-kô-dûr′mă): abnormal white patches on the skin; absence of pigment in the skin.

leuconychia (lū-kô-nĭk′ē-ă): a whitish discoloration of nails; white spots.

levator (lê-vā′tôr): a muscle that elevates a part.

ligament (lĭg′ă-mênt): a tough band of fibrous tissue, serving to connect bones, or to hold an organ in place.

lightener (bleach): the chemical employed to remove color from hair.

lightening (bleaching): see hair lightening.

light therapy (līt thĕr′ă-pē): the application of light rays for treatment of disorders.

liniment (lĭn′ĭ-mênt): a liquid intended for application to the skin by gentle friction.

lipophilic (lĭp-ō-fĭl′ĭk): having an affinity or attraction to fat and oil.

liquefy (lĭk′wĕ-fī): to reduce to the liquid state; said of both solids and gases.

liquid dry shampoo (lĭk′wĭd drī shăm-poō′): a shampoo made from a dry cleaning product; used for cleaning the scalp and hair when the patron is unable to receive a regular shampoo.

liquor cresolis compound (lĭk′ĕr krē-sōl′ĭs kŏm′pound): a powerful germicide.

litmus paper (lĭt′mûs): a blue coloring matter that is reddened by acids and turned blue again by alkalies.

lock-jaw: tetanus; specifically trismus; a firm closing of the jaw due to spasm of the muscles of mastication.

lotion (lō′shûn): a liquid solution used for bathing the skin.

louse (lous); pl., **lice** (līs): pediculus; an animal parasite infesting the hairs of the head.

lubricant lū′brĭ-kânt): anything that makes things smooth and slippery, such as oil.

lucidum (lū′sĭ-dŭm): the clear layer of the epidermis.

lung (lŭng): one of the two organs of respiration.

lunula (lū′nû-lă): the half-moon shaped area at the base of the nail.

lymph (lĭmf): a clear yellowish or light straw colored fluid, which circulates in the lymph spaces, or lymphatics of the body.

lymphatic system (lĭm-făt′ĭk): consists of lymph flowing through the lymph spaces, lymph vessels, lacteals, and lymph nodes or glands.

Lysol (lī′sōl): a trade name; a disinfectant and antiseptic; a mixture of soaps and phenols.

M

macroscopic (măk-rô-skŏp′ĭk): visible to the unaided eye.

macula (măk′û-lă); pl., **maculae** (-lē): a spot or discoloration level with skin; a freckle; macule.

magnetism (măg′nĕ-tĭz′m): the power possessed by a magnet to attract or repel other masses.

malar (mā′lăr): of or pertaining to the cheek; the cheek bone.

malformation (măl-fôr-mā′shûn): an abnormal shape or structure; badly formed.

malignant (mă-lĭg′nânt): resistant to treatment; growing worse; occurring in severe form; a tumor recurring after removal.

malpighian layer (măl-pĭg′ē-ân): stratum germinativum; the deeper portion of the epidermis.

mandible (măn′dĭ-b′l): the lower jaw bone.

mandibular nerve (măn-dĭb′û-lăr): the seventh cranial nerve which supplies the muscles and skin of the lower part of the face.

manicurist (măn′ĭ-kŭr-ĭst): one who professionally attends to the care of the hands and nails.

manipulation (mă-nĭp-û-lā′shûn): various hand. or mechanical movements employed in facials, and scalp and body massage for their beneficial effects.

Marcel irons (mär′sĕl ĭ′rônz): an implement used to create curls or waves in the hair with the aid of heat.

marrow: a soft, fatty substance filling the cavities of bone.

mask: a special cosmetic formula used to beautify the face.

massage (mă-säzh′): manipulation of the body by rubbing, pinching, kneading, tapping, etc., to increase metabolism, promote absorption, relieve pain, etc.

masseter (mă-sē′tĕr): a chewer; one of the muscles of the jaw used in mastication.

match test (măch tĕst): a test employed to determine whether hair fibers are human or synthetic.

matting (măt′ĭng): tangling together into a thick mass.

matrix (mā′trĭks): the formative portion of a nail.

maxilla (măk-sĭl′ă): upper jaw bone.

maximum (măk′sĭ-mŭm): the greatest or highest degree or amount of anything.

medial; median (mē′dē-âl; -ân): pertaining to the middle.

medulla (mĕ-dŭl′ă): the marrow in the various bone cavities; the pith of the hair.

medulla oblongata (ŏb-lŏn-gä′tă): the lowest, or posterior part of the brain, continuous with the spinal cord.

melanin (mĕl′ă-nĭn): the dark or black pigment in the epidermis and hair, and in the choroid or coat of the eye.

membrane (mĕm′brān): a thin sheet or layer of pliable tissue, serving as a covering.

mental nerve (mĕn′tâl nûrv): a nerve which supplies the skin of the lower lip and chin.

mentalis (mĕn-tā′lĭs): the muscle that elevates the lower lip, and raises and wrinkles the skin of the chin.

mesh (mĕsh): an open weave foundation used to attach hair in a hairpiece.

metabolism (mĕ-tăb′ô-lĭz′m): the constructive and destructive life process of the cell.

metallic salts (mĕ-tăl′ĭk sôlts): a compound of a base and an acid.

meta-toluene-diamine (mĕt′ă-tŏl′ū-ēn-dī-ăm′ĭn): the name given to an oxidation dye used to provide lighter shades of red and blonde; it is an aniline derivative type.

micro (mĭ′krô): a prefix denoting very small; slight; millionth part of.

microbe (mĭ′krōb): a micro-organism; a minute one-celled animal or vegetable bacterium.

micrococcus (mī-krô-kŏk′ŭs): a minute baterial cell having a round shape.

micro-organism (m-′krô-ôr′gân-ĭz′m): microscopic plant or animal cell; a bacterium.

microscope (mĭ′krô-skōp): an instrument for making enlarged views of minute objects.

miliaria rubra (mĭl-ē-ā′rē-ă rōōb′ră): prickly heat; burning and itching usually caused by exposure to excessive heat.

milium (mĭl-ē-ŭm); pl., **milia** (-ă): a small whitish pearl-like mass due to a retention of sebum beneath the epidermis; a whitehead.

milliampere (mĭl-ē-ăm′pâr): one thousandth of an ampere.

milliamperemeter (-mē′tĕr): an instrument employed to measure the rate of flow of an electric current.

mineral salts (mĭn′ĕr-âl sôlts): salts derived from an inorganic chemical compound.

miscible (mĭs′ĭ-b'l): the property of certain liquids to mix with each other in equal proportions.

mitosis (mĭ-tō′sĭs): indirect nuclear division; the usual process of cell reproduction of the human tissues.

mole (mōl): a small brownish spot on the skin.

molecule (mŏl′ē-kūl): the smallest possible unit of existence of any substance.

monilethrix (mô-nĭl′ĕ-thrĭks): beaded hair; a condition in which the hairs show a series of constrictions, giving the appearance of a string of fusiform beads.

mordant (môr′dânt): a substance, such as alum, phenol, aniline oil, which fixes the dye used in coloring.

motor nerves (efferent nerves): carry impulses from nerve centers to muscles for certain motions.

mould: to form or to shape into a definite pattern.

mucous membrane (mū′kŭs mĕm′brān): a membrane secreting mucus which lines passages and cavities communicating with the exterior.

mucus (mū′kŭs): the clear viscid secretion of mucous membrane.

muscle (mŭs″l): the contractile tissue of the body by which movement is accomplished.

muscle oil (oil): a vegetable oil in which either lecithin or cholesterin is dissolved; used in conjunction with massage to soften the skin and to help prevent fine lines.

muscle strapping (străp′ĭng): a heavy massage treatment used to reduce fatty deposits.

muscle tone (tōn): the normal degree of tension in a healthy muscle.

myology (mī-ŏl′ô-jē): the study of the function, structure, and diseases of muscles.

— N —

naevus; nevus (nē′vŭs); pl., **naevi; nevi** (-vī): a birthmark; a congenital skin blemish.

nail (nāl): unguis; the horny protective plate located at the end of the finger or toe.

nail-bed: that portion of the skin on which the body of the nail rests.

nail-body: the horny nail blade resting upon the nail-bed.

nail-grooves: the furrows on the sides of the nail upon which the nail moves as it grows.

nail lacquer: a thick liquid which forms a glossy film on the nail.

nail-mantle: the fold of the skin into which the nail-root is lodged.

nail matrix (mā′trĭks): the portion of the nail-bed extending beneath the nail-root.

nail-root: located at the base of the nail, imbedded underneath the skin.

nail-wall: folds of skin overlapping sides and base of the nail-body.

nape: the back of the neck.

naris (nā′r-s); pl., **nares** (-rēz): a nostril.

nasalis (nâ-zā′lĭs): a muscle of the nose.

neck line: in haircutting, where the hair growth of the head ends and the neck begins; hairline.

negative (nĕg′ă-tĭv): the opposite of positive; the absence of a normal condition.

negative pole, N. or — (pōl): the pole from which negative galvanic current flows.

nerve (nûrv): a whitish cord, made up of bundles of nerve fibers, through which sensory or motor impulses are transmitted.

neuritis (nû-rī′tĭs): inflammation of nerves, marked by neuralgia.

neurology (nû-rŏl′ô-jē): the science of the structure, function and pathology of the nervous system.

neuron (nū′rŏn): the unit of the nervous system, consisting of the nerve cell and its various processes.

neutral: exhibiting no positive properties; indifferent; in chemistry, neither acid nor alkaline.

neutralization (nū-trăl-ĭ-zā'shŭn): a chemical reaction between an acid and a base; rehardening the hair in cold waving or in chemical hair relaxing.

neutralizer (nū'trâl-īz-ẽr): an agent capable of neutralizing another substance. (See fixative.)

nit: the egg of a louse, usually attached to a hair.

nitrate (nī'trāte): an oxidizing agent.

nitric acid (nī'trĭk): concentrated acid employed as a caustic.

nitrite (nī'trīte): a reducing agent; sodium nitrite is used as a sanitizing agent and acts as an anti-rusting agent.

nitrogen (nī'trŏ-jĕn): a colorless, gaseous element, tasteless and odorless, found in air and living tissue.

nodule (nŏd'yūle): a small, circumscribed, solid elevation that usually extends into the deeper layers of the skin.

non (nŏn): a prefix denoting not.

non-conductor (kŏn-dŭk'tẽr): any substance that resists the passage of electricity, light or heat towards or through it.

non-pathogenic (păth-ō-jĕn'ĭk): non-disease producing; growth promoting.

non-striated (-strī'ăt-ēd): involuntary muscle; functions without the action of the will; consists of spindle-shaped cells without striations; smooth muscle.

non-vascular (-văs'kû-lâr): not supplied with blood vessels.

nucleus (nū'klē-ŭs); pl., **nuclei** (-ī): the active center of cells.

nutrition (nū-trĭsh'ŭn): the process of nourishment.

O
---

obesity (ō-bē'sĭ-tē): a condition characterized by having too much body fat.

objective symptom (ŏb'jĕk-tĭv sĭm'tôm): a visible irregular skin condition that indicates or helps to diagnose a skin disorder.

oblique (ŏb-lēk'; -līk); **obliquus** (-ŭs); slanting, or inclined.

obsolete (ŏb-sŏ-lēt'): old; gone out of date.

occipital (ŏk-sĭp'ĭ-tâl): pertaining to the back part of the head; the bone which forms the back and lower part of the cranium.

occipital artery (är'tẽr-ē): artery which supplies blood to the back of the head, up to the crown.

occipitalis (ŏk-sĭp'ĭ-tâl-ĭs): the muscle at the back part of the head.

occipito-frontalis (ŏk-sĭp'ĭ-tō-frŏn-tā'lĭs): epicranius; the scalp muscle.

occupational disease (ŏk-û-pā'shŭn-âl dĭ-zēz'): due to certain kinds of employment, such as coming into contact with chemicals, dyes, etc.

oculomotor (ŏk'û-lō-mō'tẽr): third cranial nerve; controlling the motion of the eye.

oculus (ŏk'û-lŭs); pl., **oculi** (-lī): the eye.

ohm (ōm): a unit of measurement used to denote the amount of resistance in an electrical system or device.

Ohm's law (ōmz lô): the simple statement that the current in an electric circuit is equal to the pressure divided by the resistance.

ointment (oint'mĕnt): a fatty, medicated mixture used externally.

olfactory (ŏl-făk'tŏ-rē): relating to the sense of smell; first cranial nerve, the special nerve of smell.

one process tints: see single application tints.

opaque (ō-pāk'): impervious to light rays; neither transparent nor translucent.

ophthalmic (ŏf-thăl'mĭk): pertaining to the eye; fifth cranial nerve.

optic (ŏp'tĭk): second cranial nerve; the nerve of sight; pertaining to the eye, or to vision.

orbicularis oculi (ôr-bĭk-û-lā'rĭs ŏk'û-lī): orbicularis palpebrarum; the ring muscle of the eye.

orbicularis oris (ō'rĭs): orbicular muscle; muscle of the mouth.

orbit (ôr'bĭt): the bony cavity of the eyeball; the eye-socket.

organ (ôr'găn): a part of the body, such as the heart, which has a specific function to perform.

organic (ôr-găn'ĭk): relating to an organ; pertaining to substances derived from living organisms.

organism (ôr'găn-ĭz'm): any living being, either animal or vegetable.

origin (ôr'ĭ-jĭn): the beginning; the starting point of a nerve; the place of attachment of a muscle to a bone.

oris (ō'rĭs): pertaining to the mouth; an opening.

orris root (ôr'ĭs rōot): a special powder used to give a dry shampoo.

os (ŏs): a bone.

oscillation (ŏs-ĭ-lā'shŭn): movement like a pendulum; a swinging or vibration.

osmidrosis (ŏs-mĭ-drŏ'sĭs; ŏz-): bromidrosis; foul smelling perspiration.

osmosis (ŏs-mō'sĭs; ŏz-): the passage of fluids and solutions through a membrane or other porous substance.

osseous; osseus (ŏs'ē-ŭs): bony

osteology (ŏs-tē-ŏl'ō-jē): study of the anatomy, structure, and function of bones.

overlap (ō-vẽr-lăp'): when tint or lightener is allowed to run on to the previously tinted or lightened hair during applications.

over-process (prä'cĕs): to subject the hair or skin to over-exposure to a chemical cosmetic; i.e., in permanent waving keeping the perming solution on too long or using a solution which is too strong.

oxidation (ŏk-sī-dā'shŭn): the act of combining oxygen with another substance, with or without generation.

oxygen (ŏk'sĭ-jĕn): a gaseous element, essential to animal and plant life.

oxymelanin (ŏk'sĭ-mĕl'ă-nĭn): a compound formed by a combination of an oxidizing agent with the dark melanin (color) pigments in the hair; (generally found in the red to yellow shades).

P
---

pack (păk): a special cosmetic formula used to beautify the face.

palate (păl'ât): the roof of the mouth and the floor of the nose.

palatine bones (păl′ă-tĭn bōnz): situated at the back part of the nasal fossae.

pancreas (păn′krē-ăs): a gland connected with the digestive tract.

papilla, hair (pă-pĭl′ă, hâr): a small cone-shape elevation at the bottom of the hair follicle in the dermis.

papillary layer (păp′ĭ-lâ-rē lā′ĕr): the outer layer of the dermis.

papule (păp′ūl): a pimple; a small red elevation on the skin containing fluid.

para-phenylene-diamine (păr-ă-fēn′ĭ-lēn-dī-ăm′ĭn; dī′ă-mēn): an aniline derivative used in hair tinting.

parasite (păr′ă-sīt): a vegetable or animal organism which lives on or in another organism, and draws its nourishment therefrom.

parasiticide (păr-ă-sĭt′ĭ-sīd): a substance that destroys parasites.

para tint: a tint made from an aniline derivative.

para toluene diamine (păr′ă tŏl′ū-ēn dī-ăm′ĭn): a variety of aniline derivative dyes commonly used in preparations compounded to provide red and blonde tones.

parietal (pă-rī′ĕ-tăl): a bone at the side of the head.

parotid (pă-rŏt′ĭd): near the ear; a gland near the ear.

patch test (păch tĕst): see predisposition test.

pathogenic (păth-ō-jĕn′ĭk): causing disease.

pathology (păth-ŏl′ō-jē): the study which treats with modifications of the functions and changes in structure caused by disease.

pattern (păt′ĕrn): a head shape or design from which the hairpiece is constructed.

pediculosis capitis (pē-dĭk′ū-lō′sĭs kăp′ĭ-tĭs): lousiness of the hair of the head.

penetrating tint (pĕn′ĕ-trā-tĭng): a tint which penetrates through the cuticle and deposits color in the cortex.

pepsin (pĕp′sĭn): an enzyme which digests protein.

peptide bonds: see end bonds.

percarbonate (pĕr-kär′bŏ-nāt): quantity of salts or esters of carbonic acid.

percussion (pĕr-kŭsh′ûn): a form of massage consisting of repeated light blows or taps of varying force.

pericardium (pĕr-ĭ-kär′dē-ûm): the membranous sac around the heart.

peripheral nervous system (pē-rĭf′ĕr-ăl): consists of the nerve endings in the skin and sense organs.

permanent hair color: a penetrating hair tint; an aniline derivative product which is mixed with hydrogen-peroxide. See penetrating tint.

permanent wave, acid balanced: a system of permanent waving employing a solution acid in pH but uses heat to cause penetration of the hair and reduce processing time.

permanent wave, cold: a system of permanent waving employing chemicals rather than heat; solution used is highly alkaline.

permeable (pûr′mē-ă-b'l): permitting the passage of liquids.

peroxide of hydrogen: a powerful oxidizing agent; in liquid solution it is used as an antiseptic; used in tinting and lightening treatments.

peroxide rinse (rĭns): it is used to lighten the color of the hair.

perspiration (pûr′spĭ-rā′shŭn): sweat; the fluid excreted from the sweat glands of the skin.

petrissage (pĕt-rĭ′säj): the kneading movement in massage.

petrolatum (pĕt-rō-lā′tûm): petroleum jelly; vaseline; a purified, yellow mixture of semi-solid hydrocarbons obtained from petroleum.

pH: symbol for potential hydrogen concentration; the relative degree of acidity or alkalinity.

pH number: a measure of the degree of acidity or alkalinity of a solution.

phagocyte (făg′ō-sīt): a cell possessing the property of ingesting bacteria, particles, and other cells.

pharynx (făr′ĭnks): the upper portion of the digestive tube, behind the nose and mouth.

phenol (fē′nōl): carbolic acid; caustic poison; in dilute solution is used as an antiseptic and disinfectant.

phoresis (fō-rē′sĭs): the process of introducing solutions into the tissues through the skin by the use of galvanic current.

phosphorus (fŏs′fôr-ûs): an element found in the bones, muscles and the nerves.

physiology (fĭz-ē-ŏl′ō-jē): the study of the functions of living things.

pigment (pĭg′mĕnt): any organic coloring matter, as that of the red blood cells, the hair or the skin.

pigmentation (pĭg′mĕn-tā′shŭn): the deposition of pigment in the skin or tissues.

pilus (pī′lûs); pl., **pili** (-lī): hair

pimple (pĭm′p'l): any small pointed elevation of the skin; a papule or small pustule.

pin "T" (pĭn): a "T" shaped pin used to attach a hairpiece to a block.

pituitary (pĭ-tū′ĭ-târ-ē): a ductless gland located at the base of the brain.

pityriasis (pĭt-ĭ-rī′ă-sĭs): dandruff

pityriasis capitis simplex (kăp′ĭ-tĭs sĭm′plĕks): dry dandruff.

pivot, hair shaping: the exact point from which the hair is directed in forming a curvature or shaping.

plasma (plăz′mă): the fluid part of the blood and lymph.

platelets (plāt′lĕts): blood cells which aid in the clotting process.

platysma (plă-tĭz′mă): a broad, thin muscle of the neck.

pledget (plĕj′ĕt): a compress or small, flat mass of lint, absorbent cotton, or the like.

pliability (plī-ă-bĭl′ĭ-tē): flexibility.

pneumogastric nerve (nū-mō-găs′trĭk nûrv): vagus nerve; tenth cranial nerve.

polypeptide (pŏl-ē-pĕp′tĭd): strings of amino-acids joined together by peptide bonds, the prefix "poly" meaning many.

pomade (pō-mād′): a medicated ointment for the hair.

pore: a small opening of the sweat glands of the skin.

porosity (pō-rŏs′ĭ-tē): ability of the hair to absorb moisture.

porous: full of pores.

positive: affirmative; not negative; the presence of abnormal condition.

posterior (pŏs-tē′rē-ẽr): situated behind; toward the back.

posterior auricular (ô-rĭk′û-lăr): a nerve which supplies muscles behind the ear.

posterior auricularis: the muscle behind the ear.

posterior auricular artery: the artery which supplies blood to the area behind the ears.

postiche (pŏs-tēsh′): artificial hairpiece; curls, braids, or other extra hairpiece used in creating coiffures.

posture (pŏs′tûr): the position of the body as a whole.

potassium hydroxide (pô-tăs′ē-ûm hī-drŏk′sīd): a powerful alkali, used in the manufacture of soft soaps.

precipitate (prē-sĭp′ĭ-tāt): to cause a substance in solution to settle down in solid particles; to decrease solubility.

predisposition test: a skin test designed to determine an individual's over-sensitivity to certain chemicals (patch test, allergy test, skin test).

pre-lightening (prē-līt′ĕn-ĭng): a hair lightening service required when the patron desires a drastic change in color to a much lighter shade; also required before the application of a toner.

pre-softening (prē-sŏf-tĕn′ĭng): a hair treatment required when hair is resistant; the hair is softened in order that the tint readily penetrates into the cortex.

pressing: a method of straightening over-curly or kinky hair with a heated comb or iron.

prickly heat (prĭk′lē hēt): see miliaria rubra.

primary colors: pigments or colors that are, or thought to be, fundamental; red, yellow and blue are the primary colors in pigments.

primary hair: the baby fine hair that is present over almost the entire smooth skin of the body.

prism (prĭz′m): a transparent solid with triangular ends and two converging sides; it breaks up white light into its component colors.

procerus (prô-sē′rûs): muscle that covers bridge of the nose.

processes (prŏs′ĕ-sēz): the threadlike fibers of a nerve cell which convey the nerve impulses throughout the body.

processing (prŏs′ĕs-ĭng): the action of a chemical in softening and reforming the structure of the hair. (In permanent waving and hair relaxing.)

processing machine: an apparatus employed to hasten the action of the chemical in hair tinting or lightening.

prognosis (prŏg-nō′sĭs): the foretelling of the probable course of a disease.

progressive tints (prô-grĕs′ĭv): hair restorers requiring time to oxidize; color develops gradually.

prong: the round rod of the thermal (marcel) iron.

properties (prŏp′ĕr-tēz): the identifying characteristics of a substance which are observable; a peculiar quality of anything; i.e., color, taste, smell, etc.

prophylaxis (prô-fĭ-lăk′sĭs): prevention of disease.

protective base (prô-tĕk′tĭv): a petroleum base, applied to the entire scalp in order to protect

it from the active agents contained in he chemical hair relaxer.

protein: a complex organic substance present in all living tissues, such as skin, hair and nails.

protoplasm (prō′tô-plăz′m): the material basis of life; a substance found in all living things.

protozoa (prō-tô-zō′ă) subkingdom of animals, including all the unicellular animal organisms.

psoriasis (sô-rī′ă-sĭs): a skin disease with circumscribed red patches, covered with adherent white ilver scales.

pull burn: scalp irritation resulting from uneven winding of the hair during permanent waving.

pull test: a test to determine the degree of elasticity of the hair.

pulmonary (pûl′mô-nâ-rē): relating to the lungs; an artery that carries blood from the heart to the lungs to be oxygenated.

pumice (pŭm′ĭs): substance used for buffing in manicuring; also called pumice stone.

purification (pū-rĭ-fĭ-kā′shŭn): the act of cleaning or removing foreign matter.

pus: a fluid product of inflammation, consisting of a liquid containing leucocytes and the debris of dead cells and tissue elements.

pusher: a steel instrument used to loosen the cuticle from the nail.

pustule (pŭs-tūl): an inflamed pimple containing pus.

Q

quadratus labii inferioris (kwŏd-rā′tŭs lā′bē-ī ĭn-fê-rē-ŏr′ĭs): a muscle of the lower lip.

quadratus labii superioris (sû-pē′rē-ŏr′ĭs): a muscle of the upper lip.

quarantine (kwŏr′ân-tēn): the isolation of a person to prevent spread of a contagious disease.

quaternary ammonium compounds (kwä-tẽr′năh-rē âh-mō′nē-ŭm kŏm′pŏundz): a chemical compound very effective as an agent for sanitizing implements.

quats (kwätz): the popular term for the sanitizing solution—quaternary ammonium compounds.

quinine (kw-′nīn): enters into the composition of many hair lotions in small quantities; its effect is slightly antiseptic.

R

radiation (rā-dē-ā′shŭn): the process of giving off light or heat rays.

rash (răsh): a skin eruption having little or no elevation.

reconditioning (rē-kŏn-dĭ′shŭn-ĭng): the application of a special substance to the hair in order to improve its condition.

receptors (rē-cĕp′tŏrz): sensory nerves of the skin which are sensitive to touch, pain, pressure, heat or cold.

rectifier (rĕk′tĭ-fĭ-ẽr): an apparatus to change an alternating current of electricity into a direct current.

reddish cast: a tinge of red.

reducing agent: a substance capable of adding hydrogen; in cosmetology, a cold wave solution would be a reducing agent.

reflex: an involuntary nerve reaction.

relaxer (rē-lăk'sĕr): a chemical applied to the hair to remove the natural curl.

relaxer testing: checking the action of the relaxer in order to determine the speed at which the natural curl is being removed.

reproductive (rē-prŏ-dŭk'tĭv): pertaining to reproduction or the process by which plants and animals give rise to offspring.

resilient (rĕ-zĭl'ĭ-ĕnt): elastic.

resistance (rē-zĭst'ăns): the difficulty of moisture or chemical solutions to penetrate the hair shaft.

resistant hair (rē-zĭs'tănt hâr): hair with the cuticle scales lying very close to the hair shaft resisting the penetration of moisture into the hair cortex.

respiration (rĕs-pĭ-rā'shŭn): the act of breathing; the process of inhaling air into the lungs and expelling it.

respiratory system (rē-spīr'ă-tô-rē): consists of the nose, pharynx, larynx, trachea, bronchi and lungs which assist in breathing.

reticular layer (rē-tĭk'û-lâr): the inner layer of the dermis.

retina (rĕt'ĭ-nă): the sensitive membrane of the eye which receives the image formed by the lens.

retouch: application of hair color, lightener or chemical hair relaxer to new growth of hair.

reversible (rē-vĕrs'ĭ-b'l): capable of going through a series of changes in either direction, forward or backward, as a reversible chemical reaction.

rhagades (răg'ă-dēz): cracks, fissures or chaps on the skin.

rheostat (rē'ô-stăt): a resistance coil; an instrument used to regulate the strength of an electric current.

rickettsia (rĭk-ĕt'sē-ä): a type of pathogenic microorganism, capable of producing disease.

ringed hair: a variety of canities in which the hair appears white or colored in rings.

ringworm: a vegetable parasitic disease of the skin and scalp which appears in circular lesions and is contagious.

rinse: to cleanse with a second or repeated application of water after washing; a prepared rinse water.

risorius (rĭ-zôr'ē-ûs): muscle at the side of the mouth.

rod (rŏd): that part of the thermal curling iron which is a perfectly round, solid steel bar.

rolling: a massage movement in which the tissues are pressed and twisted.

rolling massage cream (rō'lĭng mă-säzh krēm): a massage cream (pink in color) which becomes dry and flakes off as it is being massaged over the skin.

root: in anatomy, the base; the foundation or beginning of any part.

rotary (rō'tă-rē): circular motion of the fingers as in massage.

ruffing (rŭf'ĭng): back combing; teasing the hair.

S

Sabouraud Rousseau (să'bōō-rō rōō'sō): a discoverer of a 24-hour skin test used in hair coloring to determine whether or not a patron can tolerate an aniline derivative hair tint.

saline (sā'lĭn): salty; containing salt.

saliva (să-lī'vă): the secretion of the salivary glands; spit.

salivary gland (săl'ĭ-vâ-rē glănd): the gland in the mouth secreting saliva (spit).

salt (sôlt): the union of a base with an acid, used to season food.

sanitary (săn'ĭ-tă-rē): pertaining to cleanliness in relation to health; tending to promote health.

sanitation (săn-ĭ-tā'shŭn): the use of methods to bring about favorable conditions of health.

sanitize (săn'ĭ-tīz): to make sanitary.

sanitizer, dry: see dry sanitizer

sanitizer, wet (wĕt): a receptacle containing a disinfectant solution in which articles to be sanitized are completely immersed.

saprophyte (săp'rō-fīt): a micro-organism which grows normally on dead matter, as distinguished from a parasite.

S-bonds: see: sulphur bonds.

scab: a crust formed on the surface of a sore.

scabies (skā'bĭ-ēz): a skin disease caused by an animal parasite, attended with intense itching; the itch.

scalp (skălp): the thick skin covering of the head.

scalp cream (krēm): a special cream designed to help restore some of the natural oils to the scalp and hair.

scapula (skăp'û-lă): the shoulder blade; a large flat triangular bone of the shoulder.

scar (skär): a mark remaining after a wound has healed.

scarf skin (skärf skĭn): epidermis.

science (sī'ĕns): knowledge duly arranged and systematized.

scurf (skûrf): thin dry scales or scabs on the body, especially on the scalp; dandruff.

sebaceous cyst (sē-bā'shûs sĭst): a distended oily or fatty follicle or sac.

sebaceous glands (glăndz): oil glands of the skin; oil secreted by these glands are vital to the well-being of the skin and hair.

seborrhea (sĕb-ō-rē'ă): over-action of the sebaceous glands.

seborrhea capitis (kăp'ĭ-tĭs): seborrhea of the scalp, commonly called dandruff; pityriasis.

seborrhea oleosa (ō-lē-ō'să): excessive oiliness of the skin, particularly of the forehead and nose.

seborrhea sicca (sĭk'ă): an accumulation on the scalp ,of greasy scales or crusts, due to over-action of the sebaceous glands, dandruff or pityriasis.

seborrheic (sĕb-ō-rē'ĭk): seborrhea; pertaining to the over-action of the sebaceous glands.

sebum (sē,'bŭm): the fatty or oily secretions of the sebaceous glands.

secretion (sē-krē'shŭn). a product manufactured by a gland for a special purpose.

sectioning (sĕk'shŭn-ĭng): dividing the hair into separate parts or sections in preparation for haircutting or styling.

semi-permanent tints (sĕ′mĭ-pûr′măn-ĕnt tīntz): a formulated hair coloring material designed to last from four to six weeks—no peroxide is required with this type of tint.

senility (sē-nĭl′ĭ-tē): quality or state of being old.

sensation (sĕn-sā′shŭn): a feeling or impression arising as the result of the stimulation of an afferent nerve.

sensitivity (sĕn-sĭ-tĭv′ĭ-tē): the state of being easily affected by certain chemicals or external conditions.

sensory nerve (sĕn′sô-rē nûrv): afferent nerve; a nerve carrying sensations from sense organs to the brain.

sepsis (sĕp′sĭs): the presence of various pus-forming and other pathogenic organisms, or their poisons, in the blood or tissues; septicemia.

septic (sĕp′tĭk): relating to or caused by sepsis.

septum (sĕp′tŭm): a dividing wall; a partition.

setting lotion (sĕt′tĭng lō′shŭn): also called waving lotion; a lotion which is an aid to hairsetting and styling; the lotion makes the hair more pliable, provides hair control and manageability.

seventh cranial nerve (sĕ′vĕnth krā′nē-âl nûrv): the facial nerve controlling the motion of face, scalp, neck, ear and sections of the palate and tongue.

shaft (shăft): slender stem-like structure; the long slender part of the hair above the scalp.

shampoo (shăm-pōō′): to subject the scalp and hair to washing and massaging with some cleansing agent such as soap and water.

shampoo basin (bā′sĭn): an open, circular vessel, usually attached to the wall, used for shampooing.

shaper (shāp′ẽr): an implement with an attached blade, used in razor haircutting.

shaping, haircutting (shāp′ĭng, hâr′kŭt-ĭng): the process of shortening and thinning the hair to a particular style or to the contour of the head.

shaping, hairstyling (hâr′stīl-ĭng): the formation of uniform arcs or curves in wet hair; thus providing a base for various patterns in hairstyling.

shears (shẽrz): an implement employed to cut or shape hair (scissors).

sheath (shēth): a covering enclosing or surrounding some organ.

sheen (shē′n): shine, brightness, luster.

shell (shĕl): the bowl part of a marcel (curling) iron which is curved (grooved) to fit around the rod when the iron is closed.

shingling (shĭng′lĭng): cutting the hair close to the nape of the neck and gradually longer toward the crown.

shortwave (shôrt′wāv): a form of high-frequency current used in permanent hair removal.

sideburn (sīd′bûrn): continuation of the hairline in front of the ears.

siding (sīd′ĭng): a common term used to indicate the process of tapering and shaping the sides and back of head.

silking (sĭlk′ĭng): see hair pressing.

singeing: process of lightly burning hair ends with a lighted wax taper.

single application tints: products which lighten and add color to the hair in a single application; also called one process or one step tints.

sinus (sī′nŭs): a cavity or depression; a hollow in bone or other tissue.

skeletal muscles (skĕl′ē-tâl): muscles connected to the bones.

skeleton: the bony framework of the body.

skin: the external covering of the body.

skin texture: the general feel and apparance of the skin.

skull: the bony case or the framwork of the head.

slicing: carefully removing a section of hair from a shaping in preparation for making a pin curl.

slip: a smooth and slippery feeling imparted by talc to face powder.

slippage: the shifting and changing of position of the sulphur bonds.

slithering (slĭth′ẽr-ĭng): tapering the hair to graduated lengths with scissors.

smaller occipital (ŏk-sĭp′ĭ-tâl): sensory nerve affecting skin behind the ear.

soap cap: a solution of equal parts of shampoo, hydrogen peroxide and tint; employed when a slight change in color is desired.

soapless shampoo: a shampoo made with sulfonated oil, alcohol, mineral oil and water; this type of shampoo does not foam, and is usually alkaline in reaction.

sodium (sō′dē-ûm): a metallic element of the alkaline group.

sodium bicarbonate (bī-kär′bŏn-ât): baking soda; it relieves burns, bites; is often used in bath powders as an aid to cleansing oily skin.

sodium carbonate (kär′bŏn-ât): washing soda; used to prevent corrosion of metallic instruments when added to boiling water.

sodium hydroxide (hī-drŏk′sīd): a powerful alkaline product used in some chemical hair relaxers; caustic soda.

sodium lauryl sulfite (lô′rĕl sŭl′fīt): a metallic element of the alkaline group, in white or light yellow crystals; used in detergents.

sodium nitrite (nī′trīt): a chemical used for the prevention of corrosion; metal cleaner.

sodium perborate (pẽr′bô-rāt): a compound, formed by treating sodium peroxide with boric acid; on dissolving the substance in water, peroxide of hydrogen is generated; used as an antiseptic.

sodium sulphite (sûl′fīt): a soft, white metallic salt of sulphurous acid.

softening: the application of a chemical product to hair in order to make it more receptive to hair coloring or permanent waving.

soft press (sŏft prĕs): thermal hair straightening, performed with a pressing comb.

soft water (wô′tẽr): water which readily lathers with soap.

solubility (sŏl-û-bĭl′ĭ-tē): the extent to which a substance (solute) dissolves in a liquid (solvent) to produce a homegeneous system (solution).

solute (sŏl′ūt): the dissolved substance in a solution.

solution: the act or process by which a substance is absorbed into a liquid.

solvent (sŏl′vĕnt): an agent capable of dissolving substances.

spatula (spăt′ū-lă): a flexible, knife-like implement for handling creams and pomades, etc.

spectrum (spĕk′trŭm): the band of rainbow colors produced by decomposing light by means of a prism.

sphenoid (sfē′noid): wedge-shaped; a bone in the cranium.

spinal accessory (spī′nâl ăk-sĕs′ô-rē): eleventh cranial nerve.

spinal column: the backbone or vertebral column.

spinal cord: the portion of the central nervous system contained within the spinal, or vertebral canal.

spinal nerves: the nerves arising from the spinal cord.

spine: a short process of bone; the backbone.

spiral: coil; winding around a center, like a watch spring.

spirillum (spī-rĭl′ŭm); pl., **spirilla** (-ă): curved bacterium.

splash neutralizer: a chemical agent capable of stopping the action of the cold waving solution and setting or hardening the hair in its new form.

spore (spôr): a tiny bacterial body having a protective wall to withstand unfavorable conditions.

spray gum: a sticky juice applied as a liquid going through the air in small drops.

squama (skwā′mă): an epidermic scale made up of thin, flat cells.

stabilized: made stable or firm, preventing changes.

stabilizer: see fixative.

stable: in a balanced condition; not readily destroyed or decomposed; resisting molecular change.

stain: an abnormal skin discoloration.

staphylococcus (stăf-ĭ-lô-kŏk′ŭs): cocci which are grouped in clusters like a bunch of grapes; found in pustules and boils.

static electricity: a form of electricity generated by friction.

steamer, facial: an apparatus, used in place of hot towels, for steaming the scalp or face.

steatoma (stē-ă-tō′mă): a sebaceous cyst; a fatty tumor.

stem direction: the direction in which the stem moves from the base to the first arc.

stem, pin curl: that part of the pin curl between the base and the first arc of the circle.

sterilization: the process of making sterile; the destruction of germs.

sterno-cleido-mastoideus (stûr′nô-klī′dô-măs-toid′ê-ŭs): a muscle of the neck which depresses and rotates the head.

stimulation (stĭm-û-lā′shŭn): the act of arousing increased functional activity.

stomach: the dilated portion of the alimentary canal, in which the first process of digestion takes place.

strand test: a preliminary test given before a tint or lightening application to determine the required development time; a test to determine the degree of porosity and elasticity of the hair ,as well as the ability of the hair to withstand the effects of chemicals.

stratum (strā′tŭm); pl., **strata** (-ă): layer of tissue.

stratum corneum (kôr′nê-ŭm): horny layer of the skin.

stratum germinativum (jûr-mĭ-nā′tĭv-ŭm): the deepest layer of the epidermis resting on the corneum.

stratum granulosum (grăn-û-lō′sŭm): granular layer of the skin.

stratum lucidum (lū′sĭ-dŭm): clear layer of the skin.

streaking (strēk′ĭng): lightening broad sections of hair attractively placed around the face.

streptococcus (strĕp-tô-kŏk′ŭs): pus-forming bacteria that arrange in curved lines resembling a string of beads; found in erysipelas and blood poisoning.

striated (str-′āt-ĕd): marked with parallel lines or bands; ·striped; voluntary muscle.

stripping: the removal of color from the hair shaft; lightening. Strong shampoos or soap removing some of the color from the hair is also known as stripping.

stroking: a gliding movement over a surface; to pass the fingers or any instrument gently over a surface; effleurage.

structure (strŭk′tûr): construction; manner of building or form.

styptic (stĭp′tĭk): an agent causing contraction of living tissue; used to stop bleeding; an astringent.

subcutaneous (sŭb-kū-tā′nē-ŭs): under the skin.

subcutis (sŭb-kū′tĭs): subdermis; subcutaneous tissue; under or beneath the corium or dermis, the true skin.

subdermis (sŭb-dûr′mĭs): see subcutis.

subjective symptom (sŭb′jĕk-tĭv sĭm′tôm): evidence of a disorder which is felt by the person affected but is not visible to others; the opposite of objective symptom.

submental artery (sŭb-mĕn′tâl är′tĕr-ē): supplies blood to the chin and lower lip.

sudamen (sū-dā′mĕn); pl., **sudamina** (sū-dăm′ĭ-nă): a disorder of the sweat glands with obstruction of their ducts.

sudoriferous glands (sū-dôr-ĭf′ĕr-ŭs glăndz): sweat glands of the skin.

sulfite (sŭl′fīt): any salt or sulfurous acid.

sulfonated oil (sŭl′fôn-āt-êd): an organic substance prepared by reacting oils with sulphuric acid; has an alkaline reaction and is miscible with water; used as a base in soapless shampoos.

sulphide (sŭl′fīd): a compound of sulphur with another element or base.

sulphur (sŭl′fûr): a chemical element whose compounds are used in lightening, in hair preparations and in medicine.

sulphur bonds: sulphur cross bonds in the hair, which hold the chains of amino-acids together in order to form a hair strand.

superficial temporal (sōō-pĕr-fĭsh′âl tĕm′pô-râl): the primary artery which supplies blood to the muscles, skin and scalp to the front, side and top of the head.

superfluous (sōō-pĕr′flōō-ŭs): more than is necessary, excessive, extra.

superior auricularis (sōō-pē′rē-ôr ău-rĭk-ū-lär′ĭs): muscle above the ear.

suppuration (sŭp-û-rā′shŭn): the formation of pus.

supraorbital (sū-prắ-ôr′bĭ-tâl): above the orbit or eye.

supra-trochlear (sū-prắ-trŏk′lē-âr): aflects the skin between the eyes and the upper side of the nose.

surface tension: the tension or resistance to rupture possessed by the surface film of a liquid.

susceptible (sŭ-sĕp′tĭ-b′l): capable of being influenced or easily acted on.

suspension (sû-spĕn′shûn): a mixture of a liquid and insoluble particles which have a tendency to settle on standing.

sweat pore (swĕt): see pore.

swirl: formation of a wave in a diagonal direction from back to side of head.

sympathetic nervous system (sĭm-pă-thĕt′ĭk): controls the involuntary muscles which affect respiration, circulation and digestion.

symptom, objective (sĭmp′tôm, ŏb-jĕk′tĭv): that which can be seen, as in pimples, pustules, etc.

symptom, subjective (sŭb-jĕk′tĭv): can be felt, as in itching.

synthetic (sĭn-thĕt′ĭk): any man-made chemical or material.

system (sĭs′tĕm): a group of organs which especially contribute toward one of the more important vital functions; an assemblage of objects united by regular interdependence.

systematic (sĭs-tĕm-ât′ĭk): proceeding according to system or regular method.

systemic (sĭs-tĕm′ĭk): pertaining to a system or to the body as a whole.

--------------------- T ---------------------

tactile corpuscle (tăk′tĭl kôr′pŭs-′l): touch nerve endings found within the skin.

tannic acid (tăn′ĭk): a plant extract used as an astringent.

taper (tā′pĕr): regularly narrowed to a point.

tapotement (tà-pôt-män′): a massage movement using a short, quick slapping or tapping movement.

tapping (tăp′ĭng): a massage movement; striking lightly with the partly flexed fingers.

tartaric acid (tär′tà-rĭk): a colorless crystalline acid compound.

teasing: combing small sections of hair from the ends toward the scalp, causing the shorter hair to mat at the scalp, forming a cushion or base; also known as ratting, French lacing or ruffing.

temple: the flattened space on the side of the forehead.

temporal bone (tĕm′pô-râl): the bone at the side and base of the skull.

temporalis (tĕm-pô-rā′lĭs): the temporal muscle.

temporary color (tĕmp′ôr-âr-ē kŭl′ĕr): a hair coloring which coats the hair shaft and lasts only until the next shampoo.

tendon: fibrous cord or band connecting muscle with bone.

tensile (tĕn′sĭl): capable of being stretched.

tension: stress caused by stretching or pulling.

tepid (tĕp′ĭd): lukewarm; moderately warm.

terminology (tĕr-mĭ-nŏl′ô-jē): the special words or terms used in science, art or business.

tertiary (terminal) hair (tĕr′shê-à-rē hâr): the long, soft hair found on the scalp.

test curls: a method to determine how the patron's hair will react to permanent waving solution and neutralizer.

test, hair tint: a test made upon the scalp, behind the ear, or in the bend of the arm, for predisposition to the agent used; a test to determine the reaction of the color upon the sample strand, regarding both color and breakage.

test strand (strănd): a method to determine how the patron's hair will react to hair relaxing product and stabilizer or neutralizer.

tetanus (tĕt′à-nŭs): a disease with spasmodic and continuous contraction of the muscles; lock-jaw.

textometer (tĕks-tŏm′ê-tĕr): a device used to measure the elasticity and reaction of the hair to alkaline solutions.

texture of the hair: the general quality as to coarse, medium or fine; feel of the hair.

texture of skin: the general feel and appearance of the skin.

theraputic lamp (thĕr-ă-pū′tĭk): an electrical apparatus producing any of the various rays of the spectrum; used for skin and scalp treatments.

therapy (thĕr′à-pē): the science and art of healing.

thermal (thûr′mâl): relating to heat

thermal cap (kâp): see heating cap.

thermal curling: the process of forming curls with thermal irons.

thermal hair straightening: staightening over-curly hair with heated thermal irons.

thermal irons: an implement used to curl, wave or straighten hair by the application of heat.

thermal waving: forming waves in the hair with heated thermal iron.

thermostat (thûr′mô-stăt): an automatic device for regulating temperature.

thinning, hair: decreasing the thickness of the hair where it is too heavy.

thio (thī′ō): see ammonium thioglycolate.

thioglycolic acid (thī-ō-glī′kô-lĭk): a colorless liquid or white crystals with a strong unpleasant odor, miscible with water, alcohol or ether; (used in permanent wave solutions, hair relaxers and depilatories.)

thorax (thō′răks): the part of the body between the neck and the abdomen; the chest.

thrombocyte (thrŏm′bô-sīt): a blood platelet which aids in clotting.

thyroid gland (thī′roid): a large ,ductless gland situated in the neck.

tincture (tĭnk′tûr): an alcoholic solution of a medicinal substance.

tinea (tĭn′ê′à): a skin disease, especially ringworm.

tint: to give a coloring to; hair tinting; to color the hair by means of a hair tint or color rinse.

tinting: the process of adding artificial color to hair.

tipping: similar to frosting, but the darkening or lightening is confined to small strands of hair at the front of the head.

tissue: a collection of similar cells which perform a particular function.

tissue, connective (kŏ-nĕk′tĭv): binding and supporting tissue.

toner (tōn′ēr): an aniline derivative tint applied to highly lightened hair to produce a blonde, silver or pastel shade.

tonic (tōn′ĭk): increasing the strength or tone of the system.

topper (tŏp′ēr): a hairpiece designed for use on the top of the head.

topping (tŏp′ĭng): the process of cutting the hair on top of the head.

toupee (tōō-pē′): a small wig used to cover the top or crown of a man's head.

toxemia (tŏk-sē′mē-ȧ): form of blood poisoning.

toxin; toxine (tŏk′sĭn; -sēn): a poisonous substance of undetermined chemical nature which enters the tissues and the bloodstram.

T-pin (tē pĭn): a pin which is employed to hold a hairpiece on a block while it is being worked upon; pin is shaped like the letter T.

trachea (trā′kē-ȧ; trȧ-kē′ȧ): wind-pipe.

transformer (trăns-fôr′mēr): used for the purpose of increasing or decreasing the voltage of the current used; it can only be used on an alternating current.

translucent (trăns-lū′sênt): somewhat transparent.

transverse facial (trăns-vûrs′ fā′shȧl): an artery supplying the skin, the parotid gland and the masseter muscle.

trapezius (trȧ-pē′zē-ûs): muscle that draws the head backward and sideways.

triangularis (trī-ăn-gû-lā′rĭs): depressor anguli oris; a muscle that pulls down corners of the mouth.

trichology (trĭ-kŏl′ō-jē): the science of the care of the hair.

trichophytosis (trĭ-kŏf-ĭ-tō′sĭs): ringworm of the skin and scalp, due to growth of a fungus parasite.

trichoptilosis (trĭ-kŏp-tĭ-lō′sĭs): a splitting of the hair ends, giving them a feathery appearance.

trichorrhexis (trĭk-ô-rĕk′sĭs): brittleness of the hair.

trichosis (trĭ-kō′sĭs): abnormal growth of hair.

trifacial (trī-fā′shȧl): the fifth cranial nerve; trigeminus nerve.

trigeminal (trī-jĕm′ĭ-nȧl): relating to the fifth cranial or trigeminus nerve.

true skin (trōō skĭn): the corium.

trypsin (trĭp′sĭn): an enzyme in the digestive juice secreted by the pancreas; trypsin changes proteins into peptones.

tubercle (tū′bēr-k′l): a rounded, solid elevation on the skin or membrane.

tumor: a swelling; an abnormal enlargement.

turbinal; turbinate (tûr′bĭ-nȧl; -nāt): a bone in the nose; turbinated body.

tweezers: a pair of small forceps to remove or extract hair.

two process tints: see double application tints.

tyrosine (tī-rō′sĭn): an amino-acid widely distributed in proteins, particularly in casein.

— **U** —

ulcer (ŭl′sēr): an open sore not caused by a wound.

ultra (ŭl′trȧ): a prefix denoting beyond; on the other side; excessively.

ultra-violet (ŭl′trȧ-vī′ō-lĕt): invisible rays of the spectrum which are beyond the violet rays.

unadulterated (ŭn-ȧ-dŭl′tēr-āt-ĕd): pure.

undulation (ŭn-dû-lā′shûn): a wave-like movement or shape.

unipolar (ū-nĭ-pō′lȧr): a term used when one electrode of a direct current is applied to the body.

unit (ū′nĭt): a single thing or value.

United States Pharmacopeia (û-nīt′ĕd stāts fär-mȧ-kô-pē′yȧ): an official book of drug and medicinal standards.

unstable: liable to fade; not firm or constant; readily decomposing or changing.

urea (ū-rē′ȧ): a diuretic; also employed externally in treating infected wounds; occurs as colorless to white crystals or powder; soluble in water.

urea peroxide: a combination of urea and peroxide in the form of a cream developer or activator; employed in hair tinting.

— **V** —

vaccination (văk-sĭ-nā′shûn): inoculation with the virus of cowpox, or vaccina, as a means of producing immunity against small pox.

vaccine (văk′sĭn; -sēn): any substance used for preventive inoculation.

vacuum (văk′ū-ûm): a space from which most of the air has been exhausted.

vagus (vā′gûs): pneumogastric nerve; tenth cranial nerve.

vapor: the gaseous state of a liquid or solid.

vascular (văs′kû-lȧr): supplied with small blood vessels; pertaining to a vessel for the conveyance of a fluid as blood or lymph.

Vaseline (văs′ê-lĭn; -lēn): a trade name; petrolatum; a semi-solid greasy or oily mixture of hydrocarbons obtained from petroleum.

vegetable tints (vĕj′ê-tȧ-b′l tĭnts): comprised of Egyptian henna, indigo, or camomile; used as hair tints or hair rinses.

vein; vena (vān; vē′nȧ): a blood vessel carrying blood toward the heart.

vena cava (kā′vȧ): one of the large veins which carry the blood to the right auricle of the heart.

ventilate (vĕn′tĭ-lāt): to renew the air in a place; to oxygenate the blood in the capillaries of the lungs.

ventricle (vĕn′trĭ-k′l): a small cavity; particularly in the brain or heart.

vermin (vûr′mĭn): parasitic insects, as lice and bedbugs.

verruca (vĕ-rōō′kȧ): a wart.

vertebra (vûr′tê-brȧ); pl., **vertebrae** (-brē): a bony segment of the spinal column.

vertex (vûr′tĕks): the crown on top of the head.

vesicle (vĕs′ĭ-k′l): a small blister or sac; a small elevation on the skin.

vibrator (vī′brȧ-tēr): an electrically driven massage apparatus causing a swinging, shaking sensation on the body, producing stimulation.

violet-ray: high-frequency; Tesla; an electric current of medium voltage and medium amperage.

virgin hair: normal hair which has had no previous lightening or tinting treatments.

virus (vī'rs): poison; the specific poison of an infectious disease.

viscid (vĭs'ĭd): sticky or adhesive.

viscosity (vĭs-kŏs'ĭ-tē): the degree of density, thickness, stickiness and adhesiveness of a substance.

viscous (vĭs'kûs): sticky or gummy.

visible rays: light rays which can be seen; are visible to the eye.

vitamin (vī'tå-mĭn): one of a group of organic substances present in a very small quantity in natural food-stuffs, which are essential to normal metabolism, and the lack of which in the diet causes deficiency diseases.

vitiligo (vĭt-ĭ-lī'gō): milky-white spots of the skin.

volatile (vŏl'å-tĭl): easily evaporating; diffusing freely; not permanent.

volt (vōlt): the fractional unit of electromotive force.

voltage (vōl'tåj): electrical potential difference expressed in volts.

voluntary (vŏl'ûn-tå-rē): under the control of the will; voluntary muscles.

vomer (vō'mĕr): the thin plate of bone between the nostrils.

W

wall plate (wôl plāt): an apparatus equipped with indicators and controlling devices to produce various currents.

wall socket (sŏk'ĕt): a wall receptacle into which may be fitted the plug of an electrical appliance.

wart (wôrt): verruca; a circumscribed hypertrophy of the papillae of the corium, usually of the hand, covered by thickened epidermis.

water, hard: water containing certain minerals; does not lather with soap.

water, soft: water which readily lathers with soap; relatively free of minerals.

water softener: certain chemicals, such as the carbonate or phosphate of sodium, used to soften hard water to permit the lathering of soap.

watt (wät): a unit of electric power.

wattage (wŏt'åj): amount of electric power expressed in watts.

wave, cold: a method of permanent waving requiring the use of certain chemicals rather than heat.

wave, finger: arranging waves into the hair, which has been wet, with finger and comb.

wave, marcel: thermal wave produced by means of heated thermal irons.

wave, permanent: a wave given to the hair which is of permanent duration.

wave, pin curl: alternating the direction of rows of pin curls in order to form a wave pattern.

wave, shadow: a wave with low ridges and shallow waves.

wave, skip: a pattern formed by a combination of alternating ridges and curls.

weft (wĕft): an artificial section of woven hair used for practice work or as a substitute for natural hair.

wen (wĕn): a sebaceous cyst, usually on the scalp.

wetting agent: a substance that causes a liquid to spread more readily on a solid surface, chiefly through a reduction of surface tension.

wheal (whēl): a raised ridge on the skin, usually caused by a blow, a bite of an insect, uticaria, or sting of a nettle.

whitehead (whīt'hĕd): milium.

whorl (whûrl; whôrl): a spiral turn, in general; a hair whorl or cowlick; a spiral turn causing a tuft of hair which goes contrary to the usual growth of the hair.

wig: an artificial covering for the head consisting of a network of interwoven hair.

wiglet: a hairpiece with a flat base which is used in special areas of the head.

winding, croquignole (krō'kwĭ-nōl): winding under the hair, from the hair ends towards the scalp.

winding, spiral (spī'rĕl): winding the hair from the scalp to the ends.

wrapping: winding hair on rollers or rods in order to form curls.

wrinkle: a small ridge or a furrow.

wrist electrode (rĭst ê-lĕk'trōd): an electrode connected to the wrist.

X

x-ray (ĕks'rā): the Roentgen rays; these rays were discovered by the German physicist Wilhelm Roentgen and were called x-rays by him.

Y

yak (yäk): a long haired ox found in Tibet; the long, white hairs of this animal are used for the manufacture of wigs and hairpieces.

Z

zinc oxide (zĭnk ŏks'īd): a chemical used in facial packs to minimize or neutralize the effects of excess acid or alkali.

zinc sulphate (sŭl'fāt): a salt often employed as astringent, both in lotions and creams.

zinc sulphocarbonate (sŭl-fô-kär'bôn-āt): a fine white powder having the odor of carbolic acid; used as an antiseptic and astringent in deodorant preparations.

zygoma (zī-gō'må): a bone of the skull which extends along the front or side of the face, below the eye; the malar or cheek bone.

zygomatic (zī-gô-măt'ĭk): pertaining to the zygoma; pertaining to the malar or cheek bone.

zygomaticus (zī-gô-măt'ĭ-kûs): a muscle that draws the upper lip upward and outward.

CROSS INDEX

525

THE THEORY OF COLOR

To become successful in the art of hair coloring, the hair colorist must have a clear knowledge of the theory of color. It is essential that the colorist understand colors and how they react when combined. Only with this knowledge and understanding can the colorist make sound judgments concerning color selection, correct hair color problems when they occur and, preferably, prevent such problems.

PRIMARY COLORS

All colors originate from three basic colors called *primary colors:* red, yellow and blue. These are called primary colors because every other color can be developed from them.

Red   Yellow   Blue

SECONDARY COLORS

When equal proportions of any two of the primary colors are mixed, they form a new color called a secondary color. Thus:

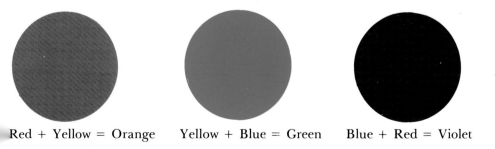

Red + Yellow = Orange   Yellow + Blue = Green   Blue + Red = Violet

Now, we have six separate colors: Primary colors—Red, Yellow, Blue. Secondary colors—Orange, Green, Violet.

TERTIARY COLORS

If equal proportions of a primary color and its adjacent (on the color wheel) secondary color are mixed, they form yet a new color called a tertiary color, and six new combinations, or color patterns, are formed:

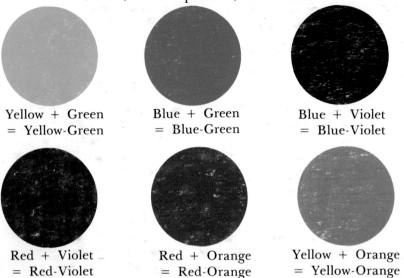

| Yellow + Green = Yellow-Green | Blue + Green = Blue-Green | Blue + Violet = Blue-Violet |
| Red + Violet = Red-Violet | Red + Orange = Red-Orange | Yellow + Orange = Yellow-Orange |

Thus, we can visualize that by continually intermixing these colors, an infinite number of colors and shades can be created. By thoroughly understanding the combination of colors, primary colors, secondary colors, and tertiary colors, the colorist is in a position to correct hair coloring problems effectively and even to avoid them entirely.

COLOR WHEEL

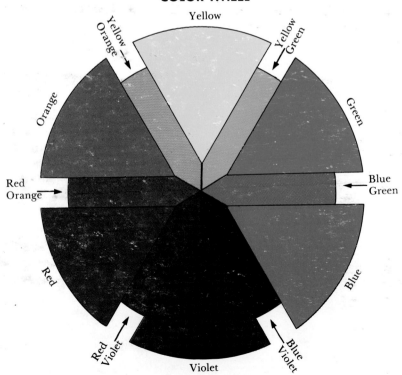